MATHEMATICS
for
AQA GCSE (Modular)

Intermediate Tier

Tony Banks and David Alcorn

Causeway Press Limited

Published by Causeway Press Ltd
P.O. Box 13, Ormskirk, Lancashire L39 5HP

First published 2003

British Library Cataloguing-in-Publication Data.
A catalogue record for this book is available from the British Library.

ISBN 1-902796-72-1

Acknowledgements
Past exam questions, provided by the *Assessment and Qualifications Alliance*, are denoted by the letters AQA. The answers to all questions are entirely the responsibility of the authors/publisher and have neither been provided nor approved by AQA.

Every effort has been made to locate the copyright owners of material used in this book. Any omissions brought to the notice of the publisher are regretted and will be credited in subsequent printings.

Page design
Billy Johnson

Reader
Anne Alcock

Artwork
David Alcorn

Cover design
Waring-Collins Partnership

Typesetting by Billy Johnson, San Francisco, California, USA

Printed and bound by Scotprint, Haddington, Scotland

preface

Mathematics for AQA GCSE (Modular) - Intermediate Tier has been written to meet the requirements of the National Curriculum and provides full coverage of **AQA Specification B (Modular)**.

The book is suitable for students preparing for assessment at the Intermediate Tier of entry on either a 1-year or 2-year course or as a revision text.

The book has been carefully organised into 40 chapters to provide complete coverage of the specification for Modules 1, 3 and 5.
Modules 2 and 4 are coursework tasks.

In preparing the text, full account has been made of the requirements for students to be able to use and apply mathematics in written examination papers and be able to solve problems in mathematics both with and without a calculator. Some chapters include ideas for investigational, practical and statistical tasks and give the student the opportunity to improve and practice their skills of using and applying mathematics.

Module 1   Chapters   1 - 7
Module 3   Chapters   8 - 18
Module 5   Chapters 19 - 40

Each chapter consists of fully worked examples with explanatory notes and commentary, carefully graded questions, a summary of key facts and skills and a review exercise.
The review exercises provide the opportunity to consolidate topics introduced within the chapter and consist of exam-style questions, which reflect how AQA assess the work, plus lots of past examination questions (marked AQA).

At the end of Module 1 and Module 3 there is an examination questions section with a compilation of exam and exam-style questions, organised for non-calculator and calculator practice, in preparation for the exams.

In Module 5 a section review is provided at the end of Chapters 19 - 26 (Algebra) and another at the end of Chapters 27 - 40 (Shape, Space and Measures) to give further opportunities to consolidate skills.
At the end of the module there is a further compilation of exam and exam-style questions, organised for non-calculator and calculator practice, in preparation for the exams.

> The book has been designed so that it can be used in conjunction with the companion book
> ***Mathematics for AQA GCSE (Modular) - Student Support Book: Intermediate Tier***
> ***Without Answers: ISBN 1-902796-57-8***
> ***With Answers: ISBN 1-902796-56-X***

contents

Chapter 12 Working with Number

Chapter 13 Standard Index Form

Chapter 14 Fractions

Module 5

Collection and Organisation of Data

To answer questions such as:

Which is the most popular colour of car?
Is it going to rain tomorrow?
Which team won the World Cup in 2002?

we need to collect data.

Primary and secondary data

When data is collected by an individual or organisation to use for a particular purpose it is called **primary data**.
Primary data is obtained from experiments, investigations, surveys and by using questionnaires.

Data which is already available or has been collected by someone else for a different purpose is called **secondary data**.
Sources of secondary data include the Annual Abstract of Statistics, Social Trends and the Internet.

Data

Data is made up of a collection of **variables**.
Each variable can be described, numbered or measured.

Data which can only be **described** in words is **qualitative**. Such data is often organised into categories, such as make of car, colour of hair, etc.

Data which is given **numerical** values, such as shoe size or height, is **quantitative**.
Quantitative data is either **discrete** or **continuous**.

> **Discrete** data can only take certain values, usually whole numbers, but may include fractions (e.g. shoe sizes).
>
> **Continuous** data can take any value within a range and is measurable (e.g. height, weight, temperature, etc.).

EXAMPLES

The taste of an orange is a qualitative variable.
The number of pips in an orange is a discrete quantitative variable.
The surface area of an orange is a continuous quantitative variable.

Exercise **1.1**

State whether the following data is qualitative or quantitative.
If the data is quantitative state whether it is discrete or continuous.

1 The colours of cars in a car park.

2 The weights of eggs in a carton.

3 The numbers of desks in classrooms.

4 The names of students in a class.

5 The sizes of spanners in a toolbox.

6 The depths that fish swim in the sea.

7 The numbers of goals scored by football teams on a Saturday.

8 The brands of toothpaste on sale in supermarkets.

9 The sizes of ladies dresses in a store.

10 The heights of trees in a wood.

Collection of data

Data can be collected in a variety of ways: by observation, by interviewing people and by using questionnaires. The method of collection will often depend on the type of data to be collected.

Data collection sheets

Data collection sheets are used to record data.
To answer the question, "Which is the most popular colour of car?" we could draw up a simple data collection sheet and record the colours of passing cars by observation.

EXAMPLE

A **data collection sheet** for colour of car is shown, with some cars recorded.

Colour of car	Tally	Frequency
Black	||	2
Blue	⊦⊦⊦⊦ ⊦⊦⊦⊦ |||	13
Green	||||	4
Red	⊦⊦⊦⊦ ⊦⊦⊦⊦ |	
Silver	⊦⊦⊦⊦ ||	
White	⊦⊦⊦⊦ ⊦⊦⊦⊦ ||||	
	Total	

The colour of each car is recorded in the **tally** column by a single stroke.

To make counting easier, groups of 5 are recorded as ⊦⊦⊦⊦.

How many red cars are recorded?
How many cars are recorded altogether?

The total number of times each colour appears is called its **frequency**.
A table for data with the totals included is called a **frequency distribution**.

For large amounts of discrete data, or for continuous data, we organise the data into **groups** or **classes**. When data is collected in groups it is called a **grouped frequency distribution** and the groups you put the data into are called **class intervals**.

EXAMPLE

The weights of 20 boys are recorded in the grouped frequency table shown below.

Weight w kg	Tally	Frequency
$50 \leqslant w < 55$	|	1
$55 \leqslant w < 60$	|||	3
$60 \leqslant w < 65$	⊦⊦⊦⊦ ||||	9
$65 \leqslant w < 70$	⊦⊦⊦⊦ |	6
$70 \leqslant w < 75$	|	1
	Total	20

Weights are grouped into class intervals of equal width.

$55 \leqslant w < 60$

means 55 kg, or more, but less than 60 kg.

John weighs 54.9 kg. *In which class interval is he recorded?*
David weighs 55.0 kg. *In which class interval is he recorded?*

What is the width of each class interval?

Collection and Organisation of Data

1 The colours of 40 cars in a car park are shown.

red	red	blue	green	white	grey
blue	red	red	grey	white	green
red	white	white	blue	red	white
blue	blue	green	black	white	blue
red	silver	silver	blue	red	red
silver	white	white	red	blue	green
red	blue	silver	white		

(a) Make a frequency table for the data.
(b) Which colour of car is most popular?
(c) How many **more** white cars than black cars are in the car park?

2 The days of the week on which some students were born are recorded.

Monday	Monday	Sunday	Wednesday	Thursday
Friday	Saturday	Tuesday	Monday	Friday
Thursday	Sunday	Monday	Friday	Tuesday
Thursday	Wednesday	Tuesday	Monday	Wednesday
Friday	Monday	Saturday	Friday	Thursday
Tuesday	Thursday	Monday	Sunday	Tuesday
Saturday	Wednesday	Friday	Thursday	Tuesday
Monday	Wednesday	Friday	Sunday	Thursday
Tuesday	Wednesday	Sunday		

(a) Make a frequency table for the data.
(b) How many students are included?
(c) On which day of the week did most births occur?
(d) How many of these students were born on either a Saturday or a Sunday?

3 The ages, in years, of 40 people are shown below.

27	34	54	57	3	12	15	19
29	30	33	47	35	20	39	28
9	11	26	42	50	26	10	7
33	49	21	18	1	25	24	34
19	20	27	37	43	56	37	34

(a) Copy and complete the grouped frequency table for the data given.

Age (years)	Tally	Frequency
0 - 9		
10 - 19		
20 - 29		

(b) What is the width of each class interval?
(c) How many people are in the class interval 30 - 39?
(d) How many people are less than 20 years old?
(e) How many people are 40 years old, or older?

4 The heights, in centimetres, of 36 girls are recorded as follows.

148	161	175	156	155	160	178	159	170
163	147	150	173	169	170	174	166	163
162	158	155	165	168	154	156	163	167
172	170	165	160	164	172	157	173	161

(a) Copy and complete the grouped frequency table for the data.

Height h cm	Tally	Frequency
$145 \leqslant h < 150$		
$150 \leqslant h < 155$		

(b) What is the width of each class interval?
(c) How many girls are in the class interval $155 \leqslant h < 160$?
(d) How many girls are less than 160 cm?
(e) How many girls are 155 cm or taller?

5 Draw up a data collection sheet to record the month in which people were born.
Collect data from 50 people.
(a) Make a frequency table for the data.
(b) In which month did most births occur?

Databases

If we need to collect data for more than one type of information, for example: the make, colour, number of doors and mileage of cars, we will need to collect data in a different way.

We could create a **data collection card** for each car.

Car	1
Make	Vauxhall
Colour	Grey
Number of doors	3
Mileage	18 604

Alternatively, we could use a data collection sheet and record all the information about each car on a separate line.

This is an example of a simple **database**.

Car	Make	Colour	Number of doors	Mileage
1	Vauxhall	Grey	3	18 604
2	Ford	Blue	2	33 216
3	Ford	White	5	27 435
4	Nissan	Red	4	32 006

When all the data has been collected, separate frequency or grouped frequency tables can be drawn up.

Collection and Organisation of Data

1 The database gives information about the babies born at a maternity hospital one day.

Baby's name	Time of birth	Weight (kg)	Length (cm)
Alistair	0348	3.2	44
Francis	0819	3.5	48
Louisa	1401	3.7	47

(a) Which baby is the longest?
(b) Which baby is the heaviest?
(c) Which baby was born first?

2 A database of cars is shown.

Car	Make	Colour	Number of doors	Mileage
1	Vauxhall	Grey	3	18 604
2	Ford	Blue	2	33 216
3	Ford	White	5	27 435
4	Nissan	Red	4	32 006
5	Vauxhall	Blue	4	31 598
6	Ford	Green	3	37 685
7	Vauxhall	Red	3	21 640
8	Nissan	White	2	28 763
9	Ford	White	3	30 498
10	Vauxhall	White	5	9 865
11	Nissan	Red	3	7 520
12	Vauxhall	Grey	5	16 482

(a) (i) Draw up separate frequency tables for make, colour and number of doors.
   (ii) Draw up a grouped frequency table for mileage.
      Use class intervals of 5000 miles,
      starting at $0 \leqslant m < 5000$, $5000 \leqslant m < 10\,000$, …
(b) (i) Which make of car is the most popular?
   (ii) How many Ford cars are white?
   (iii) How many cars have a mileage of 30 000 or more?
   (iv) How many cars have exactly 3 doors?

3 Use data collection cards to collect information about students in your class.
Include gender, height, shoe size and pulse rate.
(a) What is the smallest shoe size for students in your class?
(b) What is the gender of the student with the highest pulse rate?
(c) What is the difference between the highest pulse rate and the lowest pulse rate?
(d) What is the height of the tallest student?
(e) What differences are there in the data collected for male and female students?

4 (a) Design a data collection card to collect information on the leisure time activities
   of students.
(b) Draw up frequency or grouped frequency tables for the data.
(c) Which leisure time activity is the most popular?
(d) What differences are there in the leisure time activities of male and female students?

Questionnaires

Questionnaires are frequently used to collect data.
In business they are used to get information about products or services and in politics they are frequently used to test opinion on a range of issues and personalities.

When constructing questions for a questionnaire you should:

(1)   use simple language, so that everyone can understand the question;

(2)   ask short questions which can be answered precisely, with a "yes" or "no" answer, a number, or a response from a choice of answers;

(3)   provide tick boxes, so that questions can be answered easily;

(4)   avoid open-ended questions, like: "What do you think of education?"
      which might produce long rambling answers which would be difficult to collate or process;

(5)   avoid leading questions, like: "Don't you agree that there is too much bad language on television?" and ask instead:
      "Do you think that there is too much bad language on television?"   Yes ☐   No ☐

(6)   ask questions in a logical order.

Multiple-response questions

In many instances a choice of responses should be provided.

Instead of asking, "How old are you?" which does not indicate the degree of accuracy required and many people might consider personal, we could ask instead:

Which is your age group?

under 18 ☐   18 to 40 ☐   41 to 65 ☐   over 65 ☐

Notice there are no gaps and only **one** response applies to each person.

Sometimes we invite **multiple responses** by asking questions, such as:

Which soaps do you watch?

Coronation Street ☐   EastEnders ☐   Emmerdale ☐   Brookside ☐   Hollyoaks ☐

Tick as many as you wish.

Exercise 1.4

❶   Susan wants to find out what people think about the Health Service.
    Part of the questionnaire she has written is shown.

> Q4. What is your date of birth?
>
> Q5. Don't you agree that waiting lists for operations are too long?
>
> Q6. How many times did you visit your doctor last year?
>   ☐ less than 5   ☐ 5 - 10   ☐ 10 or more

(a)   Why should Q4 not be asked?
(b)   Give a reason why Q5 is unsuitable.
(c)   (i)   Explain why Q6 is unsuitable in its present form.
      (ii) Rewrite the question so that it could be included in the questionnaire.

❷   In preparing the questions for a questionnaire on radio listening habits the following questions were rejected.
(a)   When do you listen to the radio?
(b)   What do you like about radio programmes?
(c)   Don't you agree that the radio gives the best news reports?
Explain why each question is unsuitable and rewrite the question so that it could be included in the questionnaire.

3 In preparing questions for a survey on the use of a library the following questions were considered. Explain why each question in its present form is unsuitable and rewrite the question.
(a) How old are you?
(b) How many times have you used the library?
(c) Which books do you read?
(d) How could the library be improved?

4 A mobile phone company wants to carry out a survey.
It wants to find out the distribution of the age and sex of customers and the frequency with which they use the phone.
The company intends to use a questionnaire.
Write three questions and responses that will enable the company to carry out the survey.

5 A school is to conduct a homework survey.
Suggest five questions which could be included.

6 A survey of reading habits is to be conducted.
Suggest five questions which could be included.

7 A survey of eating habits is to be conducted.
Suggest five questions which could be included.

Hypothesis

A **hypothesis** is a statement that may or may not be true.
To test a hypothesis we can construct a questionnaire, carry out a survey and analyse the results.

EXAMPLE

A questionnaire to test the hypothesis, *"People think it is better to give than to receive"*, could include questions like these.

1. **Gender:**   male ☐   female ☐
2. **Age (years):** 11 - 16 ☐   17 - 21 ☐   22 - 59 ☐   60 & over ☐
3. **Do you think it is better to give than to receive?**
   Yes ☐   No ☐
4. **To which of the following have you given in the last year?**
   School ☐   Charities ☐   Church ☐
   Hospital ☐   Special appeals ☐   Homeless ☐
   Other (please list) _____

Suggest another question which could be included.

Sampling

When information is required about a small group of people it is possible to survey everyone.
When information is required about a large group of people it is not always possible to survey everyone and only a **sample** may be asked. The sample chosen should be large enough to make the results meaningful and representative of the whole group or the results may be **biased**.
For example, to test the hypothesis, *"Girls are more intelligent than boys"*,
you would need to ask equal numbers of boys and girls from various age groups.
The results of a survey may also be biased if there is any form of deliberate selection or if the sample is incomplete.

We have already seen that the results of a survey can be recorded on data collection sheets and then collated using frequency or grouped frequency tables. We can also illustrate data using **two-way tables**.

A two-way table is used to illustrate the data for two different features (variables) in a survey.

EXAMPLE   The two-way table shows the results of a survey.

(a) How many boys wear glasses?
(b) How many children wear glasses?
(c) Do the results prove or disprove the hypothesis:
        "More boys wear glasses than girls"?

	Wear Glasses	
	Yes	No
Boys	4	14
Girls	3	9

(a) 4   (b) 7   (c) Disprove. Boys: $\frac{4}{18} \times 100 = 22\%$ Girls: $\frac{3}{12} \times 100 = 25\%$

Exercise 1.5

1 George is investigating the cost of return journeys by train.
He plans to ask ten passengers who are waiting at a station at midday the cost of their return journeys.
Give two reasons why he might get biased results.

2 Judy is investigating shopping habits.
She plans to interview 50 women at her local supermarket on a Tuesday morning.
Give three reasons why she might get biased results.

3 State one advantage and one disadvantage of a postal survey.

4 Design a questionnaire to test the hypothesis: "Children watch more television than adults."
Consider: (a)   does gender affect people's opinions?
                  (b)   do people's opinions change with age?

5 Design a questionnaire to test the hypothesis:
"People think that everyone should take part in sport."
Describe the sample you could use to test this hypothesis.

6 Design a questionnaire to test the hypothesis:
"People think that animals should not be used to test drugs."
Describe the sample you could use to test this hypothesis.

7 Design a questionnaire to test the hypothesis: "Children have too much homework."
Describe the sample you could use to test this hypothesis.

8 The two-way table shows information about the ages of people in a retirement home.

Age (years)

	60 - 64	65 - 69	70 - 74	75 - 79	80 and over
Men	0	2	5	8	1
Women	2	5	6	5	6

(a) How many men are aged 75 - 79?
(b) How many men are included?
(c) How many people are aged 75 or more?
(d) How many people are included?
(e) What percentage of these people are aged 75 or more?

9 A group of 25 students were each asked how many brothers and sisters they had.
The table shows the results.

		Number of sisters			
		0	1	2	3
	0	5	1	2	0
Number of brothers	1	4	3	2	1
	2	2	3	1	0
	3	0	1	0	0

  (a) How many students have no brothers or sisters?
  (b) How many students have one sister?
  (c) How many students have one brother and one sister?
  (d) How many students have more brothers than sisters?

10 The two-way table shows information about a class of pupils.

  (a) How many boys can swim?
  (b) How many boys are in the class?
  (c) What percentage of the boys can swim?
  (d) What percentage of the girls can swim?
  (e) Do the results prove or disprove the hypothesis:
"More boys can swim than girls"?
Explain your answer.

	Can swim	Cannot swim
Boys	14	6
Girls	8	2

11 The two-way table shows the results of a survey to test the hypothesis:

        "More girls are left-handed than boys."

Do the results prove or disprove the hypothesis?
Explain your answer.

	Left-handed	
	Yes	No
Boys	3	18
Girls	2	12

12 The two-way table shows the results of a survey.

	A			1	2	2
	B		1	2	5	2
Grade in Mathematics	C		1	8	3	
	D		3	3	2	
	E	2	1	2		
		E	D	C	B	A

                            Grade in English

  (a) How many students achieved the same grade in both subjects?
  (b) How many students got a grade A, B or C in Mathematics?
  (c) Do the results prove or disprove the hypothesis:
"Students get better grades in English than Mathematics"? Explain your answer.

13 In a survey, 100 people were asked: "Would you like to be taller?"
      58 of the people asked were men.
      65 of the people asked said, "Yes."
      24 of the women asked said, "No."

  (a) Construct a two-way table to show the results of the survey.

  (b) A newspaper headline stated:

        | Over 80% of men would like to be taller. |

  Do the results of the survey support this headline?
  Give a reason for your answer.

14 The two-way table shows the number of boys and girls in families taking part in a survey.

Number of girls	0	1	2	3	4
3	1	2			
2	1	2	3		
1	5	9		1	1
0		3		2	

Number of boys

(a) (i) How many families have two children?
   (ii) Does the data support the hypothesis:
   "More families have less than 2 children than more than 2 children"?
   Explain your answer.
(b) (i) How many girls are included in the survey?
   (ii) Does the data support the hypothesis: "More boys are born than girls"?
   Explain your answer.

15 The two-way table shows the age and gender of people taking part in a survey.

	Age (years)				
	Under 18	18 - 25	26 - 40	41 - 64	65 and over
Female	0	2	7	9	7
Male	0	4	17	19	10

Give two reasons why the data collected may not be representative of the whole population.

What you need to know

- **Primary data** is data collected by an individual or organisation to use for a particular purpose. Primary data is obtained from experiments, investigations, surveys and by using questionnaires.
- **Secondary data** is data which is already available or has been collected by someone else for a different purpose. Sources of secondary data include the Annual Abstract of Statistics, Social Trends and the Internet.
- **Qualitative** data – Data which can only be described in words.
- **Quantitative** data – Data that has a numerical value. Quantitative data is either **discrete** or **continuous**. **Discrete** data can only take certain values. **Continuous** data has no exact value and is measurable.
- **Data Collection Sheets** – Used to record data during a survey.
- **Tally** – A way of recording each item of data on a data collection sheet. A group of five is recorded as ⵜⵜⵜⵜ.
- **Frequency Table** – A way of collating the information recorded on a data collection sheet.

- **Grouped Frequency Table** – Used for continuous data or for discrete data when a lot of data has to be recorded.
- **Database** – A collection of data.
- **Class Interval** – The width of the groups used in a grouped frequency distribution.
- **Questionnaire** – A set of questions used to collect data for a survey. Questionnaires should:
  (1) use simple language,
  (2) ask short questions which can be answered precisely,
  (3) provide tick boxes,
  (4) avoid open-ended questions,
  (5) avoid leading questions,
  (6) ask questions in a logical order.
- **Hypothesis** – A hypothesis is a statement which may or may not be true.
- When information is required about a large group of people it is not always possible to survey everyone and only a **sample** may be asked. The sample chosen should be large enough to make the results meaningful and representative of the whole group (population) or the results may be **biased**.
- **Two-way Tables** – A way of illustrating two features of a survey.

Collection and Organisation of Data

1 Jane does a survey about vehicles passing her school.
She wants to know about the types of vehicles and their colours.

Design a suitable observation sheet to record this information.
Fill in your observation sheet as if you had carried out this survey.
You should invent suitable data for 25 vehicles. AQA

2 The weights, in grams, of 24 bananas are shown.

128	120	184	113	170	206	179	99
92	156	234	192	106	163	180	100
119	150	173	232	115	200	166	196

Copy and complete the grouped frequency table for these bananas.

Weight (g)	Tally	Frequency
$80 \leqslant g < 120$		
$120 \leqslant g < 180$		
$180 \leqslant g < 250$		

AQA

3 Kath writes a questionnaire to survey opinion on whether cars should be banned from the town centre.

(a) Which two of the following points are important when she is deciding which people to ask?

A Ask people who look friendly.

B Ask people at different times of the day.

C Ask some men and some women.

D Ask the first people she sees.

(b) Which two of the following points are important when she is writing the questionnaire?

E Write polite questions.

F Write as many questions as she can think of.

G Write questions for car drivers only.

H Write questions that do not require long answers. AQA

4 Claire carried out a survey about smoking.
She included the following questions.

1. How many cigarettes do you smoke?

2. Do you agree that smoking is bad for your health?

(a) Make **one** criticism of each question.

(b) Rewrite question 2 so that it is suitable for use in Claire's survey. AQA

5 The table shows the age and gender of people taking part in a survey to test the hypothesis "Children have too much homework."

	Age (years)				
	Under 11	11 - 16	17 - 25	26 - 50	Over 50
Male	0	4	6	5	5
Female	0	0	0	0	0

Give three reasons why the sample is biased.

6 This statement is made on a television programme about health.

"Three in every eight pupils do not take any exercise outside school."

(a) A school has 584 pupils.
According to the television programme, how many of these pupils do not take any exercise outside school?

(b) Claire says, "I go to the gym twice a week after school."
She decides to do a survey to investigate what exercise other pupils do outside school.
Write down **two** questions that she could ask.

(c) Matthew decides to do a survey in his school about the benefits of exercise.
He decides to ask the girls' netball team for their opinion.
Give **two** reasons why this is **not** a suitable sample to take.

(d) This is part of Matthew's questionnaire.

Question	*Don't you agree that adults who were sportsmen when they were younger suffer more from injuries as they get older?*
Response	*Tick one box*
	☐ *Yes* ☐ *Usually* ☐ *Sometimes* ☐ *Occasionally*

(i) Write down one criticism of Matthew's question.
(ii) Write down one criticism of Matthew's response section.

AQA

7 A travel agent says, "More women prefer holidays abroad than men."
The table shows the results of a survey to test this statement.

	Men	Women
Prefer holidays abroad	18	21
Prefer holidays in the UK	6	7

Do these results support the statement made by the travel agent?
Explain your answer.

8 The number of shops and the number of churches are recorded for each of twenty small villages.
The results are shown in the table.

		Number of churches			
		0	1	2	3
Number of shops	0	0	0	0	1
	1	0	1	0	5
	2	0	2	8	0
	3	2	1	0	0

(a) How many of the villages have 3 churches?
(b) How many of the villages have more shops than churches?
(c) Calculate the total number of churches in the twenty villages.

AQA

CHAPTER 2

Presentation of Data 1

Most people find numerical data easier to understand if it is presented in a pictorial or diagrammatical form. For this reason television reports, newspapers and advertisements frequently use graphs and diagrams to present data.

Bar charts

Bar charts are a simple but effective way of displaying data.
Bars can be drawn either horizontally or vertically.

EXAMPLE

The table shows how a group of boys travelled to school one day.

Method of travel	Bus	Cycle	Car	Walk
Number of boys	2	7	1	5

(a) Draw a bar chart to show this information.
(b) Which method of travel is the mode?

(a)

How boys travel to school

Notice that:
Bars are the same width.

There are gaps between the bars because data that can be counted is discrete.

The height of each bar gives the **frequency**.

The tallest bar represents the most frequent variable (category).

(b) The most frequently occurring variable is called the **mode** or **modal category**.
Cycle is the modal category for these boys.

Bar-line graphs

Instead of drawing bars to show frequency we could draw vertical lines.
Such graphs are called **bar-line graphs** or **vertical line graphs**.
The lines can be drawn either horizontally or vertically.

EXAMPLE

The graph shows the number of goals scored by a football team in 10 matches.

(a) In how many matches was only one goal scored?
(b) What is the difference between the largest number of goals scored in a match and the smallest number of goals scored?

The frequency represents the number of matches played.

Goals scored by a football team

(a) 5
(b) The difference between the largest and smallest variable is called the **range**.
The range for the number of goals scored is $4 - 1 = 3$.

1 The bar chart shows the time Jim spent watching television each day last week.

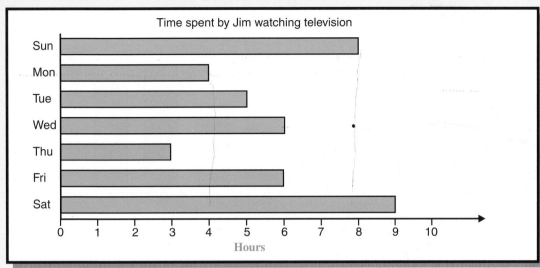

(a) On which day did Jim watch the most television?
(b) How many hours did Jim spend watching television on Tuesday?
(c) How many hours did Jim spend watching television last week?
(d) On which day did Jim spend a third of the day watching television?
(e) What fraction of the day did Jim spend watching television on Wednesday?
(f) What is the range of the number of hours per day Jim spent watching television?

2 The table shows the amount of pocket money given each week to a number of girls.

Amount (£)	1	2	3	4	5	6	7	8	9	10
Number of girls	0	0	1	5	10	4	0	3	0	7

(a) Draw a bar-line graph of the data.
(b) What is the modal amount of pocket money?
(c) What is the range of the amount of pocket money given each week?
(d) What percentage of the girls got less than £5?

3 The bar-line graph illustrates the number of goals scored per match by a hockey team.

(a) How many matches have the team played?
(b) Which number of goals scored is the mode?
(c) What is the range of the number of goals scored?
(d) In what percentage of games were no goals scored?

4 The bar chart shows the day of birth for a group of children.

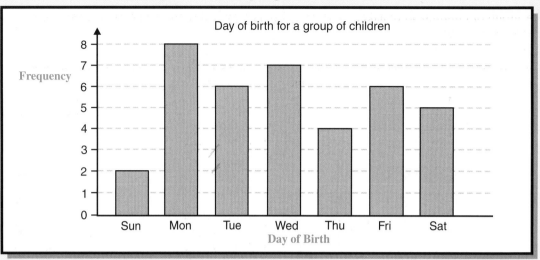

(a) How many children are in the group?

(b) Which day of birth is the mode?

The table shows the day of birth for the girls.

Day of birth	Sun	Mon	Tue	Wed	Thu	Fri	Sat
Number of girls	1	5	2	3	3	1	4

(c) Draw up a table to show the day of birth for the boys.

5 Record the day of birth for all the students in your class.
Draw a bar chart of the data.
Compare your data with the data given in question 4.

Comparing data

Bar charts can also be used to compare data.
The table shows how a class of children travelled to school one day.

Method of travel	Bus	Cycle	Car	Walk
Boys	2	7	1	5
Girls	3	1	5	6

To make it easier to compare the information given for boys and girls we can draw both bars on the same diagram, as shown.

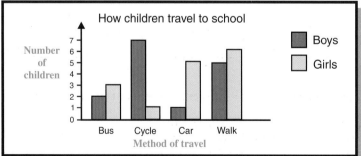

Eight children cycle to school.
How many children travel to school by car?
Walking is the most popular method of travelling to school.
Which method of travel is the least popular?
What percentage of girls walk to school?
Compare and comment on the method of travel of these boys and girls.

① A group of children were asked how many hours they had spent watching television on a particular Sunday.
The bar chart shows the results.

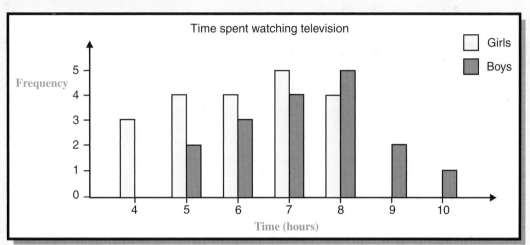

(a) What was the modal time for the girls?
(b) What was the range in time for the boys?
(c) How many boys watched television for more than 8 hours?
(d) (i) How many girls were included in the survey?
  (ii) What percentage of the girls watched television for 6 hours?
(e) Compare and comment on the time spent watching television for these boys and girls.

② The bar chart shows the results of a survey of the shoe sizes of pupils in a Year 9 class.

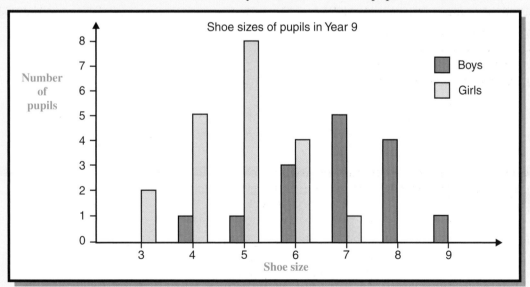

(a) Which size of shoe is the mode for the girls?
(b) Which size of shoe is the mode for the boys?
(c) How many pupils have shoe size 6?
(d) What percentage of boys have shoe size 8 or 9?
(e) What percentage of girls have shoe size 3 or 4?
(f) What is the range of shoe size for girls?
(g) What is the range of shoe size for boys?
(h) Compare and comment on the shoe sizes of boys and girls.

Bar charts are useful for comparing the various types of data (categories) with each other.
To compare each category with **all** the data collected we use a **pie chart**.

A pie chart is a circle which is divided up into sectors.
The whole circle represents the total frequency and each sector represents the frequency of one part (category) of the data.

Drawing pie charts

The table shows the ways in which some children like to eat eggs.

Method of cooking	Poached	Boiled	Scrambled	Fried
Number of children	5	8	6	11

To show this information in a pie chart we must find the angles of the sectors which represent each category. First calculate the angle which represents each child.

30 children are represented by 360°.
1 child is represented by 360° ÷ 30 = 12°.
Sector angle = Number of children in category × 12°

Method of cooking	Poached	Boiled	Scrambled	Fried	**Total**
Number of children	5	8	6	11	**30**
Sector angle	60°	96°	72°	132°	**360°**

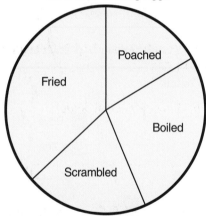

Method of Cooking Eggs

Using a table allows you to keep your work tidy and to make checks.

The whole circle represents the total frequency of 30.

Each sector represents the frequency of one category (method of cooking).

Exercise 2.3

1 The table shows information about the trees in a wood.

Type of tree	Ash	Beech	Maple
Number of trees	20	25	15

Draw a pie chart for this data.

2 The colour of eyes of 90 people were recorded.
The table shows the results.

Colour of eyes	Brown	Blue	Green	Other
Number of people	40	25	15	10

Draw a pie chart for this data.

3 The table shows the sales of ice-cream cornets at a kiosk one day.

Ice-cream cornet	Vanilla	Strawberry	99
Frequency	94	37	49

Draw a pie chart for this data.

4 The table shows the results of a survey to find the most popular takeaway food.

Type of takeaway	Fish & chips	Chicken & chips	Chinese meal	Pizza
Number of people	165	204	78	93

Draw a pie chart for this data.

5 The results of a survey to find the most popular terrestrial television channel are shown.

Television channel	BBC1	BBC2	ITV	Ch4	Ch5
Percentage of people	33	14	32	13	8

Show the information in a pie chart.

6 The breakfast cereal preferred by some adults is shown.

Breakfast cereal	Cornflakes	Muesli	Porridge	Branflakes
Number of adults	25	20	12	15

Show the information in a pie chart.

Interpreting pie charts

Pie charts are useful for showing and comparing proportions of data. However, they do not show frequencies. Such information can be found by interpreting the pie chart.

To interpret a pie chart we need to know:
● the sector angles (which can be measured from an accurately drawn pie chart), **and**
● the total frequency represented by the pie chart, **or**
the frequency represented by one of the sectors.

EXAMPLE

The pie chart shows the makes of 120 cars.

(a) Which make of car is the mode?

(b) How many of the cars are Ford?

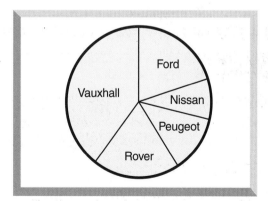

(a) The sector representing Vauxhall is the largest.
Therefore, Vauxhall is the mode.

(b) The angle of the sector representing Ford is 72°.

The number of Ford cars $= \frac{72}{360} \times 120 = 24$.

1 The pie chart shows the type of holiday chosen by 36 people.

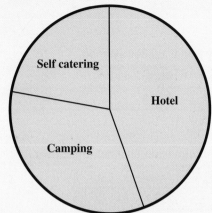

(a) How many people chose a camping holiday?

(b) How many people chose a self-catering holiday?

(c) What type of holiday is the mode?

2 The pie chart shows the resorts chosen by 60 skiers to Italy.

(a) How many skiers chose Sauze d'Oulx?

(b) How many skiers chose Foppollo?

(c) Which resort is the mode?

3 The pie chart shows the holiday destinations of 180 people.

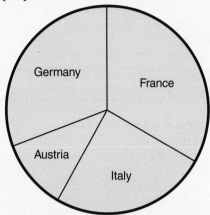

(a) Which holiday destination is the mode?

(b) How many people went to Italy?

(c) How many people went to Germany?

(d) How many people went to Austria?

4 The pie chart shows the membership of an international committee.

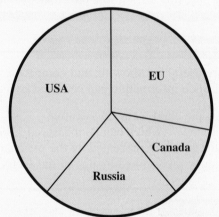

The USA has 7 committee members.

(a) How many committee members has the EU?

(b) How many committee members has Canada?

(c) How many committee members are there altogether?

5 The pie chart shows the different types of tree in a forest.

There are 54 oak trees and these are represented by a sector with an angle of 27°.

(a) The pine trees are represented by an angle of 144°.
How many pine trees are there?

(b) There are 348 silver birch trees.
Calculate the angle of the sector representing silver birch trees.

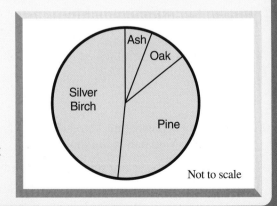

Not to scale

Stem and leaf diagrams

Data can also be represented using a **stem and leaf diagram**.

EXAMPLE

The times, in seconds, taken by 20 students to complete a puzzle are shown.

| 15 | 9 | 23 | 32 | 17 | 12 | 27 | 19 | 26 | 15 |
| 20 | 11 | 24 | 31 | 10 | 17 | 15 | 28 | 33 | 18 |

Construct a stem and leaf diagram to represent this information.

A stem and leaf diagram is made by splitting each number into two parts.
As the data uses 'tens' and 'units', the stem will represent the 'tens' and the leaf will represent the 'units'.
To draw the stem and leaf diagram begin by drawing a vertical line.
The digits to the left of the line make the **stem**.
The digits to the right of the line are the **leaves**.

> The first number is 15.
> Next to the stem of 1 record 5.

9 is recorded as 0 9 →

```
0 | 9
1 | 5  7  2  9  5  1  0  7  5  8
2 | 3  7  6  0  4  8
3 | 2  1  3
```

Once the data has been recorded, it is usual to redraw the diagram so that the leaves are in numerical order.

```
                          1 | 5   means 15 seconds
0 | 9
1 | 0  1  2  5  5  5  7  7  8  9
2 | 0  3  4  6  7  8
3 | 1  2  3
```

> Stem and leaf diagrams are often drawn without column headings in which case a key is necessary.
> e.g. 1|5 means 15 seconds

Exercise 2.5

1 The amount of petrol, in litres, bought by 20 motorists is shown.

| 16 | 23 | 27 | 10 | 35 | 42 | 26 | 25 | 24 | 17 |
| 23 | 41 | 33 | 35 | 25 | 19 | 16 | 31 | 12 | 29 |

Construct a stem and leaf diagram to represent this information.

2 The times, in seconds, taken to answer 24 telephone calls are shown.

| 3.2 | 5.6 | 2.4 | 3.5 | 4.3 | 3.6 | 2.8 | 5.8 | 3.3 | 2.6 | 3.2 | 2.8 |
| 5.6 | 3.5 | 4.2 | 1.5 | 2.7 | 2.5 | 3.7 | 3.1 | 2.9 | 4.2 | 2.4 | 3.0 |

Copy and complete the stem and leaf diagram to represent this information.

```
              3 | 2   means 3.2 seconds
1 |
2 |
3 | 2
4 |
5 |
```

> For this data
> the stem represents 'units',
> the leaf represents 'tenths'.

3 The number of press-ups completed by 18 students in one minute is shown.

21	36	41	25	18	32	40	36	22
9	16	24	33	36	27	32	20	28

Draw a stem and leaf diagram to represent this information.

4 The heights, in centimetres, of the heels on 20 different pairs of shoes are shown.

2.7	3.4	2.0	6.0	4.5	3.6	3.1	2.4	4.2	1.8
3.5	2.5	2.6	2.1	4.0	3.5	4.2	2.6	3.9	5.4

Construct a stem and leaf diagram to represent this information.

5 David did a survey to find the cost, in pence, of a loaf of bread.
The stem and leaf diagram shows the results of his survey.

```
                                    2 | 7  means 27 pence
        2 | 7  9
        3 | 1  1  2  9  9  9
        4 | 2  5  9
        5 | 0
```

(a) How many loaves of bread are included in the survey?
(b) What is the range of the prices?
(c) Which price is the mode?

Back to back stem and leaf diagrams

Back to back stem and leaf diagrams can be used to compare two sets of data.

EXAMPLE

The results for examinations in Mathematics and English for a group of students are shown.
The marks are given as percentages.

Mathematics:

91	27	55	69	83	25	45	53	67	71
30	52	45	59	86	73	65	47	54	38

English:

45	40	48	65	75	55	36	85	76	69
64	58	47	64	67	72	83	74	62	51

(a) Construct a back to back stem and leaf diagram for this data.
(b) Compare and comment on the results in Mathematics and English.

(a)
```
   Mathematics                   English          3 | 6  means 36%
              7  5 | 2 |
              8  0 | 3 | 6
           7  5  5 | 4 | 0  5  7  8
  9  5  4  3  2 | 5 | 1  5  8
           9  7  5 | 6 | 2  4  4  5  7  9
              3  1 | 7 | 2  4  5  6
              6  3 | 8 | 3  5
                 1 | 9 |
```

For Mathematics:
5 | 2 means 25%

(b) The range of marks in Mathematics is larger than in English.
The modal group in English is 60 to 69, in Mathematics it is 50 to 59.

1 The stem and leaf diagram shows the distribution of marks for a test marked out of 50.

Boys						Girls							1	7 means 17 marks
				0	9									
		6	2	1	0	1	2	7						
7	6	4	3	2	1	3	5	5	6	7	8			
9	5	3	2	0	3	2	5	9						
		5	1	4	1									
			0	5										

(a) What is the lowest mark for the girls?
(b) What is the highest mark for the boys?
(c) How many pupils scored more than 25 marks?
(d) Compare and comment on the marks for boys and girls.

2 The time taken to complete a computer game is recorded to the nearest tenth of a minute.
The times for a group of 20 adults and 20 children are shown.

Adults					Children				
7.9	8.2	7.3	9.2	6.4	6.4	5.4	4.9	6.6	7.1
6.5	6.1	8.2	7.8	7.0	5.1	6.5	6.3	7.4	6.5
9.4	8.0	7.3	5.4	7.7	8.2	7.7	5.9	6.8	7.6
10.1	5.9	6.7	7.3	6.0	5.3	6.2	8.0	4.7	7.9

(a) Construct a back to back stem and leaf diagram for this data.
(b) Compare and comment on the times for adults and children.

What you need to know

- **Bar chart**. Used for data which can be counted.
  Often used to compare quantities of data in a distribution.
  Bars can be drawn horizontally or vertically.
  Bars are the same width and there are gaps between bars.
  The length of each bar represents frequency.
  The longest bar represents the **mode**.
  The difference between the largest and smallest variable is called the **range**.

- **Bar-line graph**. Instead of drawing bars, horizontal or vertical lines are drawn to show frequency.

- **Pie chart**. Used for data which can be counted.
  Often used to compare proportions of data, usually with the total.
  The whole circle represents all the data.
  The size of each sector represents the frequency of data in that sector.
  The largest sector represents the **mode**.

- **Stem and leaf diagrams**. Used to represent data in its original form.
  Data is split into two parts. The part with the higher place value is the stem,
  e.g.   15   stem 1 leaf 5.
  The data is shown in numerical order on the diagram.

  e.g. 2│3 5 9 represents 23, 25, 29. A key is given to show the value of the data.

  e.g. 3│4 means 34 cm   or   3│4 means 3.4 cm etc.

  Back to back stem and leaf diagrams can be used to compare two sets of data.

1 Some families on holiday at a seaside resort were questioned about their holiday accommodation.

Type of accommodation	Hotel	Bed & Breakfast	Self-catering	Caravan	Camping	Other
Number of families	9	17	11	8	2	3

(a) Draw a bar chart to show this information.
(b) What type of accommodation is the mode?
(c) How many families were questioned?
(d) What percentage of these families had Bed & Breakfast?

2 In one week Ronnie rents out 90 items from his shop as shown in the table below.

Item	Televisions	Videos	Computers	Other equipment
Frequency	35	30	17	8

Draw a pie chart to show all the week's rentals.

AQA

3 The pie chart shows the different types of trees in a wood.
(a) What fraction of the trees in the wood are Ash?

There are 459 Oak trees in the wood.
(b) How many trees are there in the wood altogether?
(c) How many Elm trees are there?

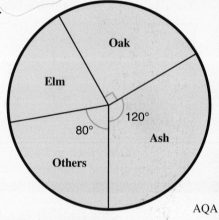

AQA

4 (a) The table shows the fuels used for heating in all the houses in a large town.

Fuel	Number of houses (in 1000's)
Solid fuel	8
Electricity	42
Gas	70
TOTAL	120

Draw a clearly labelled pie chart to represent this information.

(b) This pie chart shows the fuels used for heating in all the houses in a small village.
   (i) What fraction of these houses use gas?
   (ii) Solid fuel is used in 24 houses.
        How many houses are in the village?

(c) Use the information from these two pie charts to say which fuel is most likely to be the mode. Give a reason for your answer.

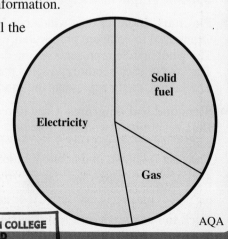

AQA

5 The weights in grams of 20 cherry tomatoes are shown.

5.4	4.6	6.7	3.9	4.2	5.0	6.3	5.4	4.8	3.5
4.6	5.6	5.8	6.0	2.8	4.4	4.7	5.6	5.1	4.8

Draw a stem and leaf diagram to represent this information.

6 A group of students took a test and their results were graded.

$\frac{1}{6}$ were awarded grade A, $\frac{1}{4}$ were awarded grade B,

$\frac{3}{8}$ were awarded grade C, and the rest were ungraded.

(a) Draw accurately a clearly labelled pie chart to represent this information.
(b) Twenty four students took the test.
How many students were awarded grade C?
The distribution of grades for boys in the group is shown in the bar chart.

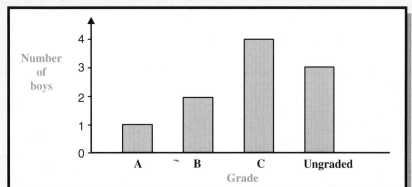

(c) Copy and complete the following table to show the distribution of grades for girls in the group.

Grade	A	B	C	Ungraded
Number of girls				

AQA

7 The frequency diagram shows the distribution of shoe sizes for a class of 40 pupils.

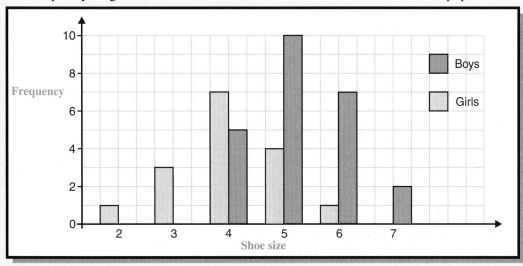

(a) What is the ratio of girls to boys in the class?
Give your answer in its simplest form.
(b) What percentage of the class have shoe size 6?
(c) By working out the range and mode for the boys and for the girls, compare and comment on the shoe sizes for boys and girls.

AQA

Averages and Range

Activity

Some friends went on a school trip.
They each brought different amounts of spending money, as follows:

Penny £25	Keith £35	Nishpal £40	Jayne £20	Stephen £50	Ben £60
Charlotte £35	Suzie £50	Dan £55	Vicki £35	Jack £55	

Ben brought the most and Jayne the least.
What was the difference in the amounts of spending money Ben and Jayne brought?
Which was the most common amount of money?
Who brought the middle amount of money? How much was this?
If the friends shared out their money equally, how much would each person get?

Range

The difference between the highest and lowest amounts is called the **range**.
Range = highest amount − lowest amount

Types of average

The most common amount is called the **mode**.
When the amounts are arranged in order of size, the middle one is called the **median**.
If the money is shared out equally, the amount each person gets is called the **mean**.

EXAMPLE   The price, in pence, of a can of cola in eight different shops is shown.

$$35, \quad 39, \quad 39, \quad 32, \quad 37, \quad 35, \quad 35, \quad 40.$$

Find   (a)   the mode,   (b)   the median,   (c)   the mean price.

(a)   The **mode** is the most common amount.
The most common price is 35.
The mode is 35 pence.
We sometimes say the modal price is 35p.

(b)   The **median** is found by arranging the data in order of size and taking the middle amount.
Arrange the data in order of size.
32,   35,   35,   35,   37,   39,   39,   40.

The middle amount is $\frac{35 + 37}{2} = 36$

The median is 36 pence.

> Where there are an even number of values the median is the average of the middle two.

(c)   The **mean** is found by finding the total of all the data and dividing the total by the number of data values.
Add the data.
$35 + 39 + 39 + 32 + 37 + 35 + 35 + 40 = 292$

The mean $= \frac{292}{8} = 36.5$

The mean is 36.5 pence.

Do not use a calculator for questions 1 to 3.

1 Tony recorded the number of birthday cards sold each day.

3   4   8   1   4

(a) Work out the range of the number of cards sold each day.
(b) Write down the mode.
(c) Find the median number of cards sold each day.

2 Claire recorded the number of e-mail messages she received each day.

2   1   7   4   1

(a) Write down the mode.
(b) Find the median number of messages received each day.
(c) Calculate the mean number of messages received each day.

3 Gail noted the number of stamps on parcels delivered to her office.

3   2   4   5   7   3   4   3   5   3

(a) Write down the mode.
(b) Find the range of the number of stamps on a parcel.
(c) Find the median number of stamps on a parcel.
(d) Calculate the mean number of stamps on a parcel.

4 Sanjay played a computer game 8 times and recorded his scores.

140   135   125   125   130   135   140   135

(a) Which score is the mode?
(b) Calculate the median of his scores.
(c) Find the mean score. Give your answer to the nearest whole number.

5 Frank counted the number of books on different shelves in a library.
He recorded the following numbers.

38   40   26   49   37   43

(a) Find the median number of books on a shelf.
(b) What is the range of the number of books on a shelf?
(c) Calculate the mean number of books on a shelf.
   Give your answer correct to one decimal place.

6 The boot sizes of players in a rugby team are:

9   8   10   11   9   8   10   9   10   9   10   10   8   9   10

(a) Which boot size is the mode?
(b) Find the median boot size.
(c) Calculate the mean boot size. Give your answer correct to one decimal place.

7 The weights of 8 men in a rowing team are:

86 kg   95 kg   89 kg   93 kg   84 kg   78 kg   91 kg   79 kg

Calculate the mean of their weights correct to one decimal place.

8 The mean of six numbers is 5. Five of the numbers are: 2, 3, 7, 8 and 6.
What is the other number?

9 The mean length of 8 rods is 75 cm. An extra rod is added.
The total length of the 9 rods is 729 cm.
What is the length of the extra rod?

10 A class of 10 boys and 15 girls take a test.
The mean mark for the boys is 14.3.
The mean mark for the girls is 15.8.
Calculate the mean mark for the whole class.

After data is collected it is often presented using a **frequency distribution table**.

Johti measured the lengths of some twigs. He recorded the following results.

2 3 2 6 3 6 2 3 5 4 3
2 2 3 5 6 2 6 5 6 2

Johti then presented his results as shown in this frequency distribution table.

Length (cm)	2	3	4	5	6
Number of twigs (frequency)	7	5	1	3	5

Using the frequency distribution table we can find the mode, median, mean and range of the lengths of the twigs that Johti measured.

To find the mode:
The mode is the amount with the greatest frequency.
There were 7 twigs of length 2 cm.
This is more than any other length of twigs.
The mode of the lengths is 2 cm.

To find the median:
The median is the middle amount.
We could list the 21 twigs in order of length and split them up like this:

10 shortest twigs	middle twig	10 longest twigs

This shows that the median length is the length of the 11th twig.
From the table we can see that:

the first 7 twigs are each 2 cm long,
and the next 5 twigs are each 3 cm long.

So the 11th twig is 3 cm long.
The median length is 3 cm.

To find the mean:
$$\text{Mean} = \frac{\text{Total of all lengths}}{\text{Number of lengths}}$$

The best way to do this is to extend the frequency distribution table.

Length (cm) x	Number of twigs (frequency) f	Number of twigs × Length $f \times x$
2	7	14
3	5	15
4	1	4
5	3	15
6	5	30
Totals	$\Sigma f = 21$	$\Sigma fx = 78$

$$\text{Mean} = \frac{\text{Total of all lengths}}{\text{Number of lengths}} = \frac{\Sigma fx}{\Sigma f}$$

Mean $= \frac{78}{21} = 3.714...$

Mean length = 3.7 cm, correct to 1 decimal place.

To find the range:
Range = longest length − shortest length
= 6 − 2 = 4 cm

The range of the lengths is 4 cm.

Σ is the Greek letter 'sigma'.
Σf means the sum of frequencies.
Σfx means the sum of the values of fx.
$$\text{Mean} = \frac{\Sigma fx}{\Sigma f}$$

Calculating averages from diagrams

EXAMPLE   Calculate the range, mode, median and mean of the ages for the data shown in the bar chart.

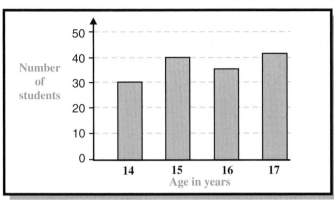

The range is the difference between the highest and lowest ages.
Range = 17 - 14
= 3 years

The most common age is shown by the tallest bar.
So the modal age is 17 years.

Use a table to find the median and the mean.

Age (years) x	Frequency f	Frequency × Age $f \times x$
14	30	420
15	40	600
16	36	576
17	41	697
Totals	$\Sigma f = 147$	$\Sigma fx = 2293$

The middle student is given by: $\frac{147 + 1}{2} = 74$

The 74th student in the list has the median age.
The first 70 students are aged 14 or 15 years.
The 74th student has age 16 years.
Median age is 16 years.

Mean = $\frac{\text{Total of all ages}}{\text{Number of students}} = \frac{\Sigma fx}{\Sigma f}$

Mean = $\frac{2293}{147} = 15.598...$

Mean age is 15.6 years, correct to 1 d.p.

Exercise 3.2

Try to do questions 1 and 4 without using a calculator.

1 Hilary observed customers using the express checkout at a supermarket.

(a) Find the range of the number of items bought.
(b) What is the mode of the number of items bought?
(c) Work out the median number of items bought.
(d) Calculate the mean number of items bought.

Averages and Range

2 Mark asked some students, "How many keys do you have on your key ring?"
The data collection sheet shows the responses he recorded.

Number of keys	Tally
2	II
3	III
4	ℍℍℐ III
5	ℍℍℐ
6	II

(a) Use Mark's data to make a frequency distribution table.
(b) How many students did Mark ask?
(c) Write down the mode of the number of keys on a key ring.
(d) Find the median number of keys.
(e) Calculate the mean number of keys on a key ring.

3 Pat recorded the weekly earnings of a group of students. Her results were as follows:

£25   £40   £30   £45   £25   £25   £30   £35   £45   £25

£35   £30   £35   £25   £35   £30   £35   £25   £45

(a) Show the data in a frequency distribution table.
(b) Find the range of the weekly earnings.
(c) What is the modal weekly earnings?
(d) How many people were in the group?
(e) What is the median weekly earnings?
(f) Calculate the total weekly earnings of the group.
(g) Calculate the mean weekly earnings. Give your answer to the nearest penny.

4 A group of students took part in a quiz on the Highway Code. The bar chart shows their scores.

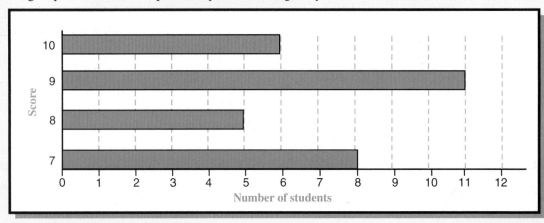

(a) Which score is the mode?
(b) What is the median score?
(c) How many students took part in the quiz?
(d) Calculate the mean score.

5 Find the mode, median and mean for the following sets of data.

(a)

Number of letters delivered	1	2	3	4	5	6
Number of days	6	9	6	6	2	1

(b)

Number of siblings	0	1	2	3	4	5
Frequency	1	4	10	4	1	1

(c)

Number of days absent in a year	0	1	2	3	4	5	6	7	8	9	10	11
Number of students	56	0	0	4	14	10	24	11	21	15	8	2

Grouped frequency distributions

When there is a lot of data, or the data is continuous, **grouped frequency distributions** are used.

Calculating the mean

For a grouped frequency distribution the true value of the mean cannot be found as the actual values of the data are not known.

To **estimate the mean**, we assume that all the values in each class are equal to the midpoint of the class.

$$\text{Estimated mean} = \frac{\Sigma\,(\text{frequency} \times \text{midpoint})}{\text{Total frequency}} = \frac{\Sigma fx}{\Sigma f}$$

Modal class

For a grouped frequency distribution with equal class width intervals, the **modal class** is the class (or group) with the highest frequency.

EXAMPLE

The table shows the masses of a group of children.
(a) Calculate an estimate of the mean mass.
(b) Find the modal class.

Mass (m kg)	Frequency
$40 \leqslant m < 50$	3
$50 \leqslant m < 60$	10
$60 \leqslant m < 70$	6
$70 \leqslant m < 80$	12

(a)

Mass (m kg)	Midpoint x	Frequency f	Frequency × Midpoint $f \times x$
$40 \leqslant m < 50$	45	3	135
$50 \leqslant m < 60$	55	10	550
$60 \leqslant m < 70$	65	6	390
$70 \leqslant m < 80$	75	12	900
	Totals	$\Sigma f = 31$	$\Sigma fx = 1975$

Midpoints of the class $40 \leqslant m < 50$ is given by:
$$\frac{40 + 50}{2} = \frac{90}{2} = 45$$

Estimate of mean $= \dfrac{\Sigma fx}{\Sigma f} = \dfrac{1975}{31} = 63.709\ldots$

Estimate of mean mass $= 63.7$ kg, correct to 3 sig. figs.

(b) The modal class is 70 - 80 kg.

Exercise 3.3

1 Give the modal class and calculate an estimate of the mean for each of the following.

(a)

Salary (s) (£000's)	Number of employees
$10 \leqslant s < 20$	79
$20 \leqslant s < 30$	32
$30 \leqslant s < 40$	14
$40 \leqslant s < 50$	0
$50 \leqslant s < 60$	2

(b)

Time spent watching TV per week (hours)	Number of students
0 -	2
10 -	8
20 -	5
30 -	14
40 - 50	7

2 The table shows the distribution of the weights of some turkeys.

Weight (w kg)	$2 \leqslant w < 4$	$4 \leqslant w < 6$	$6 \leqslant w < 8$	$8 \leqslant w < 10$
Frequency	7	9	5	3

Calculate an estimate of the mean weight of these turkeys.
Give your answer correct to one decimal place.

3 The table shows the distribution of the prices of houses for sale in a particular neighbourhood.

Price (p £000's)	$60 \leqslant p < 80$	$80 \leqslant p < 100$	$100 \leqslant p < 120$	$120 \leqslant p < 140$
Number of houses	3	7	4	1

Calculate an estimate of the mean price of these houses.
Give your answer to an appropriate degree of accuracy.

4 The table shows the distribution of the heights of
trees in a wood.
Calculate an estimate of the mean height.

Height in metres (to nearest 0.1 m)	Number of trees
3.0 - 3.4	12
3.5 - 3.9	10
4.0 - 4.4	23
4.5 - 4.9	18
5.0 - 5.4	13

5 The table shows the distribution of marks in a test.
Calculate an estimate of the mean mark.
Notice that the class intervals are not all equal.

Mark	Number of students
0 - 19	12
20 - 29	23
30 - 34	25
35 - 39	14
40 - 50	3

Comparing distributions

The table shows the marks gained in a test.
We can use the range and the mean to compare the
marks obtained by boys and girls in the test.

Mark (out of 10)	7	8	9	10
Number of boys	2	5	3	0
Number of girls	4	0	2	1

Boys: Range = 9 − 7 = 2
Girls: Range = 10 − 7 = 3

The girls had the higher range of marks.

Boys: Mean $= \dfrac{2 \times 7 + 5 \times 8 + 3 \times 9 + 0 \times 10}{10} = \dfrac{81}{10} = 8.1$

Girls: Mean $= \dfrac{4 \times 7 + 0 \times 8 + 2 \times 9 + 1 \times 10}{7} = \dfrac{56}{7} = 8$

The boys had the higher mean mark.

Overall the boys did better as:
the girls' marks were more spread out with a lower average mark,
the boys' marks were closer together with a higher average mark.

Note:
To compare the
overall standard,
the median could
be used instead of
the mean.

1 The weights of a sample of Cherry tomatoes have a range of 30 g and a mean of 45 g.
The weights of a sample of Moneymaker tomatoes have a range of 90 g and a mean of 105 g.
Compare and comment on the weights of Cherry and Moneymaker tomatoes.

2 The times, in minutes, taken by 8 boys to swim 50 metres are shown.

$$1.8 \quad 2.0 \quad 1.7 \quad 2.2 \quad 2.1 \quad 1.9 \quad 1.8 \quad 2.1$$

(a) (i) What is the range of these times?
  (ii) Calculate the mean time.

The times, in minutes, taken by 8 girls to swim 50 metres are shown.

$$2.1 \quad 1.9 \quad 1.8 \quad 2.3 \quad 1.6 \quad 2.0 \quad 2.6 \quad 1.9$$

(b) Comment on the times taken by these boys and girls to swim 50 m.

3 Use the mean and the range to compare the number of goals scored per match by these teams.

Jays

Number of goals scored per hockey match	Number of matches
0	3
1	5
2	2
3	2
4	1
5	2

Wasps

Number of goals scored per hockey match	Number of matches
0	0
1	2
2	3
3	1
4	2
5	0

4 Use the mean and the range to compare the number of visits to the cinema by these women and men.

Number of visits to the cinema last month	0	1	2	3	4	5	6	More than 6
Number of women	8	9	7	3	2	1	1	0
Number of men	0	12	7	1	0	0	0	0

5 Deepak thought that the girls in his class wore smaller shoes than the boys on average,
but that the boys' shoe sizes were less varied than the girls'.
He did a survey to test his ideas.
The table shows his results. Was he correct?

Shoe size	$4\frac{1}{2}$	5	$5\frac{1}{2}$	6	$6\frac{1}{2}$	7	$7\frac{1}{2}$	8	$8\frac{1}{2}$	9	$9\frac{1}{2}$
Number of boys	1	0	5	4	4	2	1	0	1	0	0
Number of girls	0	2	0	2	3	0	2	0	3	1	1

6 (a) Find the modal class for the ages of customers in each of these two restaurants.
(b) Which restaurant attracts more younger people?
(c) Why is it only possible to find an approximate value for the age range of customers?

Age (years)	0 - 9	10 - 19	20 - 29	30 - 39	40 - 49	50 - 59	60 - 69	70 - 79	80 - 89
MacQuick	8	9	10	7	1	1	3	1	0
Pizza Pit	2	4	12	15	5	3	3	2	1

7 The graphs show the monthly sales of bicycles before and after a marketing campaign.
Calculate the medians and the ranges.
Use your results to compare 'Before' with 'After'.

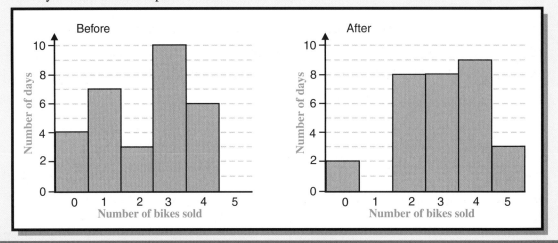

Which is the best average to use?

Many questions in mathematics have definite answers. This one does not.
Sometimes the mean is best, sometimes the median and sometimes the mode.
It all depends on the situation and what you want to use the average for.

EXAMPLE

A youth club leader gets a discount on cans of drinks if she buys all one size.
She took a vote on which size people wanted.
The results were as follows:

Size of can (ml)	100	200	330	500
Number of votes	9	12	19	1

Mode = 330 ml
Median = 200 ml
Mean = 245.6 ml, correct to one decimal place.

Which size should she buy?

The mean is no use at all because she can't buy cans of size 245.6 ml.
Even if the answer is rounded to the nearest whole number (246 ml), it's still no use.
The median is possible because there is an actual 200 ml can.
However, only 12 out of 41 people want this size.
In this case the **mode** is the best average to use, as it is the most popular size.

Exercise **3.5**

In questions 1 to 3 find all the averages possible. State which is the most sensible and why.

1 On a bus: 23 people are wearing trainers,
10 people are wearing boots,
8 people are wearing lace-up shoes.

2 20 people complete a simple jigsaw. Their times, in seconds, are recorded.

5,	6,	8,	8,	9,	10,	11,	11,	12,	12,
12,	15,	15,	15,	15,	18,	19,	20,	22,	200.

3 Here are the marks obtained by a group of 11 students in a mock exam.
The exam was marked out of 100.

5,   6,   81,   81,   82,   83,   84,   85,   86,   87,   88.

4 The times for two swimmers to complete each of ten 25 m lengths are shown below.

| Swimmer A | 30.1 | 30.1 | 30.1 | 30.6 | 30.7 | 31.1 | 31.1 | 31.5 | 31.7 | 31.8 |
| Swimmer B | 29.6 | 29.7 | 29.7 | 29.9 | 30.0 | 30.0 | 30.1 | 30.1 | 30.1 | 44.6 |

Which is the better swimmer? Explain why.

5 The table shows the number of runs scored by two batsmen in several innings.

| Batsman A | 0 | 0 | 10 | 12 | 20 | 22 | 50 | 51 | 81 | 104 | | |
| Batsman B | 0 | 24 | 25 | 27 | 28 | 30 | 33 | 34 | 44 | 45 | 46 | 96 |

Which is the better batsman? Explain why.

6 A teacher sets a test.
He wants to choose a minimum mark for a distinction so that 50% of his students get this result.
Should he use the modal mark, the median mark or the mean mark?
Give a reason for your answer.

7 The cost of Bed and Breakfast at 10 different hotels is given.

£39.50   £55   £60   £50   £49   £42   £95   £59   £39.50   £45

(a) Wyn says, "The average cost of Bed and Breakfast is £39.50."
Which average is he using?
Give a reason why this is not a sensible average to use for this data.
(b) Which of the mode, median and mean best describes the average cost of
Bed and Breakfast?
Give a reason for your answer.

What you need to know

- There are three types of **average**: the **mode**, the **median** and the **mean**.
The **mode** is the most common amount.
The **median** is the middle amount (or the mean of the two middle amounts) when the amounts are arranged in order of size.

$$\textbf{Mean} = \frac{\text{Total of all amounts}}{\text{Number of amounts}}$$

- The **range** is a measure of **spread**.
Range = highest amount − lowest amount

- To find the mean of a **frequency distribution** use: $\text{Mean} = \frac{\text{Total of all amounts}}{\text{Number of amounts}} = \frac{\Sigma fx}{\Sigma f}$

- To find the mean of a **grouped frequency distribution**, first find the value of the midpoint of each class.
Then use: $\text{Estimated mean} = \frac{\text{Total of all amounts}}{\text{Number of amounts}} = \frac{\Sigma fx}{\Sigma f}$

- Choosing the best average to use:
When the most **popular** value is wanted use the **mode**.
When **half** of the values have to be above the average use the **median**.
When a **typical** value is wanted use either the **mode** or the **median**.
When all the **actual** values have to be taken into account use the **mean**.
When the average should not be distorted by a few very small or very large values do **not** use the mean.

1 The lateness of 12 buses is recorded.
The results, in minutes, are shown.

                5   6   7   8   8   10   10   10   11   12   13   14

(a) (i)   What is the range of lateness for these buses?
     (ii) Calculate the mean lateness for these buses.

The lateness of 12 trains is also recorded.
The range in lateness for these trains is 14 minutes and the mean lateness is 5 minutes.
(b)   Compare and comment on the lateness for these buses and trains.

2 (a)   Find the range and mode of these prices.
(b)   Calculate the median and mean price of a bottle of milk.

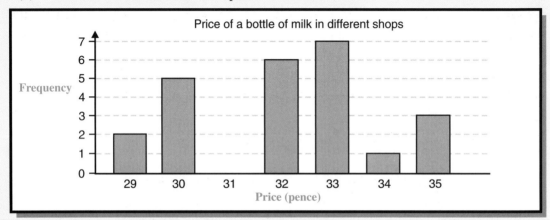

3 David is playing cricket.
The table shows the number of runs he has scored off each ball so far.

Number of runs	0	1	2	3	4	5	6
Number of balls	3	8	4	3	5	0	2

(a) (i)   What is the median number of runs per ball?
     (ii) Calculate the mean number of runs per ball.

Off the next five balls, David scores the following runs: 4, 4, 5, 3 and 6.
(b) (i)   Calculate the new median.
     (ii) Calculate the new mean.
(c)   Give a reason why the mean is used, rather than the median, to give the average number
      of runs scored per ball.
                                                                              AQA

4 Sita plays in the school netball team.
After 8 games her mean score is 6.5 goals.
(a)   What is the total number of goals that Sita has scored in these 8 games?
(b)   Selection for the County team is made after 9 games have been played.
      Sita will be chosen for the County team if her mean score is 7 goals or more.
      What is the smallest number of goals she must score in the
      ninth game in order to be chosen?
(c)   In the ninth game she actually scores 10 goals.
      Does her mean score of goals increase or decrease?
      Explain your answer.

                                                                              AQA

34

5 In an experiment 50 people were asked to estimate the length of a rod to the nearest centimetre. The results were recorded.

Length (cm)	20	21	22	23	24	25	26	27	28	29
Frequency	0	4	6	7	9	10	7	5	2	0

(a) Find the value of the median.
(b) Calculate the mean length.
(c) In a second experiment another 50 people were asked to estimate the length of the same rod.
The most common estimate was 23 cm.
The range of the estimates was 13 cm.
Make **two** comparisons between the results of the two experiments.   AQA

6 The weekly wages of employees are recorded.

Wage (£)	100 -	200 -	300 -	400 -	500 -	600 - 1000
Frequency	2	13	4	0	2	12

(a) Which is the modal group?
(b) In which group is the median value?
(c) Without calculating, state which of the mean, mode or median is the largest.
Explain your answer.   AQA

7 On holiday Val records the length of time people stay in the pool.
The results are shown in the table.

Time (t mins)	Number of people
$0 < t \leqslant 10$	4
$10 < t \leqslant 20$	7
$20 < t \leqslant 30$	3
$30 < t \leqslant 40$	2
	16

Calculate an estimate of the mean time spent in the pool.
Give your answer to an appropriate degree of accuracy.   AQA

8 Mrs Wilson wants to sell her herd of dairy cows.
A buyer will need to know the herd's average daily yield of milk.
The daily milk yield, p litres, is monitored over 5 weeks.
The table shows the results of this survey.

Milk yield (p litres)	Frequency (f)
$140 \leqslant p < 145$	3
$145 \leqslant p < 150$	5
$150 \leqslant p < 155$	9
$155 \leqslant p < 160$	6
$160 \leqslant p < 165$	8
$165 \leqslant p < 170$	4
Total	35

(a) Mrs Wilson finds the modal class for the daily yield. What is this value?
(b) Calculate the estimated mean daily milk yield.
(c) Which is the more suitable average for Mrs Wilson to use?
Give a reason for your answer.

CHAPTER 4

Presentation of Data 2

Time series

The money spent on shopping **each day**, the gas used **each quarter** and the rainfall **each month** are all examples of **time series**.
A time series is a set of readings taken at time intervals.

A time series is often used to monitor progress and to show the **trend** (increases and decreases) so that future performance can be predicted.
The type of graph used in this situation is called a **line graph**.

EXAMPLE

The table shows the temperature of a patient taken every half-hour.

Time	0930	1000	1030	1100	1130	1200
Temperature °C	36.9	37.1	37.6	37.2	36.5	37.0

Draw a line graph to illustrate the data.

To draw a line graph of this information, the given values are plotted and then joined to show the trend.

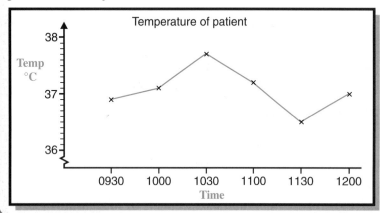

Only the plotted points show **known values**.

Lines are drawn to show the **trend**.

What is the highest temperature recorded?

*Explain why the graph can only be used to give an **estimate** of the patient's temperature at 1115.*

Exercise 4.1

1 The midday temperature at a seaside resort was recorded each day for one week.
The line graph shows the results.

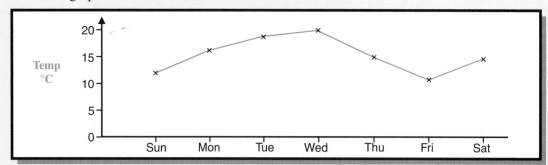

(a) What was the midday temperature on Thursday?
(b) Explain why you cannot use this line graph to estimate the temperature at midnight on Monday.

2 The number of cars sold by a car dealer is recorded each month.
The line graph shows the results for the first six months of a year.

(a) How many cars were sold in February?
(b) In which months were more than 5 cars sold?
(c) Explain why you cannot estimate how many cars were sold halfway through April.

3 Each year, on his birthday, a teenager records his height.
The table shows the results.

Age (yrs)	13	14	15	16	17	18	19
Height (cm)	145	151	157	165	174	179	180

(a) Draw a line graph to represent this information.
(b) Use your graph to estimate:
  (i) the height of the teenager when he was $14\frac{1}{2}$ years of age,
  (ii) the age of the teenager when he reached 160 cm in height.

4 Joan is a member of Weight Watchers.
She records her weight at the beginning of each week.
The line graph shows a record of her weight for six weeks.

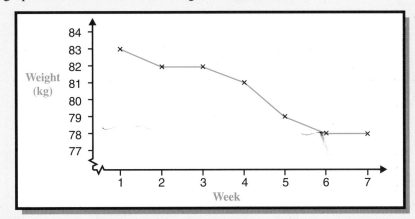

(a) What was Joan's weight at the beginning of Week 2?
(b) What was Joan's weight at the end of Week 2?
(c) How much weight did Joan lose in 6 weeks?
(d) In which week did Joan's weight first fall below 80 kg?

Seasonal variation

The graph below shows the amount of gas used by a householder each quarter over a period of 3 years.

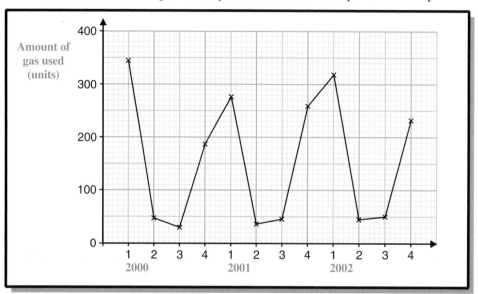

The graph shows high points for winter months and low points for summer months. These ups and downs occur because more (or less) gas is used at certain times of the year. As these ups and downs vary with the seasons of the year they are called **seasonal variations**.

To get a better idea of the average number of units of gas used each quarter we need to smooth out these seasonal variations.

Moving averages

To smooth out seasonal variations we need to find the average for every four quarters moving forward one quarter at a time. These are called **moving averages**.

The first moving average is found by calculating the mean for the four quarters of 2000.

$$\frac{345 + 49 + 30 + 188}{4} = \frac{612}{4} = 153$$

The second moving average is found by calculating the mean of the last three quarters in 2000 and the first quarter in 2001.

$$\frac{49 + 30 + 188 + 277}{4} = \frac{544}{4} = 136$$

This process is repeated moving forward one quarter at a time.

Because these averages are calculated for four consecutive quarters at a time they are called **4-point moving averages**.

The table opposite shows a useful way of setting out the calculations.

Copy and complete the table.

The number of points chosen for the moving average depends on the pattern in the data.

In the example given a 4-point moving average was chosen because the pattern was repeated every 4 quarters.

	Gas used		Moving average calculations			
Year	Quarter	Units				
2000	1	345	345			
	2	49	49	49		
	3	30	30	30	30	
	4	188	188	188	188	
2001	1	277		277	277	
	2	37			37	
	3	46				
	4	260				
2002	1	319				
	2	45				
	3	50				
	4	232				
4-point moving sum			612	544	532	
4-point moving average			153	136		

38

1 These values have been taken at equal time intervals.
Calculate the 3-point moving averages.

| 17 | 58 | 30 | 14 | 61 | 33 | 23 | 55 | 42 |

2 These values have been taken at equal time intervals.
Calculate the 5-point moving averages.

| 27 | 26 | 15 | 34 | 42 | 26 | 24 | 17 | 44 | 54 |

3 The number of new cars sold each quarter by a garage for the last three years is shown.

Year	2000				2001				2002			
Quarter	1	2	3	4	1	2	3	4	1	2	3	4
Number of cars sold	20	15	25	12	18	13	21	8	14	9	17	5

Calculate the 4-quarterly moving averages.

4 Calculate the value of the third average in a 5-point moving average for these values.

| 5 | 7 | 10 | 4 | 1 | 7 | 11 | 13 | 6 | 7 |

5 These values have been taken at equal time intervals.

| 160 | 640 | 310 | 145 | 670 | 355 | 175 | 640 | 385 |

Calculate an appropriate moving average.

Moving average graphs

Moving averages are calculated in order to investigate the general **trend** in a time series.

To investigate the trend the moving averages are plotted on the same diagram as the original graph.

Each moving average is plotted at the midpoint of the period to which it refers, so in the case of the gas used, the first moving average is plotted midway between the 2nd and 3rd quarters of 2000, the second is plotted midway between the 3rd and 4th quarters of 2000 and so on.

When all the points have been plotted a line of best fit is drawn for the moving averages to show the general **trend**.

The graph below shows the moving average values and trend line for the amount of gas used over a three-year period.

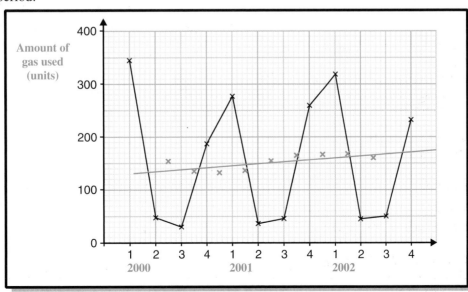

The trend shows a slight increase in the amount of gas used.

1 The table shows the amount of water used every 6 months by a householder over a period of 5 years.

Year	1998		1999		2000		2001		2002	
Month	Feb	Sept	Feb	Sept	Feb	Sept	Feb	Sept	Feb	Sept
Water used (cubic metres)	46	57	33	55	46	57	72	83	42	57

(a) Plot these values on graph paper.
(b) Calculate a 2-point moving average.
(c) Plot the moving averages on your graph.
(d) Comment on the trend in the amount of water used.

2 The table shows the quarterly electricity bills for a householder

Quarterly electricity bills

		Feb	May	Aug	Nov
	2000	£64.75	£72.16	£57.71	£67.80
Year	2001	£60.51	£74.43	£46.33	£67.39
	2002	£81.39	£75.69	£48.24	£61.65

(a) Use the data to draw a graph.
(b) Calculate a 4-point moving average.
(c) Plot the moving averages on your graph.
(d) Comment on the trend in the cost of electricity.

3 The table shows the termly absences from school for a class over a four-year period.

Termly absences

		Autumn	Spring	Summer
	Year 8	19	54	32
	Year 9	22	132	35
Year	Year 10	28	57	47
	Year 11	25	51	62

(a) Use the data to draw a graph.
(b) Calculate the values of a suitable moving average.
(c) Plot the moving averages on your graph.
(d) Comment on the trend in the number of absences for this class.

4 The table gives the daily sales (in £100's) for a new shop during the first three weeks of trading.

Daily sales

	Mon	Tue	Wed	Thu	Fri	Sat
Week 1	57	39	27	34	56	74
Week 2	38	34	28	32	61	83
Week 3	43	37	31	43	67	92

(a) Plot these values on graph paper.
(b) Calculate a 6-point moving average.
(c) Plot the moving averages on the same graph.
(d) Draw a trend line.
(e) Comment on the trend in sales.
(f) Estimate the daily sales for Monday in Week 4.

5 The number of new homes completed each quarter by a builder for the last three years is shown.

Year	2000				2001				2002			
Quarter	1	2	3	4	1	2	3	4	1	2	3	4
Number of new homes	21	35	36	18	19	23	28	14	15	19	22	9

(a) Plot these values on graph paper.
(b) Calculate the values of a suitable moving average.
(c) Plot the moving averages on the same graph.
(d) Draw a trend line by eye.
(e) Comment on the trend.
(f) Estimate the number of new homes completed by the builder in the first quarter of 2003.

Frequency diagrams

We use **bar charts** when data can be counted and there are only a few different items of data.
If there is a lot of data, or the data is continuous, we draw a **histogram** or **frequency polygon**.

Histograms

Histograms are used to present information contained in **grouped frequency distributions**. In this section we will only be drawing histograms for grouped frequency distributions that have equal class width intervals.

> Histograms with equal class width intervals look like bar charts with no gaps.

Frequency polygons

Frequency polygons are often used instead of histograms when we need to compare two, or more, groups of data.
To draw a frequency polygon:

- plot the frequencies at the midpoint of each class interval,
- join successive points with straight lines.

To compare data, frequency polygons for different groups of data can be drawn on the same diagram.

EXAMPLE

1 The frequency distribution of the heights of some boys is shown.

Height (cm)	130 -	140 -	150 -	160 -	170 -	180 -
Frequency	1	7	12	9	3	0

> **Note:**
> 130 - means 130 or more but less than 140.

Draw a histogram and a frequency polygon to illustrate the data.

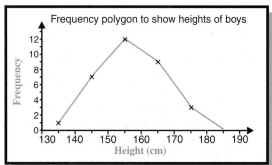

Individual bars are not labelled because the horizontal axis represents a **continuous** variable.

Presentation of Data 2

EXAMPLE

2 A supermarket opens at 0800. The frequency diagram shows the distribution of the times employees arrive for work.

(a) How many employees arrive before 0730?
(b) How many employees arrive between 0730 and 0800?
(c) How many employees arrive after 0800?
(d) What is the modal class?

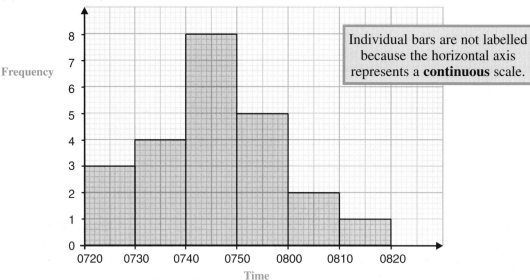

Individual bars are not labelled because the horizontal axis represents a **continuous** scale.

(a) 3 employees arrive before 0730.
(b) Between 0730 and 0740, 4 employees arrive.
Between 0740 and 0750, 8 employees arrive.
Between 0750 and 0800, 5 employees arrive.
Employees arriving between 0730 and 0800 = 4 + 8 + 5 = 17.
(c) 3 employees arrive after 0800.
(d) The modal class is the time interval with the highest frequency.
The class interval 0740 to 0750 has the highest frequency.
The modal class is therefore, "0740 and less than 0750".

Exercise 4.4

1 The frequency diagram shows information about the weights of 100 people.
10 people weigh 80 kg or more.

(a) How many people weigh between 60 kg and 70 kg?
(b) How many people weigh less than 60 kg?
(c) How many people weigh 70 kg or more?
(d) Harry is included in the survey. He weighs 80 kg. In which class interval has his weight been recorded?

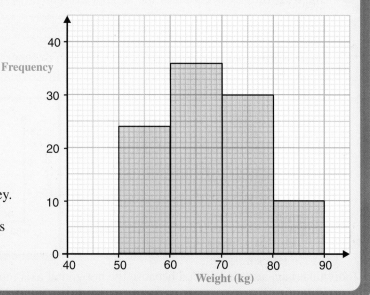

② The frequency polygon shows the distribution of the distances travelled to work by the employees at a supermarket.

When drawing frequency polygons, frequencies are plotted at the midpoints of the class intervals.

(a) How many employees travel between 2 km and 3 km to work?

(b) How many employees travel more than 4 km to work?

③ The distances, in metres, recorded in a long jump competition are shown.

5.46	5.80	5.97	5.43	6.72	5.93	6.26	6.64
5.13	6.05	6.36	6.88	6.11	5.50	6.38	5.71
6.55	6.10	5.84	5.49	6.20	5.67	6.34	6.00

(a) Copy and complete the following frequency distribution table.

Distance (m metres)	$5.00 \leqslant m < 5.50$	$5.50 \leqslant m < 6.00$	$6.00 \leqslant m < 6.50$	$6.50 \leqslant m < 7.00$
Frequency				

(b) Draw a histogram to illustrate the data.

(c) Which is the modal class?

④ The table shows the grouped frequency distribution of the marks of 200 students.

Mark (%)	1 - 10	11 - 20	21 - 30	31 - 40	41 - 50	51 - 60	61 - 70	71 - 80	81 - 90	91 - 100
Number of Students	0	2	16	24	44	50	35	20	8	1

Draw a frequency diagram to show these results.

⑤ A frequency distribution of the heights of some girls is shown.

Height (h cm)	$130 \leqslant h < 140$	$140 \leqslant h < 150$	$150 \leqslant h < 160$	$160 \leqslant h < 170$	$170 \leqslant h < 180$
Frequency	3	5	12	4	1

Draw a histogram to illustrate the data.

⑥ The frequency polygon shows the distribution of the ages of pupils who attend a village school.

(a) How many pupils are under 4 years of age?

(b) How many pupils are between 5 and 6 years of age?

(c) How many pupils are over 7 years of age?

(d) How many pupils attend the school?

7 The frequency polygon shows the distribution of the marks scored in a science test.

Copy and complete the frequency distribution table for these results.

Mark	Frequency
0 and less than 10	
10 and less than 20	
20 and less than 30	
30 and less than 40	

8 Here are the marks of pupils for a test in French.

44	23	36	60	50	45	35	56	41	37
31	57	43	29	67	45	34	54	29	25
46	52	27	36	39	45	41	54	49	37

(a) Copy and complete the frequency distribution table for these results.

Mark	Tally	Frequency
20 and less than 30		
30 and less than 40		
40 and less than 50		
50 and less than 60		
60 and less than 70		

(b) Which is the modal class?
(c) Draw a frequency polygon to illustrate the data.

9 The table shows the distances travelled to school by 100 children.

Distance (k km)	$0 \leqslant k < 2$	$2 \leqslant k < 4$	$4 \leqslant k < 6$	$6 \leqslant k < 8$	$8 \leqslant k < 10$
Frequency	27	35	22	10	6

Draw a frequency polygon to illustrate this information.

10 The frequency distribution of the weights of some students is shown.

Weight (kg)	40 -	50 -	60 -	70 -	80 -	90 - 100
Number of males	0	6	11	5	2	1
Number of females	3	14	8	0	0	0

(a) On the same diagram draw a frequency polygon for the males and a frequency polygon for the females.
(b) Compare and comment on the weights of male and female students.

11 The table shows the results of students in tests in English and Mathematics.

Marks	English	Mathematics
0 and less than 10	0	1
10 and less than 20	4	4
20 and less than 30	9	9
30 and less than 40	12	7
40 and less than 50	0	4

(a) Draw a frequency polygon for the English marks.
(b) On the same diagram draw a frequency polygon for the Mathematics marks.
(c) Compare and comment on the marks of the students in these two tests.

12 The table shows the results for competitors in the 2001 and 2002 Schools' Javelin Championship.
Only the best distance thrown by each competitor is shown.

Distance thrown (m metres)	Number of competitors 2001	Number of competitors 2002
$10 \leqslant m < 20$	0	1
$20 \leqslant m < 30$	3	4
$30 \leqslant m < 40$	14	19
$40 \leqslant m < 50$	21	13
$50 \leqslant m < 60$	7	11
$60 \leqslant m < 70$	0	2

(a) On the same diagram draw a frequency polygon for the 2001 results and then a frequency polygon for the 2002 results.
(b) Compare and comment on the results.

Misleading graphs

Television programmes, newspapers and advertisements frequently use graphs and diagrams to present information.
Many of the graphs and diagrams they use are well presented and give a fair interpretation of the facts, others are deliberately drawn to mislead.

Look at the graph below.
Why is it misleading?

You should notice that the vertical scale does not begin at zero.
The actual increase in profits is only £200 but the graph makes it appear much more.

Sales

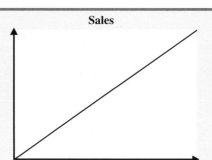

1 The following graph is misleading.
Explain why.

2

This graph is drawn to compare the money
raised for charity by two schools.
School A has raised £400.
School B has raised £500.
Why is the graph misleading?

3 This graph shows how the price of a litre of petrol
has increased.
Why is the graph misleading?

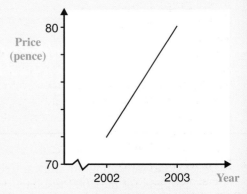

4

| **PASS WITH US** |
| Our learners only need an average of 8 lessons before they can take the driving test. |

Give a reason why this advertisement may be misleading.

5 This diagram is used to compare the average
price of a house in two different years.
Why is the diagram misleading?

Big growth in house prices

6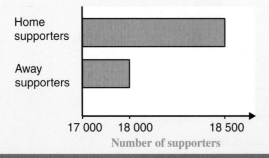

The graph shows the number of
"Home" supporters and the number of
"Away" supporters at a football match.
Why is the graph misleading?

7

Kite sales take off

Number of kites sold (1000's)

120

100

80

1980   1990   2000

Year

Why is this diagram misleading?

8 The graph shows the votes cast for a political party in five elections.
Why is the graph misleading?

Votes cast

1990 1992 1995 1996 2000 Year

What you need to know

- A **time series** is a set of readings taken at time intervals.
- A **line graph** is used to show a time series. Only the plotted points represent actual values.
  Points are joined by lines to show the **trend**.
- Variations in a time series which recur with the seasons of the year are called **seasonal variations**.
- **Moving averages** are used to smooth out variations in a time series so that the trend can be seen.
- **Histogram**. Used to illustrate **grouped frequency distributions.**
  The horizontal axis is a continuous scale.
- **Frequency polygon**. Used to illustrate grouped frequency distributions.
  Often used to compare two or more distributions on the same diagram.
  Frequencies are plotted at the midpoints of the class intervals and joined with straight lines.
  The horizontal axis is a continuous scale.
- **Misleading graphs**. Graphs may be misleading if:
  the scales are not labelled,   the scales are not uniform,   the frequency does not begin at zero.

Review Exercise 4

1 Jim bought his house in 1985.
The table shows the value of Jim's house on January 1st at 5-yearly intervals.

Year	1985	1990	1995	2000
Value of house (£)	60 000	95 000	68 000	84 000

(a) Draw a line graph to show this information.
(b) Estimate the value of Jim's house on July 1st 1988.
(c) Jim uses the graph to estimate the value of his house on January 1st 2005.
    Give a reason why his estimate may not be very accurate.

2 A factory operates 5 days a week.
The table shows the number of workers absent each day over the last 3 weeks.

Week	1					2					3				
Day	M	Tu	W	Th	F	M	Tu	W	Th	F	M	Tu	W	Th	F
Number of absences	6	5	2	3	11	4	3	1	4	13	5	3	2	4	12

(a) Plot these values on graph paper.
(b) Calculate a 5-point moving average.
(c) Plot the moving averages on the same graph.
(d) Draw a trend line by eye.
(e) Comment on the trend.

3 The following graph appeared in a newspaper advert.

Computer Sales

Write down **two** ways in which the graph is misleading.

AQA

4 Aimee does a survey of the distances people travel to work.
The frequency diagram shows the results.

(a) Which is the modal class?
(b) How many people travel between 4 km and 5 km?
(c) How many people were included in the survey?

5 The frequency polygon illustrates the time taken by students to complete a puzzle.
Copy and complete the table for the data.

Time (seconds)	Frequency
10 and less than 20	
20 and less than 30	
30 and less than 40	

48

6 A school holds a 'mini marathon'.
Every pupil who finishes the marathon gains points.
The table shows the times taken, the number of pupils and the points gained.

Time interval	Number of pupils	Points gained
1 hour or less	0	60
More than 1 hour but less than or equal to 2 hours	10	50
More than 2 hours but less than or equal to 3 hours	15	40
More than 3 hours but less than or equal to 4 hours	40	30
More than 4 hours but less than or equal to 5 hours	57	20
More than 5 hours but less than or equal to 6 hours	23	10

(a) What was the most common time interval?
(b) Ann and her brother Ben both take part.
      Ann finishes only 5 minutes before Ben but gains twice as many points.
      Explain how this could have happened.
(c) Draw a frequency diagram to show the number of pupils and the time taken.   AQA

7 The grouped frequency table shows the results of a survey about the distance travelled to work by people each day.

Distance (km)	0 -	4 -	8 -	12 -	16 -	20 - 24
Number of people	10	24	30	8	7	1

(a) Draw a histogram to illustrate this information.
(b) How many people travelled less than 8 kilometres?

8 The table gives information about the weight of the potato crop produced by 100 potato plants of two different types.

Weight of potatoes per plant w kg	Number of plants Type X	Number of plants Type Y
$0 \leqslant w < 0.5$	0	0
$0.5 \leqslant w < 1.0$	3	0
$1.0 \leqslant w < 1.5$	12	6
$1.5 \leqslant w < 2.0$	55	39
$2.0 \leqslant w < 2.5$	23	32
$2.5 \leqslant w < 3.0$	7	23
$3.0 \leqslant w < 3.5$	0	0

(a) On the same diagram draw a frequency polygon for each type of potato.
(b) Which type of potato produces the heavier crop?
(c) (i)   Which type of potato has more variation in the weight of the crop?
      (ii) Give a reason for your answer.   AQA

CHAPTER 5

Scatter Graphs

When we investigate statistical information we often find there are connections between sets of data, for example height and weight. In general taller people weigh more than shorter people.

To see if there is a connection between two sets of data we can plot a **scatter graph**.
The scatter graph below shows information about the heights and weights of ten boys.

○ ○ ○ ○ ○ ○ ○ ○ ○ ○
Each cross plotted on the graph represents the weight and height of one boy.

The diagram shows that taller boys generally weigh more than shorter boys.

Exercise 5.1

1 The scatter graph shows the shoe sizes and heights of a group of girls.

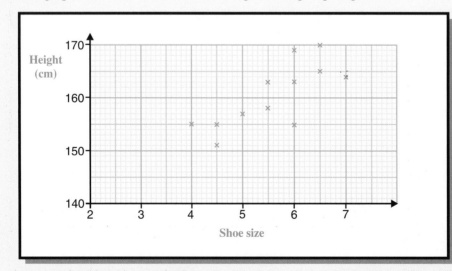

(a) How many girls wear size $6\frac{1}{2}$ shoes?

(b) How tall is the girl with the largest shoe size?

(c) Does the shortest girl wear the smallest shoes?

(d) What do you notice about the shoe sizes of taller girls compared to shorter girls?

2 The scatter graph shows the marks obtained by a group of students in a test in English and a test in French.

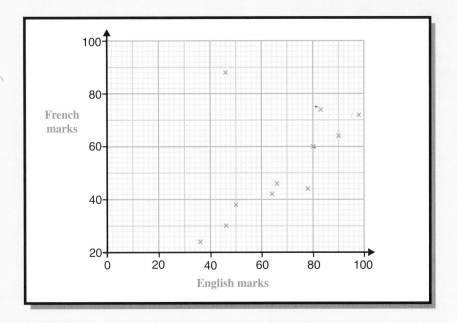

(a)   Janice got the top mark in English. What mark did she get in French?

(b)   The results of one student look out of place.
   (i)   What marks did the student get in English and in French?
   (ii)   Give a possible reason why this student has different results from the rest of the group.

3 The scatter graph shows the pulse rates of a group of women after doing aerobics for one minute and their weight.

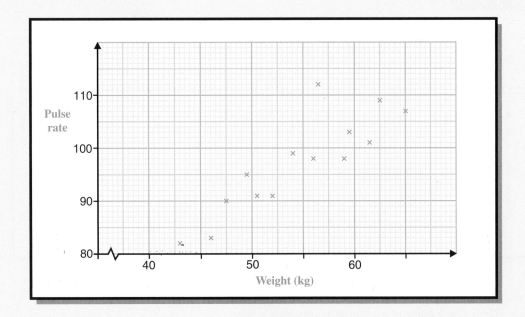

(a)   How many of these women weigh less than 50 kg?

(b)   What is the weight of the woman with the lowest pulse rate?

(c)   What do you notice about the pulse rates of heavier women compared to lighter women?

Correlation

The relationship between two sets of data is called **correlation**.

In general the scatter graph of the heights and weights shows that as height increases, weight increases. This type of relationship shows there is a **positive correlation** between height and weight.

But if as the value of one variable increases the value of the other variable decreases, then there is a **negative correlation** between the variables.

When no relationship exists between two variables there is **zero correlation**.

The following graphs show types of correlation.

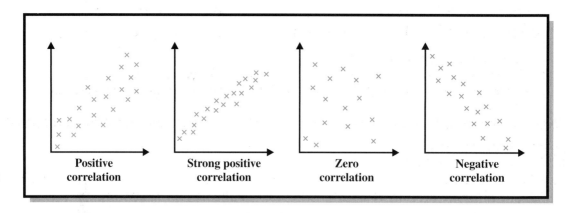

As points get closer to a straight line the stronger the correlation.
Perfect correlation is when all the points lie on a straight line.

Exercise 5.2

 (a) Which of these graphs shows the strongest positive correlation?
(b) Which of these graphs shows perfect negative correlation?
(c) Which of these graphs shows the weakest correlation?

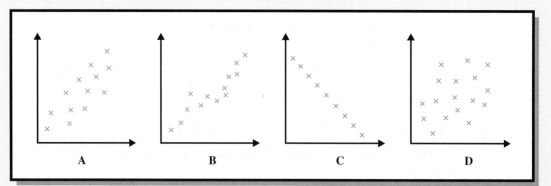

2 Describe the type of correlation you would expect between:
(a) the age of a car and its secondhand selling price,
(b) the heights of children and their ages,
(c) the shoe sizes of children and the distance they travel to school,
(d) the number of cars on the road and the number of road accidents,
(e) the engine size of a car and the number of kilometres it can travel on one litre of fuel.

3 The table shows the distance travelled and time taken by motorists on different journeys.

Distance travelled (km)	30	45	48	80	90	100	125
Time taken (hours)	0.6	0.9	1.2	1.2	1.3	2.0	1.5

(a) Draw a scatter graph for the data.
(b) What do you notice about distance travelled and time taken?
(c) Give one reason why the distance travelled and the time taken are not perfectly correlated.

4 Tyres were collected from a number of different cars. The table shows the distance travelled and depth of tread for each tyre.

Distance travelled (1000 km)	4	5	9	10	12	15	18	25	30
Depth of tread (mm)	9.2	8.4	7.6	8	6.5	7.4	7	6.2	5

(a) Draw a scatter graph for the data.
(b) What do you notice about the distance travelled and the depth of tread?
(c) Give one reason why the distance travelled and the depth of tread are not perfectly correlated.

Line of best fit

We have seen that **scatter graphs** can be used to illustrate two sets of data and, from the distribution of points plotted, an indication of the relationship which exists between the data can be seen.

The scatter graph of heights and weights has been redrawn below and a **line of best fit** has been drawn, by eye, to show the relationship between height and weight.

Lines of best fit

● The slope of the line shows the trend of the points.

● A line is only drawn if the correlation (positive or negative) is strong.

● The line does not have to go through the origin of the graph.

Where there is a relationship between the two sets of data the line of best fit can be used to estimate other values.

A boy is 132 cm tall.
Using the line of best fit an estimate of his weight is 40 kg.

In a similar way we can use the line to estimate the height of a boy when we know his weight.
A boy weighs 43 kg. Estimate his height.

1 The table shows the ages and weights of ten babies.

Age (weeks)	2	4	9	7	13	5	6	1	10	12
Weight (kg)	3.5	3.3	4.2	4.7	5	3.8	4	3	5	5.5

(a) Use this information to draw a scatter graph.
(b) What type of correlation is shown on the scatter graph?
(c) Draw a line of best fit.
(d) Mrs Wilson's baby is 11 weeks old.
   Use the graph to estimate the weight of her baby.

2 The table shows the temperature of water as it cools in a freezer.

Time (minutes)	5	10	15	20	25	30
Temperature (°C)	36	29	25	20	15	8

(a) Use this information to draw a scatter graph.
(b) What type of correlation is shown?
(c) Draw a line of best fit.
(d) Use the graph to estimate the time when the temperature of the water reaches 0°C.

3 The table shows the weights and fitness factors for a number of women.
The higher the fitness factor the fitter a person is.

Weight (kg)	45	48	50	54	56	60	64	72	99	112
Fitness Factor	41	48	40	40	35	40	34	30	17	15

(a) Use this information to draw a scatter graph.
(b) What type of correlation is shown on the scatter graph?
(c) Draw a line of best fit.
(d) Use the graph to estimate:
   (i) the fitness factor for a woman whose weight is 80 kg,
   (ii) the weight of a woman whose fitness factor is 22.

4 The following table gives the marks obtained by some candidates taking examinations in French and German.

Mark in French	53	35	39	53	50	59	36	43
Mark in German	64	32	44	70	56	68	40	48

(a) (i) Use this information to draw a scatter graph.
   (ii) Draw the line of best fit by eye.
(b) Use the graph to estimate:
   (i) the mark in German for a candidate who got 70 in French,
   (ii) the mark in French for a candidate who got 58 in German.
(c) Which of the two estimates in (b) is likely to be more reliable?
   Give a reason for your answer.

5 The table shows the times taken by some boys to run 200 metres and their inside-leg measurements.

Time (seconds)	31	33	34	38	38	38	42	43	45	47
Inside-leg (cm)	69	65	72	63	69	75	70	65	74	69

(a) Plot a scatter graph of these data.
(b) Explain why a line of best fit for these data would not be useful in estimating the time for a different boy to run 200 metres by taking his inside-leg measurement.

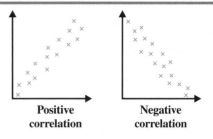

- A **scatter graph** can be used to show the relationship between two sets of data.

- The relationship between two sets of data is referred to as **correlation**.

- You should be able to recognise **positive** and **negative** correlation.

| Positive correlation | Negative correlation |

- When there is a relationship between two sets of data a **line of best fit** can be drawn on the scatter graph.
  The correlation is stronger as points get closer to a straight line.
  Perfect correlation is when all the points lie on a straight line.

- The line of best fit can be used to **estimate** the value from one set of the data when the corresponding value of the other set is known.

IDEAS FOR INVESTIGATION

Shoe size and height
Record the heights and shoe sizes of 20 male students.

Plot a scatter graph of "shoe size" against "height".

What type of correlation exists between the shoe sizes and heights of these students?

Take the shoe size of another student.
Can you use the graph to estimate the height of the student?

Investigate further.
You might like to consider age and gender.

Review Exercise 5

① The data from a survey of cars was used to plot several scatter graphs.

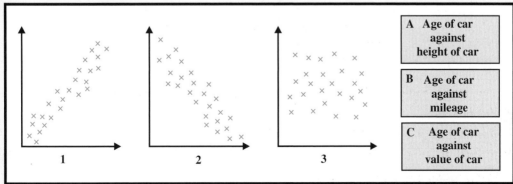

A	Age of car against height of car
B	Age of car against mileage
C	Age of car against value of car

Match each scatter graph to the correct description.

Scatter Graphs . . . Scatter Graphs . . . Scatter Graphs . . .

2 Sandra did a survey of the price of some mathematics books and how many pages they have. She put her results onto a scatter graph as shown.

(a) What does the scatter graph tell you about the connection between the price of a mathematics book and the number of pages?

(b) Copy the scatter graph and draw a line of best fit.

(c) Use your scatter graph to help you to answer these questions.
   (i) A publisher produces a new mathematics book with 340 pages.
   What price would you expect the book to be?
   (ii) You see another new mathematics book advertised in the newspaper.
   It is priced at £7.50.
   How many pages would you expect the book to have?

AQA

3 The scatter graph shows the heights of some plants, d days after germinating.

A line of best fit has been drawn on the graph.

(a) Use the line of best fit to estimate the height of a plant:
   (i) 10 days after germination,
   (ii) 20 days after germination.

(b) Which of your two answers in (a) is likely to be more reliable?
   Give a reason for your answer.

AQA

4 "Bridgit" and "Pong K'I" are two Chinese games. Each game is for two players.
A class of children played each other at
these games.
The table shows the number of wins
obtained by some of the children.

Child	Number of wins at Bridgit	Number of wins at Pong K'I
Ann	14	1
Ben	7	10
Ciri	10	5
Dawn	5	14
Erin	12	3
Fay	7	12
Gil	10	7
Hue	3	16
Ian	5	12
Jo	12	5

(a) Plot these results as a scatter graph.
(b) What does the scatter graph tell you?
(c) Draw a line of best fit.
(d) Sue won 6 games of Bridgit.
Use the scatter graph to estimate the number of games of Pong K'I that Sue won. AQA

5 A number of women do aerobics for one minute.
Their ages and pulse rates are shown in the table.

Age (years)	16	17	22	25	38	42	43	50
Pulse rate (per minute)	82	78	83	90	99	97	108	107

(a) Use this information to draw a scatter graph.
Label the horizontal axis **Age (years)** from 0 to 50.
Label the vertical axis **Pulse rate (per minute)** from 60 to 120.
(b) What type of correlation is there between the ages and pulse rates of these women?
(c) Draw a line of best fit.
(d) Betty is 35 years old.
Use the line of best fit to estimate her pulse rate after doing aerobics for one minute. AQA

6 The table gives information about the age and value of a number of cars of the same type.

Age (years)	1	$4\frac{1}{2}$	6	3	5	2	4
Value (£)	8200	4900	3800	6200	4500	7600	5200

(a) Use the information to draw a scatter graph.
(b) What type of correlation is there between the age and value of these cars?
(c) Draw a line of best fit.
(d) Jo has a car of this type which is 7 years old and is in average condition.
Use the graph to estimate its value.

7 The table gives information about the petrol used for car journeys.

Petrol (litres)	3	5	6	8	4	11	10	9	2
Distance (km)	28	50	70	110	50	110	120	130	24

(a) Draw a scatter graph for this information.
(b) Draw a line of best fit.
(c) Use your graph to estimate:
(i) the distance a car travels on 7 litres of petrol.
(ii) the number of litres of petrol used by a car travelling a distance of 150 km.
(d) Which of the estimates in (c) is likely to be more reliable?
Give a reason for your answer. AQA

Scatter Graphs . . . Scatter Graphs . . . Scatter Graphs . . .

CHAPTER 6

Cumulative Frequency

Cumulative frequency tables

This **frequency table** shows the masses of some stones recorded during an experiment.

Mass (kg)	20 -	30 -	40 -	50 -	60 - 70
Frequency	3	5	10	8	4

The first class is 20 - 30 kg. The **upper class boundary** of this class is 30 kg.

What are the upper class boundaries of the other classes?

Note: If the question does not give the upper class boundaries, then the upper class boundary of each class is equal to the lower class boundary of the next class.

The information given in a frequency table can be used to make a **cumulative frequency table**.

Mass (kg), less than	20	30	40	50	60	70
Cumulative frequency	0	3	8	18	26	30

Mass of stone (less than)	Number of stones
20 kg	0
30 kg	0 + 3 = 3
40 kg	0 + 3 + 5 = 8
50 kg	0 + 3 + 5 + 10 = 18

Cumulative frequency graph

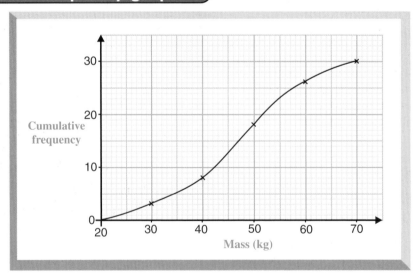

To draw a **cumulative frequency graph**:
1. Draw and label: the **variable** on the horizontal axis,   **cumulative frequency** on the vertical axis.
2. Plot the cumulative frequency against the upper class boundary of each class.
3. Join the points with a smooth curve.

Using a cumulative frequency graph

Median

The median of 13 numbers is the 7th number.
The median of 14 numbers is between the 7th and 8th numbers.
We could call this the "$7\frac{1}{2}$ th" number.

For n numbers, the rule for finding the median is:

Median = $\frac{1}{2}(n + 1)$th number

> The median of a frequency distribution is the value of the middle number.
> On a cumulative frequency graph this value is read from the horizontal axis.

Interquartile range

The **range** of a set of data was covered in Chapter 2 and again in Chapter 3.
It measures how spread out the data is.
Range = highest value − lowest value.
The range is influenced by extreme high or low values of data and can be misleading.

A better way to measure spread is to find the range of the **middle 50%** of the data.
This is called the **interquartile range**.
Interquartile range IQR = Upper Quartile − Lower Quartile

For n numbers the rules for finding the quartiles are:

Lower Quartile = $\frac{1}{4}(n + 1)$th number

Upper Quartile = $\frac{3}{4}(n + 1)$th number

> On a cumulative frequency graph the values of the Upper Quartile and the Lower Quartile are read from the horizontal axis.

EXAMPLE

Using the cumulative frequency graph from the previous page, estimate:

(a) the median mass of the stones,
(b) the interquartile range of the masses of the stones.

(a) There are 30 stones.
$\frac{1}{2}(30 + 1) = 15.5$, so the median is the mass of the 15.5th stone.

Read along from 15.5 on the vertical axis and down to the horizontal axis.
This is shown on the graph.
Median = 48 kg.

(b) $\frac{1}{4}(30 + 1) = 7.75$,
so the lower quartile is the mass of the 7.75th stone.
$\frac{3}{4}(30 + 1) = 23.25$,
so the upper quartile is the mass of the 23.25th stone.
Read these values from the graph.
IQR = Upper Quartile − Lower Quartile
= 55 − 39
= 16 kg
The interquartile range is 16 kg.

> **When n is large**
> When the total frequency, n, is 'large' you need not bother with '+1' in the rules for the median, lower quartile and upper quartile.
>
> Instead use:
>
> median = $\frac{1}{2}n$th number
>
> lower quartile = $\frac{1}{4}n$th number
>
> upper quartile = $\frac{3}{4}n$th number
>
> 'Large' means greater than 50.

1 Silvia made a record of the times students took to walk to school in the morning.

Time (minutes)	0 -	5 -	10 -	15 -	20 -	25 - 30
Number of students	4	12	18	15	8	3

(a) Copy and complete this cumulative frequency table.

Time (minutes), less than	0	5	10	15	20	25	30
Cumulative frequency							

(b) Draw a cumulative frequency graph for the data.
(c) Use your graph to find:
   (i)   the median time,
   (ii) the upper quartile time,
   (iii) the lower quartile time.
(d) Calculate the interquartile range of the times.

2 A secretary weighed a sample of letters to be posted.

Weight (g)	20 -	30 -	40 -	50 -	60 -	70 -	80 - 90
Number of letters	2	4	12	7	8	16	3

(a) How many letters were in the sample?
(b) Draw a cumulative frequency graph for the data.
(c) Use your graph to find:
   (i) the median weight of a letter,
   (ii) the interquartile range of the weights.

3 The times spent by students on mobile phones one day is shown.

Time (t minutes)	$0 \leqslant t < 5$	$5 \leqslant t < 10$	$10 \leqslant t < 15$	$15 \leqslant t < 20$	$20 \leqslant t < 25$
Number of students	34	22	12	8	4

(a) Draw a cumulative frequency graph for the data.
(b) Use your graph to find
   (i) the median time,
   (ii) the interquartile range of the times.

Another look at cumulative frequency graphs

Some variables are discrete and can only take certain values.
In many cases these are whole numbers. For these variables there are gaps between the classes.

For example, this frequency distribution table shows the number of spelling mistakes found in some essays.

Number of mistakes	0 - 5	6 - 10	11 - 15	16 - 20
Number of essays	9	17	8	3

The first class ends at 5. The highest number of spelling mistakes in the class 0 - 5 is 5.
The second class starts at 6.
We take the upper class boundary for the class 0 - 5 to be halfway between 5 and 6, at 5.5.
What are the upper class boundaries for the other classes?

In the following example there are gaps between the classes, because the lengths are measured to the nearest centimetre.

EXAMPLE

In an experiment Sophie measured and recorded the longest roots of plants.

Length (to nearest cm)	0 - 2	3 - 5	6 - 8	9 - 11	12 - 14
Number of plants	0	14	33	23	10

(a) Make a cumulative frequency table for the data Sophie collected.

(b) Draw a cumulative frequency graph for the data.

(c) Use your graph to find:
   (i)   the median length,
   (ii) the interquartile range of lengths.

(d) How many plants had roots at least 11.2 cm long?

> The class 3 - 5 includes measurements from 2.5 cm to 5.5 cm. The upper class boundary is 5.5 cm.

(a)

Length (cm) less than	2.5	5.5	8.5	11.5	14.5
Cumulative frequency	0	14	47	70	80

(b)

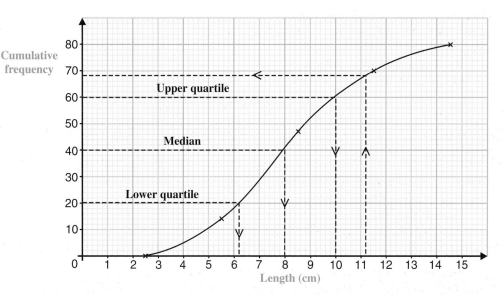

(c) (i) There are 80 plants.
$\frac{1}{2}$ of 80 = 40, so the median is the length of the roots of the 40th plant.
Median = 8.0 cm

   (ii) For the lower quartile use $\frac{1}{4}$ of 80 = 20.
Lower quartile = 6.2 cm
For the upper quartile use $\frac{3}{4}$ of 80 = 60.
Upper quartile = 10.0 cm
IQR = Upper Quartile − Lower Quartile = 10.0 − 6.2 = 3.8 cm

> **Remember**
> Cumulative frequency is plotted against the upper class boundary for each class.

(d) From 11.2 cm on the horizontal axis read upwards to the graph and across to the vertical axis.
There are 68 plants of length less than 11.2 cm.
So the number of plants with roots at least 11.2 cm long is 80 − 68 = 12 plants.

1 The times taken by competitors to complete the crossword in an annual competition were recorded to the nearest minute.

Time (minutes)	10 - 14	15 - 19	20 - 24	25 - 29	30 - 34
Frequency	7	21	37	12	3

(a) Copy and complete the cumulative frequency table.

Time (minutes)	< 9.5	< 14.5	< 19.5	< 24.5	< 29.5	< 34.5
Cumulative frequency						

(b) Draw a cumulative frequency graph for the data.
(c) Use your graph to find:
    (i) the interquartile range of times,
    (ii) the number of competitors who took less than last year's winning time of 16 minutes to complete the crossword.

2 Draw a cumulative frequency graph for the results shown in this table.

Number of marks	0 - 20	21 - 25	26 - 30	31 - 40
Number of students	10	17	23	14

(a) Find the median mark.
(b) Find the interquartile range of marks.
(c) The minimum mark for a Grade A is 33.
    What percentage of students gained Grade A?
(d) 10% of students failed.
    What was the minimum mark for a pass?

3 A survey was made of the heights of plants produced by a batch of seed.

Height (h cm)	$80 \leqslant h < 85$	$85 \leqslant h < 90$	$90 \leqslant h < 95$	$95 \leqslant h < 100$	$100 \leqslant h < 105$
Frequency	20	35	15	11	14

(a) How many plants were measured in the survey?
(b) Draw a cumulative frequency graph for the data.
    Label the horizontal axis from 70 cm to 110 cm.
(c) Use your graph to estimate:
    (i) the median height,
    (ii) the interquartile range of heights,
    (iii) the number of plants taller than 97.5 cm.
(d) The shortest 10 plants are used for testing.
    Estimate the height of the tallest of these 10 plants.

4 The times spent listening to the radio last week by some students is shown.

Time (t hours)	Number of students
$0 \leqslant t < 5$	7
$5 \leqslant t < 10$	15
$10 \leqslant t < 15$	18
$15 \leqslant t < 20$	24
$20 \leqslant t < 30$	12
$30 \leqslant t < 40$	4

(a) Draw a cumulative frequency graph for the data.
(b) Use your graph to find the interquartile range of times.
(c) What percentage of the students spent more than 25 hours per week listening to the radio?

5 The heights of a number of men are shown in the table.

Height (h cm)	Frequency
$140 \leqslant h < 150$	1
$150 \leqslant h < 160$	6
$160 \leqslant h < 170$	8
$170 \leqslant h < 180$	21
$180 \leqslant h < 190$	14

Draw a cumulative frequency graph for the data.
Use your graph to find:
(a) the median and interquartile range of heights,
(b) the number of men less than 155 cm,
(c) the number of men at least 163 cm,
(d) the maximum height of the shortest 20 men,
(e) the minimum height of the tallest 10% of men.

Comparing distributions

EXAMPLE

A firm tested a sample of electric motors produced by an assembly line.
They kept a running total of the numbers of motors which had failed at any time.
This cumulative frequency graph was plotted using the data collected.

(a) Find the median lifetime of a motor.
(b) Find the interquartile range of lifetimes.
(c) A sample of motors, produced by another assembly line, was tested and found to have:
Median lifetime = 1900 hours,   Upper quartile = 2000 hours,   Lower quartile = 1700 hours.
Compare the two samples of motors.

(a) Median lifetime = 2100 hours

(b) IQR = Upper Quartile − Lower Quartile = 2300 − 1700 = 600 hours

(c) For the second sample: Median = 1900 hours
$\qquad\qquad\qquad\qquad$ IQR = 2000 − 1700 = 300 hours
The first sample has a greater median time.
On average, they lasted 200 hours longer than motors in the second sample.

The spread of the second sample (given by the IQR) is much smaller.
It is 300 hours, compared with 600 hours for the first sample.

1 The heights of a group of boys and a group of girls were recorded separately.
The results are shown by the cumulative frequency graphs.

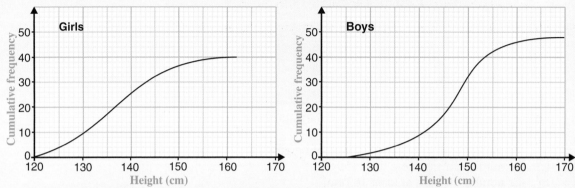

(a) How many girls were measured?
(b) Find the interquartile range of heights of the girls.
(c) Find the interquartile range of heights of the boys.
(d) Use your answers to parts (b) and (c) to comment on the heights of the girls compared
with the boys.
(e) How many boys are taller than the tallest girl?

2 The milk yields of a herd of cows is shown in the table below.

Milk yield (x litres)	$5 \leqslant x < 10$	$10 \leqslant x < 15$	$15 \leqslant x < 20$	$20 \leqslant x < 25$	$25 \leqslant x < 30$
Number of cows	15	28	37	26	25

(a) Use the data to draw a cumulative frequency graph.
(b) Use your graph to estimate:
  (i) the median milk yield,
  (ii) the interquartile range of milk yields.
(c) A neighbouring farmer calculated the following results for his herd of cows.
Median yield = 22 litres, Lower quartile = 9 litres, Upper quartile = 28 litres.
Compare and comment on the data for the two herds.

3 A sample of potatoes of Variety X and a sample of potatoes of Variety Y are weighed.
The cumulative frequency graphs show information about the weight distribution of each sample.

By finding the median and interquartile range of each sample, compare and comment on the
weights of these varieties of potato.

Box plots (or **box and whisker diagrams**) provide a useful way of representing the range, the median and the quartiles of a set of data.
They are also useful for comparing two (or more) distributions.

The graph shows the cumulative frequency distribution of the masses of 80 fish.

From the graph we can read off the following information:

- the minimum mass is 0.2 kg,
- the maximum mass is 5.6 kg,
- the median mass is 1.4 kg,
- the lower quartile is 0.8 kg,
- the upper quartile is 2.4 kg.

This information can now be represented as a box plot.

Begin by drawing a horizontal line and marking a scale from 0 to 6 kg.
Above your line, draw a box from the lower quartile to the upper quartile and mark in the median with a line across the box.
Draw lines (sometimes called whiskers) from the lower end of the box to 0.2 kg and from the upper end of the box to 5.6 kg to represent the range.

A box plot for the masses of these fish is shown below.

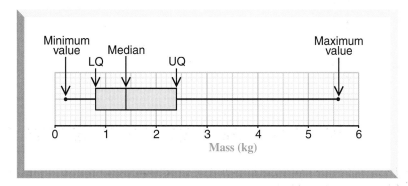

The box plot shows how the masses of these fish are spread out and how the middle 50% are clustered.

The number of points scored by the 11 players in a basketball team during a competition are shown.

13   12   5   34   8   10   11   46   25   23   4

Draw a box plot to illustrate the data.

Begin by putting the data in order and then locate the median, lower quartile and upper quartile.

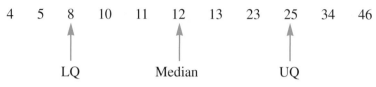

Then use these values to draw the box plot.

Exercise 6.4

1 The midday temperatures, in °C, for 11 cities around the world are:

9   12   20   24   25   28   28   30   31   32   35

Draw a box plot to represent these temperatures.

2 A group of 15 people were asked to estimate the weight of a large tortoise.
Their estimates, in kilograms, are shown.

2.8	3.0	3.2	3.3	3.5	3.6	3.8	3.8
4.0	4.0	4.2	4.2	4.4	4.5	4.7	

Draw a box plot to represent these estimates.

3 The cumulative frequency graph shows information about the distances travelled by children to get to school.

Draw a box plot to illustrate the data.

4 The table gives information about the heights of players in a rugby team.

Median	188 cm	Tallest	198 cm
Lower quartile	185 cm	Shortest	175 cm
Upper quartile	193 cm		

Draw a box plot to represent this information.

5 The box plot illustrates the reaction times of a group of people.

(a) What was the minimum reaction time?
(b) What is the value of the interquartile range?

6 A group of students took examinations in Mathematics and English.
The box plots illustrate the results.

(a) What was the highest mark scored in English?
(b) What was the lowest mark scored in Mathematics?
(c) Which subject has the higher median mark?
(d) What is the value of the interquartile range for English?
(e) Comment on the results of these examinations.

7 The cumulative frequency graphs show the times taken by students to run 100 m.

(a) Draw box plots to compare the times for males and females.
(b) Comment on the times for males and females.

8 A sample of 23 people were asked to record the amount they spent on food last week. The amounts, in £'s, are shown.

| 47 | 56 | 65 | 73 | 29 | 73 | 26 | 32 | 52 | 57 | 33 | 28 |
| 61 | 48 | 37 | 43 | 52 | 74 | 66 | 58 | 67 | 47 | 32 | |

(a) Find the median and quartiles of this distribution.
(b) Draw a box plot to represent the data.

What you need to know

- The information given in a frequency table can be used to make a **cumulative frequency table**.
- To draw a **cumulative frequency graph**:

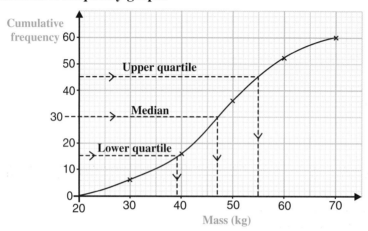

1. Draw and label: the variable on the horizontal axis,
   cumulative frequency on the vertical axis.
2. Plot the cumulative frequency against the upper class boundary of each class.
3. Join the points with a smooth curve.

- If the question does not give the upper class boundaries, then the upper class boundary of each class is equal to the lower class boundary of the next class.
- When the classes have gaps between them then the upper class boundary is halfway between the end of one class and the beginning of the next.
- The **median** is the value of the middle number.

  The **lower quartile** is the value located at $\frac{1}{4}$ of the total frequency.

  The **upper quartile** is the value located at $\frac{3}{4}$ of the total frequency.

  The **interquartile range** measures the spread of the middle 50% of the data.

  Interquartile range = Upper Quartile − Lower Quartile

- A **box plot** is used to represent the range, the median and the quartiles of a distribution.

- The box plot shows how the data is spread out and how the middle 50% of data is clustered.
- Box plots can be used to compare two (or more) distributions.

1 This cumulative frequency diagram shows information about the distances travelled to work each day by a group of adults.

(a) What is the median distance travelled?
(b) Find the interquartile range.
  Explain how you obtain your answer.
(c) Give a reason why the interquartile range is a better measure of spread than the range for this data.

AQA

2 In a school examination, 96 students each took two maths papers.
Each paper was marked out of 100. The results for Paper 1 are given in the table.

Exam mark (M)	Number of students
$0 \leqslant M \leqslant 20$	0
$20 < M \leqslant 30$	2
$30 < M \leqslant 40$	9
$40 < M \leqslant 50$	19
$50 < M \leqslant 60$	25
$60 < M \leqslant 70$	20
$70 < M \leqslant 80$	10
$80 < M \leqslant 90$	8
$90 < M \leqslant 100$	3

(a) Draw a cumulative frequency diagram.
(b) Showing your method clearly, use your diagram to estimate
  (i) the median mark,
  (ii) the interquartile range.
(c) The students' results on Paper 2 have a median of 61 marks and an interquartile range of 17 marks.
  Which exam paper did the students find easier? Give a reason for your answer.

AQA

3 A sample of 40 trout is taken at a fish farm.

Mass (g)	40 -	50 -	60 -	70 -	80 -	90 - 100
Frequency	2	3	8	9	13	5

(a) Copy and complete the cumulative frequency table.

Mass (g)	< 50	< 60	< 70	< 80	< 90	< 100
Cumulative frequency						

(b) Draw the cumulative frequency graph.
(c) Find the median mass of the trout.
(d) Find the interquartile range of the mass of the trout.
(e) A second sample of trout has a median mass of 75 g, an upper quartile of 93 g and a lower quartile of 55 g.
Compare and comment on the spread of the data in these two samples.

AQA

4 Farmer Jack has two fields.
In one field, he plants lettuce seeds by hand.
In the other, he plants lettuce seeds using a machine.

A sample of lettuce is taken from each field.
The diameter of each lettuce is measured.
The mean and interquartile range are calculated for each sample.
The results are shown below.

	Hand	Machine
Mean diameter	15.3 cm	14.7 cm
Interquartile range	3.2 cm	1.2 cm

(a) Farmer Jack says, "It's better to plant by hand."
Using the data given in the table, give a reason to justify his statement.
(b) His son Peter says, "No, dad, the machine is better."
Using the data given in the table, give a reason to justify his statement.

AQA

5 The box plot shows information about the price of a pint of milk in a number of shops.

(a) What is the range in price?
(b) What is the median price?
(c) What is the value of the interquartile range?

6 The times taken by students to access a website gave the following information.

Maximum time	5.1 minutes	Lower quartile	2.8 minutes
Minimum time	1.5 minutes	Upper quartile	4.2 minutes
Median time	3.8 minutes		

Draw a box plot to represent this information.

Probability

What is probability?

Probability, or **chance**, involves describing how likely something is to happen.
For example:

How likely is it to rain tomorrow?

We often make forecasts, or judgements, about how likely things are to happen.
When trying to forecast tomorrow's weather the following **outcomes** are possible:

sun,   cloud,   wind,   rain,   snow,   …

We are interested in the particular **event**, rain tomorrow.

> In any situation, the possible things that can happen are called **outcomes**. An outcome of particular interest is called an **event**.

The chance of an event happening can be described using these words:
Impossible   **Unlikely**   **Evens**   **Likely**   **Certain**

Use one of the words in the box to describe the chance of rain tomorrow.

Probability and the probability scale

Estimates of probabilities can be shown on a **probability scale**. The scale goes from 0 to 1.
A **probability of 0** means that an event is **impossible**.
A **probability of 1** means that an event is **certain**.
Probabilities are written either as a fraction, a decimal or a percentage.

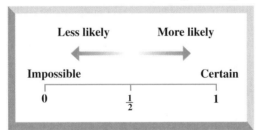

Describe the likelihood that an event will occur if it has a probability of $\frac{1}{2}$.

Exercise 7.1

1 Describe each of the following events as:

Impossible   **Unlikely**   **Evens**   **Likely**   **Certain**

(a) You roll a normal dice and get an odd number.
(b) You roll a normal dice and get a 7.
(c) A 6 is scored at least 80 times when a normal dice is rolled 600 times.
(d) It will rain on three days running in August.
(e) Somewhere in the world it is raining today.
(f) A coin is tossed five times and lands heads up on each occasion.
(g) A coin is tossed five times and lands heads up at least once.

2 The probabilities of four events have been
marked on a probability scale.
Copy the probability scale.

Event V   A coin lands 'heads' up.
Event W   A person is over 3 metres tall.
Event X   Rolling an ordinary dice and getting a score less than 7.
Event Y   There is a 35% chance that it will rain tomorrow.

Label the arrows on your diagram to show which event they represent.

Calculating probabilities using equally likely outcomes

Probabilities can be **calculated** in situations where
each outcome is **equally likely** to occur.

In such situations, the probability of an event, X,
occurring is given by:

$$P(X) = \frac{\text{Number of possible outcomes in the event}}{\text{Total number of possible outcomes}}$$

In this book P(X) stands for the probability of X.

In many probability situations
things are taken or picked at
random.

For example:
A boy is picked at random from
a group.
This means that any boy in the
group is equally likely to be picked.

EXAMPLES

1 A fair dice is rolled. What is the probability of getting:
(a)   a 6,
(b)   an odd number,
(c)   a 2 or a 3?

Total number of possible outcomes is 6   (1, 2, 3, 4, 5 and 6).
The dice is fair so each of these outcomes is equally likely.

(a)   The number of outcomes in the event getting a 6 is 1. $P(6) = \frac{1}{6}$

(b)   The total number of outcomes in the event is 3   (1, 3, 5).   P(an odd number) $= \frac{3}{6} = \frac{1}{2}$

(c)   The total number of outcomes in the event is 2   (2, 3).   P(2 or 3) $= \frac{2}{6} = \frac{1}{3}$

2 This table shows how 100 counters are coloured red or blue and numbered 1 or 2.

	Red	Blue
1	23	19
2	32	26

The 100 counters are put in a bag and a counter is taken from the bag at random.
(a)   Calculate the probability that the counter is red.
(b)   Calculate the probability that the counter is blue and numbered 1.

Total number of possible outcomes = 100

(a)   Red counters = 23 + 32 = 55   P(red) $= \frac{55}{100} = \frac{11}{20}$
This could be written as 0.55 or 55%.

(b)   There are 19 counters that are blue and numbered 1.   P(blue and 1) $= \frac{19}{100}$
This could be written as 0.19 or 19%.

1 A bag contains a red counter, a blue counter and a green counter.
A counter is taken from the bag at random.
What is the probability of taking:
(a) a red counter,
(b) a red or a green counter,
(c) a counter that is not blue?

2 A bag contains 3 red sweets and 7 black sweets.
A sweet is taken from the bag at random.
What is the probability of taking:
(a) a red sweet,
(b) a black sweet?

3 This fair spinner is used in a game.

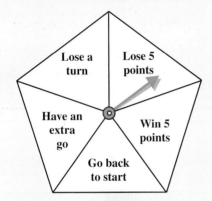

In the game a player spins the arrow.
What is the probability that the player:
(a) loses a turn,
(b) wins 5 points or loses 5 points?

4 The eleven letters of the word
MISSISSIPPI are written on separate tiles.
The tiles are placed in a bag and mixed up.
One tile is selected at random.
What is the probability that the tile selected shows:
(a) the letter M,
(b) the letter I,
(c) the letter P?

5 The letters of the word TRIGONOMETRY are written on separate cards.
The cards are shuffled and dealt, face down, onto a table.
A card is selected at random.
What is the probability that the card shows:
(a) the letter Y,
(b) the letter R?
Write your answers in their simplest form.

6 A card is taken at random from a full pack of 52 playing cards with no jokers.
What is the probability that the card:
(a) is red,
(b) is a heart,
(c) is the ace of hearts?

7 A bag contains 4 red counters, 3 white counters and 3 blue counters.
A counter is taken from the bag at random.
What is the probability that the counter is:
(a) red,
(b) white or blue,
(c) red, white or blue,
(d) green?

8 In a hat there are twelve numbered discs.

Nina takes a disc from the hat at random.
What is the probability that Nina takes a disc:
(a) with at least one 4 on it,
(b) that has not got a 4 on it,
(c) that has a 3 or a 4 on it?

9 This table shows how fifty counters are numbered either 1 or 2 and coloured red or blue.

	Red	Blue
1	12	8
2	8	22

One of the counters is chosen at random.
What is the probability that the counter is:
(a) a 1,
(b) blue,
(c) blue and a 1?

A blue counter is chosen at random.
(d) What is the probability that it is a 1?

A counter numbered 1 is chosen at random.
(e) What is the probability that it is blue?

10 Tim plays a friend at Noughts and Crosses.
He says: "I can either win, draw or lose, so the probability that I will win must be $\frac{1}{3}$."
Explain why Tim is wrong.

11 The table shows the way that 120 pupils from Year 7 travel to Linfield School.
A pupil from Year 7 is chosen at random.
What is the probability that the pupil:
(a) walks to school,
(b) is a girl who travels by car,
(c) is a boy who does not travel by bus?

A girl from Year 7 is chosen at random.
What is the probability that:
(d) she walks to school,
(e) she does not travel by car?

A Year 7 pupil who travels by bike is chosen at random.
(f) What is the probability that the pupil is a boy?

	Boys	Girls
Walk	23	17
Bus	15	20
Car	12	8
Bike	20	5

Estimating probabilities using relative frequency

In question 10 in Exercise 7.2, probabilities **cannot** be calculated using equally likely outcomes.
In such situations probabilities can be estimated using the idea of **relative frequency**.

It is not always necessary to perform an experiment or make observations.
Sometimes the information required can be found in past records.

> The relative frequency of an event is given by:
>
> $$\text{Relative frequency} = \frac{\text{Number of times the event happens in an experiment (or in a survey)}}{\text{Total number of trials in the experiment (or observations in the survey)}}$$

EXAMPLES

1 Jamie does the following experiment with a bag containing 2 red and 8 blue counters.

> **Take a counter from the bag at random.**
> **Record the colour then put the counter back in the bag. Repeat this for 100 trials.**

Jamie calculates the relative frequency of getting a red counter every 10 trials and shows his results on a graph. Draw a graph showing the results that Jamie might get.
This is the sort of graph that Jamie might get.

The dotted line shows the **calculated probability**.

$P(\text{Red}) = \frac{2}{10} = 0.2$

As the number of trials increases, relative frequency gives a better estimate of calculated probability.

Try Jamie's experiment yourself and see what sort of results you get.

2 In an experiment a drawing pin is dropped for 100 trials.
The drawing pin lands "point up" 37 times.
What is the relative frequency of the drawing pin landing "point up"?

$\text{Relative frequency} = \frac{37}{100} = 0.37$

Relative frequency gives a better estimate of probability the larger the number of trials.

EXAMPLE

3 A counter was taken from a bag of counters and replaced.
The relative frequency of getting a blue counter was found to be 0.4.
There are 20 counters in the bag.
Estimate the number of blue counters.

Relative frequency of taking a blue counter is 0.4.
Total number of counters in the bag = 20
Number of blue counters = 20 × 0.4 = 8
There are 8 blue counters in the bag.

Exercise 7.3

1 50 cars are observed passing the school gate. 14 red cars are observed.
What is the relative frequency of a red car passing the school gate?

2 In an experiment a gardener planted 40 daffodil bulbs of which 36 grew to produce flowers.
Use these results to find the relative frequency that a daffodil bulb will produce a flower.

3 Gemma keeps a record of her chess games with Helen.
Out of the first 10 games, Gemma wins 6. Out of the first 30 games Gemma wins 21.
Estimate the probability that Gemma will win her next game of chess with Helen.

4 There are 50 cars in the school car park. 5 of the cars are black.
(a) What is the relative frequency of a black car in the car park?

The relative frequency of a red car in the school car park is 0.2.
(b) How many red cars are in the car park?

5 The results of games of chess played by four children at a chess club are shown in this table.

Player	Games won	Games drawn	Games lost
Tom	4	2	6
Sam	8	1	7
Kim	3	0	1
Pam	9	2	9

(a) Calculate the relative frequency of a win for each player.
(b) Which of these relative frequencies is most likely to give the best estimate of the probability that the child will win their next game?
Explain your answer.
(c) If Tom plays Pam, who do you think is more likely to win?
Explain your answer.

6 A counter was taken from a bag of counters and replaced.
The relative frequency of getting a red counter was found to be 0.3.
There are 30 counters in the bag.
Estimate the number of red counters.

7 500 tickets are sold for a prize draw.
(a) Samantha buys one ticket.
What is the probability that she wins first prize?
(b) The probability that Greg wins first prize is $\frac{1}{20}$.
How many tickets did he buy?

8 A bypass is to be built to avoid a town.
There are three possible routes that the road can take.
A survey was carried out in the town.

Route	A	B	C
Relative frequency	0.4	0.5	0.1

30 people opted for Route C.
(a) How many people were surveyed altogether?
(b) How many people opted for Route A?
(c) How many people opted for Route B?

9 Rachel selects 40 holiday brochures at random.
The relative frequency of the brochure being for a holiday in Italy is 0.2.
How many brochures did Rachel select for holidays in Italy?

10 A counter is taken from a bag at random.
Its colour is recorded and the counter is then put back in the bag.
This is repeated 300 times.
The number of red counters taken from the bag after every 100 trials is shown in the table.

Number of trials	Number of red counters
100	52
200	102
300	141

(a) Calculate the relative frequency after each 100 trials.
(b) Estimate the probability of taking a red counter from the bag.

11 The diagram shows a spinner which is spun a number of times.
The graph shows the relative frequency of the spinner landing on the number 1 plotted against the number of times the spinner is spun.

(a) The spinner is a fair spinner.
How can you tell from the graph?
(b) How might the relative frequency of the spinner landing on the number 3 change with the number of trials?
Show your answer on a graph with relative frequency plotted after every 20 trials.

Mutually exclusive events

Events which **cannot happen at the same time** are called **mutually exclusive events**.
For example, the event 'Heads' cannot occur at the same time as the event 'Tails'.

> When A and B are events which cannot happen at the same time:
> P(A or B) = P(A) + P(B)

The probability of an event not happening

> The events A and not A cannot happen at the same time.
> Because the events A and not A are certain to happen:
> P(not A) = 1 − P(A)

EXAMPLES

1 A bag contains 3 red (R) counters, 2 blue
(B) counters and 5 green (G) counters.
A counter is taken from the bag at random.
What is the probability that the counter is:
(a) red,
(b) green,
(c) red or green?

Find the total number of counters in the bag.
5 + 2 + 3 = 10
Total number of possible outcomes = 10.

(a) Number of possible outcomes = 3.

$P(R) = \frac{3}{10}$

(b) Number of possible outcomes = 5.

$P(G) = \frac{5}{10} = \frac{1}{2}$

(c) Events R and G cannot happen at the
same time.
P(R or G) = P(R) + P(G)

$= \frac{3}{10} + \frac{5}{10} = \frac{8}{10} = \frac{4}{5}$

2

A bag contains 10 counters.
3 of the counters are red (R).
A counter is taken from the bag at random.
What is the probability that the counter is:
(a) red,
(b) not red?

Total number of possible outcomes = 10.

(a) Number of possible outcomes = 3.

$P(R) = \frac{3}{10}$

(b) P(not R) = 1 − P(R)

$= 1 - \frac{3}{10} = \frac{7}{10}$

Exercise **7.4**

1 A fish is taken at random from a tank.
The probability that the fish is black is $\frac{2}{5}$.
What is the probability that the fish is not black?

2 Tina has a bag of beads.
She takes a bead from the bag at random.
The probability that the bead is white is 0.6.
What is the probability that the bead is not white?

3 The probability of a switch working is 0.96.
What is the probability of a switch not working?

4 Six out of every 100 men are taller than 1.85 m.
A man is picked at random.
What is the probability that he is not taller than 1.85 m?

5 A bag contains red, white and blue balls.
A ball is taken from the bag at random.
The probability of taking a red ball is 0.4.
The probability of taking a white ball is 0.35.
What is the probability of taking a white ball or a blue ball?

6 Tom and Sam buy some tickets in a raffle.
The probability that Tom wins 1st prize is 0.03.
The probability that Sam wins 1st prize is 0.01.
(a)   What is the probability that Tom or Sam win 1st prize?
(b)   What is the probability that Tom does not win 1st prize?

7 A spinner can land on red, white or blue.
The probability of the spinner landing on red is 0.2.
The probability of the spinner landing on red or on blue is 0.7.
The spinner is spun once.
What is the probability that the spinner lands:
(a)   on blue,
(b)   on white?

8 A bag contains red, green, blue, yellow and white counters.
The table shows the probabilities of obtaining each colour when a counter is taken from the bag at random.

Red	Green	Blue	Yellow	White
30%	25%	20%	20%	10%

(a)   (i)   How can you tell that there is a mistake in the table?
      (ii) The probability of getting a white counter is wrong. What should it be?

A counter is taken from the bag at random.
(b)   (i)   What is the probability that it is either green or blue?
      (ii) What is the probability that it is either red, green or blue?
      (iii) What is the probability that it is not yellow?

9 Some red, white and blue cubes are numbered 1 or 2.
The table shows the probabilities of obtaining each colour and number when a cube is taken at random.

	Red	White	Blue
1	0.1	0.3	0
2	0.3	0.1	0.2

A cube is taken at random.
(a)   What is the probability of taking a red cube?
(b)   What is the probability of taking a cube numbered 2?
(c)   State whether or not the following pairs of events are mutually exclusive.
      Give a reason for each answer.
      (i)   Taking a cube numbered 1 and taking a blue cube.
      (ii) Taking a cube numbered 2 and taking a blue cube.
(d)   (i)   What is the probability of taking a cube which is blue or numbered 1?
      (ii) What is the probability of taking a cube which is blue or numbered 2?
      (iii) What is the probability of taking a cube which is numbered 2 or red?

Combining two events

EXAMPLES

1 A fair coin is thrown twice.
Identify all of the possible outcomes and
write down their probabilities.

Method 1
List the outcomes systematically.
1st throw	2nd throw
Head (H)	Head (H)
Head (H)	Tail (T)
Tail (T)	Head (H)
Tail (T)	Tail (T)

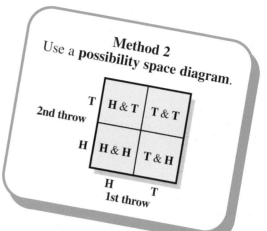

Method 2
Use a **possibility space diagram**.

2nd throw	T	H & T	T & T
	H	H & H	T & H
		H	T

1st throw

When a fair coin is tossed
twice, there are four
possible outcomes.
Because the coin is fair all
the possible outcomes are
equally likely.
Because all the outcomes
are equally likely their
probabilities can be
worked out.

Method 3
Use a **tree diagram**.

1st throw	2nd throw	Outcome
	H	**H** and **H**
H	T	**H** and **T**
T	H	**T** and **H**
	T	**T** and **T**

The lines are called
the **branches** of the
tree diagram.

$$P(H \text{ and } H) = P(H \text{ and } T) = P(T \text{ and } H) = P(T \text{ and } T) = \frac{1}{4}.$$

2 A fair dice is rolled twice.
Use a possibility space diagram to show all the possible outcomes.
What is the probability of getting a 'double six'?
What is the probability of getting any 'double'?
What is the probability that exactly one 'six' is obtained?

2nd roll

6	1 and 6	2 and 6	3 and 6	4 and 6	5 and 6	6 and 6
5	1 and 5	2 and 5	3 and 5	4 and 5	5 and 5	6 and 5
4	1 and 4	2 and 4	3 and 4	4 and 4	5 and 4	6 and 4
3	1 and 3	2 and 3	3 and 3	4 and 3	5 and 3	6 and 3
2	1 and 2	2 and 2	3 and 2	4 and 2	5 and 2	6 and 2
1	1 and 1	2 and 1	3 and 1	4 and 1	5 and 1	6 and 1
	1	2	3	4	5	6

1st roll

The dice is fair so there are 36 equally likely
outcomes.

P(double 6)
There is one outcome in the event (6 and 6).
$P(\text{double } 6) = \frac{1}{36}$

P(any double)
The 6 outcomes in the event are shaded blue.
$P(\text{any double}) = \frac{6}{36} = \frac{1}{6}$

P(exactly one six)
The 10 outcomes in the event are shaded grey.
$P(\text{exactly one six}) = \frac{10}{36} = \frac{5}{18}$

1 A red car (R), a blue car (B) and a green car (G) are parked on a narrow drive, one behind the other.
   (a) List all the possible orders in which the three cars could be parked.

   The cars are parked on the drive at random.
   (b) What is the probability that the blue car is the first on the drive?

2 Two fair dice are rolled and the numbers obtained are added.
   (a) Draw a possibility space diagram to show all of the possible outcomes.
   (b) Use your diagram to work out:
       (i) the probability of obtaining a total of 10,
       (ii) the probability of obtaining a total greater than 10,
       (iii) the probability of obtaining a total less than 10.
   (c) Explain why the probabilities you worked out in (b) should add up to 1.

3 A fair coin is tossed and a fair dice is rolled.
   Copy and complete the table to show all the possible outcomes.

Dice

		1	2	3	4	5	6
Coin	H		H2				
	T						

What is the probability of obtaining:
   (a) a head and a 5,
   (b) a tail and an even number,
   (c) a tail and a 6,
   (d) a tail and an odd number,
   (e) a head and a number more than 4,
   (f) an odd number?

4 Sanjay has to travel to school in two stages.
   Stage 1: he can go by bus or train or he can get a lift.
   Stage 2: he can go by bus or he can walk.
   (a) List all the different ways that Sanjay can travel to school.

   Sanjay decides the way that he travels on each stage at random.
   (b) What is the probability that he goes by bus in both stages?

5 The diagram shows an unbiased spinner.
   It is divided into four equal sections numbered as shown.
   The spinner is spun twice and the numbers the arrow lands on each time are added to obtain a score.
   (a) Copy and complete this table to show all the possible scores.

2nd spin

		1	2	3	4
1st spin	1	2	3		
	2	3			
	3				
	4				

   (b) Calculate the probability of getting a score of:
       (i) 2,   (ii) 3,   (iii) 6.

6 Bag A contains 2 red balls and 1 white ball.
Bag B contains 2 white balls and 1 red ball.
A ball is drawn at random from each bag.

(a) Copy and complete the table to show all possible pairs of colours.

(b) Explain why the probability of each outcome is $\frac{1}{9}$.

(c) Calculate the probability that the two balls are the same colour.

Bag A

	R	R	W
W	RW		
W			
R			

Bag B

7 The diagram shows two sets of cards A and B.

One card is taken at random from set A.
One card is taken at random from set B.

(a) List all the possible outcomes.

The two numbers are added together.
(b) (i) What is the probability of getting a total of 5?
    (ii) What is the probability of getting a total that is not 5?

All the cards are put together and one of them is taken at random.
(c) What is the probability that it is labelled A or 2?

8 Students at a college must choose to study two subjects from the list:

> Maths   English   Science   Art

(a) Write down all the possible pairs of subjects that the students can choose.

David chooses both subjects at random.
(b) What is the probability that one of the subjects he chooses is Maths?

James chooses Maths and one other subject at random.
(c) What is the probability that he chooses Maths and Science?

9 A spinner has an equal probability of landing on either red, green, blue, yellow or white.
The spinner is spun twice.
(a) List all the possible outcomes.
(b) (i) What is the probability that, on both spins, the spinner lands on white?
    (ii) What is the probability that, on both spins, the spinner lands on white at least once?
    (iii) What is the probability that, on both spins, the spinner lands on the same colour?

10 The diagram shows two unbiased spinners.
Each spinner is divided into equal sections and numbered as shown.
Each spinner is spun and the numbers that each arrow lands on are added together.

(a) Draw a possibility space diagram to show all the possible outcomes.
(b) Calculate the probability of getting a total of 2.
(c) Calculate the probability of getting a total of 6.

Probability . . . Probability . . . Probability . . .

Independent events

When two coins are tossed, the outcome of the first toss has no effect on the outcome of the second toss.
One person being left-handed does not influence another person being left-handed.
These are examples of events which can happen together but which do not affect each other.
Events like this are called **independent** events.

> When A and B are **independent** events then the probability of A and B occurring is given by:
> $$P(A \text{ and } B) = P(A) \times P(B)$$
>
> This rule can be extended to any number of independent events. For example:
> $$P(A \text{ and } B \text{ and } C) = P(A) \times P(B) \times P(C)$$

Using tree diagrams to work out probabilities

A **tree diagram** can be used to find all the possible outcomes when two or more events are combined.
It can also be used to help calculate probabilities when outcomes are not equally likely.

EXAMPLE

1 **Box A** contains 1 red ball (R) and 1 blue ball (B).
Box B contains 3 red balls (R) and 2 blue balls (B).

Box A

Box B

A ball is taken at random from Box A.
A ball is then taken at random from Box B.

(a) Draw a tree diagram to show all the possible outcomes.
(b) Calculate the probability that two red balls are taken.

(a)

Box A	Box B	Outcome
$\frac{1}{2}$ R	$\frac{3}{5}$ R	RR
	$\frac{2}{5}$ B	RB
$\frac{1}{2}$ B	$\frac{3}{5}$ R	BR
	$\frac{2}{5}$ B	BB

Remember:
When drawing a tree diagram probabilities must be put on the branches.
Using equally likely outcomes:
In Box A
$P(R) = \frac{1}{2}$ $\qquad P(B) = \frac{1}{2}$
In Box B
$P(R) = \frac{3}{5}$ $\qquad P(B) = \frac{2}{5}$

(b) The numbers of red and blue balls are unequal in Box B.
This means that the outcomes RR, RB, BR and BB are not equally likely.

Multiply the probabilities along the branches of the tree diagram.

$$P(RR) = \frac{1}{2} \times \frac{3}{5} = \frac{1 \times 3}{2 \times 5} = \frac{3}{10}$$

The probability that two red balls are taken is $\frac{3}{10}$.

EXAMPLE

2 The probability that Amanda is late for school is 0.4.
Use a tree diagram to find the probability that on two days running:
(a) she is late twice,
(b) she is late exactly once.

Day 1	**Day 2**	**Probability**

0.4 — late
late
0.4 — late   0.4 × 0.4 = **0.16**
0.6 — not late   0.4 × 0.6 = **0.24**

0.6 — not late
0.4 — late   0.6 × 0.4 = **0.24**
0.6 — not late   0.6 × 0.6 = **0.36**

(a) The probability that Amanda is late twice.
The outcome included in this event is: (late **and** late)   P(late twice) = 0.16

(b) The probability that Amanda is late exactly once.
The outcomes included in this event are: (late **and** not late)   **or**   (not late **and** late)
These outcomes are mutually exclusive.
P(late exactly once) = 0.24 + 0.24 = 0.48

Exercise **7.6**

1 A bag contains 3 red counters and 2 blue counters.
A counter is taken at random from the bag and then replaced.
Another counter is taken at random from the bag.

(a) Copy and complete the tree diagram to show all the
possible outcomes. Write the probability of each of the
events on the branches of the tree diagram.

1st counter   **2nd counter**

$\frac{3}{5}$ — red

blue

(b) (i) Calculate the probability that both counters taken are blue.
(ii) Calculate the probability that at least one counter taken is blue.

2 A manufacturer makes an electrical circuit which contains two switches.
The probability that a switch is faulty is 0.1.

(a) Copy and complete the tree diagram.

1st switch   **2nd switch**

0.1 — faulty

not faulty

(b) (i) Calculate the probability that both switches are faulty.
(ii) Calculate the probability that exactly one switch is faulty.

The circuit works if both switches are not faulty.
(c) The manufacturer makes 1000 circuits.
Estimate the number that work.

3 Five people in a group of 50 people are left handed.
There are 20 females in the group.
A person is picked at random from the group.

    (a)   (i)   What is the probability that the person is left handed?
          (ii)   What is the probability that the person is right handed?
          (iii) What is the probability that the person is female?
          (iv) What is the probability that the person is male?

    (b) Copy and complete the tree diagram.

    (c)   (i)   Calculate the probability that the person picked is a left handed female.
          (ii)   Calculate the probability that the person picked is a left handed female or is a
              right handed male.

4 Bag A contains 3 blue counters, 5 red counters and 2 white counters.
Bag B contains 2 blue counters and 3 red counters.
A ball is taken at random from Bag A.
A ball is taken at random from Bag B.

    (a) Copy and complete the tree diagram to show the possible pairs of colours.
        Write the probability of each of the events on the branches.

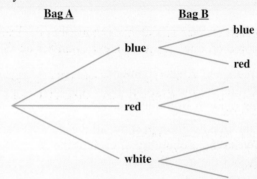

    (b) Calculate the probability that a blue counter is taken from Bag A and a red counter is
        taken from Bag B.

    (c) Calculate the probability that both counters are the same colour.

5 The probability that a car fails an MOT test on lights is $\frac{1}{10}$.

The probability that a car fails an MOT test on brakes is $\frac{1}{5}$.
A car is stopped at random and given an MOT test.
The tree diagram shows the possible outcomes.

    (a) Copy and complete the tree diagram.

    (b) Calculate the probability that the car will fail the MOT test on lights or brakes.

6 A fair spinner can land on either black or white.
The probability that it lands on white when it is spun is 0.3.
(a) What is the probability that it lands on black when it is spun?

The spinner is spun twice.
(b) Find the probability of getting two blacks.
(c) Find the probability of getting the same colour on both spinners.

7 In box A there are 3 red and 5 blue counters.
In box B there are 2 red and 3 blue counters.
A counter is taken at random from each box.
Calculate the probability that:
(a) both counters are red,
(b) at least one of the counters is red.

8 Colin takes examinations in Maths and in English.
The probability that he passes Maths is 0.7.
The probability that he passes English is 0.8.
The results in each subject are independent of each other.
Calculate the probability that:
(a) he passes Maths and fails English,
(b) he fails both subjects.

9 Dice A and Dice B are two normal dice. Dice A is a fair dice.
Dice B is biased so that the probability of getting an even number is $\frac{2}{3}$.
Both of the dice are tossed.
Find the probability that:
(a) an odd number is scored on dice A and an even number on dice B,
(b) an odd number is scored on one dice and an even number on the other.

10 A box contains cubes which are coloured red (R), white (W) or blue (B) and numbered 1, 2 or 3.
The table shows the probabilities of obtaining each colour and each number when a cube is taken from the box at random.

A single cube is taken from the box at random.
(a) What is the probability that the cube is:
   (i) red and numbered 2,
   (ii) white or numbered 1,
   (iii) white or numbered 3?

	Colour of cube		
	R	W	B
1	0.2	0	0.1
2	0.1	0.3	0
3	0	0.1	0.2

Number on cube

A cube is taken from the box at random and then replaced.
Another cube is then taken from the box at random.
(b) Calculate the probability that:
   (i) both cubes are blue and numbered 1,
   (ii) both cubes are blue.

11 A bag contains red, white and blue cubes.
The cubes are numbered 1, 2, 3 and 4.
The probabilities of taking cubes from the box at random are shown in the table.

A single cube is taken from the box at random.
(a) What is the probability that:
   (i) the cube is white,
   (ii) the cube is red and numbered 4,
   (iii) the cube is white or numbered 3?

	Colour of cube		
	Red	White	Blue
1	0.1	0	0
2	0.1	0.1	0.1
3	0	0.2	0.2
4	0.1	0	0.1

Number on cube

A cube is taken from the box at random and then replaced.
Another cube is then taken from the box at random.
(b) Calculate the probability that both cubes are the same colour.

Probability · · · · Probability · · · · Probability · · · ·

- You need to know the meaning of these terms:

  impossible, unlikely, evens, likely, certain

  outcome, event   fair, unbiased, biased, taken at random

  equally likely outcomes   trial

- **Probability** describes how likely or unlikely it is that an event will occur.
  Probabilities can be shown on a probability scale.
  Probability **must** be written as a fraction, a decimal or a percentage.

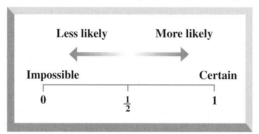

- How to work out probabilities using **equally likely outcomes**.
  The probability of an event is given by:

$$\text{Probability} = \frac{\text{Number of outcomes in the event}}{\text{Total number of possible outcomes}}$$

- How to estimate probabilities using **relative frequency**.
  The relative frequency of an event is given by:

$$\text{Relative frequency} = \frac{\text{Number of times the event happens in an experiment (or in a survey)}}{\text{Total number of trials in the experiment (or observations in the survey)}}$$

- How to use probabilities to **estimate** the number of times an event occurs in an **experiment** or **observation**.

  Estimate = total number of trials (or observations) $\times$ probability of event

- **Mutually exclusive events** cannot occur at the same time.
  When A and B are mutually exclusive events:

$$P(A \text{ or } B) = P(A) + P(B)$$

- A general rule for working out the probability of an event, A, **not happening** is:

$$P(\text{not } A) = 1 - P(A)$$

- How to find all the possible outcomes when two events are combined.
  By **listing** the outcomes systematically.
  By using a **possibility space diagram**.
  By using a **tree diagram**.

- The outcomes of **independent events** do not influence each other.
  When A and B are independent events:

$$P(A \text{ and } B) = P(A) \times P(B)$$

1 A game is played with two fair spinners.
In each turn of the game both spinners are spun
and the numbers are added to get a score.
  (a) Copy and complete the table to show
      each possible score.
  (b) What is the probability of:
      (i)   scoring 6,
      (ii) not scoring 6?
  (c) To start the game a player needs to score
      either 2 or 5.
      What is the probability that the game starts on the first throw?

	1	2	3	4
1				
2				
3				

2 A fair spinner has eight sides. The sides are numbered 1, 2, 2, 3, 3, 4, 5 and 6.
The spinner is spun once.
  (a) What is the probability that the spinner lands on a 3?

Michael and Sheila play a game using the spinner.
The spinner is spun once.
Michael wins if the spinner lands on 1 or 2 or 3.
Sheila wins if it lands on 4 or 5 or 6.
  (b) What is the probability that Sheila will win the game?
  (c) Explain why this game is **not** fair.

AQA

3 Brenda has a bag of fruit sweets.
There are 4 lemon, 5 orange, 8 strawberry and 3 blackcurrant sweets.
Brenda chooses one sweet at random.
What is the probability that the sweet is
  (a) a lemon sweet, (Give your answer as a fraction in its lowest terms.)
  (b) not an orange sweet? (Give your answer as a fraction in its lowest terms.)

AQA

4 Jaspal has one white turban and one blue turban.
He also has one green shirt, one red shirt and one yellow shirt.
  (a) List all the possible colour combinations if he wears one turban with one shirt.
  (b) He chooses one shirt and one turban at random.
      What is the probability he chooses
      (i)   the blue turban,
      (ii) the white turban and the yellow shirt,
      (iii) the white turban but not the red shirt?

Dalia has 4 red saris, 5 blue saris and 2 green saris.
She chooses one sari at random.
  (c) What is the probability that she chooses a blue sari?

AQA

5 A fair six-sided dice has its faces painted red, white or blue.
The dice is thrown 36 times. Here are the results.

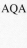

Colour	Red	White	Blue
Frequency	7	11	18

Based on the results, how many faces do you think are painted in each colour?

AQA

6 A spinner gives a score of 1, 2, 4 or 6 with the following probabilities.

Score	1	2	4	6
Probability	0.4	0.2	0.1	...

  (a) Calculate the probability that the score is 6.
  (b) Calculate the probability that the score is either 1 or 2.

AQA

7 A fair coin is thrown 20 times. It lands heads 12 times.
(a) What is the relative frequency of throwing a head?

The coin continues to be thrown.
The table shows the number of heads recorded for 20, 40, 60, 80 and 100 throws.

Number of throws	20	40	60	80	100
Number of heads	12	18	30	42	49

(b) Draw a graph to show the relative frequency of throwing a head for these data.
(c) Estimate the relative frequency of throwing a head for 1000 throws.   AQA

8 The table shows information about a group of adults.
(a) One of these adults is chosen at random.
    What is the probability that the adult can drive?
(b) A man in the group is chosen at random.
    What is the probability that he can drive?
(c) A woman in the group is chosen at random.
    The probability that she can drive is 0.76.
    What is the probability that she cannot drive?

	Can drive	Cannot drive
Male	32	8
Female	38	12

(d) Does the information given support the statement: "More women can drive than men"?
    Explain your answer.   AQA

9 Two ordinary six-sided dice are thrown. What is the probability that two fives are thrown.   AQA

10 There are two parts to a driving test. The first part is a theory test.
You must pass the theory test before you take the practical test.
Rob takes his driving test.
The probability that he passes the theory is 0.8.
The probability that he passes the practical is 0.6.
(a) The tree diagram shows the possible outcomes.
    Copy and complete the tree diagram.

(b) (i) Calculate the probability that Rob passes both parts of the driving test.
    (ii) Calculate the probability that he fails the driving test.   AQA

11 An office has two photocopiers, A and B.
On any one day: the probability that A is working is 0.8,
                      the probability that B is working is 0.9.
(a) Calculate the probability that, on any one day, both photocopiers will be working.
(b) Calculate the probability that, on any one day, only one of the photocopiers will be working.   AQA

12 Boxes P and Q each contain five numbered balls. The balls in each box are numbered as shown.
A ball is taken from each box at random.
(a) What is the probability that both balls are numbered 2?
(b) What is the probability that both balls have the same number?
(c) What is the probability that the number on the ball from box P is greater than the number on the ball from box Q?   AQA

Do not use a calculator for this exercise.

1 The graph shows the results of a survey of the times at which pupils arrived at school one day.

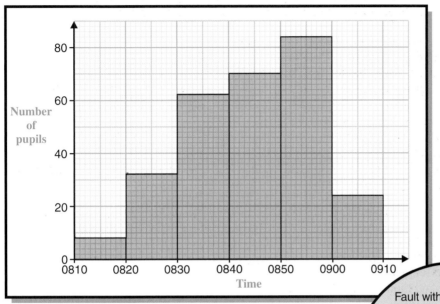

(a) (i) How many pupils arrived for school between 0830 and 0850?
(ii) How many pupils attended school that day?

There were 24 pupils who were late for school.
The reasons given for being late are shown in the pie chart.

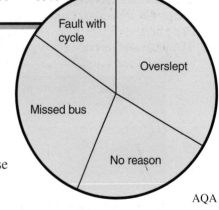

(b) (i) Which reason for lateness is the mode?
(ii) Use the pie chart to work out how many of these pupils overslept.

AQA

2 Jo measures the lengths, in centimetres, of a sample of runner beans.
The stem and leaf diagram shows the results.

(a) How many runner beans are included in the sample?
(b) What is the range of their lengths?
(c) Which length is the median?

```
                              1 | 3 means  13 cm
   1 | 3   5   7   9
   2 | 0   3   4   6   7   7   7   8
   3 | 0   1   1
```

3 (a) Write down four whole numbers whose mode is 10 and whose range is 8.
(b) Write down four whole numbers whose mode is 10 and whose mean is 9.
(c) Write down four whole numbers whose mode is 10, whose mean is 9 and whose range is 8.

AQA

4 A box contains 20 plastic ducks.
3 of the ducks are green, 10 are blue and the rest are yellow.
A duck is taken from the box at random.
(a) What is the probability that it is green?
(b) What is the probability that it is yellow?

5 A group of students were each asked how many books they had read last month.
The frequency diagram shows the results.

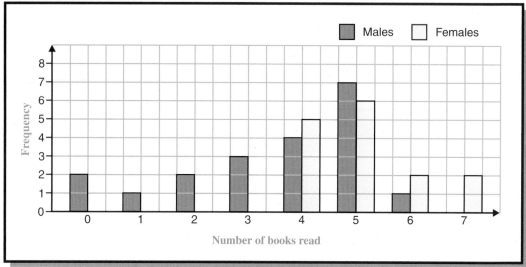

(a) How many students were included?
(b) What is the range in the number of books read by females?
(c) Calculate the mean number of books read by females.
(d) Compare and comment on the number of books read by males and the number of books read by females.

6 An artist showed four paintings to 60 people and asked them which one they liked best.
The table shows how many people chose each painting.

Painting	Frequency
A	15
B	20
C	10
D	15

(a) Draw and label a pie chart to represent the information in the table.
(b) The artist says that the probability that a person likes picture B best is $\frac{1}{4}$.
Show that this is not true for the above data.

AQA

7 A spinner is labelled as shown.
The results of the first 30 spins are given below.

1 2 3 3 5 1 3 2 2 4
5 3 2 1 2 5 2 4 1 5
1 5 2 2 4 2 5 4 2 3

(a) What is the relative frequency of getting the number 1?
(b) Is the spinner fair?
Give a reason for your answer.

8 The diagram shows two sets of cards A and B.

One card is taken from set A and one card is taken from set B.
List all the possible outcomes.

9 The table shows information about a group of children.

	Can swim	Cannot swim
Boys	16	4
Girls	19	6

(a) One of these children is chosen at random.
What is the probability that the child can swim?
(b) A girl in the group is chosen at random.
What is the probability that she cannot swim?
(c) Tony says, "These results show a higher proportion of girls can swim."
Is he correct?
Give reasons for your answer.

10 A class survey found the probability of having brown eyes is 0.6.
   (a) What is the probability of not having brown eyes?
   (b) There are 30 children in the class.
       Estimate the number with brown eyes.

11 The table gives information about the age and mileage of a number of cars.
The mileages are given to the nearest thousand miles.

Age (years)	1	3	5	3	5	4	7	$4\frac{1}{2}$
Mileage (nearest 1000 miles)	9000	24 000	46 000	27 000	41 000	39 000	62 000	40 000

   (a) Use this information to draw a scatter graph.
   (b) What type of correlation is there between the age and mileage of these cars?
   (c) (i) Draw a line of best fit.
       (ii) Use your graph to estimate the age of the car with a mileage of 54 000.   AQA

12 Sue does a survey about the time that people spend watching TV and reading.
Two questions on her questionnaire are:

> **Question 1** How much do you read?
>
> **Question 2** There are more and more TV channels.
>   More and more TV programmes are being made.
>   We are watching more and more TV, so now we don't read enough.
>   Don't you agree?

   (a) Explain why each question is **not** a good one for this questionnaire.
   (b) Rewrite Question 1 so that it is more suitable for the questionnaire.   AQA

13 The maximum load for a lift is 1200 kg.
The table shows the distribution of the
weights of 22 people waiting for the lift.
Will the lift be overloaded if all of these people get in?
You **must** show working to support your answer.

Weight (w kg)	Frequency
$30 \leqslant w < 50$	8
$50 \leqslant w < 70$	10
$70 \leqslant w < 90$	4

AQA

14 The weights of 80 bags of rice are measured.
The table summarises the results.
   (a) Draw a box plot to show this information.
   (b) Write down the interquartile range for these data.
   (c) How many bags weigh
       (i) less than 480 g,
       (ii) less than 500 g?
   (d) Draw a cumulative frequency diagram to
       show the information.

Minimum	480 g
Lower quartile	500 g
Median	540 g
Upper quartile	620 g
Maximum	720 g

AQA

15 The diagram shows a fair five-sided spinner.
The spinner has two black sections and three white sections.
The sections are numbered as shown.

The spinner is spun twice.
   (a) What is the probability of getting two black sections?
   (b) What is the probability of getting a black section on the
       first spin and a 3 on the second spin?
   (c) What is the probability of getting a black 3 and a white 3?   AQA

Module 1 Exam Practice Calculator Paper

You may use a calculator for this exercise.

1 A fair coin is thrown and a fair dice is rolled.

> If the coin shows heads, the score is the number shown on the dice.
> If the coin shows tails, the score is double the number shown on the dice.

(a) Copy and complete the table to show each possible score.

Dice

		1	2	3	4	5	6
Coin	Heads	1					
	Tails			8			

(b) What is the probability of getting a score of 10?

(c) What is the probability of getting a score of less than 6?

AQA

2 The lengths, in centimetres, of a sample of leaves are shown.

4.7	5.0	6.4	5.6	6.1	4.9	5.8	6.5	7.2	6.7	6.5	5.3

(a) Calculate the mean length of these leaves.

(b) Draw a stem and leaf diagram to represent this information.

3 The pie chart shows the results of a survey about the takeaway foods students like best.

(a) Fish and chips is liked best by 80 students.
How many students like Pizza best?

(b) The table shows the results of a survey about the takeaway foods liked best by 100 pensioners.

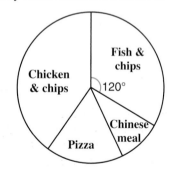

Takeaway	Frequency
Fish and chips	40
Chicken and chips	43
Pizza	9
Chinese meal	8

Do these surveys support the hypothesis:
"More pensioners than students like fish and chips"?
Explain your answer.

AQA

4 The table shows the ages and weights of chickens.

Age (days)	10	20	40	50	70	80	100
Weight (g)	100	300	1000	1300	2000	2000	2400

(a) Use this information to draw a scatter graph.

(b) Draw a line of best fit.

(c) (i) Use the line of best fit to estimate the weight of a chicken aged 140 days.

(ii) Give a reason why your answer may not be very reliable.

AQA

5 Jamal, Des, William and Sue play a board game. There is only one winner.
The probability that Jamal wins is 0.3.
The probability that Des wins is 0.1.

   (a)   Calculate the probability that either William or Sue wins.
   (b)   William is twice as likely to win as Sue. What is the probability that Sue wins?   *AQA*

6 Brian does a survey on what pupils eat for breakfast.
Here are three questions from his questionnaire.

> 1. What time do you get up?
>   Before 7.00 ☐   Between 7.00 and 8.00 ☐   After 8.00 ☐
> 2. Which of these do you have for breakfast?   Bacon ☐   Eggs ☐   Cereal ☐
> 3. How long does it take you to eat your breakfast? . . . .

Write down one **criticism** of each question.   *AQA*

7 Four scatter graphs are shown.

      A   B   C   D

   (a)   Which graph shows negative correlation?
   (b)   Which graph shows no correlation?
   (c)   Which graph could show the relationship between the engine size of cars and their top speeds?

8 The two-way table shows the results of a survey among adults at an out of town supermarket.

	Can drive	Cannot drive
Male	22	4
Female	15	4

A town has 27 953 adults.
   (a)   Give a reason why the sample may not be representative of the town.
   (b)   Use the results of the survey to estimate the number of adults in the town who can drive.
        Give your answer to a suitable degree of accuracy.   *AQA*

9 A college records the number of people who sign up for adult educational classes each term.
The table shows the numbers from Autumn 2000 to Summer 2002.

Term	Autumn 2000	Spring 2001	Summer 2001	Autumn 2001	Spring 2002	Summer 2002
Number of people	520	300	380	640	540	500

   (a)   Calculate the first value of the three-point moving average for these data.
   (b)   Explain why a **three-point** moving average is appropriate.   *AQA*

10 Nick travels to work by train on two days.
The probability that the train is late on any day is 0.3.
   (a)   Draw a tree diagram to show all the possible outcomes for the two days.
   (b)   What is the probability that the train is late on at least one of the two days?

11 Pupils in Year 7 are all given the same test. The test is marked out of 100.
The results for the boys are:

Lowest score	7 marks
Highest score	98 marks
Lower quartile	36 marks
Median	53 marks
Upper quartile	66 marks

Girls

(a) The diagram shows the box plot for the girls' results.
Draw a box plot to show the information for the boys.
(b) Comment on the differences between the boys' and girls' results.

AQA

12 A survey was made of the time taken by 100 people to do their shopping at a local supermarket on a Monday.

(a) Calculate an estimate of the mean time taken by these people to do their shopping.
(b) Draw a frequency polygon to illustrate this information.

Time taken (t minutes)	Number of people
$0 \leqslant t < 10$	43
$10 \leqslant t < 20$	35
$20 \leqslant t < 30$	17
$30 \leqslant t < 40$	5

13 The cumulative frequency table gives the age distribution of people living in a village.

Age (years)	< 10	< 20	< 30	< 40	< 50	< 60	< 70	< 80	< 100
Cumulative frequency	5	30	70	120	180	260	350	380	400

(a) Draw a cumulative frequency graph to illustrate the data.
(b) Estimate the number of people less than 25 years old.
(c) Use your graph to estimate
   (i) the median,
   (ii) the interquartile range.
(d) The age distribution of people living in a town has a median of 45 years and an interquartile range of 20 years.
   Compare and comment on the ages of people living in the village and the town.

AQA

14 The number of mobile phones sold each quarter by a retailer for the last three years is shown.

Year	2000				2001				2002			
Quarter	1	2	3	4	1	2	3	4	1	2	3	4
Number of phones sold	18	28	22	36	20	32	28	42	24	42	40	76

(a) Plot these values on graph paper.
(b) Calculate the 4-quarterly moving averages.
(c) Plot the moving averages on the same graph.
(d) Draw a trend line by eye.
(e) Comment on the trend.
(f) Estimate the number of mobile phones sold by the retailer in the first quarter of 2003.

15 Sue has two bags of sweets.
Bag A contains 6 toffees and 3 chocolates.
Bag B contains 5 toffees and 2 chocolates.
Sue takes one sweet from each bag.
What is the probability that she gets two sweets of the same sort?

AQA

Whole Numbers

The numbers 0, 1, 2, 3, 4, 5, … can be used to count objects.
Such numbers are called **whole numbers**.
There are other types of numbers, including fractions, decimals and negative numbers which you will meet in later chapters.

Place value

Our number system is made up of the digits 0, 1, 2, 3, 4, 5, 6, 7, 8 and 9.
The position a digit has in a number is called its **place value**.
In the number 5384 the digit 8 is worth 80, but in the number 4853 the digit 8 is worth 800.

Reading and writing numbers

$8543 = 8 \times 1000 + 5 \times 100 + 4 \times 10 + 3 \times 1$
The number 8543 is written or read as, "eight thousand five hundred and forty-three."
For numbers bigger than one thousand split the number into groups of three digits, starting from the units column.

EXAMPLES

1 Write the number 56843 in words.

Fifty-six *thousand* eight hundred and forty-three.

2 Write the number 4567205 in words.

Four *million* five hundred and sixty-seven *thousand* two hundred and five.

1. Split the numbers into groups of 3 digits.
2. Combine the numbers of millions and thousands with the number less than 1000.

Exercise 8.1

1 Write the following numbers in figures.
  (a) three hundred and ninety-six
  (b) five thousand and ten
  (c) seventy thousand two hundred
  (d) nine million two thousand and fifty-one
  (e) seven hundred and sixty-two million five hundred and four thousand and nineteen
  (f) twenty million two hundred and two thousand and twenty

2 Write the following numbers in words.
  (a) 84   (b) 23590   (c) 93145670   (d) 764809   (e) 6049   (f) 9080004

3 Write answers to the following using figures.
  (a) Ten less than one thousand and fourteen.
  (b) One hundred more than nine hundred and thirty-five.
  (c) Eighty less than one thousand and ninety-four.

4 In the number 3<u>8</u>4 the value of the underlined figure is 80.
  Give the value of the underlined figure in the following.
  (a) 62<u>3</u>4   (b) 12<u>3</u> 456 789   (c) 95 <u>6</u>70   (d) <u>2</u>003   (e) 9<u>4</u> 705   (f) 423<u>6</u>

5 Look at these numbers. 97, 32, 23, 28, 302, 203.
  (a) Which is the largest **odd** number?   (b) Which is the smallest **even** number?

6 Write the following numbers in ascending order.
(a) 74, 168, 39, 421.
(b) 3842, 5814, 3874, 3801, 4765.

7 Write the following numbers in descending order.
(a) 399, 425, 103, 84, 429.
(b) 9434, 9646, 9951, 9653.

| Smallest number | ascending order | Largest number |
| Largest number | descending order | Smallest number |

8 Using the digits 4, 6, 7, 1 and 5
(do not use the same digit more than once)
(a) make the biggest five-digit number,
(b) make the smallest five-digit number.
In each case explain your method.

9 By using each of the digits 5, 4, 9 and 6
(a) make the largest four-digit **even** number,
(b) make the smallest four-digit **odd** number.

10 Using the digits 8, 5, 4 and 3 make as many four-digit numbers as you can.
Use each digit just once in each four-digit number, e.g. 8543.
Put your numbers in ascending order.
How many numbers begin with eight?

Non-calculator methods for addition

Writing numbers in columns

Write the numbers in tidy columns
according to place value.
Add together the numbers of units, tens,
hundreds, etc.
If any of these answers comes to more
than 10 then something is carried to the
next column.

EXAMPLE

Work out 4567 + 835.

```
  4 5 6 7     7 + 5 = 12                   which is 2 carry 1.
+   8 3 5     6 + 3 + carried 1 = 10,  which is 0 carry 1.
  5 4 0 2     5 + 8 + carried 1 = 14,  which is 4 carry 1.
  1 1 1       4 + carried 1 = 5.
```

Using a number line

A number line shows a different method
for adding numbers.
With practice you should not need to
draw a number line.

EXAMPLE

Work out 26 + 37.

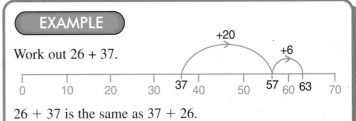

26 + 37 is the same as 37 + 26.
37 + 20 = 57 (adding 20)
57 + 6 = 63   (adding 6)
So 26 + 37 = 63.

Working in context

1. Identify the calculation required by the question.
2. Do the calculation.
3. Give the answer to the question using a short sentence.

EXAMPLE

In Year 7 the class attendances were as follows:
28   30   27   30   25
What was the total attendance?

The total attendance was 140.

```
    2 8
    3 0
    2 7
    3 0
+   2 5
  1 4 0
    1 2
```

1 Here is a number line for 18 + 15.

+10   +5

0   10   18 20   28 30 33   40

(a) What is 18 + 10?
(b) What is 18 + 15?

2 Draw a number line for each of the following sums and work out the answers.
(a) 14 + 15   (b) 13 + 18
(c) 7 + 36   (d) 18 + 25
(e) 24 + 29   (f) 19 + 27

3 What must be added to each of these numbers to make 100?
(a) 9   (b) 96
(c) 45   (d) 37
(e) 62   (f) 83

4 Work these out by writing the numbers in columns.
(a) 765 + 23   (b) 27 + 56
(c) 76 + 98   (d) 324 + 628
(e) 1273 + 729   (f) 3495 + 8708
(g) 67 + 89 + 45
(h) 431 + 865 + 245
(i) 187 + 54 + 3210
(j) 123 456 + 876 544

5 Work these out in your head.
(a) 15 + 12   (b) 24 + 32
(c) 19 + 16   (d) 37 + 17
(e) 26 + 48   (f) 29 + 41
(g) 63 + 57   (h) 13 + 99

6 This signpost is between Poole and London.

POOLE 47 Miles   LONDON 65 Miles

How far is it from Poole to London?

7

Computer Package

PC   £349
Printer   £125
Software   £65

What is the total cost of this computer package?

8

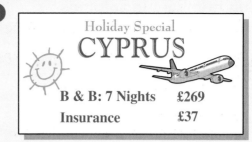

Holiday Special
CYPRUS

B & B: 7 Nights   £269
Insurance   £37

What is the total cost of the holiday?

9 The chart shows the distances in kilometres between some towns.

Bath

| 153 | Woking | |
| 362 | 367 | York |

Kathryn drives from Bath to Woking and then from Woking to York.
Calculate the total distance she drives.

10 The class attendance in Year 7, Year 8 and Year 9 is shown.

Year 7		Year 8		Year 9	
7A	28	8A	27	9A	30
7B	29	8B	30	9B	28
7C	29	8C	28	9C	27

What is the total attendance in these 9 classes?

11 What is the total weight of these packages?

49 grams   257 grams   724 grams

12 The table shows the number of tickets sold each day last week at a cinema.

Mon	Tue	Wed	Thu	Fri	Sat	Sun
125	87	95	105	278	487	201

How many tickets were sold altogether?

13 The last four attendances at a football stadium were:

21 004,   19 750,   18 009,   22 267.

What is the total attendance?

Whole Numbers . . . Whole Numbers . . .

Non-calculator methods for subtraction

Writing numbers in columns

Write the numbers in columns according to place value.
The order in which the numbers are written down is important.
Then, in turn, subtract the numbers of units, tens, hundreds, etc.
If the subtraction in a column cannot be done, because the number being subtracted is greater, borrow 10 from the next column.

Work out $7238 - 642$.

$$
\begin{array}{r}
{}^{6}\!\!\!\not7\,{}^{11}\!\!\!\not2\,{}^{1}\!3\,8 \\
-\quad 6\,4\,2 \\
\hline
6\,5\,9\,6
\end{array}
$$

Units: $8 - 2 = 6$
Tens: $3 - 4$ cannot be done, so borrow 10 from the 2 in the next column.
Now $10 + 3 - 4 = 9$.
Hundreds: $1 - 6$ cannot be done, so borrow 10 from the 7 in the next column.
Now $10 + 1 - 6 = 5$.
Thousands: $6 - 0 = 6$.

You can use addition to check your subtraction.
Does $6596 + 642 = 7238$?

$$
\begin{array}{r}
6\,5\,9\,6 \\
+\quad 6\,4\,2 \\
\hline
7\,2\,3\,8 \\
{}_{1}\ {}_{1}
\end{array}
$$

EXAMPLES

1

$$
\begin{array}{r}
{}^{0}\!\!\not1\,{}^{16}\!\!\not7\,{}^{15}\!\!\not6\,{}^{1}2 \\
-\quad 8\,7\,3 \\
\hline
8\,8\,9
\end{array}
$$

2

$$
\begin{array}{r}
{}^{2}\!\!\not3\,{}^{9}\!\!\not0\,{}^{9}\!\!\not0\,{}^{1}6 \\
-\quad 1\,8\,4\,7 \\
\hline
1\,1\,5\,9
\end{array}
$$

3

$$
\begin{array}{r}
{}^{8}\!\!\not9\,{}^{9}\!\!\not0\,{}^{10}\!\!\not1\,{}^{1}2 \\
-\quad 5\,6\,7\,8 \\
\hline
3\,3\,3\,4
\end{array}
$$

Check the answers by addition.

Addition is the opposite (inverse) operation to subtraction.
If $\quad a - b = c$,
then $\quad c + b = a$.

Exercise 8.3

Do not use a calculator for this exercise.

1 Here is a number line for $43 - 16$.
(a) What is $43 - 10$?
(b) What is $43 - 16$?

2 Draw a number line for each of the following questions and work out the answers.
(a) $56 - 28$ (b) $64 - 18$ (c) $44 - 19$ (d) $73 - 38$

3 Write down the answers to the following by working them out in your head.
(a) $100 - 95$ (b) $100 - 8$ (c) $100 - 57$ (d) $100 - 32$
(e) $100 - 24$ (f) $100 - 83$ (g) $100 - 41$ (h) $100 - 79$

4 Work these out in your head.
(a) $26 - 10$ (b) $26 - 9$ (c) $87 - 37$ (d) $87 - 38$
(e) $200 - 110$ (f) $204 - 99$ (g) $500 - 350$ (h) $500 - 199$
(i) $1000 - 425$ (j) $1003 - 999$

5 Work these out by writing the numbers in columns. Use addition to check your answers.
(a) $978 - 624$ (b) $843 - 415$ (c) $1754 - 470$ (d) $407 - 249$
(e) $5070 - 2846$ (f) $2345 - 1876$ (g) $8045 - 1777$ (h) $10\,000 - 6723$

6 A car park has spaces for 345 cars. On Tuesday 256 spaces are used. How many spaces are not used?

7 A school has 843 pupils. How many are boys if there are 459 girls?

8 The table shows the milometer readings for three cars at the start and end of a year.

	Start	End
Car A	2501	10980
Car B	55667	67310
Car C	48050	61909

Which car has done the most miles in the year?

9 Here is a price list for some electrical goods.

(a) How much more does it cost to buy the TV and Video separately than to buy the Combined TV/Video?

(b) I have £500. How much more do I need to buy the Combined TV/Video, and the Music System?

TV	**£299**
Video	**£150**
Combined TV/Video	**£375**
Music System	**£185**

Multiplication of whole numbers

It is very useful to know your Multiplication Tables up to 10×10.

×	1	2	3	4	5	6	7	8	9	10
1	1	2	3	4	5	6	7	8	9	10
2	2	4	6	8	10	12	14	16	18	20
3	3	6	9	12	15	18	21	24	27	30
4	4	8	12	16	20	24	28	32	36	40
5	5	10	15	20	25	30	35	40	45	50
6	6	12	18	24	30	36	42	48	54	60
7	7	14	21	28	35	42	49	56	63	70
8	8	16	24	32	40	48	56	64	72	80
9	9	18	27	36	45	54	63	72	81	90
10	10	20	30	40	50	60	70	80	90	100

Activity

How quickly can you answer the following questions?

9×5

6×6

7×4

9×6

8×7

9×7

8×8

Working with a partner ask each other questions from the table.

Non-calculator method for short multiplication

Short multiplication is when the multiplying number is less than 10, e.g. 165×7.
One method multiplies the units, tens, hundreds, etc. in turn.

```
  1 6 5
×     7
-------
1 1 5 5
1 4 3
```

Units: $7 \times 5 = 35$, which is 5 carry 3.

Tens: $7 \times 6 = 42 +$ carried $3 = 45$, which is 5 carry 4.

Hundreds: $7 \times 1 = 7 +$ carried $4 = 11$, which is 1 carry 1.

There are no more digits to be multiplied by 7, the carried 1 becomes 1 thousand.

EXAMPLES

1
```
  1 6 2
×     4
-------
  6 4 8
    2
```

2
```
  9 0 7 1
×       7
---------
6 3 4 9 7
      4
```

3
```
  4 8 3 5
×       8
---------
3 8 6 8 0
  6 2 4
```

Multiplying a whole number by 10, 100, 1000, ...

When you multiply a whole number by:

10   The units become 10s, the 10s become 100s, the 100s become 1000s, and so on.

100   The units become 100s, the 10s become 1000s, the 100s become 10 000s, and so on.

1000   The units become 1000s, the 10s become 10 000s, the 100s become 100 000s, and so on.

EXAMPLES

$753 \times 10 = 7530$
$753 \times 100 = 75\ 300$
$753 \times 1000 = 753\ 000$

We can show these multiplications in a table.

100 000s	10 000s	1000s	100s	10s	Units
			7	5	3
		7	5	3	0	← 753 × 10
	7	5	3	0	0	← 753 × 100
7	5	3	0	0	0	← 753 × 1000

$100 = 10 \times 10$
Multiplying a number by 100 is the same as multiplying the number by 10 and then by 10 again.

Explain any patterns you can see.

Multiplying a whole number by multiples of 10 (20, 30, 40, ...)

Work out 753×20.

This can be written as:
$$753 \times 20 = 753 \times 10 \times 2$$
$$= 7530 \times 2$$
$$= 15\ 060$$

$20 = 10 \times 2$

Exercise 8.4   Do not use a calculator for this exercise.

1   I get 8 doughnuts for £1.
How many doughnuts will I get for £5?

2   When John uses a store card he gets 4 points for every pound he spends. He spends £18.
How many points does he get?

3   A machine makes 24 jigsaws in an hour.
How many jigsaws will it make in 6 hours?

4   Linda is paid 3p for each leaflet she delivers. She delivers 184 leaflets.
How much is she paid?

5   Work these out using a method you find easiest.
   (a) 21×4 (b) 17×5 (c) 36×7 (d) 183×3
   (e) 264×8 (f) 3179×5 (g) 4012×6 (h) 6012×7

6   Write down the answers to the following questions. You do not have to show any working.
   (a) 132×10 (b) 123×100 (c) 47×1000 (d) 384×100

7   What number should be put in the box to make each of these statements correct?
   (a) $231 \times 10 = \square$ (b) $\square \times 1000 = 514\ 000$ (c) $172 \times \square = 17\ 200$

8   A packet of 24 custard cream biscuits costs 39 pence. I buy 10 packets.
   (a)   How many biscuits do I buy?   (b)   How much will they cost altogether?

9   There are 7 classrooms in a school. In each classroom there are 30 chairs and 20 tables.
Find the total number of
   (a)   chairs,   (b)   tables.

10 Calculate the number of seconds in
(a) 5 minutes, (b) 19 minutes.

11 A farmer has 32 bags of turnips.
Each bag weighs 50 kg.
What is the total weight?

12 A caretaker puts out 30 rows of chairs.
There are 24 chairs in each row.
How many chairs are put out?

13 There are 400 metres in one lap of a
running track.
How many metres are there in 25 laps?

14 Use a non-calculator method to calculate
these products.
(a) 253 × 30   (b) 357 × 20
(c) 537 × 40   (d) 615 × 20
(e) 186 × 70   (f) 239 × 90
(g) 412 × 80   (h) 142 × 70
(i) 632 × 30   (j) 260 × 50

15 (a) Describe a method of multiplying
by 200, 300, 400, and so on.
(b) Describe a method of multiplying
by 2000, 3000, 4000, and so on.
(c) Work out (i) 347 × 500
(ii) 743 × 6000

Non-calculator method for short division

The process of dividing a number by a number less than 10 is called **short division**.
Short division relies on knowledge of the Multiplication Tables.
What is   32 ÷ 8,   42 ÷ 7,   72 ÷ 9,   54 ÷ 6 ?

Work out 882 ÷ 7.

7)8 ^{1}8 ^{4}2   Starting from the left:
$\overline{1\ 2\ 6}$ 8 ÷ 7 = 1 remainder 1, which is 1 carry 1.
18 ÷ 7 = 2 remainder 4, which is 2 carry 4.
42 ÷ 7 = 6, with no remainder.
So 882 ÷ 7 = 126.

You may set your
working out like
this:
$$\frac{1\ 2\ 6}{7)8\ ^{1}8\ ^{4}2}$$

You can check your division by multiplying.
Does 126 × 7 = 882?

Multiplication is the
opposite (inverse) operation
to division.
If $a \div b = c$,
then $c \times b = a$.

EXAMPLES	**1** $6)1\ 4^{2}7^{3}0$ over $2\ 4\ 5$	**2** $9)2\ 7\ 6^{6}3$ over $3\ 0\ 7$

Dividing a whole number by 10, 100, 1000, ...

When you divide a whole number by:
10   The 10s become units, the 100s become 10s, the 1000s become 100s, and so on.
100   The 100s become units, the 1000s become 10s, the 10 000s become 100s, and so on.
1000   The 1000s become units, the 10 000s become 10s, the 100 000s become 100s, and so on.

Examples	10 000s	1000s	100s	10s	Units	
7530 ÷ 10 = 753						
12 400 ÷ 100 = 124		7	5	3	0	
631 000 ÷ 1000 = 631			7	5	3	← 753 ÷ 10

Draw tables to show the other division sums.
Explain any patterns you can see.

Dividing a whole number by multiples of 10 (20, 30, 40, ...)

Work out 7530 ÷ 30.

7530 ÷ 30
= (7530 ÷ 10) ÷ 3
= 753 ÷ 3   (dividing by 10)
= 251   (dividing by 3)

30 = 10 × 3
Dividing by 30 is the same as
dividing by 10 and then dividing by 3.

Do not use a calculator for this exercise.

1 Two tins of cat food cost 98p.
What is the cost of one tin?

2 Flower pots cost £5 each. I have £30.
How many flower pots can I buy?

3 Pam buys 3 watches for £42.
How much is each watch?

4 A packet of 8 crayons is 96p.
What is the cost of one crayon?

5 Candles are sold in packets of 4.
I need 60 candles.
How many packets do I need to buy?

6 Calculate these divisions.
Show your working clearly.
State the remainder if there is one.
Use multiplication to check your answers.
(a) $85 \div 5$ (b) $471 \div 3$
(c) $816 \div 6$ (d) $455 \div 6$
(e) $3146 \div 8$ (f) $824 \div 4$
(g) $9882 \div 9$ (h) $80\,560 \div 4$

7 Write down the answers to the following
questions.
You do not have to show your working.
(a) $4560 \div 10$
(b) $465\,000 \div 1000$
(c) $64\,000 \div 1000$
(d) $65\,400 \div 100$

8 What number should be put in the box to
make each of these statements correct?
(a) $56\,400 \div \square = 564$
(b) $\square \div 1000 = 702$
(c) $35\,000 \div \square = 3500$

9 A minibus holds 20 passengers.
How many minibuses are needed to carry
160 passengers?

10 How many £50 notes are needed to pay a
bill of £750?

11 A double-decker bus holds 70 passengers.
How many buses are needed to take
840 students on a trip?

12 A box holds 40 matches. How many boxes
are needed to hold 1000 matches?

13 Hannah completes a puzzle in 420 seconds.
How many minutes is this?

14 Work out.
(a) $7590 \div 30$ (b) $7110 \div 90$
(c) $21\,480 \div 40$ (d) $7560 \div 60$
(e) $900 \div 20$ (f) $30\,650 \div 50$

15 (a) Describe a method to divide by
multiples of 100 (200, 300, 400, …)
(b) Work out. (i) $13\,000 \div 500$
(ii) $329\,600 \div 800$

Long multiplication

Long multiplication is used when the multiplying
number is greater than 10, e.g. 24×17.

Work out 24×17.

$$\begin{array}{r} 24 \\ \times\ 17 \\ \hline 168 \\ +\ 240 \\ \hline 408 \end{array}$$

$\leftarrow 24 \times 7 = 168$
$\leftarrow 24 \times 10 = 240$

A standard non-calculator method for doing
long multiplication multiplies the number by:

● the units figure, then

● the tens figure, then

● the hundreds figure, and so on.

All these answers are added together.

EXAMPLES

1
$$\begin{array}{r} 145 \\ \times\ 62 \\ \hline 290 \\ +\ 8700 \\ \hline 8990 \end{array}$$
$\leftarrow 145 \times 2$
$\leftarrow 145 \times 60$

2
$$\begin{array}{r} 273 \\ \times\ 234 \\ \hline 1092 \\ 8190 \\ +\ 54600 \\ \hline 63882 \end{array}$$
$\leftarrow 273 \times 4$
$\leftarrow 273 \times 30$
$\leftarrow 273 \times 200$

Long division

Long division works in exactly the same way as short division, except that all the working out is written down.

Consider $952 \div 7$.

```
    1 3 6
7) 9 5 2
   7
   ‾‾
   2 5
   2 1
   ‾‾
     4 2
     4 2
     ‾‾
       0
```

$9 \div 7 = 1$ and a remainder.
What is the remainder?
$1 \times 7 = 7$ (write below the 9).
$9 - 7 = 2$ (which is the remainder).
Bring down the next figure (5) to make 25.
Repeat the above process.
$25 \div 7 = 3$ and a remainder.
$3 \times 7 = 21$, $25 - 21 = 4$ (remainder).
Bring down the next figure (2) to make 42 and repeat the process.
$42 \div 7 = 6$, but there is no remainder.
$6 \times 7 = 42$, $42 - 42 = 0$ (remainder).
There are no more figures to be brought down and there is no remainder.
So $952 \div 7 = 136$.

Using short division:

$$7)\overline{9^2 5^4 2}$$
$$1\ 3\ 6$$

Long division process
→ ÷ (obtain biggest answer possible)
× } calculates
− } the remainder
└── Bring down the next figure
Repeat process until there are no more figures to be brought down.

Exercise 8.6

Do not use a calculator for this exercise.

1 Work out.
(a) 17×12 (b) 23×15
(c) 42×32 (d) 76×32
(e) 143×34 (f) 718×54

2 A box holds 12 tins of soup.
How many tins will 18 boxes hold?

3 A computer prints 17 symbols on a line.
How many symbols will it print on 15 lines?

4 A restaurant charges £23 for dinner.
What is the total charge for 42 dinners?

5 A company has 47 shops.
Each shop employs 28 people.
How many people are employed altogether?

6 A coach trip costs £29 per person.
48 people go on the trip.
How much money is paid altogether?

7 Here is part of a price list.

Office Supplies

| Desk | £126 |
| Cabinet | £149 |

What is the total cost of 14 desks and 23 cabinets?

8 Work out.
(a) $473 \div 11$ (b) $480 \div 15$
(c) $324 \div 12$ (d) $544 \div 17$
(e) $624 \div 13$ (f) $943 \div 23$
(g) $777 \div 37$ (h) $841 \div 29$

9 Work these out and state the remainder each time.
(a) $410 \div 25$ (b) $607 \div 24$
(c) $800 \div 45$ (d) $754 \div 57$

10 A pint of milk costs 34 pence.
How many pints of milk can be bought for £5?
How much change will there be?

11 Tins of beans are packed in boxes of 24.
A supplier has 1000 tins of beans.
(a) How many full boxes is this?
(b) How many tins are left over?

12

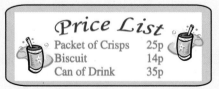

Price List
Packet of Crisps   25p
Biscuit   14p
Can of Drink   35p

I have £5 to spend.
(a) How many packets of crisps can I buy?
(b) How many biscuits can I buy?
(c) How many cans of drink can I buy?
In each case state the change if there is any.

Order of operations in a calculation

What is $4 + 3 \times 5$?	It is not sensible to have two possible answers. It has been agreed that calculations are done obeying certain rules:

First	Brackets and Division line
Second	Divide and Multiply
Third	Addition and Subtraction

EXAMPLES

1 $4 + 3 \times 5$ $=$ $4 + 15$ $=$ 19

2 $10 \div 2 + 3$ $=$ $5 + 3$ $=$ 8

3 $10 \div (2 + 3)$ $=$ $10 \div 5$ $=$ 2

4 $(5 + 6) \times 3 + 4$ $=$ $11 \times 3 + 4$ $=$ $33 + 4$ $=$ 37

5 $\dfrac{12}{11 - 8} - 3$ $=$ $\dfrac{12}{3} - 3$ $=$ $4 - 3$ $=$ 1

This is the same as $12 \div (11 - 8) - 3$.

Exercise 8.7

Do not use a calculator for this exercise.

1   Work these out.

(a) $7 + 6 \times 5$ (b) $7 - (6 - 2)$ (c) $24 \div 6 + 5$

(d) $7 \times 6 + 8 \times 2$ (e) $10 \div 5 + 8 \div 2$ (f) $(5 - 2) \times 7 + 9$

(g) $60 \div (5 + 7)$ (h) $60 \div 5 + 7$ (i) $4 \times 3 + 2$

(j) $4 \times (3 + 2)$ (k) $12 \times (20 - 2) \div 9$ (l) $36 \div (5 + 4)$

(m) $4 \times 12 \div 8 - 6$ (n) $9 \times 9 - 5 \times 5$ (o) $(9 + 5) \times (9 - 5)$

(p) $\dfrac{22 - 4}{17 - 8} + 12 \div 3$ (q) $\dfrac{6 \times 3 - 2}{2 \times 2} + 3 \times 8$ (r) $\dfrac{(3 + 7) \times 10 - 19}{(2 + 1) \times (8 - 5)} - 3 \times 3$

2   Choose from the four signs $+$, $-$, $\times$ and $\div$ to make these sums correct.

(a)   5   6   7 = 37   (b)   5   6   7 = 47   (c)   15   8   9 = 87

(d)   15   8   9 = 129   (e)   15   8   9 = 111   (f)   15   5   3 = 6

(g)   5   24   6 = 1   (h)   19   19   7   0 = 1   (i)   4   4   7   2 = 30

3   Using all the numbers 6, 3, 2 and 1 in this order, brackets and the signs $+$, $-$, $\times$ and $\div$ make all the numbers from 1 to 10.

$6 - 3 \times 2 + 1 = 1$, $6 - 3 - 2 + 1 = 2$,   and so on.

4   The caretaker set out 17 rows of chairs. There are 15 chairs in each row. How many more chairs are needed to provide seats for 280 people?

5   Claire is 16 cm taller than Rachel. Their heights add up to 312 cm. How tall is Rachel?

6   The admission charges to a zoo are £7 for a child and £12 for an adult. Zoe is organising a trip to the zoo for a group of people and worked out that the total cost would be £336. She collected £84 from the adults in the group.

(a)   How many children are in the group?

(b)   What is the total number of people in the group?

You should be able to:

- Read and write whole numbers expressed in figures and words.
- Order whole numbers.
- Recognise the place value of each digit in a number.
- Use mental methods to carry out addition and subtraction.
- Carry out accurately non-calculator methods for addition and subtraction.
- Know the Multiplication Tables up to 10×10.
- Carry out multiplication by a number less than 10 (short multiplication).
- Multiply whole numbers by 10, 100, 1000, …
- Multiply whole numbers by 20, 30, 40, …
- Carry out division by a number less than 10 (short division).
- Divide whole numbers by 10, 100, 1000, …
- Divide whole numbers by 20, 30, 40, …
- Carry out long multiplication.
- Carry out long division.
- Know the order of operations in a calculation.

Write down a three-digit number.
Write in words.
Count the letters.
Write this number in words.
Count the letters.
Write this number in words
and so on.

Example

569,	five hundred and sixty-nine
23,	twenty-three
11,	eleven
6,	six
3,	three
5,	five
4,	four

1 Start with the number 207.
What number do you end up with?

2 Repeat the process starting with a different number.

3 Do you always end up with the same number?

Review Exercise 8   Do not use a calculator for this exercise.

1 (a) Write 870302 in words.
(b) Write three million twenty-seven thousand four hundred and nine in figures.

2 By using each of the digits 4, 8, 7, 2, 9 and 5,
(a) write the biggest six-digit number you can,
(b) write the smallest six-digit **odd** number you can.

3 In the game of darts the scores of the three darts are added
together. These are then taken away from the current total
to calculate the new total. In each case work out the score
of the three darts and the new total.

	Current Total	1st dart	2nd dart	3rd dart	Score	New Total
(a)	501	60	18	19	[ ]	[ ]
(b)	420	19	57	38	[ ]	[ ]
(c)	301	50	25	17	[ ]	[ ]

Whole Numbers . . . Whole Numbers . . .

4 Work out the following. Show your working.
  (a) $465 + 12 + 1582$ (b) $2465 - 1878$

5 Write down the answers to these questions.
  (a) 735×100 (b) 214×30 (c) $3\,020\,000 \div 1000$ (d) $18\,480 \div 40$

6 The chart shows the distances in miles between some towns.

Isaac drives from Liverpool to Nottingham, from Nottingham to York and then from York back to Liverpool.
Calculate the total distance he drives.

Liverpool				
35	Manchester			
109	70	Nottingham		
77	37	44	Sheffield	
102	71	87	61	York

7 Work out the following. Show your working clearly.
  (a) 718×9 (b) $1446 \div 6$

8 Calculate these. Remember to do the operations in the right order.
  (a) $2 + 6 \times 8$ (b) $(9 - 4) \times (3 + 7)$

  (c) $72 \div 8 + 1$ (d) $\dfrac{(5 \times 6 - 3) - 21 \div 3}{2 \times 3 + 4}$

9 John's dog eats two meals a day, every day for a year.
Each meal costs 75p.
How much money will John need to feed his dog for a year?   AQA

10 Lauren does a paper round.
She delivers 47 newspapers, 6 days a week for 52 weeks a year.
How many newspapers does she deliver altogether in one year?

11 A supermarket orders 1800 kg of potatoes.
The potatoes are delivered in 15 kg bags.
How many bags are delivered?

12 One thousand chocolate biscuits are packed in boxes of 6.
  (a) How many full boxes will there be?   (b) How many biscuits will be left over?

13 A company is organising a holiday for 274 workers.
Each worker pays £53 as part of the cost.
Work out exactly the total amount paid by the workers. You **must** show all your working.   AQA

14 Angelique is taking 149 pupils to the theatre to see the Royal Ballet.
The cost of the theatre ticket is £23 per person.
Work out the total cost of the tickets.   AQA

15 Joe wants to save £884 to pay for his holiday.
He saves the same amount each week for 52 weeks.
How much does Joe save each week?   AQA

16 Sue has collected £544 from her friends at work for theatre tickets.
The tickets cost £17 each.
Work out the number of theatre tickets she can buy.   AQA

17 A survey counted the number of visitors to a website on the Internet.
Altogether it was visited 30 million times.
Each day it was visited 600 000 times.
Based on this information, for how many days did the survey last?   AQA

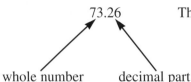

Decimals

Numbers and quantities are not always whole numbers.
The number system you met in Chapter 8 can be extended to include **decimal numbers**, such as tenths, hundredths, thousandths, and smaller numbers.
A **decimal point** is used to separate the whole number part from the decimal part of the number.

73.26   This number is read as seventy-three point two six.

whole number   decimal part
73   2 tenths + 6 hundredths
                             (which is the same as 26 hundredths)

Place value

In the number 1.53 the digit 1 is worth 1 unit = 1
                          the digit 5 is worth 5 tenths = 0.5
                          the digit 3 is worth 3 hundredths = 0.03

1.53 = 1 + 0.5 + 0.03

○○○○○○○○○○
1 unit = 10 tenths
1 tenth = 10 hundredths
1 hundredth = 10 thousandths
… and so on.

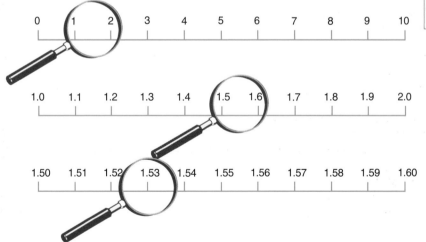

The first digit after the decimal point represents **tenths**.

The second digit after the decimal point represents **hundredths**.

The number 1.53 can be represented by a diagram.

 1 unit   **5 tenths**   **3 hundredths**

Ordering decimals

Compare the numbers 52.359 and 52.36. Which number is the bigger?

You can use a grid to compare the numbers.

tens	units	.	tenths	hundredths	thousandths
5	2	.	3	5	9
5	2	.	3	6	

Start by comparing the digits with the greatest place value, the tens.
Both numbers have 5 tens, so move down to compare the units.
Both numbers have 2 units, so move down to the tenths.
Both numbers have 3 tenths, so move down to the hundredths.
52.359 has 5 hundredths but 52.36 has 6 hundredths.
So 52.36 is bigger than 52.359.

A similar method can be used to place a list of decimal numbers in order.

Exercise 9.1

1 $2.564 = 2 + 0.5 + 0.06 + 0.004$
Write these numbers in the same way.
(a) 7.62   (b) 37.928
(c) 7.541   (d) 20.503

2 In the number 17.4<u>6</u>2 the value of the underlined figure is 0.06.
Give the value of the underlined figures in the following.
(a) 27.<u>4</u>3   (b) 36.42<u>9</u>
(c) 2<u>8</u>5.03   (d) 0.7<u>5</u>3

3 Write down the numbers shown by these diagrams.

(a)

(b)

(c)

4 Look at these decimals.
0.07, 0.6, 0.09, 0.1.
(a) Which is the smallest number?
(b) Which is the largest number?

5 On these scales what numbers are shown by the arrows?

(a)

(b)

(c)

(d)

6 Compare the numbers 47.5074 and 47.506. Which is the bigger number?

7 Compare the numbers 93.07 and 93.072. Which is the smaller number?

8 List the following decimals in ascending order.
(a) 3.1, 3.01, 3.001, 3.15, 3.2.
(b) 3.567, 3.657, 3.576, 3.675.
(c) 0.1, 0.55, 0.45, 0.5, 0.15.

9 List the following decimals in descending order.
(a) 9.87, 8.79, 9.78, 8.97.
(b) 0.00015, 0.15, 1.5, 0.015.
(c) 2.67, 2.7, 2.599, 2.701.

Writing numbers in columns

Write the numbers in tidy columns according to place value.
This is easily done by keeping the decimal points in a vertical column.
Start the addition or subtraction from the right, just as you did for whole numbers.
Use the same methods for carrying and borrowing as well.

EXAMPLES

1 Work out $42.6 + 0.75 + 9$

$$\begin{array}{r} 4\,2.6 \\ 0.7\,5 \\ +\ \ 9.0 \\ \hline 5\,2.3\,5 \\ \hline {\scriptstyle 1\ \ 1} \end{array}$$

2 Work out $17.1 - 8.72$

$$\begin{array}{r} 1\,\overset{6}{7}.\overset{10}{1}\overset{1}{0} \\ -\ \ 8.7\,2 \\ \hline 8.3\,8 \end{array}$$

Use addition to check this answer.

You can write 9 as 9.0 or 9.00 to keep your figures tidy. This does not change the value of the number.
42.6 can be written as 42.60
17.1 can be written as 17.10

Working mentally

Addition and subtraction of decimals can be carried out mentally, in your head.
For example, using place value, we know that $2.5 = 2 + 0.5$.
So, adding 2.5 to a number is the same as adding 2 and then adding 0.5.

EXAMPLES

1 Work out $8.31 + 3.58$.

$3.58 = 3 + 0.5 + 0.08$
$8.31 + 3.58$
$= 8.31 + 3 + 0.5 + 0.08$
$= 8.39 + 3 + 0.5$ (adding 8.31 and 0.08)
$= 8.89 + 3$ (adding 8.39 and 0.5)
$= 11.89$

$3.58 = 3 + 0.5 + 0.08$
The adding of 3, 0.5 and 0.08 can be carried out in any order.
Here, we have added the numbers in order of size, starting with the smallest.
Choose a method you find easiest.

2 Work out $25.4 - 8.7$.

$25.4 - 8.7$
$= 25.4 - 8 - 0.7$
$= 24.7 - 8$ (subtracting 0.7 from 25.4)
$= 16.7$

$8.7 = 8 + 0.7$
To subtract 8.7, first subtract 0.7 and then **subtract** 8.
Alternatively, first subtract 8 and then **subtract** 0.7.

Money

1360p can be written as £13.60

£13.60
complete number of pounds, 13   number of pence, 60

£6 can be written as £6.00
There must be exactly **two** figures after the decimal point when a decimal point is used to record amounts of money.

Other uses of decimal notation

Many measurements are recorded using decimals, including time, distance, weight, volume, etc.
The same rules for addition and subtraction can be applied if all the measurements involved are recorded using the same units.

I buy a newspaper for 45p, a set of batteries for £2.50 and a book of stamps for £2.
What is the total cost? How much change should I get from £5?

Working in pounds.

$$
\begin{array}{r}
0.4\,5 \\
2.5\,0 \\
+\ 2.0\,0 \\
\hline
4.9\,5
\end{array}
\qquad
\begin{array}{r}
5.0\,0 \\
-\ 4.9\,5 \\
\hline
0.0\,5
\end{array}
$$

The total cost is £4.95.
The change is £0.05 or 5p.

Exercise 9.2

Do this exercise without using your calculator, showing your working clearly.
Having completed the exercise you can use a calculator to check your answers.

1 (a) Work out.
(i) 5.14 + 3.72   (ii) 7.065 + 5.384   (iii) 11.8 + 5.69
(b) Show how subtraction can be used to check each of the answers in part (a).

2 (a) Work out.
(i) 9.47 − 3.24   (ii) 37.6 − 13.28   (iii) 45.04 − 20.36
(b) Show how addition can be used to check each of the answers in part (a).

3 Work these out in your head.
(a) 2.5 + 8.4   (b) 0.7 + 0.95   (c) 0.36 + 0.54   (d) 6.47 + 4.53
(e) 2.7 − 1.5   (f) 1.3 − 0.7   (g) 0.4 − 0.16   (h) 15.3 − 6.4

4 Work out.
(a) 6.54 + 0.27 + 0.03   (b) 79.1 + 7 + 0.23   (c) 10 − 4.78
(d) 9.57 − 4.567   (e) 2.22 + 0.78   (f) 9.13 − 7.89
(g) 5.564 + 0.017 + 10.2   (h) 17.1 − 8.82   (i) 9.123 + 0.71 + 6.2
(j) 9.123 − 2.85

5 Add these amounts of money. Calculate the change from the given amount.
(a) (i) 45p, 63p, 79p, £1.43   (ii) What is the change from £5?
(b) (i) £2.47, £6, £1.50, £1.27   (ii) What is the change from £15?
(c) (i) 31p, £0.25, 27p   (ii) What is the change from £10?
(d) (i) £12, £3.57, 67p   (ii) What is the change from £50?

6 I have 2.5 kg of potatoes, 0.5 kg of butter, 0.75 kg of grapes and 0.6 kg of cheese in my
shopping bag. What is the total weight of my shopping?

7 Fred cuts three pieces of wood of length 0.95 m, 1.67 m and 2.5 m from a plank 10 m long.
How much wood is left?

8 Kevin is 0.15 m shorter than Sally. Sally is 1.7 m tall. How tall is Kevin?

9 In bobsleigh the times of four runs are added together.
Team A records: 37.03 sec   37.76 sec   36.89 sec   37.25 sec
Team B records: 37.27 sec   37.45 sec   37.64 sec   36.72 sec
Team C records: 36.87 sec   37.51 sec   37.03 sec   38.12 sec
(a) Work out the total time for each team.
(b) The team with the lowest time wins. Put the teams in order 1st, 2nd and 3rd.

10 Swimmer A finishes the 100 m freestyle in 51.371 seconds. Swimmer B finishes in
52.090 seconds. How long after Swimmer A does Swimmer B finish?

11 In skiing the times of two runs are added together.
(a) Skier A has times of 47.12 seconds and 48.09 seconds. What is her total time?
(b) Skier B completes her first run in 47.49 seconds.
What time does she have to do in her second run to equal the total time of Skier A?

Multiplying and dividing decimals by powers of 10 (10, 100, 1000, ...)

When you multiply a decimal by:
10	Each figure moves 1 place to the left.
100	Each figure moves 2 places to the left.
1000	Each figure moves 3 places to the left.
	... and so on.

When you divide a decimal by:
10	Each figure moves 1 place to the right.
100	Each figure moves 2 places to the right.
1000	Each figure moves 3 places to the right.
	... and so on.

EXAMPLES

Multiplication

		2	•	7	6
	2	7	•	6	
	2	7	6	•	
2	7	6	0	•	

←2.76 × 10 = 27.6

←2.76 × 100 = 276

←2.76 × 1000 = 2760

Division

3	•	4	5		
0	•	3	4	5	
0	•	0	3	4	5
0	•	0	0	3	4	5

←3.45 ÷ 10 = 0.345

←3.45 ÷ 100 = 0.0345

←3.45 ÷ 1000 = 0.00345

276 has the same value as 276.0

Noughts can be used as place fillers to locate the decimal point, as in 2.76 × 1000 = 2760. If the nought was omitted the value of all other figures would change.

Exercise 9.3

Do this exercise without using a calculator.

1 Work out the following.
(a) 25.06 × 10	(b) 25.06 × 100	(c) 25.06 × 1000
(d) 0.93 × 10	(e) 0.93 × 100	(f) 0.93 × 1000
(g) 0.0623 × 10	(h) 0.0623 × 100	(i) 0.0623 × 1000
(j) 9.451 × 10	(k) 9.451 × 100	(l) 9.451 × 1000

2 Work out the following.
(a) 37.7 ÷ 10	(b) 37.7 ÷ 100	(c) 37.7 ÷ 1000
(d) 0.27 ÷ 10	(e) 0.27 ÷ 100	(f) 0.27 ÷ 1000
(g) 189.02 ÷ 10	(h) 189.02 ÷ 100	(i) 189.02 ÷ 1000
(j) 9 ÷ 10	(k) 9 ÷ 100	(l) 9 ÷ 1000

3 (a) Multiply 0.064 by (i) 10 (ii) 100 (iii) 1000
   (b) Divide 6.4 by (i) 10 (ii) 100 (iii) 1000

4 An ice cream costs £1.35.
(a) How much will 10 cost? (b) How much will 100 cost? (c) How much will 1000 cost?

5 A biro costs 25 pence.
(a) How much will 10 cost? (b) How much will 100 cost? (c) How much will 1000 cost?

6 One lap of a cycling track is 0.504 km.
(a) How far is 10 laps? (b) How far is 100 laps? (c) How far is 1000 laps?

Decimals . . . Decimals . . . Decimals . . . Decimals . . .

7 (a) 100 calculators cost £795. How much does one cost?

(b) 1000 pencils cost £120. How much does one cost?

(c) 10 litres of petrol cost £7.69. How would the cost of 1 litre be advertised?

8 Write down pairs of calculations which give the same answer.

| 12.3×1000 | $12.3 \div 100$ | 12.3×0.1 | $12.3 \div 0.01$ | 12.3×10 | $12.3 \div 0.1$ |
| 12.3×100 | 12.3×0.001 | $12.3 \div 0.001$ | $12.3 \div 10$ | $12.3 \div 1000$ | 12.3×0.01 |

Multiplying decimals

The result of multiplying two numbers is called the **product**.

Activity

Use a calculator to multiply these decimals.

$$5.924 \times 2.34 \qquad 5.2 \times 6.4 \qquad 6 \times 3.7 \qquad 5.1 \times 6.02 \qquad 2.16 \times 5.79$$

Count the total number of decimal places in the numbers to be multiplied together.
For example, 5.924 has three decimal places (there are three figures to the right of the decimal point) and 2.34 has two decimal places. The product of 5.924 and 2.34 has five decimal places.
Can you find a rule?

How many decimal places does your rule predict 0.5×0.5 should have?

Non-calculator method for multiplying decimals

To multiply decimals without using a calculator:

1 Ignore the decimal points and multiply the numbers using long multiplication.

2 Count the total number of decimal places in the numbers being multiplied together.

3 Place the decimal point so that the answer has the same total number of decimal places.

EXAMPLES

1 Work out 1.752×0.23.

```
      1.7 5 2
    × 0.2 3
   ─────────
     5 2 5 6   ←1752 × 3
   3 5 0 4 0   ←1752 × 20
   ─────────
   0.4 0 2 9 6   The answer must have 5 decimal places because 1.752 has 3 and 0.23 has 2.
   ─────────
```

$1.752 \times 0.23 = 0.40296$

2 Work out 4.25×0.18.

```
      4.2 5
    × 0.1 8
   ─────────
     3 4 0 0   ←425 × 8
     4 2 5 0   ←425 × 10
   ─────────
   0.7 6 5 0   The answer must have 4 decimal places because 4.25 has 2 and 0.18 has 2.
   ─────────
```

$4.25 \times 0.18 = 0.7650$ This can be written as 0.765 which has the same value as 0.7650.

EXAMPLE

3 Work out 0.2 × 0.4.

$$\begin{array}{r} 0.2 \\ \times\ 0.4 \\ \hline 0.0\,8 \\ \hline \end{array}$$

0.2 has 1 decimal place.

0.4 has 1 decimal place.

The answer has 2 decimal places.

4 × 2 = 8
The answer must have 2 decimal places. Noughts are used in the answer to locate the decimal point and to preserve place value.

Exercise **9.4**

Do this exercise without using your calculator, showing your working clearly.
Having completed the exercise you can use a calculator to check your answers.

1 Work these out in your head.
(a) 1.7 × 5
(b) 1.2 × 0.3
(c) 2.6 × 0.5
(d) 0.6 × 0.8
(e) 0.3 × 0.2
(f) 1.2 × 1.2

2 Calculate these products.
(a) 2.5 × 3.5
(b) 28.7 × 1.9
(c) 4.12 × 0.25
(d) 6.9 × 4.32
(e) 0.01 × 0.07
(f) 0.1 × 0.1
(g) 0.01 × 0.01
(h) 134 × 0.73
(i) 10.7 × 5.4
(j) 0.074 × 0.0024

3 (a) Multiply each of these numbers by 0.6.
(i) 5
(ii) 2.5
(iii) 0.4
(iv) 25
(b) What do you notice about the original numbers and each of your answers?

4 Work out the cost of these vegetables.
(a) 0.6 kg of carrots at 35p per kilogram.
(b) 4.6 kg of potatoes at 40p per kilogram.
(c) 1.2 kg of cabbage at 65p per kilogram.

5 What is the cost of each of these lengths of material?
(a) 7 metres of sheeting at £2.99 a metre.
(b) 4.5 metres of linen at £3.24 a metre.
(c) 7.8 metres of satin at £6.95 a metre.
(d) 3.2 metres of silk at £8.20 a metre.

6 (a) £1 can be exchanged for 1.45 euros.
What is the value in euros of
(i) £3.60,
(ii) 60p,
(iii) £54.20?
(b) £1 can be exchanged for $1.64 US dollars.
What is the value in US dollars of
(i) £7.50,
(ii) 75p,
(iii) £36.50?

7 (a) Work out the cost for each of these portions of cheese.
(i) 0.7 kg of Stilton.
(ii) 1.6 kg of Cheddar.
(iii) 0.8 kg of Sage Derby.
(iv) 0.45 kg of Cotherstone.
(b) Corrine buys:
0.25kg of Stilton and 1.4kg of Cheddar.
She pays with a £10 note.
How much change will she get?

Select
CHEESES
Price per kilogram

Cheddar	£3.20
Cotherstone	£5.20
Sage Derby	£3.25
Stilton	£6.20

Non-calculator method for dividing decimals

Work out $2.4 \div 0.4$.
In other words, how many 0.4's add up to 2.4?

$0.4 + 0.4 + 0.4 + 0.4 + 0.4 + 0.4 = 2.4$
So $2.4 \div 0.4 = 6$

$2.4 \div 0.4$ can be written as $\frac{2.4}{0.4}$

$\frac{2.4}{0.4} = \frac{2.4 \times 10}{0.4 \times 10} = \frac{24}{4} = 6$

It is easier to divide by a whole number than by a decimal.

To divide by a decimal:
1. Multiply the dividing number by a power of 10 (10, 100, 1000, …) so that it becomes a whole number.
2. Multiply the number to be divided by the same number.
3. If necessary the answer will have a decimal point in the same place.

EXAMPLES

1 Work out the following.

(a) $4 \div 0.8$
Multiply both numbers by 10.
$40 \div 8 = 5$

(b) $2 \div 0.25$
Multiply both numbers by 100.
$200 \div 25 = 8$

(c) $9 \div 4$

$$4\overline{)9.\overset{1}{0}\overset{2}{0}}$$
$$2.2\,5$$

(d) $16 \div 5$

$$5\overline{)1\,6.\overset{1}{0}}$$
$$3.2$$

Noughts are added until the division is finished.

2 8 video tapes cost £14.
How much does each tape cost?

You must work out $14 \div 8$.

$$8\overline{)1\,4.\overset{6}{0}\overset{4}{0}}$$
$$1.7\,5$$

One video tape costs £1.75.

Noughts can be added to the end of a decimal. Adding noughts does not change the value of the number. 14 has the same value as 14.00. Continue dividing until either there is no remainder or the required accuracy is obtained.

3 Work out $2.898 \div 0.23$.

$0.23 \times \mathbf{100} = 23$ (whole number)
$2.898 \times \mathbf{100} = 289.8$

289.8 ÷ 23 has the same value as 2.898 ÷ 0.23 and can be worked out using long division.

$2.898 \div 0.23 = 12.6$

$$
\begin{array}{r}
1\,2.6 \\
23\overline{)2\,8\,9.8} \\
-\,2\,3 \\
\hline
5\,9 \\
-\,4\,6 \\
\hline
1\,3\,8 \\
-\,1\,3\,8 \\
\hline
0
\end{array}
$$

Exercise 9.5

Do this exercise without using a calculator, showing your working clearly.
Having completed the exercise you can use a calculator to check your answers.

1 Work out.
(a) 2 ÷ 0.5   (b) 3 ÷ 0.2   (c) 6 ÷ 0.4   (d) 10 ÷ 2.5   (e) 6 ÷ 0.12

2 Work out.
(a) 7 ÷ 4   (b) 8 ÷ 5   (c) 1.2 ÷ 0.5   (d) 10.5 ÷ 6   (e) 9 ÷ 8

3 Work out.
(a) 2.46 ÷ 0.2   (b) 0.146 ÷ 0.05   (c) 2.42 ÷ 0.4   (d) 100.1 ÷ 0.07
(e) 0.0025 ÷ 0.05   (f) 0.05 ÷ 0.004   (g) 4.578 ÷ 0.7   (h) 0.3 ÷ 0.008

4 Use long division to work out the following.
(a) 81.4 ÷ 2.2   (b) 15.12 ÷ 2.7   (c) 7 ÷ 0.16   (d) 11.256 ÷ 0.24
(e) 0.1593 ÷ 0.015   (f) 16.074 ÷ 0.47

5 (a) Divide each of these numbers by 0.6.
　　　　(i) 6   (ii) 3.6   (iii) 0.18
　　(b) What do you notice about the original numbers and each of your answers?

6 A 3-litre bottle of lemonade costs £1.41.
What is the cost of 1 litre of lemonade?

7 12 rolls cost £1.08.
How much does each roll cost?

8 25 litres of petrol cost £18.90.
What is the cost of 1 litre of petrol?

9 A bottle holds 0.25 litres.
How many bottles can be filled from a tank holding 30 litres?

10 A steel bar is 12.73 metres long.
How many pieces, each 0.19 metres long, can be cut from it?

11 A jug holds 1.035 litres.
A small glass holds 0.023 litres.
How many of the small glasses would be required to fill the jug?

Changing decimals to fractions

How to change a decimal to a fraction:

Change 0.12 to a fraction.　　　　　　　　　　　　0.12

Write the decimal without the decimal point.　　　　12
This will be the numerator (top number).

The denominator (bottom number) is a power of 10.　$\frac{12}{100}$
The number of noughts is the same as the number of
decimal places in the original decimal.

Divide both the numerator and denominator by　　　Divide by 4
the largest possible number.
This gives the fraction in its simplest form.　　　　$\frac{3}{25}$

Fractions are covered
in further detail in
Chapter 14.

EXAMPLE

Write the following decimals as fractions in their simplest form.

(a) $0.3 = \frac{3}{10}$

(b) $0.6 = \frac{6}{10} = \frac{3}{5}$

(c) $0.45 = \frac{45}{100} = \frac{9}{20}$

(d) $1.5 = 1 + 0.5$

$\qquad = 1 + \frac{5}{10}$

$\qquad = 1 + \frac{1}{2}$

$\qquad = 1\frac{1}{2}$

$1\frac{1}{2}$ is called a **mixed number**.
It is a mixture of whole numbers and fractions.

Recurring decimals

Some decimals have recurring digits.

For example, $\frac{1}{3} = 0.3333\ldots$.

The number $0.3333\ldots$ is called a **recurring decimal**.

Recurring decimals are covered in more detail in Chapter 14.

Exercise 9.6

1 Write the following decimals as fractions in their simplest form.
(a) 0.25
(b) 0.5
(c) 0.75
(d) 0.1

2 Write the following decimals as fractions in their simplest form.
(a) 0.7
(b) 0.4
(c) 0.01
(d) 0.2
(e) 0.05
(f) 0.15
(g) 0.52
(h) 0.07
(i) 0.125
(j) 0.65
(k) 0.6
(l) 0.95

3 Change these decimals into mixed numbers.
(a) 1.7
(b) 2.3
(c) 1.4
(d) 3.25
(e) 4.8
(f) 12.1
(g) 16.75
(h) 5.05

4 What fraction is equal to each of these recurring decimals?
(a) $0.6666\ldots$
(b) $0.1111\ldots$
(c) $0.5555\ldots$

What you need to know

Without using a calculator you should be able to:

- Add and subtract decimals.

- Use decimal notation for money and other measures.

- Multiply and divide decimals by powers of 10 (10, 100, 1000, …)

- Multiply decimals by other decimals.

- Divide decimals by other decimals.

- Change decimals to fractions.

- Carry out a variety of calculations involving decimals.

- Know that:
  when a number is **multiplied** by a number between 0 and 1 the result will be **smaller** than the original number,
  when a number is **divided** by a number between 0 and 1 the result will be **larger** than the original number.

Choose any positive whole number,   e.g. 20
On a calculator multiply 20 by several positive decimal numbers
e.g. 3.7,   0.24,   23.1,   0.98
20 × 3.7 = 74 (bigger than 20)
20 × 0.24 = 4.8 (smaller than 20)

Find a condition for a number to multiply 20 and make the answer **smaller** than 20.

Is the same condition true for any number other than 20?
*i.e. for a number to multiply 15 and make the answer **smaller** than 15.*

Now divide 20 by several positive decimal numbers,   e.g. 3.7,   0.24,   23.1,   0.98
20 ÷ 3.7 = 5.405405... (smaller than 20)
20 ÷ 0.24 = 83.33333... (bigger than 20)

Find a condition for a number to divide into 20 and make the answer **bigger** than 20.

Is the same condition true for any number other than 20?
*i.e. for a number to divide 15 and make the answer **bigger** than 15.*

Review Exercise 9

Do not use a calculator for questions 1 to 10.

1 (a) (i) $1.045 + 9.7 + 10$ (ii) $9.89 + 0.017 + 4.5$ (iii) $72.4 + 100.4 + 0.92 + 5.5$
  (b) (i) $9.75 - 8.88$ (ii) $10 - 5.67$ (iii) $4.1 - 2.57$
  (c) Check the subtractions in part (b) with an addition.

2 A 4×100 m relay team runs the four stages in: 10.01 s,   9.93 s,   10.15 s   and   9.91 s.
What is the overall time for the team?

3 Two pieces of wood of length 97 cm and 1.78 m are sawn from a plank 5.12 m long.
How much wood is left?

4 (a) Multiply 7.62 by (i) 10   (ii) 100   (iii) 1000
  (b) Divide 7.62 by (i) 10   (ii) 100   (iii) 1000

5 (a) Multiply 87.3 by (i) 20   (ii) 30   (iii) 40
  (b) Divide 87.3 by (i) 20   (ii) 30   (iii) 40

6 (a) A calculator costs £4.95. How much do 50 cost?
  (b) 20 textbooks cost £259.80. How much does one cost?

7 Calculate these products.
  (a) 7.4×6.3 (b) 3.76×2.7 (c) 176.5×0.6

8 Calculate these divisions.
  (a) $16.56 \div 2.3$ (b) $98.8 \div 0.08$ (c) $5480 \div 0.4$

9 Goldfish cost 85p each.   How many goldfish can you buy with £10?   AQA

10 Korky cat food costs 54p a tin. Alex buys 18 tins of Korky cat food.
He pays with a £10 note.
How much change should he receive?   AQA

11 Work out $\dfrac{24.076}{1.5 + 3.7}$ AQA

12 Tony uses his calculator to work out $\dfrac{4.2 \times 86}{3.2 \times 0.47}$
What answer should he get?   AQA

13 Work out $\dfrac{4.7 \times 20.1}{5.6 - 1.8}$
Write down your full calculator display.   AQA

CHAPTER 10

Approximation and Estimation

Approximation

In real-life it is not always necessary to use exact numbers.
A number can be **rounded** to an **approximate** number.
Numbers are rounded according to how accurately we wish to give details.
For example, the distance to the Sun can be given as 93 million miles.

Can you think of other situations where approximations might be used?

Rounding to the nearest 10, 100, 1000

The number line shows the position of 87.

87 is between 80 and 90, but is closer to 90.

87 rounded to the nearest 10 is 90.

If there were 7487 people at a football match a newspaper report could say,

"7000 at the football match".

The number 7487 can be approximated as 7490, 7500 or 7000 depending on the degree of accuracy required.

7487 rounded to the nearest 10 is 7490.

7487 rounded to the nearest 100 is 7500.

7487 rounded to the nearest 1000 is 7000.

It is a convention to round a number which is in the middle to the higher number.
75 to the nearest 10 is 80.
450 to the nearest 100 is 500.
8500 to the nearest 1000 is 9000.

EXAMPLES

1 Round the numbers: 7547, 973, 62 783 and 9125
to the nearest 10, to the nearest 100, to the nearest 1000.

	Number			
	7547	973	62 783	9125
Rounded to the nearest 10	7550	970	62 780	9130
Rounded to the nearest 100	7500	1000	62 800	9100
Rounded to the nearest 1000	8000	1000	63 000	9000

2 A lifeguard says, "There are 120 people in the pool today."
This figure is correct to the nearest 10.
What is the smallest and largest possible number of people in the pool?

The smallest whole number that rounds to 120 is 115.
The largest whole number that rounds to 120 is 124.
So, the smallest possible number of people is 115 and the largest possible number of people is 124.

1 Write each of these numbers to the nearest 10.   (a) 47   (b) 53   (c) 65

2 (a)   Which of these numbers: 4850, 4860, 4870, 4880, 4890 is closest to 4872?
   (b)   Which of these numbers: 4600, 4700, 4800, 4900, 5000 is closest to 4872?
   (c)   Which of these numbers: 3000, 4000, 5000, 6000   is closest to 4872?

3 Round the number 364   (a) to the nearest 10,   (b) to the nearest 100.

4 Round the number 7475
   (a) to the nearest 10,   (b) to the nearest 100,   (c) to the nearest 1000.

5 Copy and complete this table.

	Number								
	7613	977	61 115	9714	623	9949	5762	7509	7499
Round to the nearest 10									
Round to the nearest 100									
Round to the nearest 1000									

6 64 537 people signed a petition. A newspaper report stated:
   ‘65 000 people sign petition’
To what degree of accuracy is the number given in the newspaper report?

7 Write down these figures to appropriate degrees of accuracy.
   (a)   There were 19 141 people at the football match.
   (b)   There were 259 people on the plane.
   (c)   Tom had 141 marbles.
   (d)   The class raised £49.67 for charity.
   (e)   There are 129 students in Year 7.
   (f)   The population of the town is 24 055.
   (g)   The land area of the country is 309 123 km^2.
   (h)   The distance to London is 189 km.
   (i)   Sarah spent £50.99 on CDs.
   (j)   There were 693 students in the school.

8 Write down a number each time which fits these roundings.
   (a)   It is 750 to the nearest 10 but 700 to the nearest 100.
   (b)   It is 750 to the nearest 10 but 800 to the nearest 100.
   (c)   It is 8500 to the nearest 100 but 8000 to the nearest 1000.
   (d)   It is 8500 to the nearest 100 but 9000 to the nearest 1000.

9 Pete says, "I had 40 birthday cards." The number is correct to the nearest 10.
   (a)   What is the smallest possible number of cards Pete had?
   (b)   What is the largest possible number of cards Pete had?

10 The number of people at a concert is 2000 to the nearest 100.
   (a)   What is the smallest possible number of people at the concert?
   (b)   What is the largest possible number of people at the concert?

11 **"43 000 spectators watch thrilling Test Match."**
The number reported in the newspaper was correct to the nearest thousand.
What is the smallest possible number of spectators?

12 Carl has 140 postcards in his collection. The number is given to the nearest ten.
What is the smallest and greatest number of postcards Carl could have in his collection?

13 "You require 2700 tiles to tile your swimming pool." This figure is correct to the nearest 100.
What is the greatest number of tiles needed?

Approximation and Estimation

Rounding in real-life problems

In a real-life problem a rounding must be used which gives a common sense answer.

Penny is arranging a BBQ.
50 people have been invited.
She caters for everyone to have one burger.
Burgers are sold in packs of 12.
How many packs of burgers should she buy?

The answer is found by working out 50 ÷ 12.
In 4 packs, there are 4 × 12 = 48 burgers.
In 5 packs, there are 5 × 12 = 60 burgers.
50 ÷ 12 = 4 remainder 2.
Penny must buy 5 packs in order that everybody has one burger.
(In fact she will have 10 left over for those who might want a second burger.)

EXAMPLES

1 A Year group in a school are going to Alton Towers. There are 242 students and teachers going.
Each coach can carry 55 passengers.
How many coaches should be ordered?

242 ÷ 55 = 4.4   This should be rounded up to 5.

4 coaches can only carry 220 passengers (4 × 55 = 220).

2 Filing cabinets are to be placed along a wall. The available space is 460 cm.
Each cabinet is 80 cm wide.
How many can be fitted in?

460 ÷ 80 = 5.75   This should be rounded down to 5.

Although the answer is nearly 6 the 6th cabinet would not fit in.

Exercise 10.2   Do not use a calculator for this exercise.

1 49 students are waiting to go to the Sports Stadium. A minibus can take 15 passengers at a time. How many trips are required?

2 A classroom wall is 700 cm long.
How many tables, each 120 cm long, could be fitted along the wall?

3 76 people are waiting to go to the top of Canary Wharf. The lift can only take 8 at a time. How many times must the lift go up?

4 A group of 175 people are going to Margate. Coaches can take 39 passengers.
How many coaches should be ordered?

5 There are 210 students in a year group.
They each need an exercise book.
The exercise books are sold in packs of 25.
How many packs should be ordered?

6 Car parking spaces should be 2.5 m wide.
How many can be fitted into a car park which is 61 m wide?

7 A sweet manufacturer puts 17 sweets in a bag. How many bags can be made up if there are 500 sweets?

8 How many 26p stamps can be bought for £5?

9 How many grapefruits, each costing 29p, can be bought for £1.50?

10 Kim needs 26 candles for a cake.
The candles are sold in packs of 4.
How many packs must she buy?

11 Lauren needs 50 doughnuts for a party.
Doughnuts are sold in packs of 12.
How many packs must she buy?

Rounding using decimal places

What is the cost of 1.75 metres of material costing £1.99 a metre?

$1.75 \times 1.99 = 3.4825$

The cost of the material is £3.4825 or 348.25p.

As you can only pay in pence, a sensible answer is £3.48, correct to two decimal places (nearest penny).

This means that there are only two decimal places after the decimal point.

Often it is not necessary to use an exact answer. Sometimes it is impossible, or impractical, to use the exact answer.

To round a number to a given number of decimal places

When rounding a number to one, two or more decimal places:

1. Write the number using one more decimal place than asked for.

2. Look at the last decimal place and
   - if the figure is 5 or more round up,
   - if the figure is less than 5 round down.

3. When answering a problem remember to include any units and state the degree of approximation used.

EXAMPLES

1 Write 2.76435 to   (a)   2 decimal places,   (b)   1 decimal place.

(a)   Look at the third decimal place.   **4**
This is less than 5, so round down.
Answer 2.76

(b)   Look at the second decimal place.   **6**
This is 5 or more, so round up.
Answer 2.8

2 Write 7.104 to 2 decimal places.
7.104 = 7.10 to 2 d.p.
The zero is written down because it shows the accuracy used, 2 decimal places.

Notation
Often decimal place is shortened to d.p.

3 5.98 = 6.0 to 1 d.p.
Notice that the next tenth after 5.9 is 6.0.

Exercise **10.3**

1 Write the number 3.9617 correct to
(a)   3 decimal places,   (b)   2 decimal places,   (c)   1 decimal place.

2 Write the number 567.654 correct to
(a)   2 decimal places,   (b)   1 decimal place,   (c)   the nearest whole number.

3 Copy and complete this table

Number	2.367	0.964	0.965	15.2806	0.056	4.991	4.996
d.p.	1	2	2	3	2	2	2
Answer	2.4						

4 Work out   40 ÷ 7.
Give your answer correct to two decimal places.

Approximation and Estimation

5 The display on a calculator shows the result of 34 ÷ 7.
What is the result correct to two decimal places?

$$\boxed{4.857142857}$$

6 Carry out these calculations giving the answers correct to
    (a) 1 d.p.   (b)   2 d.p.   (c) 3 d.p.

      (i)   6.12 × 7.54   (ii) 89.1 × 0.67   (iii)   90.53 × 6.29
      (iv) 98.6 ÷ 5.78   (v) 67.2 ÷ 101.45

7 In each of these short problems decide upon the most suitable accuracy for the answer.
Then work out the answer.
Give a reason for your degree of accuracy.
    (a)   1.74 metres of cloth at £6.99 a metre.
    (b)   1.74 metres of cloth at £2.05 a metre.
    (c)   0.454 kg of cheese at £5.21 a kg.
    (d)   7 equal sticks measure 250 cm in total when lying end to end.
        How long is each stick?
    (e)   A packet of 6 videotapes costs £7.99.
        How much does one cost?
    (f)   Petrol costs 81.4 pence a litre.
        I buy 15.6 litres.
        How much will I have to pay?

Rounding using significant figures

Consider the calculation   600.02 × 7500.97 = 4500732.0194
To 1 d.p. it is 4500732.0,   to 2 d.p. it is 4500732.02.
The answers to either 1 or 2 d.p. are very close to the actual answer and are almost as long.
There is little advantage in using either of these two roundings.
The point of a rounding is that it is a more convenient number to use.

Another kind of rounding uses **significant figures**.
The **most** significant figure in a number is the figure which has the greatest place value.

Consider the number 237.
The figure 2 has the greatest place value. It is worth 200.
So 2 is the most significant figure.

In the number 0.00328, the figure 3 has the greatest place value.
So 3 is the most significant figure.

> Noughts which are used to locate the decimal point and preserve the place value of other figures are not significant.

To round a number to a given number of significant figures

When rounding a number to one, two or more significant figures:
1.   Start from the most significant figure and count the required number of figures.
2.   Look at the next figure to the right of this and
       ● if the figure is 5 or more round up,
       ● if the figure is less than 5 round down.
3.   Add noughts, as necessary, to locate the decimal point and preserve the place value.
4.   When answering a problem remember to include any units and state the degree of approximation used.

EXAMPLES

1 Write 4 500 732.0194 to 2 significant figures.

The figure after the first 2 significant figures **45** is 0.
This is less than 5, so round down, leaving 45 unchanged.
Add noughts to 45 to locate the decimal point and
preserve place value.
So 4 500 732.0194 = 4 500 000 to 2 sig. fig.

Notation
Often significant
figure is shortened to
sig. fig.

2 Write 0.000364907 to 1 significant figure.

The figure after the first significant figure 3 is 6.
This is 5 or more, so round up, 3 becomes 4.
So 0.000364907 = 0.0004 to 1 sig. fig.

Notice that the noughts before the 4 locate the decimal point and preserve place value.

Choosing a suitable degree of accuracy

In some calculations it would be wrong to use the complete answer from the calculator.
The result of a calculation involving measurement should not be given to a greater degree of accuracy
than the measurements used in the calculation.

EXAMPLE

What is the area of a rectangle measuring 4.6 cm by 7.2 cm?

$4.6 \times 7.2 = 33.12$
Since the measurements used in the calculation (4.6 cm and 7.2 cm) are given to 2 significant figures
the answer should be as well.
33 cm^2 is a more suitable answer.

Exercise 10.4

1 Write these numbers correct to one significant figure.
   (a) 17 (b) 523 (c) 0.34 (d) 0.019 (e) 24.6

2 Copy and complete this table.

Number	456 000	454 000	7 981 234	7 981 234	1290	19 602
sig. fig.	2	2	3	2	2	1
Answer	460 000					

3 Copy and complete this table.

Number	0.000567	0.093748	0.093748	0.093748	0.010245	0.02994
sig. fig.	2	2	3	4	2	2
Answer						

4 This display shows the result of $3400 \div 7$.
What is the result correct to four significant figures?

`485.7142857`

5 Carry out these calculations giving the answers correct to
  (a) 2 sig. fig.   (b)   3 sig. fig.   (c) 4 sig. fig.

  (i) 672 × 123   (ii) 6.72 × 12.3   (iii)   78.2 × 12.8
  (iv) 7.19 ÷ 987.5   (v) 124 ÷ 65300

6 A field measures 18.6 m by 25.4 m.
  Calculate the area of the field, giving your answer to a suitable degree of accuracy.

7 In each of these short problems decide upon the most suitable accuracy for the answer.
  Then work out the answer, remembering to state the units.
  Give a reason for your degree of accuracy.
  (a) The area of a rectangle measuring 7.9 cm by 6.4 cm.
  (b) The area of a rectangle measuring 13.2 cm by 11.9 cm.
  (c) The area of a football pitch measuring 99 m by 62 m.
  (d) The length of 13 tables was measured at 16 m.
       How long was each table?
  (e) The area of a farmer's field measuring 320 m by 480 m.

Estimation

It is always a good idea to find an **estimate** for any calculation.
An estimate is used to check that the answer to the actual calculation is of the right magnitude (size).
If the answer is very different to the estimate then a mistake has possibly been made.

Estimation is done by approximating every number in the calculation to 1 significant figure.
The calculation is then done using the approximated values.

EXAMPLES

1 Estimate   421 × 48.

Round 421 to one significant figure: 400
Round 48 to one significant figure: 50
400 × 50 = 20 000

Use long multiplication to calculate   421 × 48.   Comment on your answer.

2 Estimate   608 ÷ 19.

Round the numbers in the calculation to one significant figure.
600 ÷ 20 = 30

Use long division to calculate   608 ÷ 19.   Comment on your answer.

3 Estimate $\dfrac{78.5 \times 0.51}{18.7}$

Approximating: 78.5 = 80 to 1 sig. fig.
                    0.51 = 0.5 to 1 sig. fig.
                    18.7 = 20 to 1 sig. fig.

$\dfrac{80 \times 0.5}{20} = \dfrac{40}{20} = 2$ (estimate)

Remember
When you are asked to estimate, write each number in the calculation to one significant figure.

Using a calculator $\dfrac{78.5 \times 0.51}{18.7} = \dfrac{40.035}{18.7} = 2.140909\ldots$

Is 2.140909 reasonably close to 2?   Yes.

Exercise 10.5   Do not use a calculator for questions 1 to 6. Show any working clearly.

1 Make estimates to these calculations by using approximations to 1 sig. fig.
Then carry out the calculations accurately using long multiplication.
Compare your estimates with your answers.
(a) 32 × 41 (b) 12 × 66 (c) 58 × 34 (d) 72 × 45
(e) 34 × 78 (f) 17 × 219 (g) 291 × 56 (h) 312 × 23

2 Make estimates to these calculations by using approximations to 1 sig. fig.
Then carry out the calculations accurately using long division.
Compare your estimates with your answers.
(a) 594 ÷ 18 (b) 609 ÷ 21 (c) 256 ÷ 16 (d) 840 ÷ 35

3 By using approximations to 1 significant figure find estimates to these products.
Then carry out the calculations with the original figures.
Compare your estimate to the actual answer.
(a) 4.2 × 1.8 (b) 8.9 × 3.1 (c) 48.1 × 4.2 (d) 103.4 × 2.9

4 Find estimates to these divisions by using approximations to 1 significant figure.
Then carry out the calculations with the original figures.
Compare your estimate to the actual answer.
(a) 10.78 ÷ 4.9 (b) 19.68 ÷ 4.1 (c) 30.4 ÷ 3.2 (d) 203.49 ÷ 5.1

5 (a) When estimating the answer to 29 × 48 the approximations 30 and 50 are used.
How can you tell that the estimation must be bigger than the actual answer?
(b) When estimating the answer to 182 ÷ 13 the approximations 200 and 10 are used.
How can you tell if the estimate will be bigger or smaller than the actual answer?

6 Bernard plans to buy a conservatory costing £8328 and furniture costing £984.
(a) By using approximations, estimate the total amount Bernard plans to spend.
(b) Find the actual cost.

7 Find estimates to these calculations by using approximations to 1 significant figure.
Then carry out the calculations with the original figures.
Compare your estimate to the actual answer.

(a) $\dfrac{7.9 \times 3.9}{4.8}$ (b) $\dfrac{400 \times 0.29}{6.2}$ (c) $\dfrac{81.7 \times 4.9}{1.9 \times 10.3}$

Accuracy in measurement

No measurement is ever exact.
Measures which can lie within a range of possible values are called **continuous measures**.
The value of a continuous measure depends on the accuracy of whatever is making the measurement.

Jane is 160 cm tall to the nearest 10 cm.
What are the limits between which her actual height lies?

Height is a continuous measure.
When rounding to the nearest 10 cm:
The minimum value that rounds to 160 cm is 155 cm.
155 cm is the minimum height that Jane can be.

The maximum value that rounds to 160 cm is 164.$\dot{9}$ cm.
164.$\dot{9}$ cm is the maximum height that Jane can be.

For ease the value 164.$\dot{9}$ cm is normally called 165 cm.

So Jane's actual height is any height from 155 cm to 165 cm.
This can be written as the inequality:
155 cm ⩽ Jane's height < 165 cm

All possible heights for Jane can be
shown on a number line.

The hollow circle indicates that 165 is
not included

Approximation and Estimation

1 The length of a pencil is 17 cm to the nearest centimetre.
What are the limits between which the actual length of the pencil lies?

When rounding to the nearest centimetre: The smallest value that rounds to 17 cm is 16.5 cm.
The largest value that rounds to 17 cm is 17.4$\dot{9}$ cm.
So the actual length of the pencil lies between 16.5 cm and 17.5 cm.
$$16.5 \text{ cm} \leqslant \text{length of pencil} < 17.5 \text{ cm}$$

2 A concrete block weighs 1.8 kg, correct to the nearest tenth of a kilogram.
What is the minimum possible weight of the concrete block?
$$\text{Minimum weight} = 1.8 \text{ kg} - 0.05 \text{ kg} = 1.75 \text{ kg}$$

Exercise 10.6

1 A girl's height is 168 cm, correct to the nearest centimetre.
What is the minimum possible height of the girl?

2 The height of a building is 9 m, correct to the nearest metre.
Copy and complete the inequality: …… $\leqslant$ height of building < ……

3 A brick weighs 840 g, correct to the nearest 10 g.
What is the minimum and maximum possible weight of the brick?

4 An athlete completed a race in 11.6 seconds, correct to the nearest tenth of a second.
What is the minimum possible time the athlete could have taken?

5 A pane of glass weighs 9.4 kg, correct to one decimal place.
What is the minimum possible weight of the pane of glass?

6 The length of a table is 2.7 m, correct to the nearest tenth of a metre.
Write down the least and greatest possible length of the table.

7 A glass contains 24 ml of milk, correct to the nearest millilitre.
Find the minimum possible number of millilitres in four glasses.

8 Loaves of bread each weigh 0.8 kg, correct to the nearest 100 g.
Write down the minimum and maximum possible weight of ten loaves of bread.

What you need to know

- A number can be rounded to an **approximate** number.
- How to approximate using **decimal places**.
    1. Write the number using one more decimal place than asked for.
    2. Look at the last decimal place and
        - if the figure is 5 or more round up, - if the figure is less than 5 round down.
- How to approximate using **significant figures**.
    When rounding a number to one, two or more significant figures:
    1. Start from the most significant figure and count the required number of figures.
    2. Look at the next figure to the right of this and
        - if the figure is 5 or more round up, - if the figure is less than 5 round down.
    3. Add noughts, as necessary, to locate the decimal point and preserve the place value.
- When answering a problem, include any units and state the degree of approximation used.
- Use approximation to **estimate** that the actual answer to a calculation is of the right magnitude.
- You should be able to recognise limitations on the accuracy of data and measurements.

1 Round 8475 to the nearest   (a) 10,   (b) 100,   (c) 1000.

2 (a) The exact number of people who watched the cup final on TV was 6 732 125.
     (i) Copy and complete this newspaper headline with a sensible rounded number.
        "……**Watch Cup Final on TV**"
     (ii) Copy and complete this sentence. My number is rounded to the nearest ……… people.
  (b) "**110 000 Listen To New Radio Station**"
     The number is given to the nearest thousand.
     What is the **smallest** possible number of listeners?   AQA

3 (a) Mohini **estimated** 21×29 to be about 600. Explain how she did it.
  (b) Show how you would find an **estimate** for $1980 \div 43$.
     Write down your estimate for $1980 \div 43$.   AQA

4 Find **estimates** to these calculations by using approximations to one significant figure.
  (a) 86.5×1.9 (b) $2016 \div 49.8$

5 Aimee uses her calculator to multiply 18.7 by 0.96. Her answer is 19.752.
Without finding the exact value of 18.7×0.96,   explain why her answer must be wrong.

6 Jonathan uses his calculator to work out the value of 42.2×0.027.
The answer he gets is 11.394.
Use approximation to show that his answer is wrong.   AQA

7 Alun has a part-time job. He is paid £18 each day he works. In 2002 he worked 148 days.
Estimate Alun's total pay for 2002. Write down your calculation and answer.   AQA

8 Angela needs to buy 132 chocolate biscuits for a Christmas party.
The biscuits are sold in packs of nine. How many packs must Angela buy?   AQA

9 The number of people at a beach party is 90, to the nearest 10.
What is the smallest and largest possible number of people at the party?

10 The display shows the result of $179 \div 7$.
What is the result correct to
  (a)   two decimal places,
  (b)   one decimal place,
  (c)   one significant figure?

$$\boxed{25.57142857}$$

11 A bus is 18 m in length, correct to the nearest metre.
  (a)   What is the minimum possible length of the bus?
  (b)   Copy and complete this inequality: …… $\leqslant$ length of bus $<$ ……

12 Use your calculator to find the value of $\dfrac{3.81 \times 17.21}{8.49 + 7.38}$
Give your answer to two decimal places.   AQA

13 Work out $\dfrac{4.7 \times 20.1}{5.6 - 1.8}$
  (a)   Write down your full calculator display.
  (b)   Use estimation to check your answer. Show each step of your working.   AQA

14 The floor of a lounge is a rectangle which measures 5.23 m by 3.62 m.
The floor is to be carpeted.
  (a)   Calculate the area of carpet needed.
     Give your answer to an appropriate degree of accuracy.
  (b)   Explain why you chose this degree of accuracy.

15 A book weighs 3.2 kg, given to the nearest 100 g.
Find the minimum possible weight of 6 copies of the same book.   AQA

CHAPTER 11

Negative Numbers

In Chapter 8 we used a number line to show whole numbers.
This number line can be extended to include **negative whole numbers**.

Negative whole numbers, zero and positive whole numbers are called **integers**.
−5 can be read as "minus five" or "negative five".
A number written without a sign before it is assumed to be positive. +5 has the same value as 5.
Real-life situations which use negative numbers include temperature, bank accounts and depths below sea-level.
Can you think of any other situations where negative numbers are used?

Ordering numbers

The thermometer

−5°C is colder than −1°C.
−3°C is colder than   1°C.
−4°C is colder than   0°C.
  2°C is colder than   4°C.

2°C is warmer than −3°C.
4°C is warmer than −5°C.
0°C is warmer than −3°C.
5°C is warmer than   2°C.

As you move up the thermometer the temperatures become warmer.

As you move down the thermometer the temperatures become colder.

The number line

−5 is less than −1.
−3 is less than   1.
−4 is less than   0.
  2 is less than   4.

2 is more than −3.
4 is more than −5.
0 is more than −3.
5 is more than   2.

As you move from left to right along the number line the numbers become bigger.

As you move from right to left along the number line the numbers become smaller.

EXAMPLES

1 List these temperatures from coldest to hottest:

3°C,   5°C,   −2°C,   0°C,   −4°C.

−4°C,   −2°C,   0°C,   3°C,   5°C.

2 List these numbers in ascending order (from lowest to highest):

50,   −41,   −18,   −11,   28,   9.

−41,   −18,   −11,   9,   28,   50.

Exercise **11.1**

1 Copy and complete these sentences using the words 'colder' or 'warmer' as appropriate.
    (a)   −2°C is ...... than −5°C.   (b)   −1°C is ...... than   4°C.
    (c)   2°C is ...... than −4°C.   (d) −10°C is ...... than −5°C.

2 Copy and complete these sentences using the words 'less' or 'more' as appropriate.
    (a)   −3 is ...... than   2.   (b)   1 is ...... than −5.
    (c)   −4 is ...... than −1.   (d)   −4 is ...... than −10.

3 At midnight on New Year's Day the temperatures in some cities were as shown:
    (a)   Which city recorded the highest temperature?
    (b)   Which city recorded the lowest temperature?
    (c)   List the temperatures from coldest to hottest.

Edinburgh	−7°C
London	0°C
Moscow	−22°C
New York	−17°C
Rome	3°C
Colombo	21°C
Cairo	15°C

4 List these temperatures from coldest to hottest.
    (a)   23°C, −28°C, −3°C, 19°C, −13°C.   (b)   −9°C, −11°C, 12°C, 10°C, −7°C, 0°C.
    (c)   27°C, 18°C, −29°C, −15°C, 2°C.   (d)   20°C, −15°C, −20°C, 0°C, −5°C, 10°C.

5 List these numbers from lowest to highest.
    (a)   31, −78, 51, −39, −16, −9, 11.   (b)   5, 1, −1, −3, −5, −2, 0, 2, 4.
    (c)   99, −103, 104, 5, −3, 52, −63, −19.   (d)   30, 10, −30, −50, −20, 0, 40.
    (e)   27, −30, 17, 0, −15, −10, 8.

Subtracting a larger number from a smaller number

Work out 3 − 5.
To work out smaller number − larger number:
    (i)   Do the calculation the other way round. 3 − 5 becomes 5 − 3.
    (ii) Put a minus sign in front of the answer. So 3 − 5 = −2.

This is the same as starting at 3 on a number line and going 5 places to the left, to get to −2.

EXAMPLES

1 Work out 7 − 13.
Do 13 − 7 = 6.   Then 7 − 13 = −6.

2 Calculate 21 − 34.
Do 34 − 21 = 13.   Then 21 − 34 = −13.

3 Alec has £50 in his bank account. He writes a cheque for £80. What is his new balance?
His new balance is given by the calculation £50 − £80.
80 − 50 = 30.
So 50 − 80 = −30.
The new balance is −£30.   This means that Alec's account is overdrawn by £30.

Do not use a calculator for this exercise.

1 Work out the following.
- (a) 4 − 7
- (b) 8 − 12
- (c) 13 − 20
- (d) 24 − 56
- (e) 20 − 20
- (f) 23 − 50
- (g) 29 − 90
- (h) 20 − 21

2
(a) Draw a number line to show each of these statements.
- (i) 7 − 10 = −3
- (ii) 3 − 6 = −3
- (iii) −1 − 3 = −4

(b) Explain how a number line can be used to work out the following.
- (i) 5 − 6
- (ii) 4 − 8
- (iii) −2 − 2

3 What number should be put in the box to make each of these statements correct?

- (a) 7 − ☐ = −2
- (b) ☐ − 6 = −5
- (c) 9 − ☐ = −3
- (d) −3 − 7 = ☐
- (e) ☐ − 50 = −20
- (f) 10 − ☐ = −5

4
(a) Mr Armstrong has £25 in the bank. He writes a cheque for £100.
     What is his new balance?
(b) After paying a bill of £60 by cheque, Claire's bank balance is £20 overdrawn.
     What was Claire's bank balance before paying the bill?

5 Negative numbers can be used for depths
below sea level.
Use negative numbers to answer the following.
- (a) At what depth is the diver?
- (b) At what depth is the treasure chest?

What is the difference in height between
- (c) the helicopter and the parachutist,
- (d) the diver and the jellyfish,
- (e) the diver and the treasure chest,
- (f) the bird and the jellyfish,
- (g) the parachutist and the treasure chest,
- (h) the kite and the jellyfish,
- (i) the helicopter and the kite,
- (j) the diver and the helicopter,
- (k) the bird and the treasure chest?

Helicopter	160 m above
Parachute	100 m above
Bird	50 m above
Kite	30 m above
	Sea level
Jellyfish	20 m below
Diver	80 m below
Treasure chest	200 m below

Addition and subtraction using negative numbers

Think of the number line as a series of stepping stones.

What is −4 − 5?

Using the number line: Start at −4 and move 5 to the **left**.
The answer is −9.
−4 − 5 = −9

−4 − 5 can be written as: −4 + (−5) or −4 − (+5).
So −4 + (−5) = −9 and −4 − (+5) = −9.

What is −3 − (+7)?   −3 − (+7) is the same as −3 − 7.
Using the number line: Start at −3 and move 7 to the **left**.
−3 − (+7) = −10

−3 − (−7) must start at −3 and move 7 to the **right**.
−3 − (−7) is the same as −3 + 7.
So −3 − (−7) = 4 and −3 + 7 = 4.

What is $-5 + (+7)$?
$+7$ can be written as 7.
$-5 + (+7)$ is the same as $-5 + 7 = 2$.

To add or subtract negative numbers:
Replace double signs with a single sign.
Start on the number line with the first number.
Then move left or right according to the single sign.

$+\ +$	can be replaced by $+$
$-\ -$	can be replaced by $+$
$+\ -$	can be replaced by $-$
$-\ +$	can be replaced by $-$

EXAMPLES

1 Work out $2 + (-6)$.

$+ -$ can be replaced with $-$.
Start at 2 and move 6 to the left.
$2 + (-6) = 2 - 6 = -4$

2 Work out $-2 - (-8)$.

$--$ can be replaced with $+$.
Start at -2 and move 8 to the right.
$-2 - (-8) = -2 + 8 = 6$

3 Work out $-4 - (+6)$.

$-+$ can be replaced with $-$.
Start at -4 and move 6 to the left.
$-4 - (+6) = -4 - 6 = -10$

4 Work out $-4 + (-3) + 6 - (-5) - (+3)$.

Replace signs.
$= -4 - 3 + 6 + 5 - 3$
$= 1$

Exercise 11.3   Do not use a calculator for this exercise.

1 Work out.
(a) $-3 + (+5)$	(b) $5 + (-4)$	(c) $-2 + (-7)$
(d) $-1 + (+9)$	(e) $7 + (-3)$	(f) $15 + (-20)$
(g) $-11 + (+4)$	(h) $11 + (-4)$	(i) $8 + (-7)$
(j) $-8 + (-7)$	(k) $3 + (+3) + (-9)$	(l) $-7 + (-5) + 6$

2 Work out.
(a) $8 - (-5)$	(b) $-4 - (-10)$	(c) $10 - (+3)$
(d) $6 - (-1)$	(e) $-5 - (-10)$	(f) $-4 - (+8)$
(g) $-7 - (-6)$	(h) $7 - (-6)$	(i) $-2 - (+9)$
(j) $2 - (-9)$	(k) $5 - (+5) + 9$	(l) $-10 - (-6) + 4$

3 Work out.
(a) $-3 - (-8)$	(b) $5 + (-2)$	(c) $7 - (+4)$
(d) $-9 - (-5) + (-3)$	(e) $7 + (-8) - (+5)$	(f) $-2 - (-7) - 6$

4 Work out.
(a) $10 + 5 - 8 + 6 - 7$	(b) $12 + 8 - 15 + 7 - 20$	(c) $30 - 20 + 12 - 50$
(d) $6 + 12 - 14 - 4$	(e) $37 - 23 - 24 - 25$	(f) $12 + 13 + 14 - 20$

5 Work out.
(a) $5 + (-4) - (-3) + 2 - (-1)$	(b) $5 - 4 + (-3) - (-2) + (-1)$
(c) $10 - (-11) + (-12) + 13 - (-14)$	(d) $-7 - (-7) + 6 + (-3) + (-9)$
(e) $12 + 8 - (-8) + 9 - (-1)$	(f) $15 - (-5) + 5 - (-10) + (-20)$
(g) $-5 + (-5) + (-5) + (-5) - (-5)$	(h) $5 - (-5) - (-5) - (-5) - (-5)$
(i) $1 - (-2) - (-3) - (-4) - (-5)$	(j) $-6 + 7 - 8 + (-9) - (-10)$

6 The temperature inside a freezer was $-23°C$.
After two hours the temperature had risen by $8°C$.
What was the temperature in the freezer then?

Negative Numbers

11

Module 3   131

7 What is the difference in temperature between
  (a) Edinburgh and Rome,
  (b) Edinburgh and New York,
  (c) Moscow and New York,
  (d) Moscow and Cairo?

Edinburgh	$-7°C$
Moscow	$-22°C$
New York	$-17°C$
Rome	$3°C$
Cairo	$15°C$

Multiplying and dividing negative numbers

You will need to know these rules for multiplying and dividing negative numbers:

When multiplying:
$+ \times + = +$
$- \times - = +$
$+ \times - = -$
$- \times + = -$

When dividing:
$+ \div + = +$
$- \div - = +$
$+ \div - = -$
$- \div + = -$

The diagram shows the multiplication table extended to include negative numbers.

Second number

×	−5	−4	−3	−2	−1	0	1	2	3	4	5
−5	25	20	15	10	5	0	−5	−10	−15	−20	−25
−4	20	16	12	8	4	0	−4	−8	−12	−16	−20
−3	15	12	9	6	3	0	−3	−6	−9	−12	−15
−2	10	8	6	4	2	0	−2	−4	−6	−8	−10
−1	5	4	3	2	1	0	−1	−2	−3	−4	−5
0	0	0	0	0	0	0	0	0	0	0	0
1	−5	−4	−3	−2	−1	0	1	2	3	4	5
2	−10	−8	−6	−4	−2	0	2	4	6	8	10
3	−15	−12	−9	−6	−3	0	3	6	9	12	15
4	−20	−16	−12	−8	−4	0	4	8	12	16	20
5	−25	−20	−15	−10	−5	0	5	10	15	20	25

First number

Describe any patterns you can see in the table.

Division is the opposite (inverse) operation to multiplication.

If $a \times b = c$,
then $c \div b = a$
and $c \div a = b$.

If $(+5) \times (-2) = -10$,
then $(-10) \div (-2) = +5$
and $(-10) \div (+5) = -2$.

EXAMPLES

1 Work out $(+7) \times (-5)$.

Signs: $+ \times - = -$
Numbers: $7 \times 5 = 35$
So $(+7) \times (-5) = -35$.

2 Work out $(+8) \div (-2)$.

Signs: $+ \div - = -$
Numbers: $8 \div 2 = 4$
So $(+8) \div (-2) = -4$.

3 Work out $(-4) \times (-0.8)$.

Signs: $- \times - = +$
Numbers: $4 \times 0.8 = 3.2$
So $(-4) \times (-0.8) = 3.2$.

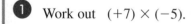

Work logically
Work out the sign first. Then work out the numbers.

4 Work out $(-6) \div (-0.3)$.

Signs: $- \div - = +$
Numbers: $6 \div 0.3$ is the same as $60 \div 3 = 20$
So $(-6) \div (-0.3) = 20$.

Exercise **11.4**

Do not use a calculator for this exercise.

1 (a) $(+7) \times (+5)$ (b) $(-7) \times (+5)$ (c) $(-7) \times (-5)$ (d) $5 \times (+2)$
   (e) $(+5) \times (-2)$ (f) $(-5) \times (-2)$ (g) $(-1) \times (-1)$ (h) $8 \times (-3)$
   (i) $(-8) \times (+3)$ (j) $(-5) \times 9$ (k) $(-8) \times (-8)$ (l) $(-7) \times 6$
   (m) $(-7) \times (-6)$ (n) $8 \times (-10)$ (o) $(-8) \times (+10)$ (p) $(-4) \times (-8)$

2 (a) $(+5) \times (-2) \times (+2)$ (b) $(+4) \times (-3) \times (-5)$ (c) $(-3) \times (-2) \times (-5)$
   (d) $(-5) \times (+3) \times (-4)$ (e) $(-5) \times (+3) \times (+4)$ (f) $(-5) \times (-4) \times (-5)$

3 (a) $(-8) \div (+2)$ (b) $(-8) \div (-2)$ (c) $(+20) \div (+4)$ (d) $(+20) \div (-4)$
   (e) $(-20) \div (+4)$ (f) $(-20) \div (-4)$ (g) $(+18) \div (+3)$ (h) $(-18) \div (+3)$
   (i) $(-24) \div (-6)$ (j) $(+24) \div (-3)$ (k) $(-30) \div (-5)$ (l) $(-30) \div (+6)$

4 (a) $6 \times (-0.3)$ (b) $(-6) \times (-0.5)$ (c) $4 \times (-0.4)$ (d) $(-4) \times (-0.8)$
   (e) $6 \div (-0.3)$ (f) $(-6) \div (-0.5)$ (g) $4 \div (-0.4)$ (h) $(-4) \div (-0.8)$

5 (a) $(-2.5) \div 5$ (b) $3.2 \div (-4)$ (c) $(-4.9) \div (-7)$
   (d) $7.5 \div (-0.5)$ (e) $(-2.8) \div 0.7$ (f) $(-3.6) \div (-0.9)$

Using a calculator

Calculations involving negative numbers can be carried out using a calculator.
Work out $5 + (-7)$.
You should get the answer -2.

Use your calculator to check your answers to questions in Exercises 11.3 and 11.4.

What you need to know

You should be able to:

● Use **negative numbers** in context such as temperatures, bank accounts.

● Realise where negative numbers come on a **number line**.

● Put numbers in order (including negative numbers).

● Add $(+)$, subtract $(-)$, multiply $(\times)$ and divide $(\div)$ with negative numbers.

You will also meet negative numbers further on: They may be solutions to equations.
   Negative coordinates on graphs.
   They may be substituted into algebraic formulae.

Review Exercise **11**

Do not use a calculator for questions 1 to 10.

1 Place the following numbers in order of size starting with the largest.

   17   34 -21 -11 132

   AQA

2 The table shows the midday temperatures in these towns one day.

Town	Selby	Poole	Woking
Temperature (°C)	-8	-2	-5

(a) Which town has the highest midday temperature?
(b) Which town has the lowest midday temperature?

3 Calculate.
   (a) $-7 - 11$ (b) $-7 + 11$ (c) $-7 - (-11)$

4 Complete the following.

(a) $-4 - \boxed{} = -9$ (b) $6 - \boxed{} = 8$

AQA

5 The temperatures at Athens and Moscow are taken at the same time.

Athens 8°C   Moscow −5°C

(a) How many degrees colder is Moscow than Athens?

(b) At the same time, Oslo is 3°C colder than Moscow.
What is the temperature in Oslo?

6 At midnight the temperature was 2°C.
At 8 am the next day the temperature was −3°C.
By how many degrees did the temperature fall?

7 The butter is stored in a cold room at −20°C.
How many degrees is this below the required
storage temperature?

CREAMERY BUTTER
Store below -9°C
Net weight 2.4 kg

AQA

8 The temperature was recorded inside a house and outside a house.

Inside temperature 16°C	Outside temperature −8°C

How many degrees warmer was it inside the house than outside?

AQA

9 A diver is 6 metres below the surface of the water.
A bird is flying 27 metres above the water.
How many metres is the bird above the diver?

AQA

10 Dawn has £30.25 in her bank account.
She buys a coat costing £64 and pays for it by a cheque which is accepted by her bank.
What is the new balance of her bank account?

AQA

11 Carry out these multiplications.

(a) $(+6) \times (+4)$ (b) $(+6) \times (-4)$ (c) $(-6) \times (+4)$ (d) $(-6) \times (-4)$
(e) 8×5 (f) $(-8) \times 5$ (g) $8 \times (-5)$ (h) $(-8) \times (-5)$

12 Carry out these divisions.

(a) $(+50) \div (-10)$ (b) $(-12) \div (-6)$ (c) $(-18) \div 3$ (d) $24 \div 6$

13 (a) Complete the boxes.

(i) $\boxed{} \times \boxed{} = \boxed{-10}$ (ii) $\boxed{} \div \boxed{} = \boxed{-1}$

(b) Work out $\dfrac{(-1) \times (-7) \times (+8)}{(-2)}$

AQA

14 The temperature inside a fridge is 3°C. The temperature inside a freezer is −18°C.

(a) How much colder is it inside the freezer than inside the fridge?

(b) Calculate $\dfrac{9 \times (-18)}{5} + 32$ to find the temperature of the freezer in degrees Fahrenheit.

AQA

15 Ama and Bob take part in a quiz. The rules are:

For each correct answer +4 points	For each wrong answer −3 points

After the first round Ama has +6 points and Bob has +13 points.
In the second round each person answers 5 more questions.
Bob scores −1 point in this round. This is added to his previous points.
What is the least number of questions Ama must answer correctly in the second round to have
more points than Bob **in total**?

AQA

Working with Number

Multiples

Numbers in the 4 times table are called **multiples** of 4.
Numbers in the 10 times table are called **multiples** of 10.

EXAMPLES

1 Write down the first five multiples of 5.

$$1 \times 5 = 5$$
$$2 \times 5 = 10$$
$$3 \times 5 = 15$$
$$4 \times 5 = 20$$
$$5 \times 5 = 25$$

The first five multiples of 5 are:
    5,   10,   15,   20   and   25.

2 What is the eighth multiple of 9?

The eighth multiple of 9 is $8 \times 9 = 72$.

3 The fifth multiple of a number is 30.
What is the number?

$5 \times 6 = 30$.
So, the number is 6.

A table of multiples

	1	2	3	4	5	6	7	8	9	10
1	1	2	3	4	5	6	7	8	9	10
2	2	4	6	8	10	12	14	16	18	20
3	3	6	9	12	15	18	21	24	27	30
4	4	8	12	16	20	24	28	32	36	40
5	5	10	15	20	25	30	35	40	45	50
6	6	12	18	24	30	36	42	48	54	60
7	7	14	21	28	35	42	49	56	63	70
8	8	16	24	32	40	48	56	64	72	80
9	9	18	27	36	45	54	63	72	81	90
10	10	20	30	40	50	60	70	80	90	100

The shaded numbers in the table are the
multiples of 2.
Multiples of 2 are called **even numbers** and
end in 0, 2, 4, 6 or 8.
Odd numbers end in 1, 3, 5, 7 or 9.
6, 12, 18, 24, … are **multiples** of 6.
The 8th **multiple** of 7 is $8 \times 7 = 56$.
3×8 has the same value as 8×3.

Exercise 12.1   Do not use a calculator.

1 Write down the first five multiples of:
  (a) 10   (b) 3   (c) 7   (d) 6   (e) 9   (f) 20

2 Copy and complete the following.
  (a) The fifth multiple of 4 is ……
  (b) The seventh multiple of 6 is ……
  (c) The …… multiple of 6 is 18.
  (d) The …… multiple of 8 is 56.
  (e) The sixth multiple of …… is 60.
  (f) The eighth multiple of …… is 72.

3 (a) What multiple of 6 is the third multiple of 4?
  (b) What multiple of 8 is the fourth multiple of 4?
  (c) What multiple of 20 is the tenth multiple of 10?
  (d) What multiple of 3 is the sixth multiple of 4?
  (e) What multiple of 12 is the fourth multiple of 9?

4 (a) Write down a multiple of 7 between 30 and 40.
  (b) Write down a multiple of 8 between 40 and 50.

5 (a) Look at the table of multiples on Page 135.
What can you say about the following?
(i) Even multiples of an even number.   (ii) Even multiples of an odd number.
(iii) Odd multiples of an even number.   (iv) Odd multiples of an odd number.

(b) Using **O** for an odd number and **E** for an even number copy and complete these multiplication tables.

(i)

×	2	3	6	7	9
2	E				
3		O	E		
6					
7					
9					

(ii)

×	O	E
O		
E		

(c) Why are there more even numbers than odd numbers in the table of multiples?

Activity

The product of 1 and 12 is $1 \times 12 = 12$.
Write down **all** the other pairs of **whole numbers** that have a product of 12.
Write down all the pairs of whole numbers that have a product of 6.
Write down all the pairs of whole numbers that have a product of 5.
Write down all the pairs of whole numbers that have a product of 48.

> When numbers are multiplied together the answer is called the **product** of the numbers.

Factors

Pairs of **whole numbers** which have a product of 6 are 1×6 and 2×3.
1,   2,   3,   and   6   are called **factors** of 6.

EXAMPLES

1 Find all the factors of 30.

Find **all** the pairs of whole numbers that have a product of 30.
$$30 \times 1 = 30 \qquad 15 \times 2 = 30$$
$$10 \times 3 = 30 \qquad 6 \times 5 = 30$$
1,   2,   3,   5,   6,   10,   15   and   30
are all factors of 30.

2 Find all the factors of 7.

Only one pair of numbers has a product of 7.
$$1 \times 7 = 7$$
7 has just two factors,   1   and   7.

Prime numbers

Numbers like 7 are called **prime numbers**.
A prime number has exactly **two** factors, 1 and the number itself.
The first few prime numbers are: 2,   3,   5,   7,   11,   13,   …
The number 1 is not a prime number because it has only one factor.

Common factors

The factors of 20 are: 1,   2,   4,   5,   10,   20.   The factors of 50 are: 1,   2,   5,   10,   25,   50.

1, 2, 5 and 10 are factors of both 20 **and** 50.
They are called the **common factors** of 20 and 50.

1 These pairs of numbers have a product of 12.
   1 × 12   2 × 6   3 × 4
   (a) List all the factors of 12.
   (b) Explain why 8 is not a factor of 12.

2 (a) Find all the pairs of whole numbers that have a product of 18.
   (b) Write down all the factors of 18.

3 (a) Find all the pairs of whole numbers that have a product of 20.
   (b) Write down all the factors of 20.

4 Find all the factors of:
   (a) 16   (b) 28   (c) 36   (d) 45
   (e) 48   (f) 50   (g) 60   (h) 80

5 (a) Find all the factors of:
   (i) 2   (ii) 3   (iii) 5
   (iv) 7   (v) 11   (vi) 13
   (b) Find two more numbers with only two factors.

6 (a) Find all the factors of:
   (i) 4   (ii) 9   (iii) 25   (iv) 49
   (b) Find two more numbers with only three factors.

7 (a) Find all the factors of:
   (i) 6   (ii) 10   (iii) 14
   (iv) 26   (v) 55   (vi) 38
   (b) Find two more numbers with only four factors.

8 Which of these numbers have common factors of 1, 2 and 3?
       6,   16,   26,   36,   46.

9 Find the common factors of
   (a) 10 and 15,   (b) 12 and 20,
   (c) 16 and 18,   (d) 24 and 36,
   (e) 12, 18 and 36.

10 Consider these numbers.
       3, 4, 5, 14, 20, 27, 35, 60.
   (a) Which number is a factor of 10?
   (b) Which number is a multiple of 9?
   (c) Which numbers are prime numbers?

11 (a) How many multiples of 6 are factors of 36?
   (b) How many multiples of 5 are factors of 120?
   (c) How many factors of 100 are multiples of 2?
   (d) How many factors of 96 are multiples of 4?

12 Draw a 100 square on squared paper.

1	2	3	4	5	6	7	8	9	10
11	12	13	14	15	16	17	18	19	20
21	22	23	24	25	26	27	28	29	30
31	32	33	34	35	36	37	38	39	40
71	72	73	74	75	76	77	78	79	80
81	82	83	84	85	86	87	88	89	90
91	92	93	94	95	96	97	98	99	100

(a) On your 100 square shade all the multiples of 2 **except** 2.

(b) Next, shade all the multiples of 3 **except** 3.

(c) All the multiples of 4 are already shaded. Explain why.

(d) Shade all the multiples of 5 **except** 5.

(e) Why have all the multiples of 6 **already** been shaded?

(f) Shade all the multiples of 7 **except** 7.

(g) Explain why 11 is the next unshaded number.
   Shade all the multiples of 11 **except** 11.

(h) Continue to shade multiples of unshaded numbers (except the unshaded number).

(i) Write a list of all the unshaded numbers less than 50 (except 1).
   How many factors has each of the numbers in your list?
   What is the special name for these numbers?

Working with Number

Activity

Cut a piece of paper into 2 **pieces**.

Put the pieces on top of each other.
Cut the pile in half.
How many pieces have you got?

Put **all** the pieces on top of each other.
Cut the pile in half again.
How many pieces?

Continue putting the pieces on top of each other and cutting the pile in half.

Copy and complete this table to show your results.

0 cuts gives 1 piece 1 cut gives 2 pieces 2 cuts gives 4 pieces 3 cuts gives 8 pieces 4 cuts gives … 5 cuts gives … 6 cuts gives …	$4 = 2 \times 2$ $8 = 2 \times 2 \times 2$	In shorthand 2×2 can be written as 2^2. In shorthand $2 \times 2 \times 2$ can be written as 2^3.

Write down the shorthand form of $2 \times 2 \times 2 \times 2 \times 2 \times 2 \times 2 \times 2 \times 2 \times 2$.
Write down the number of pieces for 20 cuts in shorthand form.
Write down the number of pieces for n cuts in shorthand form.
What are the values of 2^1 and 2^0?

Products of the same number, like $2 \times 2 \times 2 \times 2 \times 2$, can be written in a shorthand form using **powers**.
For example:

$2 \times 2 \times 2 \times 2 \times 2 = 2^5$	This is read as '2 to the power of 5'.	2^5 has the value 32.
$3 \times 3 \times 3 \times 3 = 3^4$	This is read as '3 to the power of 4'.	3^4 has the value 81.
$5 \times 5 \times 5 \times 5 \times 5 \times 5 \times 5 = 5^7$	This is read as '5 to the power of 7'.	5^7 has the value 78 125.

Use a calculator to check the values of 2^5, 3^4 and 5^7.

Index form

Numbers written in shorthand form like 2^5 are said to be in **index** form.
This is sometimes called **power** form.

An expression of the form
$a \times a \times a \times a \times a$
can be written in index form as a^5.

a^5 is read as 'a to the **power** 5'.
a is the **base** of the expression.
5 is the **index** or **power**.
(The plural of index is **indices**.)

There are two special results that you might have noticed when doing the activity.

$2^0 = 1$. Also, $3^0 = 1$, $4^0 = 1$, $5^0 = 1$, …
In general: $a^0 = 1$
Any number raised to the power zero is 1.

$2^1 = 2$. Also, $3^1 = 3$, $4^1 = 4$, $5^1 = 5$, …
In general: $a^1 = a$
Any number raised to the power one is the number itself.

EXAMPLES

Expression	Index form	Read as	Value
$4 \times 4 \times 4 \times 4 \times 4$	4^5	'4 to the power 5'	1024
$6 \times 6 \times 6$	6^3	'6 to the power 3'	216
$2.1 \times 2.1 \times 2.1 \times 2.1$	2.1^4	'2.1 to the power 4'	19.4481

Exercise **12.3**   Do not use a calculator.

1 Write each of the following as a power.
(a) $4 \times 4 \times 4 \times 4$
(b) $3 \times 3 \times 3 \times 3 \times 3 \times 3 \times 3 \times 3$
(c) $8 \times 8 \times 8 \times 8 \times 8 \times 8 \times 8$
(d) $0.3 \times 0.3 \times 0.3$
(e) $1.6 \times 1.6 \times 1.6 \times 1.6 \times 1.6$
(f) $12 \times 12 \times 12 \times 12 \times 12 \times 12 \times 12$

2 (a) Copy and complete this table of the powers of 10.

Expression	Index form	Value
$10 \times 10 \times 10 \times 10 \times 10 \times 10$	10^6	1 000 000
$10 \times 10 \times 10 \times 10 \times 10$	10^5	
	10^4	
$10 \times 10 \times 10$		
		100
10		
		1

(b) Complete a similar table for:　(i)　the powers of 5,　(ii)　the powers of 4.
(c) What do you notice about numbers raised to the power zero?

3 Work out the value of:
(a) 2^3　(b) 6^2　(c) 3^4　(d) 12^2　(e) 5^4　(f) 10^7

4 Write the following as products of powers.
For example:　$2 \times 2 \times 2 \times 3 \times 3 \times 5 = 2^3 \times 3^2 \times 5$
(a) $2 \times 2 \times 3 \times 3$
(b) $2 \times 3 \times 3 \times 3 \times 5$
(c) $2 \times 3 \times 5 \times 5$
(d) $2 \times 2 \times 2 \times 2 \times 3 \times 5 \times 5$
(e) $3 \times 3 \times 3 \times 3 \times 5 \times 5 \times 7$

Prime factors

The factors of 18 are　1,　2,　3,　6,　9　and　18.
Two of these factors, 2 and 3, are prime numbers.
The **prime factors** of 18 are 2 and 3.

Those factors of a number which are prime numbers are called **prime factors**.

Products of prime factors

All numbers can be written as the product of their prime factors.
For example:

$$6 = 2 \times 3$$
$$20 = 2 \times 2 \times 5$$
$$70 = 2 \times 5 \times 7$$
$$168 = 2 \times 2 \times 2 \times 3 \times 7$$

Powers can be used to write numbers as the product of their prime factors in a shorter form.
For example:

$$20 = 2^2 \times 5$$
$$168 = 2^3 \times 3 \times 7$$

A **factor tree** can be used to help write numbers as the product of their prime factors.
For example, this factor tree shows that:

$$40 = 2 \times 20$$
$$40 = 2 \times 2 \times 10$$
$$40 = 2 \times 2 \times 2 \times 5$$
$$40 = 2^3 \times 5$$

The branches of a factor tree stop when a prime factor is obtained.

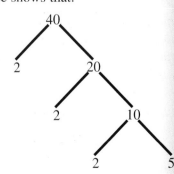

So 40 written as the product of its prime factors is $2^3 \times 5$.

1 Find the prime factors of 42.

First find the factors of 42.
$$42 \times 1 = 42$$
$$21 \times 2 = 42$$
$$14 \times 3 = 42$$
$$7 \times 6 = 42$$

Factors of 42 are:
1, 2, 3, 6, 7, 14, 21 and 42.
2, 3 and 7 are prime numbers.
The prime factors of 42 are 2, 3 and 7.

2 Write 50 as the product of its prime factors.

The factor tree shows that:
$$50 = 2 \times 25$$
$$50 = 2 \times 5 \times 5$$

50 written as the product of its prime factors is 2×5^2.

Exercise 12.4

Do not use a calculator for questions 1 to 3.

1 Find the prime factors of:
(a) 12   (b) 20   (c) 28   (d) 45   (e) 66

2 Write the following numbers as products of their prime factors.
(a) 12   (b) 20   (c) 28   (d) 45   (e) 66

3 (a) A number written as the product of its prime factors is $2^5 \times 3^3$.
Find all the factors of this number. Write them as products of their prime factors.
(b) A number written as the product of its prime factors is $5^3 \times 7^4$.
Find all the factors of this number. Write them as products of their prime factors.

4 Each of the following numbers are written as products of their prime factors:
$2^3 \times 5^3$, $2^6 \times 5^6$, $2^2 \times 3^3 \times 5^2$, $2^4 \times 3^2 \times 5^8$, $3^2 \times 5^2 \times 11^4$, $3^3 \times 5^6 \times 13^3$.
Calculate each of the numbers.

5 Numbers are made using the rule $a^3 \times b^2 \times c^2$ where a, b and c are different prime numbers.
The smallest number is 1800, which is given by $2^3 \times 3^2 \times 5^2$.
Find the next three numbers.

6 Write each of the numbers 24, 40, 54 as the product of their prime factors. What do you notice?
Find the next three numbers.

7 Write each of the numbers 60, 84, 90 as the product of their prime factors. What do you notice?
Find the next three numbers.

Least common multiples

The first few multiples of three are:
     3, 6, 9, 12, **15**, 18, 21, 24, 27, **30**, 33, 36, 39, 42, **45**, ...

The first few multiples of five are:
     5, 10, **15**, 20, 25, **30**, 35, 40, **45**, 50, ...

15, 30, 45, ... are multiples of both 3 **and** 5.
They are called **common multiples** of 3 and 5.

The smallest number that is a multiple of both 3 and 5 is 15.
The **least common multiple** of 3 and 5 is 15.

The least common multiple (**LCM**) of two numbers is the smallest number that is a multiple of them both.

EXAMPLE

Find the least common multiple of 20 and 45.
Start with the multiples of 45:   45,   90,   135,   180,   225,   270,   …
Which is the lowest multiple of 45 which is also a multiple of 20?
Multiples of 20:   20,   40,   60,   80,   100,   120,   140,   160,   **180**,   …

So the least common multiple of 20 and 45 is 180.

Highest common factors

The factors of 20 are: 1,   2,   4,   5,   10,   20.
The factors of 50 are: 1,   2,   5,   10,   25,   50.

1, 2, 5 and 10 are factors of both 20 **and** 50.
They are called the **common factors** of 20 and 50.

The largest number that is a factor of both 20 and
50 is 10.
The **highest common factor** of 20 and 50 is 10.

$$20 \times 1 = 20 \qquad 50 \times 1 = 50$$
$$10 \times 2 = 20 \qquad 25 \times 2 = 50$$
$$5 \times 4 = 20 \qquad 10 \times 5 = 50$$

The highest common factor **(HCF)** of two numbers is the largest number that is a factor of them both.

EXAMPLE

The factors of 18 are: 1,   2,   3,   6,   9,   18.
The factors of 45 are: 1,   3,   5,   9,   15,   45.

The common factors of 18 and 45 are: 1, 3 and 9.

The highest common factor of 18 and 45 is 9.

$$18 \times 1 = 18 \qquad 45 \times 1 = 45$$
$$9 \times 2 = 18 \qquad 15 \times 3 = 45$$
$$6 \times 3 = 18 \qquad 9 \times 5 = 45$$

Exercise 12.5   Do not use a calculator.

1 Find the least common multiple of:
   (a) 8 and 12   (b) 5 and 32   (c) 10 and 20   (d) 15 and 18
   (e) 30 and 45   (f) 4, 6 and 8   (g) 5, 8 and 10   (h) 45, 90 and 105

2 Find the highest common factor of:
   (a) 12 and 66   (b) 8 and 24   (c) 16 and 18   (d) 20 and 36
   (e) 33 and 88   (f) 16, 20 and 28 (g) 15, 39 and 45 (h) 45, 90 and 105

3 The table shows the highest common factors of pairs of numbers.

   (a) Copy and extend the table up to at least
        15 in each direction.
   (b) Complete the table.
   (c) Describe any patterns you see in the table.

	1	2	3	4	5	6	7
1	1						
2							
3							1
4		2					
6			3				

4 (a) Find the value of x when $2^2 \times 3^x = 108$.
   (b) Write 162 as a product of prime factors.
   (c) What is the highest common factor of 108 and 162?
   (d) What is the least common multiple of 108 and 162?

5
  (a) Write 216 as a product of prime factors.
  (b) Write 288 as a product of prime factors.
  (c) What is the highest common factor of 216 and 288?
  (d) What is the least common multiple of 216 and 288?

6
  The bell at St. Gabriel's church rings every 6 minutes.
  At St. Paul's, the bell rings every 9 minutes.
  Both bells ring together at 9.00 am. When is the next time both bells ring together?

Square numbers

Whole numbers raised to the power 2 are called **square numbers**.

$1^2 = 1 \times 1 = 1$ 1^2 is read as '1 squared'.   1 is a square number.
$2^2 = 2 \times 2 = 4$ 2^2 is read as '2 squared'.   4 is a square number.
$3^2 = 3 \times 3 = 9$ 3^2 is read as '3 squared'.   9 is a square number.

To **square a number** multiply it by itself.

Square numbers can be shown as square patterns of dots.

$1^2 = 1$ $2^2 = 4$ $3^2 = 9$

Find the next two square numbers.
Numbers that are not whole numbers can also be squared.
For example:
   $1.6^2 = 1.6 \times 1.6 = 2.56$
   2.56 is **not** a square number. *Why not?*

Squaring on a calculator
1.6^2 is read as '1.6 squared'.

To calculate 1.6^2 use this sequence of buttons:

If there is no x^2 button try this:

Cube numbers

Whole numbers raised to the power 3 are called **cube numbers**.

$1^3 = 1 \times 1 \times 1 = 1$ 1^3 is read as '1 cubed'.   1 is a cube number.
$2^3 = 2 \times 2 \times 2 = 8$ 2^3 is read as '2 cubed'.   8 is a cube number.
$3^3 = 3 \times 3 \times 3 = 27$ 3^3 is read as '3 cubed'.   27 is a cube number.

Cube numbers can be shown using small cubes.

Draw a diagram to show 4^3.
What is the value of 4^3? $1^3 = 1$ $2^3 = 8$ $3^3 = 27$

Numbers that are not whole numbers can also be cubed.
For example:
   $1.6^3 = 1.6 \times 1.6 \times 1.6 = 4.096$
   4.096 is **not** a cube number. *Why not?*

1.6^3 is read as '1.6 cubed'.

Using a calculator

Powers

The **squares** of numbers and the **cubes** of numbers can also be calculated using the $\boxed{x^y}$ button on a calculator. The $\boxed{x^y}$ button can be used to calculate the value of a number x raised to the power of y.

EXAMPLES

1 Calculate the value of 2.6^4.

To do the calculation enter the following sequence into your calculator.

| 2 | . | 6 | x^y | 4 | = |

This gives $2.6^4 = 45.6976$

2 Calculate the value of $5^3 \times (2^4 + 2^3)$.

To do the calculation enter the following sequence into your calculator.

| 5 | x^y | 3 | × | (| 2 | x^y | 4 | + | 2 | x^y | 3 |) | = |

This gives $5^3 \times (2^4 + 2^3) = 3\ 000$

3 Find the value of x in: $2^x \times 5 = 160$

$2^x \times 5 = 160$
Dividing through by 5 gives:
$2^x = 32$
$2^5 = 32$ so $x = 5$.

Reciprocals

The **reciprocal** of a number is the value obtained when the number is divided into 1.

The reciprocal of a number x is $\frac{1}{x}$.

A number times its reciprocal equals 1.

For example, the reciprocal of 2 is $\frac{1}{2}$, and $2 \times \frac{1}{2} = 1$.

The reciprocal of a number can be shown using an index of -1.

For example, $7^{-1} = \frac{1}{7}$.

> To find the reciprocal of a number on a calculator use the
> $\boxed{\frac{1}{x}}$ button.
> 0 (zero) has no reciprocal.

EXAMPLE

Find the reciprocal of   (a) 5,   (b) 0.5.

(a)   The reciprocal of 5 is $\frac{1}{5}$.

$1 \div 5 = 0.2$

The reciprocal of 5 is 0.2.

To find the reciprocal of 5 on your calculator use the sequence: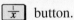

(b)   The reciprocal of 0.5 is $\frac{1}{0.5}$.

$1 \div 0.5 = 2$

The reciprocal of 0.5 is 2.

Use your calculator to check your answer.

Do not use a calculator for questions 1 and 2.

1 (a) Complete this list of square numbers from 1^2 to 20^2.

$$1^2 = 1 \times 1 = 1$$
$$2^2 = 2 \times 2 = 4$$
$$3^2 = 3 \times 3 = 9$$

(b) Explore the difference patterns in your list.

$$1 \quad 4 \quad 9 \quad 16 \quad 25 \quad ...$$
$$3 \quad 5 \quad 7 \quad 9 \quad ...$$
$$2 \quad 2 \quad 2 \quad ...$$

(c) Use the pattern to find 21^2 from 20^2.

2 (a) Complete this list of cube numbers from 1^3 to 10^3.

$$1^3 = 1 \times 1 \times 1 = 1$$
$$2^3 = 2 \times 2 \times 2 = 8$$
$$3^3 = 3 \times 3 \times 3 = 27$$

(b) Explore the difference patterns in your list.

$$1 \quad 8 \quad 27 \quad 64 \quad 125 \quad ...$$
$$7 \quad 19 \quad 37 \quad ...$$
$$12 \quad 18 \quad ...$$
$$6$$

3 (a) Calculate the value of:
(i) $(-3)^2$ (ii) $(-2)^3$
(iii) $(-4)^2$ (iv) $(-5)^3$

(b) What do you notice about the signs of your answers?

4 Consider the numbers:
8, 16, 27, 36, 64, 100.
Which of these numbers is both a square number **and** a cube number?

5 Calculate the value of:
(a) 6.7 squared   (b) 3.4 cubed
(c) 0.7 squared   (d) 0.04 cubed
(e) (−0.4) squared   (f) (−0.5) cubed

6 Calculate the value of:
(a) 0.2^0 (b) 0.3^3
(c) 0.4^1 (d) 0.5^2

7 Calculate the value of:
(a) 1.3^2 (b) 1.7^3
(c) 5.4^0 (d) 4.8^1

8 Use the $\boxed{x^y}$ button on your calculator to find the value of:
(a) (i) 13^2 (ii) 17^2 (iii) 2.5^2
    (iv) 0.8^2 (v) 9.7^2
(b) (i) 6^3 (ii) 15^3 (iii) 2.4^3
    (iv) 0.7^3 (v) 5.6^3
(c) (i) 3^7 (ii) 7^5 (iii) 9^6
    (iv) 0.5^4 (v) 3.8^5

9 Calculate:
(a) 2.4^5 (b) $(-1.2)^3$
(c) $(-0.7)^2$ (d) $3^4 + 3^2$
(e) $2^6 - 2^2$ (f) $2^5 \times 3^3$
(g) $3^5 \times 2^3$ (h) $4^5 \times 0.5^3$
(i) $4^5 \div 0.5^3$ (j) $1.4^5 \div 2.5^2$

10 Calculate:
(a) $2 + 2^2 + 2^3 + 2^4$
(b) $3 + 3^2 - 3^3 + 3^4$
(c) $3^3 \times (2^7 - 2^5)$
(d) $4^2 \times (3^4 + 3^2)$
(e) $3^3 \times 2^4 + 3^4 \times 2^3$
(f) $(5^4 + 5^2) \div (2^7 - 2^5)$
(g) $5^3 \times (4^5 - 4^2) + 6^3$
(h) $3^3 \div (2^7 - 2^5)$
(i) $(5^3 - 5^2) \times (6^3 - 2^4)$

11 (a) Find the reciprocals of these numbers without using a calculator, then use a calculator to check your answers.
(i) 2   (ii) 5   (iii) 10
(iv) 0.5   (v) 0.1   (vi) 0.2

(b) Use the $\boxed{\frac{1}{x}}$ button on your calculator to find the reciprocals of:
(i) 4   (ii) 20   (iii) 25
(iv) 0.25   (v) 0.4   (vi) 0.16

12 Show by means of an example, that a number times its reciprocal is equal to 1.

13 Calculate:
(a) 2^{-1} (b) 4^{-1}
(c) $(0.8)^{-1}$ (d) $\left(\frac{1}{4}\right)^{-1}$
Give each of your answers as a decimal.

14 Find the value of x in:
(a) $3^x \times 2 = 54$ (b) $2^x \times 7 = 7$
(c) $3^x \times 11 = 33$ (d) $5^x \times 4 = 100$
(e) $2^x \times 3 = 192$ (f) $5^x \times 7 = 875$
(g) $3^x \times 5 = 405$ (h) $7^x \times 2 = 686$

Square roots

The opposite of squaring a number is called finding the **square root**.
For example:
The square root of 16 is 4 because $4^2 = 16$.

4 $\xrightarrow{\text{square}}$ 16

4 $\xleftarrow{\text{square root}}$ 16

The square root of 3.24 is 1.8 because $1.8^2 = 3.24$.

1.8 $\xrightarrow{\text{square}}$ 3.24

1.8 $\xleftarrow{\text{square root}}$ 3.24

$\sqrt{}$ This special symbol stands for the square root.

For example:
$$\sqrt{9} = 3 \qquad\qquad \sqrt{2.56} = 1.6$$

The square root of a number can also be written in index form, using an index of $\frac{1}{2}$.
For example, $9^{\frac{1}{2}} = \sqrt{9}$.

Square roots on a calculator

To calculate $\sqrt{2.56}$ use this sequence of buttons:

[√] [2] [.] [5] [6] [=]

or:

[2] [.] [5] [6] [√]

Cube roots

The opposite of cubing a number is called finding the **cube root**.
For example:
The cube root of 27 is 3 because $3^3 = 27$.

3 $\xrightarrow{\text{cube}}$ 27

3 $\xleftarrow{\text{cube root}}$ 27

The cube root of 0.125 is 0.5 because $0.5^3 = 0.125$.

0.5 $\xrightarrow{\text{cube}}$ 0.125

0.5 $\xleftarrow{\text{cube root}}$ 0.125

$\sqrt[3]{}$ This special symbol stands for the cube root.

The cube root of a number can also be written in index form, using an index of $\frac{1}{3}$.
For example, $27^{\frac{1}{3}} = \sqrt[3]{27}$.

Square roots and cube roots can be worked out on a calculator without using special buttons.
A method called **trial and improvement** can be used.

EXAMPLE

You are asked to find the cube root of 18.6 but your calculator does not have a cube root button.
You know that $2^3 = 8$ and $3^3 = 27$.
Use trial and improvement, and a calculator, to find the cube root of 18.6 to an accuracy of
one decimal place. Show your method clearly.

2^3	$= 2 \times 2 \times 2$	$= 8$	so the cube root of 8 is 2	
3^3	$= 3 \times 3 \times 3$	$= 27$	so the cube root of 27 is 3	So try 2.5 *Why?*
2.5^3	$= 2.5 \times 2.5 \times 2.5$	$= 15.625$	so the cube root of 15.625 is 2.5	So try 2.6 *Why?*
2.6^3	$= 2.6 \times 2.6 \times 2.6$	$= 17.576$	so the cube root of 17.576 is 2.6	So try 2.7 *Why?*
2.7^3	$= 2.7 \times 2.7 \times 2.7$	$= 19.683$	so the cube root of 19.683 is 2.7	So try 2.65 *Why?*
2.65^3	$= 2.65 \times 2.65 \times 2.65$	$= 18.609625$	so the cube root of 18.609625 is 2.65	

This shows that the cube root of 18.6 lies between 2.6 and 2.65.
So correct to one decimal place the cube root of 18.6 is 2.6.

Remember. When using trial and improvement:
● Work methodically using trials first to the nearest whole number, then to one decimal place etc.
● Do at least one trial to one more decimal place than the required accuracy to be sure of your answer.

1 Write down the value of:
(a) $\sqrt{25}$ (b) $\sqrt{100}$ (c) $\sqrt{64}$ (d) $\sqrt{49}$

2 Write down the value of:
(a) $\sqrt[3]{8}$ (b) $\sqrt[3]{64}$ (c) $\sqrt[3]{125}$ (d) $\sqrt[3]{27}$

3 Work out.
(a) $\sqrt{3^2 + 4^2}$ (b) $\sqrt[3]{6^2 - 3^2}$ (c) $\sqrt[3]{8^2}$

4 (a) Use the method of trial and improvement to find the square roots of:
(i) 20   (ii) 108   (iii) 7.6
Give your answers to an accuracy of one decimal place.
(b) Check each of your answers using the square root button.

5 Use the method of trial and improvement to find the cube roots of:
(a) 45   (b) 200   (c) 4.6
Give your answers to an accuracy of one decimal place.

6 Use the method of trial and improvement to find the length of the side of a square carpet of area 55 m².
Give your answer to an accuracy of one decimal place.

7 Use the method of trial and improvement to find the length of the side of an ice cube of volume 4500 mm³.
Give your answer to an accuracy of two decimal places.

Multiplying and dividing numbers with powers

EXAMPLES

This example introduces a method for multiplying powers of the same number.

1 (a) Calculate the value of $6^5 \times 6^4$ in power form.
$6^5 = 6 \times 6 \times 6 \times 6 \times 6$ and $6^4 = 6 \times 6 \times 6 \times 6$
$6^5 \times 6^4 = (6 \times 6 \times 6 \times 6 \times 6) \times (6 \times 6 \times 6 \times 6)$
$= 6 \times 6 \times 6 \times 6 \times 6 \times 6 \times 6 \times 6 \times 6$
This gives: $6^5 \times 6^4 = 6^9$

(b) Calculate the value of $3^2 \times 3^6$ in power form.
$3^2 = 3 \times 3$ and $3^6 = 3 \times 3 \times 3 \times 3 \times 3 \times 3$
$3^2 \times 3^6 = (3 \times 3) \times (3 \times 3 \times 3 \times 3 \times 3 \times 3)$
$= 3 \times 3 \times 3 \times 3 \times 3 \times 3 \times 3 \times 3$
This gives: $3^2 \times 3^6 = 3^8$

Can you see a quick way of working out the power of the answer?

This example introduces a method for dividing powers of the same number.

2 (a) Calculate the value of $6^7 \div 6^4$ in power form.
$6^7 \div 6^4 = \dfrac{6 \times 6 \times 6 \times \cancel{6} \times \cancel{6} \times \cancel{6} \times \cancel{6}}{\cancel{6} \times \cancel{6} \times \cancel{6} \times \cancel{6}}$
$= 6 \times 6 \times 6$
$= 6^3$
This gives: $6^7 \div 6^4 = 6^{7-4} = 6^3$

(b) Calculate the value of $4^5 \div 4^3$ in power form.
$4^5 \div 4^3 = \dfrac{4 \times 4 \times \cancel{4} \times \cancel{4} \times \cancel{4}}{\cancel{4} \times \cancel{4} \times \cancel{4}}$
$= 4 \times 4$
$= 4^2$
This gives: $4^5 \div 4^3 = 4^{5-3} = 4^2$

Rules for multiplying and dividing powers of the same number

Multiplying

When multiplying:
powers of the same base are **added**.

In general: $a^m \times a^n = a^{m+n}$

Dividing

When dividing:
powers of the same base are **subtracted**.

In general: $a^m \div a^n = a^{m-n}$

EXAMPLES

1 Simplify $2^6 \times 2^{-3}$.
Leave your answer in power form.

$$2^6 \times 2^{-3} = 2^{6+-3}$$
$$= 2^{6-3}$$
$$= 2^3$$

Remember
When multiplying and dividing powers with different bases each base must be dealt with separately.
Why?

2 Simplify $3^4 \times 2^3 \times 3^{-5} \times 2^5$.
Leave your answer in power form.

$$3^4 \times 2^3 \times 3^{-5} \times 2^5 = 3^4 \times 3^{-5} \times 2^3 \times 2^5$$
$$= 3^{4+-5} \times 2^{3+5}$$
$$= 3^{-1} \times 2^8$$

3 Simplify $10^{-4} \div 10^{-2}$.
Leave your answer in power form.

$$10^{-4} \div 10^{-2} = 10^{-4--2}$$
$$= 10^{-4+2}$$
$$= 10^{-2}$$

Exercise **12.8**

Do not use a calculator in this exercise.

1 Simplify each of these expressions.
Leave your answers in power form.
- (a) $2^5 \times 2^2$
- (b) $4^3 \times 4^6$
- (c) $6^2 \times 6$
- (d) $8^4 \times 8^3$
- (e) $9^2 \times 9^{-2}$
- (f) $2^{-3} \times 2$
- (g) $5^5 \times 5^{-7}$
- (h) $3^{-2} \times 3$
- (i) $8^{-2} \times 8^{-3}$

2 Simplify.
Leave your answers in power form.
- (a) $2^5 \div 2^2$
- (b) $4^7 \div 4^5$
- (c) $6^2 \div 6$
- (d) $8^4 \div 8^3$
- (e) $3^{11} \div 3^5$
- (f) $2^{-3} \div 2$
- (g) $5^5 \div 5^{-7}$
- (h) $11^{-2} \div 11^3$
- (i) $7^{-4} \div 7^{-3}$

3 Simplify.
Leave your answers in power form.
- (a) $8^{-3} \times 8^5$
- (b) $7^2 \div 7^7$
- (c) $2.5^{-2} \div 2.5^{-1}$
- (d) $4^3 \times 4^2 \times 4^{-5}$
- (e) $10^{-3} \div 10^{-2}$
- (f) $6^{-3} \times 6^4 \div 6^5$
- (g) $0.1^{-7} \div 0.1^5$
- (h) $5^{-7} \div (5^2 \times 5^6)$
- (i) $4^2 \div (4^{-1} \times 4^{-2})$

4 Simplify.
Leave your answers in power form.
- (a) $4^{-3} \times 4^5 \times 8^5 \times 8^2$
- (b) $4^{-1} \times 5^5 \times 5^{-7} \times 4^2$
- (c) $2^{-5} \times 5^3 \times 2^3 \times 5^2$
- (d) $3^{-1} \times 8^5 \times 3^{-2} \times 8^{-1}$

5 Simplify.
Leave your answers in power form.
- (a) $\dfrac{2 \times 2^5}{2^3}$
- (b) $\dfrac{3^5 \times 3^{-2}}{3^2}$
- (c) $\dfrac{5^{-3} \times 5^4}{5^{-2}}$

Surds

A surd is the square root of a positive integer, like $\sqrt{3}$, for which the root is not exact.
$\sqrt{4}$ is not a surd because it has an exact root.

The square root of a number can be positive or negative.
For example, the square root of 4 can be $+2$ or -2.

When we use surds we take the **positive square root**.

Surds are used when we want to keep an answer **exact**.
$\sqrt{3} = 1.73205\ldots$

To keep an exact answer it is therefore necessary to keep the number in surd form and not to use a decimal approximation.

To manipulate surds we must use these rules.

$$\textbf{1.} \quad m\sqrt{a} + n\sqrt{a} = (m + n)\sqrt{a} \qquad \textbf{2.} \quad \sqrt{ab} = \sqrt{a} \times \sqrt{b} \qquad \textbf{3.} \quad \sqrt{\frac{a}{b}} = \frac{\sqrt{a}}{\sqrt{b}}$$

To simplify surds look for factors that are square numbers.

EXAMPLES

Simplify the following leaving the answer in surd form.

(a) $\sqrt{12}$

(b) $2\sqrt{3} + 3\sqrt{3}$

(c) $\sqrt{\dfrac{15}{12}}$

(a) $\sqrt{12} = \sqrt{4} \times \sqrt{3} = 2\sqrt{3}$

(b) $2\sqrt{3} + 3\sqrt{3} = 5\sqrt{3}$

(c) $\sqrt{\dfrac{15}{12}} = \dfrac{\sqrt{3} \times \sqrt{5}}{\sqrt{4} \times \sqrt{3}} = \dfrac{\sqrt{5}}{2}$

Exercise 12.9 — Do not use a calculator.

1 Which of the following are surds?
   (a) $\sqrt{2}$ (b) $\sqrt{9}$ (c) $\sqrt{7}$ (d) $\sqrt{1}$ (e) $\sqrt{18}$ (f) $\sqrt{25}$

2 Write the following surds in their simplest form.
   (a) $\sqrt{8}$ (b) $\sqrt{12}$ (c) $\sqrt{28}$ (d) $\sqrt{27}$ (e) $\sqrt{75}$ (f) $\sqrt{45}$
   (g) $\sqrt{20}$ (h) $\sqrt{72}$

3 Simplify.
   (a) $\sqrt{2} + \sqrt{2}$ (b) $2\sqrt{5} - \sqrt{5}$ (c) $5\sqrt{3} + 2\sqrt{3}$ (d) $5\sqrt{2} - 3\sqrt{2}$

4 Simplify.
   (a) $\sqrt{\dfrac{9}{4}}$ (b) $\sqrt{\dfrac{25}{16}}$ (c) $\sqrt{\dfrac{6}{4}}$ (d) $\sqrt{\dfrac{18}{9}}$ (e) $\sqrt{\dfrac{12}{15}}$

5 Simplify.
   (a) $\sqrt{3} \times \sqrt{3}$ (b) $\sqrt{3} \times 2\sqrt{3}$ (c) $3\sqrt{2} \times \sqrt{2}$ (d) $\sqrt{2} \times \sqrt{8}$
   (e) $\sqrt{18} \times \sqrt{2}$ (f) $\sqrt{12} \times \sqrt{3}$ (g) $\sqrt{5} \times \sqrt{10}$ (h) $\sqrt{3} \times \sqrt{6}$

What you need to know

- **Multiples** of a number are found by multiplying the number by   1,   2,   3,   4,   …
  For example: the multiples of 8 are $1 \times 8 = 8$, $2 \times 8 = 16$, $3 \times 8 = 24$, $4 \times 8 = 32$,   …

- **Factors** of a number are found by listing all the products that give the number.
  For example: $1 \times 6 = 6$ and $2 \times 3 = 6$.   So, the factors of 6 are: 1,   2,   3   and   6.

- A **prime number** is a number with only two factors, 1 and the number itself.
  The first few prime numbers are: 2,   3,   5,   7,   11,   13,   17,   19,   23,   29,   31,   …

- The **prime factors** of a number are those factors of the number which are themselves prime numbers.

- The **Least Common Multiple** of two numbers is the smallest number that is a multiple of them both.

- The **Highest Common Factor** of two numbers is the largest number that is a factor of them both.

- An expression such as $3 \times 3 \times 3 \times 3 \times 3$ can be written in a shorthand way as 3^5.
  This is read as '3 to the power 5'. The number 3 is the **base** of the expression. 5 is the **power**.

- Numbers raised to the power 2 are **squared**. Whole numbers squared are called **square numbers**.
  Squares can be calculated using the $\boxed{x^2}$ button on a calculator.
  The opposite of squaring a number is called finding the **square root**.
  Square roots can be calculated using the $\boxed{\sqrt{}}$ button on a calculator.
  The square root of a number can be written in index form. For example: $\sqrt{9} = 9^{\frac{1}{2}}$.

- Numbers raised to the power 3 are **cubed**. Whole numbers cubed are called **cube numbers**.
  The opposite of cubing a number is called finding the **cube root**.
  Cube roots can be calculated using the $\boxed{\sqrt[3]{}}$ button on a calculator.
  The cube root of a number can be written in index form. For example: $\sqrt[3]{27} = 27^{\frac{1}{3}}$.

- **Powers**
  The squares of numbers and the cubes of numbers can be worked out on a calculator by using the $\boxed{x^y}$ button.
  The $\boxed{x^y}$ button can be used to calculate the value of a number x raised to the power of y.

- The square root of a number can be positive or negative.
  For example, the square root of 4 can be $+2$ or -2.

- **Reciprocals**
  The reciprocal of a number is the value obtained when the number is divided into 1.
  The reciprocal of a number can be found on a calculator by using the $\boxed{\frac{1}{x}}$ button.
  A number times its reciprocal equals 1. Zero has no reciprocal.
  The reciprocal of a number can be shown using an index of -1. For example: $5^{-1} = \frac{1}{5}$.

- Square roots and cube roots can be found using a method called **trial and improvement**.

- Powers of the same base are **added** when terms are **multiplied**.
  Powers of the same base are **subtracted** when terms are **divided**.
  Any number raised to the power zero equals 1.

- A surd is the square root of a positive integer, like $\sqrt{3}$, for which the root is not exact.
  $\sqrt{4}$ is not a surd because it has an exact root.

- To manipulate surds we must use these rules.

1. $m\sqrt{a} + n\sqrt{a} = (m + n)\sqrt{a}$	**2.** $\sqrt{ab} = \sqrt{a} \times \sqrt{b}$	**3.** $\sqrt{\dfrac{a}{b}} = \dfrac{\sqrt{a}}{\sqrt{b}}$

Working with Number

1 12 written as the product of its prime factors is $2^2 \times 3$.

Find the factors of 12.

12 × 1 = 12
6 × 2 = 12
4 × 3 = 12

12 has 6 factors: 1, 2, 3, 4, 6 and 12.

Find the number of factors of some more numbers of the form $a^2 \times b$ where a and b are prime numbers. What do you notice?

Investigate the number of factors of other numbers with just two prime factors. What about numbers with any number of prime factors?

2 The squares of whole numbers can be written as the sum of consecutive odd numbers.

$$1^2 = 1 \qquad 2^2 = 1 + 3 \qquad 3^2 = 1 + 3 + 5$$

Continue this pattern. Can you find a general rule for n^2?

The cubes of whole numbers can also be written as the sum of consecutive odd numbers.

$$1^3 = 1 \qquad 2^3 = 3 + 5 \qquad 3^3 = 7 + 9 + 11$$

Continue this pattern. Can you find a general rule for n^3?

Other powers of whole numbers can also be written as the sum of consecutive odd numbers. This is how the pattern starts for the powers of 4 and 5.

$$1^4 = 1 \qquad 1^5 = 1 \qquad 2^4 = 7 + 9 \qquad 2^5 = 15 + 17$$

Investigate the connection between other powers and the sum of consecutive odd numbers.

Review Exercise 12

Do not use a calculator for questions 1 to 17.

1 Find all the factors of: (a) 12 (b) 30 (c) 96

2 Explain why 19 is a prime number.

3 Part of a sequence of numbers is shown. 3 6 9 12 15 18
(a) Which of these numbers are multiples of 9?
(b) Which of the numbers are factors of 6?
(c) Which of these numbers is a prime number?   AQA

4 What is the square of 6?

5

> 3, 9, 20, 25, 29, 75, 92, 100

Which of the numbers in the box are:
(a) square numbers, (b) factors of 100, (c) prime numbers?   AQA

6 Consider the numbers: 8, 9, 11, 17 and 121.
(a) Write down all the factors of these numbers.
(b) (i) Which of the numbers have only two factors?
    (ii) What special name is given to these numbers?
(c) (i) Which of these numbers have exactly 3 factors?
    (ii) What special name is given to these numbers?

7 (a) Write down the multiple of 6 that is larger than 105, but smaller than 111.
(b) Write down all the factors of 111.
(c) Write down the largest prime number that is smaller than 107.
(d) Write down an even prime number.   AQA

8 (a) Write as a product of prime factors:
   (i) 126, (ii) 90, (iii) 210
   (b) What is the smallest number that has 90 and 210 as factors?
   (c) What is the highest common factor of 90 and 126?

9 (a) Find the value of p when $2^p \times 3 = 48$.
   (b) Write 72 as a product of prime factors.
   (c) What is the highest common factor of 48 and 72?
   (d) What is the least common multiple of 48 and 72? AQA

10 A blue light flashes every 18 seconds and a green light flashes every 30 seconds. The two lights flash at the same time. After how many seconds will the lights next flash at the same time?

11 State the value of
   (a) 4^2,
   (b) the square root of 9. AQA

12 Work out
   (a) the cube of 5,
   (b) 2^6. AQA

13 What is the value of $2^3 - \sqrt{25}$?

14 (a) Find the square root of forty-nine.
   (b) Find the square of seventeen. AQA

15 Simplify
   (a) $3\sqrt{5} - \sqrt{5}$
   (b) $\sqrt{\dfrac{36}{25}}$
   (c) $\sqrt{2} \times 3\sqrt{2}$

16 Which is greater $\sqrt{625}$ or 3^3?
   Show working to explain your answer. AQA

17 (a) Work out the value of 0.3^2.
   (b) Work out the value of 0.5^3. AQA

18 Computer magazines often use the fact that 2^{10} is approximately equal to 10^3. To how many significant figures is this true? AQA

19 What is the value of $\sqrt{50}$? Give your answer correct to one decimal place.

20 Calculate the value of $0.7^3 + \sqrt{30}$. Give your answer correct to one decimal place.

21 (a) Calculate the exact value of 8^5.
   (b) Find the reciprocal of 6. Give your answer correct to 3 decimal places.

22 Julio is trying to find the cube root of 17. His calculator does not have a cube root button so he has to work out his answer by trial and improvement.
   He calculates
   $$2.5 \times 2.5 \times 2.5 = 15.625$$
   $$2.6 \times 2.6 \times 2.6 = 17.576$$
   Continue this method to find the cube root of 17 correct to two decimal places. You **must** show all your working. AQA

23 Write each of the following as a power of 10.
   (a) 100 (b) 1 000 000
   (c) 1 (d) 0.1
   (e) 0.001

24 Write down the value of:
   (a) 1^{10} (b) 5^4
   (c) $4^4 + 4^2$ (d) $3^4 + 3^2$
   (e) $5^4 - 5^3$ (f) $7^0 + 7^2$
   (g) $2^1 + 2^4 + 2^5$ (h) $3^0 + 3^1 + 3^2 + 3^3$

25 For each of the following equations, write down the value of n.
   (a) $2^n = 32$ (b) $n^3 = 125$
   (c) $8^n = 8$ AQA

26 Calculate the value of:
   (a) $12^5 \div 2^3$ (b) $0.3^3 + 0.3^5$
   (c) $0.3^3 \times 0.3^5$ (d) $3^4 + 2^5 \times (3^2 + 3^5)$
   (e) $2^5 \times (8^3 - 4^5)$ (f) $8^5 \times (2^3 + 4^2)$

27 Simplify fully each of these expressions. Leave your answers in power form.
   (a) $3^6 \times 3^2$ (b) $5^4 \times 5^7$
   (c) $9^5 \times 9$ (d) $4^8 \div 4^3$
   (e) $7^6 \div 7$ (f) $6^7 \div 6^3$
   (g) $2^{-5} \times 2^2$ (h) $5^{-3} \times 5^{-4}$
   (i) $4^{-2} \div 4$ (j) $2^{-4} \times 7^3 \times 2^{-3} \times 7^{-1}$
   (k) $3^8 \times 3^3 \div 3^2$

28 Calculate the value of:
   (a) $\sqrt{7}$
   (b) $(\sqrt{7})^2$
   (c) $(\sqrt{7})^6$

CHAPTER 13

Standard Index Form

Standard index form is a shorthand way of writing very small and very large numbers. Standard index form is often called **standard form** or **scientific notation**.

Very large numbers

Scientists who study the planets and the stars work with very large numbers.

Approximate distances from the Sun to some planets are:

Mercury	58 000 000 km
Venus	108 000 000 km
Earth	149 000 000 km
Mars	228 000 000 km
Pluto	5 898 000 000 km

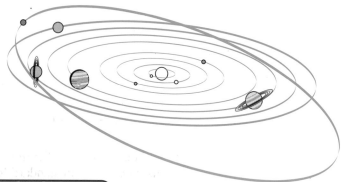

Distances to the stars are far greater.

Large numbers and your calculator

A calculator displays very large numbers in **standard form**.
To represent large numbers in standard form you need to use powers of 10.

Number	1 000 000	100 000	10 000	1000	100	10
Power of 10	10^6	10^5	10^4	10^3	10^2	10^1

For example: $2\,600\,000 = 2.6 \times 1\,000\,000 = 2.6 \times 10^6$
Therefore $2\,600\,000 = 2.6 \times 10^6$ in **standard form**.

Calculator displays

Work out $3\,000\,000 \times 25\,000\,000$ *on your calculator.*
Write down the display.

Most calculators will show the answer as | 7.5   *13* |.

In **standard form** the answer should be written as 7.5×10^{13}.

> A number written in standard form has **two** parts. The first part must be a number between 1 and 10. The second part is a power of 10. The two parts are connected by a multiplication sign.

EXAMPLES

1 Write
  (a) 370 000 in standard form,   (b) 5.6×10^7 as an ordinary number.

  (a) $370\,000 = 3.7 \times 100\,000 = 3.7 \times 10^5$ (b) $5.6 \times 10^7 = 5.6 \times 10\,000\,000 = 56\,000\,000$

2 Write the calculator display | 7.3   *05* |

  (a) in standard form,   (b) as an ordinary number.

  (a) | 7.3   *05* | means 7.3×10^5 (b) $7.3 \times 10^5 = 7.3 \times 100\,000 = 730\,000$

1   Copy the table and fill in all the different forms of each number.

	Ordinary number	Power of 10	Standard form
	300 000	3 × 100 000	3×10^5
(a)	75 000	7.5 × 10 000	
(b)		8 × 100 000 000	
(c)			3.5×10^{13}
(d)	62 300 000 000 000		
(e)			5.4×10^9
(f)		6.93 × 10 000 000	
(g)	453 100 000 000		
(h)			6.97×10^5
(i)	453 120		
(j)		1.097 × 100 000	

2   Use your calculator to work out each of the following. Write each of the answers:
   (i)   as on your calculator display,   (ii)   in standard form,   (iii)   as an ordinary number.

   (a)   300 000 × 200 000 000   (b)   120 000 × 80 000 000
   (c)   15 000 × 700 000 000   (d)   65 000 × 2 000 000 000
   (e)   480 000 × 500 000 000   (f)   50 000 × 50 000 000
   (g)   352 000 000 × 40 000 000   (h)   35 200 × 6 500 000 000
   (i)   3450 × 5200 × 45 000   (j)   550 000 × 8000 × 250 000

3   Write each of these numbers in standard form.
   (a)   300 000 000 000   (b)   80 000 000   (c)   700 000 000   (d)   2 000 000 000
   (e)   42 000 000   (f)   21 000 000 000   (g)   3 700 000 000   (h)   630
   (i)   3 219 000 000   (j)   654 120 000   (k)   897 213   (l)   42 670 000 000

4   Change each of these numbers to an ordinary number.
   (a) 6×10^5 (b) 2×10^3 (c) 5×10^7 (d) 9×10^8
   (e) 3.7×10^9 (f) 2.8×10^1 (g) 9.9×10^{10} (h) 7.1×10^4
   (i) 3.97×10^2 (j) 8.172×10^2 (k) 7.4312×10^6 (l) 1.234×10^9

5   Write these calculator displays   (a)   in standard form,   (b)   as an ordinary number.

   (i) | 4.5   03 | (ii) | 7.8   07 | (iii) | 5.3   05 | (iv) | 3.25   04 |

6   The table shows the estimated population for some countries in 2020.

Country	Estimated population in 2020
Albania	5.3×10^6
Brazil	2.5×10^8
Fiji	9.0×10^5
Greece	1.2×10^7

   (a)   (i)   Which of these countries is estimated to have the largest population in 2020?
         (ii)   Write the estimated population as an ordinary number.
   (b)   In 2020, China is estimated to have a population of 1288 million people.
         Write 1288 million in standard form.

Scientists who study microbiology work with numbers that are very small.
The smallest living cells are bacteria which have a diameter of about 0.000 025 cm.
Blood cells have a diameter of about 0.000 75 cm.

There are plenty of examples of other very small quantities.

Small numbers and your calculator

A calculator displays small numbers in **standard form**.
It does this in the same sort of way that it does for large numbers.
To represent very small numbers in standard form you need to use powers of 10 for numbers less than 1.

Number	1000	100	10	1	0.1	0.01	0.001	0.000 1	0.000 01
Power of 10	10^3	10^2	10^1	10^0	10^{-1}	10^{-2}	10^{-3}	10^{-4}	10^{-5}

For example: $0.000\ 037 = 3.7 \times 0.000\ 01 = 3.7 \times 10^{-5}$
Therefore $0.000\ 037 = 3.7 \times 10^{-5}$ in **standard form**.

Calculator displays

Work out $0.000\ 007 \times 0.000\ 9$ on your calculator.
Write down the display.

Most calculators will show the answer as $\boxed{6.3 \qquad -09}$.

In standard form the answer should be written as 6.3×10^{-9}.

Standard form

In **standard form** a number is written as: a number between 1 and 10 × a power of 10

In standard form:
a **large** number has a **positive power**.   e.g. $160\ 000\ 000 = 1.6 \times 10^8$
a **small** number has a **negative power**.   e.g. $0.000\ 000\ 06 = 6 \times 10^{-8}$

EXAMPLES

1 Write
(a) 0.000 73 in standard form,
(b) 2.9×10^{-6} as an ordinary number.

(a) $0.000\ 73 = 7.3 \times 0.000\ 1 = 7.3 \times 10^{-4}$
(b) $2.9 \times 10^{-6} = 2.9 \times 0.000\ 001 = 0.000\ 002\ 9$

2 Write the calculator display $\boxed{1.5 \qquad -03}$
(a) in standard form,
(b) as an ordinary number.

(a) $\boxed{1.5 \quad -03}$ means 1.5×10^{-3}

(b) $1.5 \times 10^{-3} = 1.5 \times 0.001 = 0.001\ 5$

Do questions 1 to 5 without using a calculator.

1 Write down the power of 10 for each of these numbers.
  (a) 0.1
  (b) 0.000 01
  (c) 0.000 000 001
  (d) 0.001
  (e) 0.000 000 000 01
  (f) 0.000 000 000 000 1

2 Copy and complete the following table.

	Ordinary number	Power of 10	Standard form
(a)	0.000 03	$3 \times 0.000\,01$	3×10^{-5}
(b)	0.007 5	7.5×0.001	
(c)	0.000 008 75	$8.75 \times 0.000\,001$	
(d)	0.000 000 003 5		
(e)	0.000 000 000 006 23		
(f)	0.000 000 5		
(g)	0.000 000 047 25		
(h)	0.05		
(i)	0.000 007 85		

3 Change each of these numbers to an ordinary number:
  (a) 3.5×10^{-1}
  (b) 5×10^{-4}
  (c) 7.2×10^{-5}
  (d) 6.1×10^{-3}
  (e) 1.17×10^{-10}
  (f) 8.135×10^{-7}
  (g) 6.462×10^{-2}
  (h) 4.001×10^{-9}

4 Write each of these numbers in standard form.
  (a) 0.007
  (b) 0.04
  (c) 0.000 000 005
  (d) 0.000 8
  (e) 0.000 000 002 3
  (f) 0.000 000 045
  (g) 0.023 4
  (h) 0.000 000 002 34
  (i) 0.006 7
  (j) 0.3
  (k) 0.000 000 073 95
  (l) 0.000 000 000 000 34

5 Change each of these numbers to an ordinary number:
  (a) 5.5×10^{-6}
  (b) 6.5×10^{-8}
  (c) 3.2×10^{7}
  (d) 2.9×10^{2}
  (e) 3.167×10^{-11}
  (f) 1.115×10^{4}
  (g) 1.412×10^{-5}
  (h) 4×10^{1}

6 Use your calculator to work out each of the following. Write each of the answers:
  (i) as on the calculator display, (ii) in standard form, (iii) as an ordinary number.
  (a) $0.000\,03 \times 0.000\,000\,2$
  (b) $0.000\,045 \times 0.000\,003$
  (c) $0.000\,75 \times 0.000\,000\,04$
  (d) $0.002\,3 \times 0.000\,000\,05$
  (e) $0.053 \times 0.000\,000\,08$
  (f) $0.000\,006\,4 \times 0.000\,015\,2$
  (g) $0.59 \times 0.000\,000\,7^{2}$
  (h) $0.067\,5 \div 15\,000^{2}$
  (i) $6\,330\,000 \div 0.000\,06$
  (j) $7400 \div 0.002^{3}$

Using large and small numbers with a calculator

Calculations with large and small numbers can be done on a calculator by:

  ● changing the numbers to standard form,
  ● entering the numbers into the calculator using the [Exp] button.

If your calculator works in a different way to the examples shown refer to the
instruction booklet supplied with the calculator or ask someone for help.

1 Calculate the value of   62 500 000 000 × 0.000 000 003
Give your answer both as an ordinary number and in standard form.

62 500 000 000 × 0.000 000 003 = $(6.25 \times 10^{10}) \times (3 \times 10^{-9})$

To do the calculation enter the following sequence into your calculator.

| 6 | . | 2 | 5 | Exp | 1 | 0 | × | 3 | Exp | 9 | +/− | = |

Giving:
62 500 000 000 × 0.000 000 003
= 187.5   (ordinary number)
= 1.875×10^{2} (standard form)

Some calculators display this result as: 187.5
Other calculators give this display: 1.875   *02*

2 Calculate the value of $0.000\ 000\ 000\ 05^{4}$.
Give your answer in standard form.

$(0.000\ 000\ 000\ 05)^{4} = (5 \times 10^{-11})^{4}$

To do the calculation enter the following sequence into your calculator.

| 5 | Exp | 1 | 1 | +/− | x^{y} | 4 | = |

This gives the calculator display: 6.25   −42

$0.000\ 000\ 000\ 05^{4} = 6.25 \times 10^{-42}$

Remember:
The calculator display **must** be changed to either **standard form** or an **ordinary number**.

Solving problems involving large and small numbers

Problems can involve numbers given in standard form.

EXAMPLE

The following figures refer to the population of China and the USA in 1993.
        China 1.01×10^{9} USA 2.32×10^{8}

(a) By how much did the population of China
exceed that of the USA in 1993?
(b) Calculate the total population of the two countries
in 1993.

$1.01 \times 10^{9} > 2.32 \times 10^{8}$
The greater the power …
… the bigger the number.

(a) You need to work out $1.01 \times 10^{9} - 2.32 \times 10^{8}$
To do the calculation enter the following sequence into your calculator.

| 1 | . | 0 | 1 | Exp | 9 | − | 2 | . | 3 | 2 | Exp | 8 | = |

Giving: $1.01 \times 10^{9} - 2.32 \times 10^{8} = 778\ 000\ 000 = 7.78 \times 10^{8}$

(b) You need to work out $1.01 \times 10^{9} + 2.32 \times 10^{8}$
Enter the following sequence into your calculator.

| 1 | . | 0 | 1 | Exp | 9 | + | 2 | . | 3 | 2 | Exp | 8 | = |

Giving: $1.01 \times 10^{9} + 2.32 \times 10^{8} = 1.242 \times 10^{9}$

*Try this example **without** a calculator.*

Use the $\boxed{\text{Exp}}$ button on your calculator to answer these questions.

1 Give the answers to the following calculations as ordinary numbers.

(a) $(5.25 \times 10^9) \times (5 \times 10^{-5})$ (b) $(5.25 \times 10^9) \div (5 \times 10^{-5})$

(c) $(8.5 \times 10^6)^2$ (d) $(5 \times 10^{-3})^3$

(e) $(7.2 \times 10^5) \div (2.4 \times 10^{-5})$ (f) $(9.5 \times 10^6) \div (1.9 \times 10^{-7})^2$

2 Give the answers to the following calculations in standard form.

(a) $33\,500\,000\,000 \times 2\,800\,000\,000$ (b) $0.000\,000\,000\,2 \times 80\,000\,000\,000$

(c) $15\,000\,000\,000\,000^2$ (d) $0.000\,000\,000\,000\,5^3$

(e) $48\,000\,000\,000 \div 0.000\,000\,000\,2$ (f) $25\,000\,000\,000 \div 500\,000\,000\,000$

3 (a) In 1992 about $1\,400\,000\,000$ steel cans and about $688\,000\,000$ aluminium cans were recycled.

What was the total number of cans that were recycled in 1992?

Give your answer in standard form.

(b) Alpha Centauri is about $40\,350\,000\,000\,000$ km from the Sun.

Alpha Cygni is about $15\,300\,000\,000\,000\,000$ km from the Sun.

How much further is it from the Sun to Alpha Cygni than from the Sun to Alpha Centauri?

Give your answer in standard form.

4 Here are the diameters of some planets.

Saturn 1.2×10^5 km   Jupiter 1.42×10^5 km   Pluto 2.3×10^3 km

(a) List the planets in order of size starting with the smallest.

(b) What is the difference between the diameters of the largest and smallest planets?

Give your answer in standard form and as an ordinary number.

5 Here are the areas of some of the world's largest deserts.

The Sahara desert in North Africa	8.6×10^6 km²
The Gobi desert in Mongolia and North East China	1.166×10^6 km²
The Patagonian desert in Argentina	6.73×10^5 km²

(a) What is the total area of the Sahara and Patagonian deserts?

(b) What is the difference in area between the Gobi and the Patagonian deserts?

Give your answer in standard form.

6 Calculate $5.42 \times 10^6 \times 4.65 \times 10^5$

giving your answer in standard form correct to 3 significant figures.

7 Calculate $1.7 \times 10^3 \div 7.6 \times 10^7$

giving your answer in standard form correct to 2 significant figures.

8 Calculate $2.3 \times 10^{-3} \times 9.8 \times 10^{-5}$

giving your answer in standard form to an appropriate degree of accuracy.

9 Calculate $2.76 \times 10^{-5} \div 9.68 \times 10^{-3}$

giving your answer in standard form to an appropriate degree of accuracy.

10 The mass of an oxygen atom is 2.7×10^{-23} grams.

The mass of an electron at rest is approximately 30 000 times smaller than this.

Estimate the mass of an electron at rest.

11 The modern human appeared on the Earth about 3.5×10^4 years ago.

The Earth has been in existence for something like 1.3×10^5 times as long as this.

(a) Estimate the age of the Earth.

Reptiles appeared on the Earth about 2.3×10^8 years ago.

(b) How many times longer than the modern human have reptiles been alive?

Give your answer in standard form.

In some standard form problems the calculations can be handled without using a calculator.

EXAMPLES

1 Calculate the value of $(3 \times 10^2) + (4 \times 10^3)$.
Give your answer in standard form.

$3 \times 10^2 = 300 \qquad 4 \times 10^3 = 4000$
$$(3 \times 10^2) + (4 \times 10^3) = 300 + 4000$$
$$= 4300$$
$$= 4.3 \times 10^3$$

> When adding or subtracting numbers in standard form without a calculator change to ordinary numbers first.

2 Calculate the value of ab where
$a = 8 \times 10^3$ and $b = 4 \times 10^5$.

$$ab = (8 \times 10^3) \times (4 \times 10^5)$$
$$= 8 \times 4 \times 10^3 \times 10^5$$
$$= 32 \times 10^8$$
$$= 3.2 \times 10 \times 10^8$$
$$= 3.2 \times 10^9$$

> When **multiplying** the powers are **added**.
> $10^3 \times 10^5 = 10^{3+5} = 10^8$
> $10 \times 10^8 = 10^{1+8} = 10^9$

3 Calculate the value of x^2 where $x = 7 \times 10^{-8}$.

$$x^2 = (7 \times 10^{-8})^2$$
$$= 49 \times 10^{-16}$$
$$= 4.9 \times 10 \times 10^{-16}$$
$$= 4.9 \times 10^{-15}$$

> **Remember:**
> $(7 \times 10^{-8})^2 = 7^2 \times (10^{-8})^2$
> $10 \times 10^{-16} = 10^{1-16} = 10^{-15}$

4 Calculate the value of $(1.2 \times 10^3) \div (4 \times 10^{-8})$.

$$(1.2 \times 10^3) \div (4 \times 10^{-8}) = (1.2 \div 4) \times (10^3 \div 10^{-8})$$
$$= 0.3 \times 10^{11}$$
$$= 3 \times 10^{-1} \times 10^{11}$$
$$= 3 \times 10^{10}$$

> When **dividing** the powers are **subtracted**.
> $10^3 \div 10^{-8} = 10^{3--8} = 10^{11}$

Exercise 13.4

Do not use a calculator. Give your answers in standard form.

1 For each of the following calculate the value of $p + q$.
(a) $p = 5 \times 10^3$ and $q = 2 \times 10^2$
(b) $p = 4 \times 10^5$ and $q = 8 \times 10^6$
(c) $p = 3.08 \times 10^4$ and $q = 9.2 \times 10^3$
(d) $p = 4.25 \times 10^4$ and $q = 7.5 \times 10^3$

2 For each of the following calculate the value of $p - q$.
(a) $p = 3 \times 10^3$ and $q = 2 \times 10^2$
(b) $p = 9.05 \times 10^5$ and $q = 5 \times 10^3$
(c) $p = 3.05 \times 10^7$ and $q = 5 \times 10^5$
(d) $p = 9.545 \times 10^8$ and $q = 4.5 \times 10^6$

3 For each of the following calculate the value of $p \times q$.
(a) $p = 4 \times 10^3$ and $q = 2 \times 10^4$
(b) $p = 2 \times 10^4$ and $q = 3 \times 10^3$
(c) $p = 4 \times 10^5$ and $q = 6 \times 10^2$
(d) $p = 9 \times 10^9$ and $q = 3 \times 10^5$

4 For each of the following calculate the value of $p \div q$.
(a) $p = 6 \times 10^5$ and $q = 2 \times 10^2$
(b) $p = 9 \times 10^5$ and $q = 3 \times 10^2$
(c) $p = 2.5 \times 10^5$ and $q = 5 \times 10^3$
(d) $p = 4 \times 10^8$ and $q = 2 \times 10^{-3}$
(e) $p = 1.2 \times 10^3$ and $q = 3 \times 10^{-3}$
(f) $p = 1.5 \times 10^{-5}$ and $q = 5 \times 10^{-3}$

5 $x = 3 \times 10^4$ and $y = 5 \times 10^{-5}$. Work out the value of each of these expressions.
(a) xy
(b) x^3
(c) x^2y
(d) y^3
(e) $\dfrac{x}{y}$

6 Find the value of each of the following.

(a) $(5 \times 10^6) \times (3 \times 10^4)$ (b) $(8 \times 10^{-5}) \times (3 \times 10^7)$

(c) $(7 \times 10^{-5}) \times (6 \times 10^{-4})$ (d) $(8 \times 10^3)^2$

(e) $(4 \times 10^5) \div (8 \times 10^3)$ (f) $(1.8 \times 10^3) \div (6 \times 10^{-7})$

(g) $(5 \times 10^{-7}) \div (8 \times 10^{-2})$ (h) $(2 \times 10^4) \div (8 \times 10^{-1})$

What you need to know

- **Standard index form**, or **standard form**, is a shorthand way of writing very large and very small numbers.

- In **standard form** a number is written as: **a number between 1 and 10 × a power of 10**.
  Large numbers (ten, or more) have a **positive** power of 10.
  Small numbers (less than one) have a **negative** power of 10.

Review Exercise 13

Try to do questions 1 and 2 without using your calculator.

1 In the box are six numbers written in standard form.

| 8.3×10^4 | 3.9×10^5 | 6.7×10^{-3} | 9.245×10^{-1} | 8.36×10^3 | 4.15×10^{-2} |

(a) (i) Write down the largest number.   (ii) Write your answer as an ordinary number.

(b) (i) Write down the smallest number.   (ii) Write your answer as an ordinary number.

AQA

2 The number p written in standard form is 8×10^5.
The number q written in standard form is 5×10^{-2}.

(a) Calculate $p \times q$. Give your answer in standard form.

(b) Calculate $p \div q$. Give your answer in standard form.   *AQA*

3 (a) Write 34 500 000 000 in standard form.

(b) Write 0.000 000 543 in standard form.

(c) Work out $\dfrac{7.2 \times 10^5}{6.4 \times 10^3}$. Give your answer in standard form.   *AQA*

4 $p = 1.65 \times 10^7$, $q = 4.82 \times 10^6$ and $r = 6.17 \times 10^{-2}$.

Calculate the value of the following. Give your answers in standard form.

(a) $2p + 3q$ (b) $p \div r$ *AQA*

5 In 1998, the population of Scotland was 5 137 000.

(a) Write this population in standard form.

(b) In 1998, there was, on average in Scotland, one doctor for every 72.2 people.
How many doctors were there in Scotland?
Give your answer in standard form to an approximate degree of accuracy.   *AQA*

6 In 2002, a company paid out a total of £1.14 × 10¹⁰ in wages to 0.63 million employees.
Calculate the average annual wage per employee.
Give your answer in standard form correct to three significant figures.

7 Last year the population of the United Kingdom was approximately 5.9×10^7.

(a) An average of £680 per person was spent on food last year in the UK.
What was the total amount spent on food last year in the UK?
Give your answer in standard form.

(b) Last year there were 1.4×10^7 car drivers in the UK.
They spent a total of £1.5 × 10¹⁰ on their cars.
What was the average amount spent by each car driver?
Give your answer to a suitable degree of accuracy.   *AQA*

CHAPTER 14

Fractions

Shaded fractions

What fraction of this rectangle is shaded?

The rectangle is divided into **eight** squares.
The squares are all the same size.
Three of the squares are shaded.

$\frac{3}{8}$ of the rectangle is shaded.

In a fraction:
The top number is called the **numerator**.
The bottom number is called the **denominator**.

Activity

What fraction of each of these rectangles is shaded?

| P | Q | R | S |

Which rectangles have the same fraction shaded?

Equivalent fractions

Fractions which are equal are called **equivalent fractions**.

Rectangle Q has $\frac{3}{12}$ shaded, $\frac{3}{12} = \frac{1}{4}$.

Rectangle S has $\frac{6}{24}$ shaded, $\frac{6}{24} = \frac{1}{4}$.

Each of the fractions $\frac{1}{4}$, $\frac{3}{12}$, $\frac{6}{24}$, is the same fraction written in different ways.

These fractions are all equivalent to $\frac{1}{4}$.

Write down two more fractions equivalent to $\frac{1}{4}$.

To write an equivalent fraction:
Multiply the numerator and denominator by the **same** number.

For example. $\frac{1}{4} = \frac{1 \times 3}{4 \times 3} = \frac{3}{12}$

$\frac{1}{4} = \frac{1 \times 6}{4 \times 6} = \frac{6}{24}$

EXAMPLES

1 Write down three fractions equivalent to $\frac{5}{7}$.

The numerators are any multiples of 5.
For example: 5, 10, 15, 20, ...

The denominators are the same multiples of 7: 7, 14, 21, 28, ...
This gives the fractions: $\frac{5}{7}$, $\frac{10}{14}$, $\frac{15}{21}$, $\frac{20}{28}$, ...

2 The fraction $\frac{2}{3}$ is equivalent to the fraction $\frac{?}{12}$.
Find the value of the unknown numerator.

3 has been multiplied by 4 to get 12.
So 2 must also be multiplied by 4 to get the unknown numerator.
The unknown numerator is 8.

Simplifying fractions

Fractions can be simplified if the numerator and denominator have a common factor.
In its **simplest form**, the numerator and denominator of a fraction have no common factor other than 1.

To write a fraction in its simplest form divide the numerator and denominator of the fraction by their highest common factor.
This is sometimes called **cancelling** a fraction.

The numerator and denominator of $\frac{15}{25}$ have a highest common factor of 5.

$$\frac{15}{25} = \frac{15 \div 5}{25 \div 5} = \frac{3}{5}$$

3 and 5 have no common factors, other than 1.

$$\frac{15}{25} = \frac{3}{5} \text{ in its simplest form.}$$

Remember:
Multiplication and division are inverse (opposite) operations.
Equivalent fractions can also be made by dividing the numerator and denominator of a fraction by the same number.

EXAMPLES

1 Simplify $\frac{24}{30}$.

The highest common factor of 24 and 30 is 6.

$$\frac{24}{30} = \frac{24 \div 6}{30 \div 6} = \frac{4}{5}$$

2 In a class of 28 pupils there are 12 boys.
What fraction of the pupils are boys?
Write this fraction in its simplest form.

There are 12 out of 28 boys.

The fraction of boys $= \frac{12}{28}$

$$\frac{12}{28} = \frac{12 \div 4}{28 \div 4} = \frac{3}{7}$$

$\frac{12}{28} = \frac{3}{7}$ in its simplest form.

3 Write 42 as a fraction of 70.

42 as a fraction of 70 is $\frac{42}{70}$

2 is a common factor of 42 and 70.

$$\frac{42}{70} = \frac{42 \div 2}{70 \div 2} = \frac{21}{35}$$

7 is a common factor of 21 and 35.

$$\frac{21}{35} = \frac{21 \div 7}{35 \div 7} = \frac{3}{5}$$

$\frac{42}{70} = \frac{3}{5}$ in its simplest form.

We could have divided by 14.

$$\frac{42}{70} = \frac{42 \div 14}{70 \div 14} = \frac{3}{5}$$

Exercise 14.1

1 What fraction of each of these diagrams is shaded?

(a)　　　(b)　　　(c)　　　(d)

2 Write three equivalent fractions for the shaded part of this rectangle.

What is the simplest form of the fraction for the shaded part?

3 Look at these diagrams.

P   Q   R   S

(a) Which diagram has $\frac{3}{12}$ shaded? (b) Which diagram has $\frac{1}{4}$ shaded?

(c) Which diagram has $\frac{6}{15}$ shaded? (d) Which diagram has $\frac{2}{5}$ shaded?

(e) Which diagram has $\frac{1}{2}$ shaded? (f) Which diagram has $\frac{1}{3}$ shaded?

4 What fraction of each of these shapes is shaded? Give your answers in their simplest form.

(a)   (b)   (c)   (d)   (e)

5 Write down three fractions equivalent to:

(a) $\frac{1}{3}$ (b) $\frac{2}{9}$ (c) $\frac{5}{8}$ (d) $\frac{4}{5}$ (e) $\frac{3}{10}$ (f) $\frac{7}{12}$

6 Each of these pairs of fractions are equivalent.
In each case find the value of n.

(a) $\frac{1}{3}, \frac{n}{6}$ (b) $\frac{n}{8}, \frac{6}{16}$ (c) $\frac{5}{n}, \frac{15}{18}$ (d) $\frac{n}{4}, \frac{12}{16}$ (e) $\frac{24}{64}, \frac{3}{n}$ (f) $\frac{n}{12}, \frac{56}{96}$

7 Write each of these fractions in its simplest form.

(a) $\frac{6}{8}$ (b) $\frac{12}{15}$ (c) $\frac{18}{27}$ (d) $\frac{22}{99}$ (e) $\frac{50}{75}$ (f) $\frac{16}{40}$ (g) $\frac{12}{50}$ (h) $\frac{52}{65}$

8 Write the first number as a fraction of the second.
Write the fractions in their simplest form.

(a) 4, 20 (b) 3, 12 (c) 8, 12 (d) 24, 60 (e) 60, 105

9 Mr Jones plans a car journey.
(a) The journey is 50 km long. Mr Jones plans to stop after 35 km.
What fraction of the total distance is this?
Give your answer in its simplest form.
(b) The journey takes 60 minutes which includes a 12-minute stop.
For what fraction of the total time does Mr Jones stop on his journey?
Give your answer in its simplest form.

10 A group of students were asked some questions about how they travelled to school.
$\frac{1}{2}$ of the students said they walked. $\frac{1}{3}$ of the students said they travelled by bus.

In the group there were more than 20 students and less than 30.
(a) How many students were in the group?

The rest of the group came by car.
(b) What fraction of the group came by car?
Give your answer in its simplest form.

Types of fractions

This diagram shows that when 5 cakes are shared equally between 2 people they get $2\frac{1}{2}$ cakes each.

This diagram shows that when 5 cakes are shared equally between 4 people they get $1\frac{1}{4}$ cakes each.

Numbers like $2\frac{1}{2}$ and $1\frac{1}{4}$ are called **mixed numbers** because they are a mixture of whole numbers and fractions.

Mixed numbers can be written as **improper** or '**top heavy**' fractions.

These are fractions where the numerator is larger than the denominator.

EXAMPLES

1 Write $3\frac{4}{7}$ as an improper fraction.

$3\frac{4}{7} = \frac{(3 \times 7) + 4}{7} = \frac{21 + 4}{7} = \frac{25}{7}$

2 Write $\frac{32}{5}$ as a mixed number.

$32 \div 5 = 6$ remainder 2.

$\frac{32}{5} = 6\frac{2}{5}$

Finding fractions of quantities

EXAMPLES

1 Find $\frac{3}{10}$ of 100.

Divide 100 into 10 equal parts.
$100 \div 10 = 10$.

10	10	10	10	10	10	10	10	10	10

Each of these parts is $\frac{1}{10}$ of 100.

Three of these parts is $\frac{3}{10}$ of 100.

10	10	10	10	10	10	10	10	10	10

So $\frac{3}{10}$ of 100 = $3 \times 10 = 30$.

2 Find $\frac{2}{5}$ of £65.

Divide £65 into 5 equal parts.
£65 $\div$ 5 = £13.

13	13	13	13	13

Each of these parts is $\frac{1}{5}$ of £65.

Two of these parts is $\frac{2}{5}$ of £65.

13	13	13	13	13

So $\frac{2}{5}$ of £65 = $2 \times £13 = £26$.

Exercise 14.2

Do not use a calculator in questions 1 to 3.

1 Change the following improper fractions to mixed numbers:

(a) $\frac{13}{10}$ (b) $\frac{3}{2}$ (c) $\frac{17}{8}$ (d) $\frac{15}{4}$ (e) $\frac{23}{5}$ (f) $\frac{34}{7}$

2 Change the following mixed numbers to improper fractions:

(a) $2\frac{7}{10}$ (b) $1\frac{3}{5}$ (c) $5\frac{5}{6}$ (d) $3\frac{3}{20}$ (e) $4\frac{5}{9}$ (f) $7\frac{4}{7}$

3 Calculate:

(a) $\frac{1}{4}$ of 12 (b) $\frac{1}{5}$ of 20 (c) $\frac{1}{10}$ of 30 (d) $\frac{1}{6}$ of 48

(e) $\frac{2}{5}$ of 20 (f) $\frac{3}{10}$ of 30 (g) $\frac{2}{7}$ of 42 (h) $\frac{5}{9}$ of 36

4 Calculate:

(a) $\frac{3}{10} \times 8$ (b) $\frac{3}{8} \times 20$ (c) $\frac{5}{6} \times 9$ (d) $\frac{4}{5} \times 12$

5 Tom earns £9 per hour. Sam earns $\frac{2}{3}$ of what Tom earns.
How much does Sam earn in 10 hours?

6 Aisha has 36 balloons. She sells $\frac{2}{9}$ of them.
How many balloons has she got left?

7 Alfie collects £120 for charity. He gives $\frac{3}{5}$ of it to Oxfam.
How much does he give to other charities?

8 A coat costing £138 is reduced by $\frac{1}{3}$.
Find the new price of the coat.

9 In a sale of electrical goods all items are reduced by $\frac{3}{8}$.
What is the sale price of a microwave which was originally priced at £212?

10 Lauren and Amelia share a bar of chocolate. The chocolate bar has 24 squares.
Lauren eats $\frac{3}{8}$ of the bar.   Amelia eats $\frac{5}{12}$ of the bar.
(a) How many squares has Lauren eaten?
(b) How many squares has Amelia eaten?
(c) What fraction of the bar is left?

11 Andy, Bill and Chris share a bag of sweets. There are 60 sweets in the bag.
Andy eats $\frac{1}{6}$ of the sweets.   Bill eats $\frac{5}{12}$ of the sweets.   Chris eats $\frac{1}{5}$ of the sweets.
(a) (i) How many sweets has Andy eaten?
     (ii) How many sweets has Bill eaten?
     (iii) How many sweets has Chris eaten?
(b) What fraction of the sweets are left?

12 A publisher offers a discount of $\frac{3}{20}$ for orders of more than 100 books.
How much would a shop pay for an order of 250 books costing £12.50 each?

Adding and subtracting fractions

There are 12 sweets in a packet. Alena eats $\frac{2}{3}$ of the sweets and Sead eats $\frac{1}{4}$ of the sweets.
What fraction of the packet of sweets have they eaten altogether?

Alena eats $\frac{2}{3}$ of the sweets in the packet.
$$\frac{2}{3} \text{ of } 12 = 8 \qquad \frac{2}{3} = \frac{8}{12}$$

Sead eats $\frac{1}{4}$ of the sweets in the packet.
$$\frac{1}{4} \text{ of } 12 = 3 \qquad \frac{1}{4} = \frac{3}{12}$$

Together Alena and Sead eat $\frac{2}{3} + \frac{1}{4}$ of the packet.
$$\frac{2}{3} + \frac{1}{4} = \frac{8}{12} + \frac{3}{12} = \frac{11}{12}$$

Together Alena and Sead eat $\frac{11}{12}$ of the packet.

How to add and subtract fractions

Calculate $1\frac{7}{10} + \frac{5}{6}$

Change mixed numbers to improper ('top heavy') fractions.

$$1\frac{7}{10} = \frac{17}{10}$$

The calculation then becomes $\frac{17}{10} + \frac{5}{6}$

Find the **least** common multiple of the denominators (bottom numbers).

Least common multiple of 10 and 6 is 30.

Change the fractions to equivalent fractions using the least common multiple as the new denominator.

$$\frac{17}{10} = \frac{51}{30} \quad \text{and} \quad \frac{5}{6} = \frac{25}{30}$$

Add the new numerators. Keep the new denominator the same.

$$\frac{51}{30} + \frac{25}{30} = \frac{51 + 25}{30} = \frac{76}{30}$$

Write the answer in its simplest form.

$$\frac{76}{30} = 2\frac{16}{30} = 2\frac{8}{15}$$

Fractions must have the **same denominator** before addition (or subtraction) can take place.

*What happens when you use a common multiple that is **not** the least?*

EXAMPLES

1 Work out $\frac{1}{2} + \frac{1}{3}$.

The least common multiple of 2 and 3 is 6.

$$\frac{1}{2} = \frac{3}{6} \quad \text{and} \quad \frac{1}{3} = \frac{2}{6}$$

$$\frac{1}{2} + \frac{1}{3} = \frac{3}{6} + \frac{2}{6}$$

$$= \frac{5}{6}$$

Remember to add the numerators only.

2 Calculate $3\frac{3}{10} - 1\frac{5}{6}$.

$$3\frac{3}{10} = \frac{33}{10} \quad \text{and} \quad 1\frac{5}{6} = \frac{11}{6}$$

The least common multiple of 10 and 6 is 30.

$$\frac{33}{10} = \frac{99}{30} \quad \text{and} \quad \frac{11}{6} = \frac{55}{30}$$

$$3\frac{3}{10} - 1\frac{5}{6} = \frac{99}{30} - \frac{55}{30} = \frac{44}{30}$$

$$\frac{44}{30} = \frac{22}{15} = 1\frac{7}{15}$$

3 Work out $\frac{3}{4} + \frac{2}{3}$.

$$\frac{3}{4} + \frac{2}{3} = \frac{9}{12} + \frac{8}{12}$$

$$= \frac{17}{12} = 1\frac{5}{12}$$

When the answer is an improper fraction change it into a mixed number.

Exercise **14.3**

Do not use a calculator in this exercise.

1 Work out:

(a) $\frac{1}{4} + \frac{1}{8}$ (b) $\frac{1}{3} + \frac{1}{4}$ (c) $\frac{1}{2} + \frac{1}{5}$ (d) $\frac{1}{3} + \frac{1}{5}$ (e) $\frac{1}{2} + \frac{1}{7}$ (f) $\frac{1}{4} + \frac{1}{5}$

2 Work out:

(a) $\frac{1}{4} - \frac{1}{8}$ (b) $\frac{1}{3} - \frac{1}{4}$ (c) $\frac{1}{2} - \frac{1}{5}$ (d) $\frac{1}{3} - \frac{1}{5}$ (e) $\frac{1}{2} - \frac{1}{7}$ (f) $\frac{1}{4} - \frac{1}{5}$

3 Work out:

(a) $\frac{1}{2} + \frac{3}{4}$ (b) $\frac{2}{3} + \frac{5}{6}$ (c) $\frac{3}{4} + \frac{4}{5}$ (d) $\frac{5}{7} + \frac{2}{3}$ (e) $\frac{3}{8} + \frac{5}{6}$ (f) $\frac{2}{5} + \frac{3}{4}$

4 Calculate:

(a) $\frac{5}{8} - \frac{1}{2}$ (b) $\frac{13}{15} - \frac{1}{3}$ (c) $\frac{5}{6} - \frac{5}{24}$ (d) $\frac{7}{9} - \frac{2}{5}$ (e) $\frac{7}{8} - \frac{2}{3}$ (f) $\frac{13}{16} - \frac{5}{12}$

5 Calculate:

(a) $2\frac{3}{4} + 1\frac{1}{2}$ (b) $1\frac{1}{2} + 2\frac{1}{3}$ (c) $1\frac{3}{4} + 2\frac{5}{8}$ (d) $2\frac{1}{4} + 3\frac{3}{5}$ (e) $4\frac{3}{5} + 1\frac{5}{6}$ (f) $3\frac{3}{10} + 2\frac{3}{20}$

6 Calculate:

(a) $2\frac{1}{2} - 1\frac{2}{5}$ (b) $1\frac{2}{3} - 1\frac{1}{4}$ (c) $3\frac{3}{8} - 2\frac{3}{4}$ (d) $5\frac{2}{5} - 2\frac{1}{10}$ (e) $4\frac{3}{10} - 2\frac{5}{8}$ (f) $3\frac{3}{16} - 2\frac{5}{24}$

7 Colin buys a bag of flour.

He uses $\frac{1}{3}$ to bake a cake and $\frac{1}{2}$ to make a loaf.

(a) What fraction of the bag of flour has he used?

(b) What fraction of the bag of flour is left?

8 Kathryn and Matt share a bottle of cola.

Kathryn drinks $\frac{1}{4}$ of the cola and Matt drinks $\frac{1}{5}$ of the cola.

What fraction of the bottle of cola is left?

9 Billy and Mary both have a packet of the same sweets.

Mary eats $\frac{2}{5}$ of her packet and Billy eats $\frac{3}{4}$ of his packet.

(a) Find the difference between the fraction Mary eats and the fraction Billy eats.

Billy gives his remaining sweets to Mary.

(b) What fraction of a packet does Mary now have?

10 A school has pupils in Years 7 to 13.

$\frac{7}{12}$ of its pupils are in Years 7 to 9 and $\frac{3}{10}$ of its pupils are in Years 10 and 11.

What fraction of the pupils in the school are in Years 12 and 13?

11 Andy, Billy and Cathy are the only candidates in a school election.

Andy got $\frac{7}{20}$ of the votes and Billy got $\frac{5}{16}$ of the votes.

(a) What fraction of the votes did Cathy get?

(b) Which candidate won the election?

12 A bag of sweets contains chocolates, toffees and mints.

$\frac{2}{5}$ are chocolates and there are an equal number of toffees and mints.

What fraction of the sweets are toffees?

Multiplying fractions

There are 12 sweets in a packet.

Alena gives $\frac{2}{3}$ of the sweets in the packet to Sead.

$\frac{2}{3}$ of 12 = 8

Sead eats $\frac{3}{4}$ of the sweets that Alena gives him.

$\frac{3}{4}$ of 8 = 6

Sead eats $\frac{6}{12}$ of the whole packet.

So ... $\frac{2}{3}$ of $\frac{3}{4} = \frac{6}{12} = \frac{1}{2}$

This shows that $\frac{2}{3} \times \frac{3}{4} = \frac{2 \times 3}{3 \times 4} = \frac{6}{12} = \frac{1}{2}$

166

How to multiply fractions

Calculate $2\frac{2}{5} \times 3\frac{1}{4}$

Change mixed numbers to improper ('top heavy') fractions.

$2\frac{2}{5} = \frac{12}{5}$ and $3\frac{1}{4} = \frac{13}{4}$

The calculation then becomes $\frac{12}{5} \times \frac{13}{4}$

Simplify, where possible, by cancelling. $\frac{\overset{3}{\cancel{12}}}{5} \times \frac{13}{\underset{1}{\cancel{4}}}$

Multiply the numerators.
Multiply the denominators. $\frac{3 \times 13}{5 \times 1} = \frac{39}{5}$

Write the answer in its simplest form. $\frac{39}{5} = 7\frac{4}{5}$

To simplify:
Divide a numerator **and** a denominator by the **same number.**

In this case:
12 and 4 can be divided by 4.
$12 \div 4 = 3$ and $4 \div 4 = 1$.

EXAMPLES

1 Work out $\frac{3}{5} \times \frac{10}{21}$

$\frac{3}{5} \times \frac{10}{21}$

Simplify by cancelling.

$= \frac{\overset{1}{\cancel{3}}}{5} \times \frac{\overset{2}{\cancel{10}}}{\underset{7}{\cancel{21}}}$

Multiply out.

$= \frac{1 \times 2}{1 \times 7}$

$= \frac{2}{7}$

2 Calculate $1\frac{1}{2} \times 1\frac{3}{5}$

Change mixed numbers to improper fractions.

$1\frac{1}{2} \times 1\frac{3}{5} = \frac{3}{2} \times \frac{8}{5}$

Simplify by cancelling.

$= \frac{3}{\underset{1}{\cancel{2}}} \times \frac{\overset{4}{\cancel{8}}}{5}$

Multiply out.

$= \frac{3 \times 4}{1 \times 5} = \frac{12}{5} = 2\frac{2}{5}$

Exercise 14.4

Do not use a calculator in this exercise.

1 Work out:

(a) $\frac{1}{2} \times \frac{1}{3}$

(b) $\frac{1}{4} \times \frac{1}{5}$

(c) $\frac{3}{5} \times \frac{1}{6}$

(d) $\frac{5}{7} \times \frac{1}{3}$

(e) $\frac{2}{3} \times \frac{1}{4}$

(f) $1\frac{1}{4} \times \frac{1}{5}$

(g) $2\frac{2}{5} \times \frac{1}{3}$

(h) $2\frac{5}{8} \times \frac{1}{6}$

2 Calculate:

(a) $\frac{1}{2} \times \frac{3}{4}$

(b) $\frac{3}{4} \times \frac{2}{5}$

(c) $\frac{2}{5} \times \frac{5}{6}$

(d) $\frac{2}{3} \times \frac{1}{2}$

(e) $\frac{3}{10} \times \frac{5}{8}$

(f) $\frac{2}{5} \times \frac{1}{7}$

(g) $\frac{3}{4} \times \frac{2}{3}$

(h) $\frac{3}{10} \times \frac{5}{6}$

3 Calculate:

(a) $1\frac{1}{2} \times \frac{3}{4}$

(b) $1\frac{1}{2} \times 1\frac{1}{3}$

(c) $2\frac{1}{4} \times 1\frac{2}{3}$

(d) $2\frac{3}{4} \times 1\frac{2}{5}$

(e) $1\frac{1}{2} \times 3\frac{1}{4}$

(f) $1\frac{3}{5} \times 1\frac{1}{6}$

(g) $6\frac{3}{10} \times 2\frac{2}{9}$

(h) $3\frac{3}{4} \times 3\frac{3}{5}$

4 Calculate:

(a) $\frac{4}{5}$ of $3\frac{1}{4}$

(b) $\frac{2}{3}$ of $5\frac{1}{4}$

(c) $\frac{3}{4}$ of $7\frac{1}{5}$

(d) $\frac{4}{5}$ of $3\frac{1}{8}$

(e) $\frac{3}{8}$ of $3\frac{5}{9}$

(f) $\frac{5}{6}$ of $4\frac{2}{7}$

(g) $\frac{5}{8}$ of $1\frac{1}{15}$

(h) $\frac{3}{10}$ of $4\frac{4}{9}$

5 Spencer has $\frac{1}{4}$ of a pint of milk. He uses $\frac{1}{2}$ of the milk.

(a) What fraction of a pint does he use?   (b) What fraction of a pint is left?

6 Kylie has $\frac{2}{3}$ of a litre of orange. She drinks $\frac{2}{5}$ of the orange.

(a) What fraction of a litre does she drink?   (b) What fraction of a litre is left?

7 Tony eats $\frac{1}{5}$ of a bag of sweets.

He shares the remaining sweets equally among Bob, Jo and David.
(a) What fraction of the bag of sweets does Bob get?
(b) What is the smallest possible number of sweets in the bag?

Dividing fractions

Activity

The diagram shows $1\frac{1}{2}$ divided into $\frac{1}{6}$'s.

Use the diagram to explain why …

(a) $1\frac{1}{2} \div \frac{1}{6} = 9$

(b) $1\frac{1}{2} \div \frac{1}{3} = 4\frac{1}{2}$

(c) $1\frac{1}{2} \div \frac{2}{3} = 2\frac{1}{4}$

Think of each of these as …

(a) How many $\frac{1}{6}$'s in $1\frac{1}{2}$?

(b) How many $\frac{1}{3}$'s in $1\frac{1}{2}$?

(c) How many $\frac{2}{3}$'s in $1\frac{1}{2}$?

How to divide fractions

The method normally used when one fraction is divided by another is to change the division to a multiplication. The fractions can then be multiplied in the usual way.

$$\text{Calculate} \quad 2\frac{2}{15} \div 1\frac{3}{5}$$

Change mixed numbers to improper ('top heavy') fractions. $\quad 2\frac{2}{15} = \frac{32}{15}$ and $1\frac{3}{5} = \frac{8}{5}$

Change the division to a multiplication. $\quad \frac{32}{15} \div \frac{8}{5} = \frac{32}{15} \times \frac{5}{8}$

Simplify, where possible, by cancelling. $\quad \dfrac{\overset{4}{\cancel{32}}}{\underset{3}{\cancel{15}}} \times \dfrac{\overset{1}{\cancel{5}}}{\underset{1}{\cancel{8}}}$

Multiply the numerators. $\quad \frac{4 \times 1}{3 \times 1} = \frac{4}{3}$
Multiply the denominators.

Write the answer in its simplest form. $\quad \frac{4}{3} = 1\frac{1}{3}$

EXAMPLES

1 Work out $\frac{2}{3} \div 5$.

$\frac{2}{3} \div 5$

$= \frac{2}{3} \times \frac{1}{5}$

$= \frac{2}{15}$

> Divide by 5 is the same as multiply by $\frac{1}{5}$.

2 Calculate $1\frac{3}{5} \div \frac{4}{9}$.

$1\frac{3}{5} \div \frac{4}{9} = \frac{8}{5} \div \frac{4}{9}$

$\qquad = \frac{8}{5} \times \frac{9}{4}$

$\qquad = \frac{\overset{2}{\cancel{8}}}{5} \times \frac{9}{\underset{1}{\cancel{4}}}$

$\qquad = \frac{18}{5} = 3\frac{3}{5}$

> Divide by $\frac{4}{9}$ is the same as multiply by $\frac{9}{4}$.

Do not use a calculator in this exercise.   ⑭

1 Work out.

(a) $\frac{1}{2} \div 5$ (b) $\frac{3}{4} \div 2$ (c) $\frac{2}{5} \div 4$ (d) $1\frac{2}{3} \div 5$ (e) $1\frac{5}{7} \div 3$ (f) $3\frac{1}{9} \div 7$

2 Calculate.

(a) $\frac{1}{2} \div \frac{1}{4}$ (b) $\frac{1}{5} \div \frac{1}{2}$ (c) $\frac{7}{8} \div \frac{1}{3}$ (d) $\frac{2}{3} \div \frac{1}{5}$ (e) $2\frac{3}{4} \div \frac{1}{8}$ (f) $1\frac{2}{9} \div \frac{1}{6}$

3 Calculate:

(a) $\frac{2}{3} \div \frac{4}{5}$ (b) $\frac{3}{8} \div \frac{2}{3}$ (c) $\frac{3}{5} \div \frac{3}{4}$ (d) $\frac{2}{5} \div \frac{3}{10}$ (e) $\frac{3}{8} \div \frac{9}{16}$ (f) $\frac{7}{12} \div \frac{7}{18}$

(g) $\frac{4}{9} \div \frac{2}{3}$ (h) $\frac{7}{10} \div \frac{3}{5}$ (i) $\frac{9}{20} \div \frac{3}{10}$ (j) $\frac{21}{25} \div \frac{7}{15}$

4 Calculate:

(a) $2\frac{3}{4} \div 4\frac{1}{8}$ (b) $1\frac{1}{2} \div 1\frac{1}{11}$ (c) $1\frac{3}{5} \div 1\frac{2}{5}$ (d) $6\frac{3}{10} \div 1\frac{7}{20}$ (e) $3\frac{3}{4} \div \frac{5}{18}$

(f) $1\frac{1}{4} \div 1\frac{9}{16}$ (g) $3\frac{1}{5} \div 2\frac{2}{15}$ (h) $2\frac{1}{4} \div 1\frac{4}{5}$ (i) $4\frac{2}{7} \div 1\frac{7}{8}$ (j) $5\frac{2}{5} \div 1\frac{2}{3}$

5 A shelf is $40\frac{3}{4}$ cm long.

(a) How many books of width $1\frac{9}{10}$ cm can stand on the shelf?

(b) How many videos of width $1\frac{3}{4}$ cm can stand on the shelf?

In each case how much space is left on the shelf?

6 (a) $3\frac{3}{4}$ is multiplied by a number to give $2\frac{2}{3}$. What is the number?

(b) The product of two numbers is 4. One of the numbers is $1\frac{2}{3}$. What is the other number?

7 A jug contains $1\frac{3}{4}$ litres of milk.

Mrs Jones makes a rice pudding with $1\frac{1}{3}$ litres of the milk in the jug.

What fraction of the milk in the jug does Mrs Jones use to make the rice pudding?

Problems involving fractions

EXAMPLES

1 Jenny spends $\frac{3}{5}$ of her money.

She has £1.40 left.

How much money did she start with?

Jenny has $1 - \frac{3}{5}$ of her money left.

$$1 - \frac{3}{5} = \frac{2}{5}$$

$\frac{2}{5}$ of Jenny's money is £1.40.

$\frac{1}{5}$ of Jenny's money is £1.40 ÷ 2.

Jenny started with $5 \times £0.70 = £3.50$.

2 In an experiment a weight is added to a spring.

The length of the spring increases by $\frac{2}{5}$.

The new length of the spring is 21 cm.

What was the length of the spring before the weight was added?

$$1 + \frac{2}{5} = \frac{7}{5}$$

$\frac{7}{5}$ of the original length is 21 cm.

$\frac{1}{5}$ of the original length is 21 ÷ 7.

The original length is $5 \times 3 = 15$ cm.

Exercise **14.6**   Do not use a calculator in this exercise.

1 Ben spends $\frac{5}{8}$ of his pocket money. He has £1.20 left.

How much pocket money did Ben get?

2 A cyclist travels from A to B in two stages. Stage 1 is 28 km which is $\frac{2}{7}$ of the total journey.

How long is stage 2?

3 Robert pays £9.60 for a CD in the sale. How much did he save?

Music Sale - $\frac{1}{4}$ off all CDs

4 Sara's hourly wage is increased by $\frac{1}{10}$. Her new hourly wage is £6.60. What was her original hourly wage?

5 A young tree is $\frac{3}{8}$ taller in August than it was in May. In August it is 132 centimetres tall. How tall was it in May?

6 A factory produced 231 sofas in May, $\frac{2}{9}$ more than the number of sofas it produced in April. How many sofas did the factory produce in April?

Fractions on a calculator

Fraction calculations can be done quickly using the fraction button on a calculator.
On most calculators the
fraction button looks like this … $\boxed{a^b/_c}$

EXAMPLES

1 Use a calculator to work out $4\frac{3}{5} \div 2\frac{1}{4}$.

This can be calculated with this calculator sequence.

$$\boxed{4}\ \boxed{a^b/_c}\ \boxed{3}\ \boxed{a^b/_c}\ \boxed{5}\ \boxed{\div}\ \boxed{2}\ \boxed{a^b/_c}\ \boxed{1}\ \boxed{a^b/_c}\ \boxed{4}\ \boxed{=}$$

This gives the answer $2\frac{2}{45}$.

2 Calculate $\frac{7}{12}$ of 32.

This can be calculated with this calculator sequence.

$$\boxed{7}\ \boxed{a^b/_c}\ \boxed{1}\ \boxed{2}\ \boxed{\times}\ \boxed{3}\ \boxed{2}\ \boxed{=}$$

This gives the answer $18\frac{2}{3}$.

Use a calculator to check your answers to some of the questions in Exercises 14.3 to 14.6.

Fractions and decimals

All fractions can be written as decimals and vice versa.

Changing decimals to fractions

$0.7 = \frac{7}{10}$ $\qquad$ $0.03 = \frac{3}{100}$ $\qquad$ $0.009 = \frac{9}{1000}$

The place value of numbers written as decimals was first covered in Chapter 9.

0.375 can be written as a fraction.
Using place value:

$0.375 = \frac{3}{10} + \frac{7}{100} + \frac{5}{1000}$

Write equivalent fractions with denominator 1000.

$\frac{3}{10} = \frac{3 \times 100}{10 \times 100} = \frac{300}{1000}$ $\qquad$ $\frac{7}{100} = \frac{7 \times 10}{100 \times 10} = \frac{70}{1000}$

$0.375 = \frac{300}{1000} + \frac{70}{1000} + \frac{5}{1000} = \frac{375}{1000}$

This can be written as a fraction in its simplest form.

$\frac{375}{1000} = \frac{375 \div 125}{1000 \div 125} = \frac{3}{8}$

$0.375 = \frac{375}{1000} = \frac{3}{8}$

Adding fractions with the same denominator
1. Add the numerators.
2. Keep the denominator the same.
Why?

EXAMPLES

Change the following decimals to fractions in their simplest form.

1 0.02 $\quad$ 0.02 $= \frac{2}{100} = \frac{2 \div 2}{100 \div 2} = \frac{1}{50}$

2 0.36 $\quad$ 0.36 $= \frac{36}{100} = \frac{36 \div 4}{100 \div 4} = \frac{9}{25}$

3 0.225 $\quad$ 0.225 $= \frac{225}{1000} = \frac{225 \div 25}{1000 \div 25} = \frac{9}{40}$

Changing fractions to decimals

EXAMPLES

Change the following fractions to decimals.

> **Method 1**
> Write an equivalent fraction with a denominator of 10, 100, 1000, …

> **Method 2**
> $\frac{1}{5}$ means $1 \div 5$.
> $1 \div 5$ can be worked out using: short division, long division or a calculator.

1 $\frac{1}{5} = \frac{1 \times 2}{5 \times 2} = \frac{2}{10} = 0.2$ $\qquad$ $\frac{1}{5} = 1 \div 5 = 0.2$

2 $\frac{11}{20} = \frac{11 \times 5}{20 \times 5} = \frac{55}{100} = 0.55$ $\qquad$ $\frac{11}{20} = 11 \div 20 = 0.55$

Remember:
$11 \div 20 = 11.00 \div 20$

$$\begin{array}{r} 0.5\,5 \\ 20\overline{)1\,1.0\,0}^{\,11\ \,10} \end{array}$$

3 $\frac{3}{8} = \frac{3 \times 125}{8 \times 125} = \frac{375}{1000} = 0.375$ $\qquad$ $\frac{3}{8} = 3 \div 8 = 0.375$

Recurring decimals

Some decimals have recurring digits.
These are shown by:
$\qquad$ a single dot above a single recurring digit,
$\qquad$ a dot above the first and last digit of a set of recurring digits.

For example:

$\frac{1}{3} = 0.3333333… = 0.\dot{3}$

$\frac{123}{999} = 0.123123123… = 0.\dot{1}2\dot{3}$

$\frac{41}{70} = 0.5857142857142… = 0.5\dot{8}5714\dot{2}$

$\frac{3}{11} = 0.27272727… = 0.\dot{2}\dot{7}$

Do not use a calculator for questions 1 to 3.

1 Change the following decimals to fractions in their simplest form.

(a) 0.12   (b) 0.6   (c) 0.32   (d) 0.175   (e) 0.45   (f) 0.65

(g) 0.22   (h) 0.202   (i) 0.28   (j) 0.555   (k) 0.625   (l) 0.84

2 Change the following fractions to decimals.

(a) (i) $\frac{1}{4}$ (ii) $\frac{1}{2}$ (iii) $\frac{3}{4}$

(b) (i) $\frac{1}{10}$ (ii) $\frac{3}{10}$ (iii) $\frac{7}{10}$

(c) (i) $\frac{2}{5}$ (ii) $\frac{3}{5}$ (iii) $\frac{4}{5}$

3 Change the following fractions to decimals.

(a) (i) $\frac{3}{20}$ (ii) $\frac{7}{20}$ (iii) $\frac{19}{20}$

(b) (i) $\frac{4}{25}$ (ii) $\frac{9}{25}$ (iii) $\frac{23}{25}$

(c) (i) $\frac{7}{100}$ (ii) $\frac{23}{100}$ (iii) $\frac{106}{200}$

4 Change these fractions to decimals.

(a) $\frac{1}{8}$ (b) $\frac{5}{8}$ (c) $\frac{9}{40}$ (d) $\frac{29}{40}$

5 Write these decimals using dots to represent recurring digits.

(a) 0.77777...   (b) 0.11111...   (c) 0.363636...   (d) 0.828282...

(e) 0.135135...   (f) 0.216216...   (g) 0.166666...   (h) 0.285714285714...

6 Write each of these fractions as recurring decimals, using dots to represent recurring digits.

(a) $\frac{8}{9}$ (b) $\frac{4}{9}$ (c) $\frac{17}{33}$ (d) $\frac{8}{11}$ (e) $\frac{1}{7}$ (f) $\frac{6}{7}$

(g) $\frac{1}{30}$ (h) $\frac{7}{15}$ (i) $\frac{5}{6}$ (j) $\frac{17}{22}$

7 Change these fractions to decimals. Give your answers correct to two decimal places.

(a) $\frac{1}{3}$ (b) $\frac{2}{3}$ (c) $\frac{3}{7}$ (d) $\frac{5}{11}$ (e) $\frac{7}{9}$ (f) $\frac{5}{13}$

What you need to know

- The top number of a fraction is called the **numerator**, the bottom number is called the **denominator**.

- To write **equivalent fractions**, the numerator and denominator of a fraction are multiplied (or divided) by the **same** number.

  e.g. $\frac{3}{8} = \frac{3 \times 4}{8 \times 4} = \frac{12}{32}$

- In its **simplest form**, the numerator and denominator of a fraction have no common factor, other than 1.

- $2\frac{1}{2}$ is an example of a **mixed number**. It is a mixture of whole numbers and fractions.

- $\frac{5}{2}$ is an **improper** (or '**top heavy**') fraction.

- Fractions must have the **same denominator** before **adding** or **subtracting**.

- Mixed numbers must be changed to **improper fractions** before **multiplying** or **dividing**.

- All fractions can be written as decimals.
  Some decimals have **recurring digits**.
  These are shown by:
    a single dot above a single recurring digit, e.g. $\frac{2}{3} = 0.6666... = 0.\dot{6}$

    a dot above the first and last digit of a set of recurring digits, e.g. $\frac{5}{11} = 0.454545... = 0.\dot{4}\dot{5}$

1 Each of these pairs of fractions are equivalent.
In each case find the value of n.

(a) $\frac{5}{8}$, $\frac{15}{n}$ (b) $\frac{n}{20}$, $\frac{5}{n}$ (c) $\frac{n}{20}$, $\frac{3}{15}$

2 A packet contains 24 biscuits.
Emily eats $\frac{3}{8}$ of the biscuits.
How many biscuits are left?

3

All types of cabins for hire	
Season	Price
Summer	Summer Price
Spring	Pay $\frac{3}{4}$ of Summer Price
Winter	Pay $\frac{1}{3}$ of Summer Price

(a) The summer price of a Standard Cabin is £360.
How much do you pay for a Standard Cabin in Spring?

(b) The winter price of a de luxe Cabin is £180.
How much do you pay for a de luxe Cabin in Spring?   AQA

4 Work out.

(a) $\frac{1}{4} + \frac{2}{3}$ (b) $\frac{2}{5} - \frac{1}{8}$

5 In Jimmy's class $\frac{1}{3}$ of the pupils have blue eyes and $\frac{2}{5}$ have brown eyes.
What fraction of the class do not have blue or brown eyes?

6 36 girls and 24 boys applied to go on a rock climbing course.
$\frac{2}{3}$ of the girls and $\frac{3}{4}$ of the boys went on the course.
What fraction of the 60 students who applied went on the course?
Write the fraction in its simplest form.

7 Change the following decimals to fractions in their simplest form.

(a) 0.4   (b) 0.24   (c) 0.45   (d) 0.125

8 A necklace is made from 60 beads.
$\frac{3}{10}$ of the beads are red.
$\frac{9}{20}$ of the beads are blue.
The rest of the beads are white.
What fraction of the beads are white?
Give this fraction in its simplest form.

9 Calculate:

(a) $2\frac{1}{4} + 3\frac{5}{6}$ (b) $2\frac{5}{7} + 1\frac{4}{9}$

(c) $3\frac{3}{5} - 1\frac{1}{2}$ (d) $4\frac{3}{10} - 1\frac{2}{3}$

(e) $3\frac{3}{4} \times 1\frac{1}{5}$ (f) $2\frac{2}{3} \times 3\frac{3}{4}$

(g) $3\frac{3}{5} \div 2\frac{1}{10}$ (h) $5\frac{1}{4} \div 2\frac{1}{10}$

10 The length of a rectangle is $\frac{2}{3}$ m.
The width of the rectangle is $\frac{3}{8}$ m.

(a) What is the perimeter of the rectangle?
(b) What is the area of the rectangle?

11 In a school $\frac{8}{15}$ of the pupils are girls.
$\frac{3}{16}$ of the girls are left-handed.
What fraction of the pupils in the school are left-handed girls?

12 The price of a coat is reduced by $\frac{2}{5}$ to £48.
What was the original price of the coat?

13 Change the following fractions to decimals.

(a) $\frac{4}{5}$ (b) $\frac{9}{20}$ (c) $\frac{21}{50}$ (d) $\frac{201}{500}$

14 (a) Convert $\frac{1}{7}$ to a decimal, giving your answer correct to three decimal places.

(b) Place the following numbers in order of size, starting with the smallest.

11.14 $1\frac{1}{7}$ 1.14   1.41   1.014
AQA

15 An examination in French is marked out of 80.

(a) Jean scored $\frac{4}{5}$ of the marks.
How many marks did she score?

(b) Tony scored 35 marks.
What fraction of the total did he score?
Give your answer in its simplest form.

16 One kilometre is approximately five eighths of a mile.
The distance by car between Southampton and Birmingham is 130 miles.
What is the distance in kilometres?   AQA

CHAPTER 15

Percentages

The meaning of a percentage

'Per cent' means 'out of 100'.
The symbol for per cent is %.
A percentage can be written as a fraction with denominator 100.

> 10% means 10 out of 100.
>
> 10% can be written as $\frac{10}{100}$.
>
> 10% is read as '10 percent'.

Changing percentages to decimals and fractions

To change a percentage to a decimal or a fraction: **divide by 100**

EXAMPLES

1 Write 38% as a fraction in its simplest form.

38% means '38 out of 100'.

This can be written as $\frac{38}{100}$.

$\frac{38}{100} = \frac{38 \div 2}{100 \div 2} = \frac{19}{50}$

$38\% = \frac{19}{50}$

> **Remember**
> To simplify a fraction divide the **numerator** (top number) and the **denominator** (bottom number) of the fraction by their highest common factor.

2 Write 72% as a fraction in its simplest form.

$72\% = \frac{72}{100} = \frac{72 \div 4}{100 \div 4} = \frac{18}{25}$

3 Write 42.5% as a decimal.

$42.5\% = \frac{42.5}{100} = 42.5 \div 100 = 0.425$

> **Remember**
> To change a fraction to a decimal divide the numerator by the denominator.

Changing decimals and fractions to percentages

To change a decimal or a fraction to a percentage: **multiply by 100**

EXAMPLES

1 Change 0.3 to a percentage.

$0.3 \times 100 = 30$
So 0.3 as a percentage is 30%.

2 Change 0.875 to a percentage.

$0.875 \times 100 = 87.5$
So 0.875 as a percentage is 87.5%.

3 Change $\frac{7}{10}$ to a percentage.

$\frac{7}{10} \times 100 = 7 \times 100 \div 10$
$= 700 \div 10 = 70\%$

4 Change $\frac{11}{25}$ to a percentage.

$\frac{11}{25} \times 100 = 11 \times 100 \div 25$
$= 1100 \div 25 = 44\%$

Comparing fractions

Fractions can be compared by first writing them as percentages.

EXAMPLE

Ben scored 17 out of 20 in a Maths test and 21 out of 25 in a History test. Which is Ben's better mark?

Change each mark to a percentage.

Maths: $\frac{17}{20}$ $\frac{17}{20} \times 100 = 17 \times 100 \div 20 = 85\%$

History: $\frac{21}{25}$ $\frac{21}{25} \times 100 = 21 \times 100 \div 25 = 84\%$

So Ben's better mark was his Maths mark of 85%.

Exercise 15.1   Do not use a calculator for questions 1 to 5.

1 Write these percentages as
    (a) fractions in their simplest form,   (b) decimals.
       (i) 10%   (ii) 20%   (iii) 25%   (iv) 75%

2 Change these percentages to fractions written in their simplest form.
    (a) 15%   (b) 5%   (c) 18%   (d) 52%   (e) 23%   (f) 12.5%

3 Change these percentages to decimals.
    (a) 15%   (b) 5%   (c) 47%   (d) 72%   (e) 87.5%   (f) 150%

4 Copy and complete this table to work out the percentage equivalents of the fractions given.

Fraction	$\frac{3}{10}$	$\frac{2}{5}$	$\frac{3}{25}$	$\frac{7}{20}$
Percentage				

5 Copy and complete this table to work out the percentage equivalents of the decimals given.

Decimal	0.7	0.45	0.05	1.2
Percentage				

6 What is $\frac{1}{3}$ as a percentage?

7 Change these fractions to percentages.
    (a) $\frac{17}{50}$ (b) $\frac{12}{25}$ (c) $\frac{30}{200}$ (d) $\frac{4}{5}$ (e) $\frac{135}{500}$ (f) $\frac{13}{20}$ (g) $\frac{2}{3}$ (h) $\frac{2}{9}$

8 Change these decimals to percentages.
    (a) 0.15   (b) 0.32   (c) 0.125   (d) 0.07   (e) 1.12   (f) 0.015

9 Write in order of size, lowest first:
    (a) $\frac{1}{2}$ 60% $\frac{2}{5}$ 0.55   (b) 43% $\frac{9}{20}$ 0.42 $\frac{11}{25}$ (c) $\frac{23}{80}$ 28% $\frac{57}{200}$ 0.2805

10 Peter scores 96 out of 120. What percentage did he get?

11 Change each of these marks to a percentage.
    (a) Maths: 27 out of 30.   (b) French: 34 out of 40.
    (c) Science: 22 out of 25.   (d) Art: 48 out of 60.

12 In an ice hockey competition Team A won 8 out of the 11 games they played whilst Team B won 5 of their 7 games.

Which team has the better record in the competition?

Percentages · · · · Percentages · · · · Percentages · · ·

Expressing one quantity as a percentage of another

To work out one number as a percentage of another there are two steps.

| **Step 1** Write the numbers as a fraction. |
| **Step 2** Change the fraction to a percentage. |

EXAMPLES

The numbers in the fraction must be in the **same** units.

1 What is 30p as a percentage of £2?

£2 = 200p

Step 1

30p as a fraction of 200p is $\frac{30}{200}$.

Step 2

$\frac{30}{200} \times 100 = 30 \times 100 \div 200 = 15\%$

So 30p as a percentage of £2 is 15%.

2 A newspaper contains 48 pages, 6 of which are Sports pages.
What percentage of the pages are Sports pages?

Step 1

6 out of 48 pages are Sports pages.

$\frac{6}{48} = 6 \div 48 = 0.125$

Step 2

$0.125 \times 100 = 12.5$
12.5% of the pages are Sports pages.

Exercise 15.2

Do not use a calculator for questions 1 to 5.

1 What is
(a) 30 as a percentage of 50,
(b) 4 as a percentage of 25,
(c) 7 as a percentage of 10,
(d) 42 as a percentage of 200,
(e) 63 as a percentage of 300?

2 What is
(a) 64 pence as a percentage of £2,
(b) 6 minutes as a percentage of 1 hour,
(c) 30 mm as a percentage of 5 cm,
(d) 150 g as a percentage of 1 kg,
(e) 18 pence as a percentage of £0.60?

3 There are 8 yellow fruit drops in a packet of 25 fruit drops.
What percentage of the fruit drops are yellow?

4 James saved £30 and then spent £9.
What percentage of his savings did he spend?

5 A Youth Club has 200 members.
80 of the members are boys.
(a) What percentage of the members are boys?
(b) What percentage of the members are girls?

6 240 people took part in a survey.
30 of them were younger than 18.
What percentage were younger than 18?

7 A bar of chocolate has 32 squares.
Jane eats 12 of the squares.
What percentage of the bar does she eat?

8 Billy earns £9 per hour.
He gets a wage rise of 27 pence per hour.
What is his percentage wage rise?

9 What is
(a) £2 as a percentage of £6,
(b) 80 km as a percentage of 120 km,
(c) 20 cm as a percentage of 160 cm,
(d) £1530 as a percentage of £3600,
(e) £105.09 as a percentage of £186?

10 A new car costs £13 500.
The dealer gives a discount of £1282.50.
What is the percentage discount?

11 There are 600 pupils in Years 9 to 13 of a High school.
360 pupils are in Years 10 and 11.
15% of pupils are in Years 12 and 13.
What percentage of pupils are in Year 9?

Percentages . . . Percentages . . . Percentages . . .

EXAMPLES

1 Find 20% of £56.

Step 1   Divide by 100.   £56 ÷ 100 = £0.56
Step 2   Multiply by 20.   £0.56 × 20 = £11.20

So 20% of £56 is £11.20.

2 The price of a car is £12 500.
A car salesman offers a 7% discount.
How much is the discount?

Discount   = 7% of £12 500
1% of £12 500 = £12 500 ÷ 100 = £125
7% of £12 500 = £125 × 7 = £875
The discount is £875.

3 David invests £500 in a building society.
He earns 6% interest per year.
How much interest does he get after one year?

Interest   = 6% of £500
1% of £500 = £500 ÷ 100 = £5
6% of £500 = £5 × 6 = £30
The interest is £30.

> To find 1% of a quantity divide the quantity by 100.
>
> To find 20% of a quantity multiply 1% of the quantity by 20.
>
> This is the same as the method you would use to find $\frac{20}{100}$ of a quantity.

Exercise 15.3

Do not use a calculator in this exercise.

1 Find:
   (a)   10% of 500   (b)   5% of 800
   (c)   20% of 700   (d)   30% of 200
   (e)   40% of 600   (f)   20% of 550
   (g)   5% of 50   (h)   15% of 80
   (i)   65% of 30   (j)   85% of 20
   (k)   12% of 500   (l)   32% of 200

2 Find:
   (a)   20% of £80   (b)   75% of £20
   (c)   30% of £220   (d)   15% of £350
   (e)   5% of £500   (f)   20% of £150
   (g)   9% of £300   (h)   20% of 20 m
   (i)   30% of 80 kg   (j)   35% of 800 m
   (k)   45% of £25   (l)   60% of 20 pence

3 Garry has 300 marbles.
20% of the marbles are blue.
35% of the marbles are red.
The rest of the marbles are white.
   (a)   How many marbles are blue?
   (b)   How many marbles are red?
   (c)   What percentage of the marbles are white?

4 Tim invests £400 in a building society.
He earns 5% interest per year.
How much interest does he get in one year?

5 There are 450 seats in a theatre.
60% of the seats are in the stalls.
How many seats are in the stalls?

6 A salesman earns a bonus of 3% of his weekly sales.
How much bonus does the salesman earn in a week when his sales are £1400?

7 Jenny gets a 15% discount on a theatre ticket.
The normal cost is £18.
How much does she save?

8 Dipak earns £350 per week.
He gets a wage rise of 3%.
How much extra does he earn each week?

9 In a school of 1200 pupils 45% are boys.
   (a)   How many are girls?

30% of the girls are under 13.
   (b)   How many girls are under 13?

10 A dozen biscuits weigh 720 g.
The amount of flour in a biscuit is 40% of the weight of a biscuit.
What is the weight of flour in **each** biscuit?

Percentage change

1 Increase £25 by 30%.

First find 30% of £25.

$\frac{30}{100} \times 25 = 0.3 \times 25 = 7.5$

30% of £25 is £7.50.
£25 increased by 30% = £25 + £7.50
= £32.50

2 Decrease £600 by 12%.

First find 12% of £600.

$\frac{12}{100} \times 600 = 0.12 \times 600 = 72$

12% of £600 is £72.
£600 decreased by 12% = £600 − £72
= £528

3 A shirt normally priced at £24 is reduced by 15% in a sale.
How much does this cost in the sale?

Reduction in price = 15% of £24
$15 \div 100 \times 24 = 0.15 \times 24 = 3.6$
15% of £24 = £3.60
The shirt costs £24 − £3.60 = £20.40.

4 A packet of cereals weighs 440 g.
A special offer packet contains 30% more.
What is the weight of a special offer packet?

Extra contents = 30% of 440 g
= 440 ÷ 100 × 30
= 132 g
$440 + 132 = 572$
A special offer packet weighs 572 g.

Exercise 15.4

Do not use a calculator for questions 1 to 5.

1 Increase:
(a) £400 by 20%   (b) £300 by 40%
(c) £2000 by 40%   (d) £600 by 80%
(e) £3000 by 15%   (f) £900 by 40%
(g) £50 by 60%   (h) £10 by 30%
(i) £15 by 10%   (j) £50 by 15%

2 Decrease:
(a) £600 by 30%   (b) £800 by 25%
(c) £2500 by 20%   (d) £250 by 40%
(e) £12 000 by 15%   (f) £7000 by 35%
(g) £600 by 15%   (h) £55 by 90%
(i) £42 by 20%   (j) £63 by 35%

3 A mobile telephone company offers a 20% discount on calls made in March. The normal cost of a peak time call is 50 pence per minute. How much does a peak time call cost in March?

4 Abdul earns £200 per week. He gets a wage rise of 7.5%. What is his new weekly wage?

5 A packet of breakfast cereal contains 660 g. A special offer packet contains an extra 15%. How many grams of breakfast cereal are in the special offer packet?

6 Prices in a sale are reduced by 18%. The normal price of a shirt is £22.50. Calculate its sale price.

7 The price of a gold watch is £278. What does it cost with a 12% discount?

8 The price of a used car is £5200. What does it cost with a 9.5% discount?

9 The price of a new kitchen is £8650. What does it cost with a 35% discount?

10 Jane's salary of £14 000 is increased by 4%. Calculate her new salary.

11 A car was valued at £13 500 when new. After one year it lost 22% of its value. What was the value of the car after one year?

12 Louisa puts £480 into a bank account. At the end of one year interest at 2.5% is added to her account. How much is in her account at the end of one year?

More complicated percentage problems

Problems involving percentages can involve more complicated calculations.

EXAMPLES

1 Calculate 4×10^6
as a percentage of 2×10^8.

$$\frac{4 \times 10^6}{2 \times 10^8} = 0.02$$

$$0.02 \times 100 = 2\%$$

2 Calculate 30% of 8×10^4.

$$30 \div 100 \times 8 \times 10^4$$
$$= 24\,000$$

3 1.2×10^{10} steel cans were used in 2002.
1.4×10^9 of these were recycled.
Calculate the percentage of steel cans
that were **not** recycled in 2002.

$$\frac{1.4 \times 10^9}{1.2 \times 10^{10}} = 0.1166\ldots$$

$$0.1166\ldots \times 100 = 11.66\ldots$$
$$= 11.7 \text{ to 3 significant figures.}$$
Percentage recycled = 11.7%
$100 - 11.7 = 88.3$
Percentage not recycled = 88.3%

Exercise **15.5**

Use a calculator in this exercise.
Where appropriate give your answers to 3 significant figures.

1 Prices in a sale are reduced by 24%. The normal price of a kettle is £25.50.
Calculate its sale price.

2 Milk costs 28 pence a pint. How much does it cost after a 14% increase?

3 Petrol costs 81.9 pence a litre. What does it cost after a 2.4% decrease?

4 A 5-litre can of paint covers an area of $28\,m^2$. Harry buys 3 cans of paint to cover $70\,m^2$.
What percentage of the paint does he use?

5 A car was valued at £13 500 when new. After one year it lost 22% of its value.
At the end of two years it was sold for £8200.
What percentage of its original value did the car lose in its second year?

6 In 2001 house prices increased by 19.6%. In 2002 house prices increased by 17.4%.
A house was valued at £78 000 at the beginning of 2001.
What was the value of the house at the end of 2002?

7 Ben invests £650 in a building society. He earns 5.25% interest in the first year.
(a) How much interest does he earn?

Ben leaves his original £650 plus the interest he has earned in the building society.
He earns 6.05% in the second year.
(b) How much interest does Ben earn in the second year?

8 There are 633 pupils in a school.
230 of the pupils walk to school, 212 travel by bus and 150 come by car.
(a) What percentage walk to school?
(b) What percentage come by car?

18% of the pupils who normally come by car start to travel on a new bus route.
(c) What percentage of the pupils now travel by bus?

9 (a) Calculate 5% of 5.4×10^3.   (b) Calculate 3.6×10^4 as a percentage of 4.8×10^5.

10 The Amazonian Rainforest covers an area of $6.5 \times 10^6\,km^2$ and is decreasing in area at a
rate of 7% per year.
Calculate the decrease in the area of the rainforest in one year.

11 The volume of water on Earth is approximately $1.436 \times 10^9 \, \text{km}^3$.
About 94% of this is contained in the Earth's oceans.
Use these figures to estimate the volume of water in the Earth's oceans.

12 The area of the surface of the Earth is about 5.095×10^9 square miles.
Approximately 29.2% of this is land.
Use these figures to estimate the area of land surface on Earth.

13 James wins a lottery prize of $£1.764 \times 10^6$.
He pays $£5.29 \times 10^5$ for a house.
What percentage of his prize did he spend on the house?
Give your answer to a suitable degree of accuracy.

14 The planet Pluto is $5.914 \times 10^9 \, \text{km}$ from the Sun. The Earth is $1.496 \times 10^8 \, \text{km}$ from the Sun.
Express the distance of the Earth from the Sun as a percentage of the distance of
Pluto from the Sun.

Percentage increase and decrease

Sadik and Chandni took Maths tests in October and June.

 My mark went up from 54% to 72%.

 My mark went up from 42% to 60%.

Who has made the most improvement?

They have both improved by a score of 18% so by one measure they have both improved equally.
Another way of comparing their improvement is to use the idea of a percentage increase.

$$\text{Percentage increase} = \frac{\text{actual increase}}{\text{initial value}} \times 100\%$$

Comparing percentage increases is the best way to decide
whether Sadik or Chandni has made the most improvement.
Explain why.

> ⊙⊙⊙⊙⊙⊙⊙⊙⊙⊙
> **Remember**
> To calculate
>   % increase or % decrease
> always use the initial value.

For Sadik
% increase $= \frac{18}{54} \times 100\% = 33.3\%$

For Chandni
% increase $= \frac{18}{42} \times 100\% = 42.9\%$

Both calculations are correct to one decimal place.

A percentage decrease can be calculated in a similar way.

$$\text{Percentage decrease} = \frac{\text{actual decrease}}{\text{initial value}} \times 100\%$$

1 A shop buys pens for 15 pence and sells
them for 21 pence.
What is their percentage profit?

Actual profit = 21 pence − 15 pence
$\quad\quad\quad\quad = 6$ pence

% profit $= \dfrac{\text{actual profit}}{\text{initial value}} \times 100$

$\quad\quad = \dfrac{6}{15} \times 100 = 40\%$

2 Pam buys a micro-scooter for £24.
She sells the micro-scooter for £15.
What is her percentage loss?

Actual loss = £24 − £15
$\quad\quad\quad\quad = £9$

% loss $= \dfrac{\text{actual loss}}{\text{initial value}} \times 100$

$\quad\quad = \dfrac{9}{24} \times 100 = 37.5\%$

1 A shop buys calculators for £5 and sells them for £6. Find the percentage profit.

2 John's weekly wage rises from £250 to £265. What is John's percentage wage rise?

3 On Monday peaches cost 15p each. On Tuesday peaches cost 12p each.
What is the percentage reduction in price?

4 The price of a book increases from £8 to £9. What is the percentage increase in price?

5 A man buys a boat for £25 000 and sells it for £18 000. Find his percentage loss.

6 The rent on Karen's flat increased from £80 to £90 per week.
(a)   Find the percentage increase in her rent.
At the same time Karen's wages increased from £250 per week to £280 per week.
(b)   Find the percentage increase in her wages.
Comment on your answers.

7 In October, Sam scored 50% in an English test. In January he improved to 66%.
In the same tests, Becky scored 40% and 56%.
Who has made the most improvement? Explain your answer.

8 A sample of soil is dried in an oven. Its mass reduces from 65 g to 45 g.
Find the percentage decrease in the mass.

9 The value of car A when new was £13 000. The value of car B when new was £16 500.
After one year the value of car A is £11 200 and the value of car B is £13 500.
Calculate the percentage loss in the values of cars A and B after one year.

10 In a school the number of pupils increased
as shown in the table:
In which year is the percentage increase in
the number of pupils the greatest?

Year	1998	1999	2000	2001	2002
Number	554	605	643	679	734

11 During 2002 the population of a village decreased from 323 to 260.
Find the percentage decrease in the population.

12 Between 1990 and 2000 the population of the UK increased from 5.7×10^7 to 5.9×10^7.
Find the percentage increase in the population of the UK between 1990 and 2000.

13 At the start of May a flower was 12.3 cm high. In May it grew by 14.5%.
At the start of July it was 16.7 cm high.
What was its percentage growth during June?

14 A rectangle has length 12 cm and width 8 cm.
The length is increased by 7.5% and the width decreased by 12.5%.
Find the change in area as a percentage of the original area of the rectangle.

15 In 2001 Miles bought £2000 worth of shares.
In 2002 the value of his shares decreased by 10%.
In 2003 the value of his shares increased by 20%.
By what percentage has the value of his shares changed from 2001 to 2003?

16 The price of a micro-scooter is reduced by 10%.
In a sale, the new price is reduced by a further 10%.
By what percentage has the original price of the micro-scooter been reduced in the sale?

17 The price of telephone calls is increased by 15%.
Companies are given a 10% discount off the new price.
What is the percentage increase in the price of calls for companies?

Reverse percentage problems

EXAMPLES

1 A shop sells videos with a 20% discount.
Petra buys a video and pays £10.
How much does the video normally cost?

Discount price is normal price less 20%.
So 80% of normal price = £10.
So 1% of normal price = £10 ÷ 80
$\qquad$ = £0.125
So normal price = £0.125 × 100
$\qquad$ = £12.50

2 Tara gets a 5% wage rise.
Her new wage is £126 per week.
What was Tara's wage before her wage rise?

New wage = old wage + 5%
So 105% of old wage = £126
1% of old wage is 126 ÷ 105 = £1.20
Old wage = 1.2 × 100 = £120

Exercise 15.7   Do questions 1 to 4 without a calculator.

1 A special bottle of pop contains 10% more than a normal bottle.
The special bottle contains 660 ml.
How much does the normal bottle contain?

2 Jim saves 15% of his monthly salary. Each month he saves £90.
What is his monthly salary?

3 May gets a 20% wage rise. Her new wage is £264 per week.
What was May's wage before her wage rise?

4 Mary and Sam take a History and a Geography test.
(a)   Sam scored 60 marks in History.
Sam's score was 20% better than his score in Geography.
What was Sam's score in Geography?
(b)   Mary scored 72 marks in History.
Mary's score was 20% worse than her score in Geography.
What was Mary's score in Geography?

5 In a high jump event, Nick jumps 1.8 metres.
This is 5% lower than the best height he can jump.
What is the best height he can jump?

6 A house is valued at £350 000.
This is a 12% increase on the value of the house a year ago.
What was the value of the house a year ago?

7 30 grams of a breakfast cereal provides 16.2 mg of vitamin C.
This is 24% of the recommended daily intake.
What daily intake of vitamin C is recommended?

8 Tom gets a 3% increase in his salary. His new salary is £1462.60 per month.
What was Tom's salary before his wage rise?

9 A one year old car is worth £6720. This is a decrease of 16% of its value from new.
What was the price of the new car?

10 Here is some data about the changes in the number of pupils in schools A and B.
School A's numbers increased by 4% to 442.
School B's numbers decreased by 6% to 423.
How many pupils were in schools A and B before the change in numbers?

11 John sells his computer to Dan and makes a 15% profit.
Dan then sells the computer to Ron for £391. Dan makes a 15% loss.
How much did John pay for the computer?
Explain why it is not £391.

12 Kim sells her bike to Sara.
Sara sells it to Tina for £121.50. Both Kim and Sara make a 10% loss.
How much did Kim pay for the bike?
Explain why it is not 20% more than £121.50.

What you need to know

- 'Per cent' means 'out of 100'.
  The symbol for per cent is %.

- A percentage can be written as a fraction with denominator 100.
  For example: 10% can be written as $\frac{10}{100}$.

- To change a decimal or a fraction to a percentage - **multiply by 100**.
  For example:
  0.12 as a percentage is $0.12 \times 100 = 12\%$.
  $\frac{3}{25}$ as a percentage is $\frac{3}{25} \times 100 = 3 \times 100 \div 25 = 12\%$.

- To change a percentage to a decimal or a fraction - **divide by 100**.
  For example:
  18% as a decimal is $18 \div 100 = 0.18$.
  18% as a fraction is $\frac{18}{100}$ which in its simplest form is $\frac{9}{50}$.

- Percentage increase $= \dfrac{\text{actual increase}}{\text{initial value}} \times 100\%$

  Percentage decrease $= \dfrac{\text{actual decrease}}{\text{initial value}} \times 100\%$

IDEAS FOR INVESTIGATION

Increasing and decreasing

200 increased by 10% and then decreased by 10%
$200 \rightarrow +10\% \rightarrow 220 \rightarrow -10\% \rightarrow 198$
Actual change $= 200 - 198$
$= $ decrease of 2
$\frac{2}{200} = \frac{2}{200} \times 100 = 2 \times 100 \div 200 = 1\%$
2 as a percentage of 200 is 1%.
The combined result of a 10% increase followed by a 10% decrease is a 1% decrease.

500 decreased by 10% and then increased by 30%
$500 \rightarrow -10\% \rightarrow 450 \rightarrow +30\% \rightarrow 585$
Actual change $= 585 - 500$
$= $ increase of 85
$\frac{85}{500} = \frac{85}{500} \times 100 = 85 \times 100 \div 500 = 17\%$
85 as a percentage of 500 is 17%.
The combined result of a 10% decrease followed by a 30% increase is a 17% increase.

Investigate increasing and decreasing different quantities by different percentages.
You might find a spreadsheet useful.

Do not use a calculator for questions 1 to 5.

1 A bag contains 60 beads.
   (a) Emily uses 30% of the beads to make a necklace. How many beads does she use?
   (b) Laura uses 12 beads to make a bracelet. What percentage of the beads does she use?

2 Joe earns £650 in May. In June he earns 20% more. How much does he earn in June?   AQA

3 A roll of carpet is 20 m long. Beryl buys 18 m of carpet from the roll.
   What percentage of the roll did she buy?

4 A train has 1200 seats. 85% of the seats are occupied. How many seats are unoccupied?

5 In a nine carat gold ring $\frac{9}{24}$ of the weight is pure gold.
   What percentage of the weight of the ring is pure gold?   AQA

6 In a local election 3750 people could have voted. 2150 people actually voted.
   What percentage of the people voted?   AQA

7 An estate agent makes the following charge for the sale of a house.

Sale price of house	Up to £50 000	Over £50 000
Charge by estate agent	3% of the sale price	3% of the first 50 000 plus 2% on the remainder

Calculate the charge made by the estate agent for a house sold for £129 000.   AQA

8 (a) A year ago Martin was 1.60 m tall. He is now 4% taller.
      Calculate his height now. Give your answer in centimetres.
   (b) Martin now weighs 58 kg. A year ago he weighed 51 kg.
      Calculate the percentage increase in his weight.
      Give your answer to an appropriate degree of accuracy.   AQA

9 (a) In the men's long jump, Leroy improved on his first jump of 8.15 m by 8%.
      What was the length of this improved jump?
   (b) In the women's long jump, Sabrina improved her jump from 6.40 m to 7.36 m.
      What was the percentage increase in her jump?   AQA

10 Brian buys 300 CDs for £1400. He sells $\frac{3}{4}$ of them at £9 each.
   He then reduces the price of the remaining CDs by 30%.
   When he has sold 290 CDs, he gives the last 10 to a charity.
   (a) How much money does he receive from selling the CDs?
   (b) Find the percentage profit which Brian made on these CDs.   AQA

11 The number of salmon in the River Derwent is expected to increase by about 15% every year
   up to the year 2000.
   At the beginning of 1996 there were approximately 6000 salmon in the River Derwent.
   (a) How many salmon are expected to be in the River Derwent at the beginning of 1997?
   (b) The River Authority stated that by the year 2000 there will be over 10 000 salmon in the
      River Derwent.
      Do you agree with this? Show all your working.   AQA

12 Calculate 18% of 2.4×10^5.

13 In a sale a dress costs £32.40. The original price was reduced by 10%.
   What was the original price?   AQA

14 In a sale, all the prices are reduced by 20%. I bought a coat for £68 in the sale.
   What was the price of the coat before the sale?   AQA

15 David has a 4% wage rise. His new wage is £220.80 per week.
   What was his weekly wage before his wage rise?

CHAPTER 16

Time and Money

The time of day is given in terms of hours, minutes and sometimes seconds.
There are 24 hours in each day, 60 minutes in each hour and 60 seconds in each minute.

24-hour clock and 12-hour clock times

The time can be given using the 12-hour clock or the 24-hour clock.

The watch and the digital clock both show the same time.
The time on the watch is 5.45 pm using 12-hour clock time.
The digital clock shows 5.45 pm as 1745 using 24-hour clock time.

12-hour clock times Times before midday are given as am. Times after midday are given as pm.	**24-hour clock times** The first two figures give the hours. The last two figures give the minutes.

EXAMPLES

1 A video recorder uses 24-hour clock times.
  (a) What time is shown by the video recorder at 6.30 pm?
  (b) The video is set to record programmes from 1120 to 1645.
     What are these times in 12-hour clock time?

(a) 6.30 pm is equivalent to 1830.

(b) 1120 is equivalent to 11.20 am.
  1645 is equivalent to 4.45 pm.

12-hour to 24-hour clock times
Times before midday:
  use the same figures.
Times after midday:
  add 12 to the hours.
	24-hour to 12-hour clock times
	Times before midday:
	  use the same figures and
	  include **am**.
	Times after midday:
	  subtract 12 from the hours and
	  include **pm**.

2 A motorist left Liverpool at 10.50 am and arrived in Birmingham at 1.20 pm.
  How long did the journey take?

Method 1 (subtraction)

```
1 3.2 0
1 0.5 0
───────

───────

   2 6 0
1 3́.2 0
1 0.5 0
───────
  2.3 0
```

1. Write the times as 24-hour clock times.
2. Subtract the minutes.
   20 − 50 cannot be done.
   Exchange 1 hour for 60 minutes.
   60 + 20 − 50 = 30 minutes.
3. Subtract the hours.
   12 − 10 = 2.

Method 2 (adding on)

10.50 to 11.00 =	10 minutes
11.00 to 13.00 = 2 hours	
13.00 to 13.20 =	20 minutes
Total time	= 2 hours 30 minutes

The journey took 2 hours 30 minutes.

1 Write these 12-hour clock times in 24-hour clock time.
  (a) 10.30 am   (b) 10.30 pm   (c) 1.45 am
  (d) 1.45 pm   (e) 7.50 am   (f) 11.50 pm

2 Write these 24-hour clock times in 12-hour clock time.
  (a) 1415   (b) 0525   (c) 2320
  (d) 1005   (e) 0940   (f) 1705

3 The times of some Sunday evening BBC 1 programmes are shown.

BBC 1
6 35 Antiques Roadshow
7 20 Holiday Guide to Australia
8 00 Ballykissangel
8 50 News

  (a) Give the times of these programmes using 24-hour clock time.
  (b) How many minutes does "Holiday Guide to Australia" last?
  (c) How many minutes does "Antiques Roadshow" last?

4 A train left Paddington at 1315 and arrived in Exeter at 1605.
  (a) At what time did the train leave in 12-hour clock time?
  (b) How long did the journey take?

5 A train left Manchester at 9.10 am and arrived in Reading at 1.25 pm.
  (a) What was the arrival time in 24-hour clock time?
  (b) How long did the journey take?

6 A coach leaves Bournemouth at 10.50 am to travel to London.
The journey takes 2 hours 40 minutes.
At what time does the coach reach London?
Give your answer in   (a) 12-hour clock time,   (b) 24-hour clock time.

7 Mrs Hill took 3 hours 56 minutes to drive from Bath to Blackpool.
She left Bath at 1045. At what time did she arrive in Blackpool?
Give your answer in   (a) the 24-hour clock,   (b) the 12-hour clock.

Timetables

Bus and rail timetables are usually given in 24-hour clock time. Here is part of a rail timetable.

Kidderminster	1035	1115	1155	1240	1325	1410
Bewdley	1050	1130	—	1300	—	1430
Arley	1105	1148	—	1318	1403	1448
Highley	1114	1158	—	1328	—	1458
Hampton Loade	1125	1210	—	1340	1425	1510
Bridgnorth	1140	1225	1310	1355	1440	1525

> Some trains do not stop at every station. This is shown by a dash on the timetable.

How many minutes does the journey take on the 1035 train from Kidderminster to Arley?

Jean catches the 1155 train from Kidderminster to Bridgnorth.
What is her arrival time in 12-hour clock time? How long does the journey take?

Alex lives in Bewdley.
What is the time of the last train he can catch to keep an appointment in Bridgnorth at 1.15 pm?

1 The times of some trains from Hastings to Charing Cross are shown.

Hastings	0702	0802	0857	0900	0957	1102	1257
Crowhurst	—	—	0908	—	1008	—	1308
Battle	0715	0815	0912	—	1012	—	1312
Tunbridge Wells	0745	0845	0943	0940	1043	1141	1342
Sevenoaks	0805	0905	1003	—	1103	1201	1403
Charing Cross	0834	0934	1032	1025	1132	1230	1432

(a) John catches the 0745 from Tunbridge Wells to Charing Cross.
How many minutes does the journey take?

(b) Aimee catches the 0857 from Hastings to Charing Cross.
How long does the journey take?

(c) Sarah catches the 1257 from Hastings to Tunbridge Wells.
What is her arrival time using the 12-hour clock?

(d) Keith wants to be in Charing Cross by 1030.
What is the latest train he can catch from Battle?

2 Some of the rail services from Manchester to Birmingham are shown.

Manchester	0925	1115	1215	1415	1555
Stockport	0933	—	1223	—	1603
Stoke	1007	1155	1255	1459	1636
Stafford	1027	—	1318	—	1656
Wolverhampton	1056	1234	1336	1535	1716
Birmingham	1121	1257	1359	1558	1742

(a) David has to be in Wolverhampton by 2 pm.
What is the time of the latest train he can catch from Manchester?

(b) Pam catches the 0933 from Stockport to Birmingham.
How long does the journey take?

(c) What time does the 1555 from Manchester arrive in Birmingham in 12-hour clock time?

3 Some of the rail services from Poole to Waterloo are shown.

Poole	0544	0602	—	0640	—	0740	0825	0846
Bournemouth	0558	0616	—	0654	0715	0754	0839	0900
Southampton	0634	0655	0714	0738	0754	0838	0908	0938
Eastleigh	0646	—	—	0750	—	0852	—	0951
Waterloo	0804	0810	0844	0901	0908	1005	1018	1112

(a) Sid arrives at Bournemouth station at 0830.
What is the time of the next train to Eastleigh?

(b) Paul catches the 0654 from Bournemouth to Southampton.
How many minutes does the journey take?

(c) Emma catches the 0544 from Poole to Waterloo.
How long does the journey take?

4 Some of the coach services from Woking to Heathrow airport are shown.

Woking	0610	0650	0720	0750	0820	Then	1830	1900	2000
Terminal 1	0650	0730	0800	0830	0900	every	1900	1930	2030
Terminal 2	0655	0735	0805	0835	0905	30	1905	1935	2035
Terminal 3	0700	0740	0810	0840	0910	mins	1910	1940	2040
Terminal 4	0710	0750	0820	0850	0920	until	1920	1950	2050

(a) Helen arrives at Woking at 3 pm.
    She catches the next coach to Heathrow.
    (i) At what time does it leave Woking?
    (ii) At what time does it arrive at Terminal 3?
(b) Leroy needs to be at Terminal 2 at 6 pm.
    What is the latest time he can catch a coach from Woking?

Wages

Hourly pay

Many people are paid by the hour for their work. In most cases they receive a **basic hourly rate** for a fixed number of hours and an **overtime rate** for any extra hours worked.

> **EXAMPLE**
>
> A car-park attendant is paid £5.20 per hour for a basic 40-hour week.
> Overtime is paid at time and a half.
> One week an attendant works 48 hours.
> How much does he earn?
>
> Basic Pay: £5.20 × 40 = £208.00
> Overtime: 1.5 × £5.20 × 8 = £62.40
>
> Total pay = £270.40
>
> Overtime paid at 'time and a half' means 1.5 × normal hourly rate.
> In this example, the hourly overtime rate is given by:
> 1.5 × £5.20
>
> Common overtime rates are 'time and a quarter', 'double time', etc.

Commission

As an incentive for their employees to work harder some companies pay a basic wage (fixed amount) plus commission. The amount of commission is usually expressed as a percentage of the value of the sales made by the employee.

> **EXAMPLE**
>
> An estate agent is paid a salary of £14 000 per year plus commission of 0.5% on the sales of all houses.
> Last year the estate agent sold houses to the value of £2 640 500.
> How much did the estate agent earn last year?
>
> Annual salary: £14 000
> Commission: 0.005 × £2 640 500 = £13 202.50
>
> Total pay = £27 202.50
>
> **Remember:**
> $0.5\% = \frac{0.5}{100} = 0.005$

1 A secretary earns £352.80 a week. She is paid £9.80 per hour.
How many hours a week does she work?

2 A chef is paid £10.40 per hour for a basic 38-hour week. Overtime is paid at time and a half.
How much does the chef earn in a week in which she works 50 hours?

3 A mechanic is paid £8.80 per hour for a basic 40-hour week.
Overtime is paid at time and a quarter.
One week the mechanic works 42 hours. How much does he earn?

4 A hairdresser is paid £7.20 per hour for a basic 35-hour week.
One week she works two hours overtime at time and a half and $3\frac{1}{2}$ hours overtime at
time and a quarter. How much is she paid that week?

5 A driver is paid £68.85 for $4\frac{1}{2}$ hours of overtime. Overtime is paid at time and a half.
What is his basic hourly rate of pay?

6 A furniture salesperson is paid an annual salary of £12 500 plus commission of 2% on sales.
Last year the salesperson sold £500 000 worth of furniture.
How much did the salesperson earn last year?

7 A car salesperson is paid an annual salary of £10 200 plus commission of 2.5% on sales.
How much does the salesperson earn in a year in which cars to the value of £868 000 are sold?

8 A double glazing salesperson is paid £480 per month plus commission of 5% on sales.
How much does he earn in a month in which he makes sales of £22 600?

9 An estate agent is paid 1.5% commission on the sales of houses.
Last month he was paid £12 000 commission.
Calculate the total value of the houses he sold.

10 A florist is paid £159.60 per week plus commission of 3% on the sales of flowers.
Last week she was paid £202.80.
Calculate the total value of the flowers she sold.

Income tax

The amount you earn for your work is called your **gross pay**.
Your employer will make deductions from your gross pay for
income tax, National Insurance, etc. Pay after all deductions
have been made is called **net pay**.

> The rates of tax and the
> bands (ranges of income)
> to which they apply vary.

The amount of **income tax** you pay will depend on how much you earn.
Everyone is allowed to earn some money which is not taxed, this is called a **tax allowance**.
Any remaining money is your **taxable income**.

EXAMPLE

George earns £6030 per year. His tax allowance is £4615 per year and he pays tax at 10p in the £ on
his taxable income.
How much income tax does George pay per year?

Taxable income: £6030 − £4615 = £1415
Income tax: £1415 × 0.10 = £141.50

> An income tax rate of 10%
> is often expressed as
> 10p in the pound (£)'.

George pays income tax of £141.50 per year.

Time and Money . . . . Time and Money . . . Time and Money . . .

1 Harry is paid £462 per week for 52 weeks.
His taxable allowance is £4615.
What is his annual taxable income?

2 Lyn earns £5800 per year.
Her tax allowance is £4615 per year and she pays tax at 10p in the £ on her taxable income.
(a) What is her annual taxable income?
(b) How much income tax does she pay per year?

3 Brian earns £644 per month.
His tax allowance is £6090 per year and he pays tax at 10p in the £ on his taxable income.
(a) What is his annual taxable income?
(b) How much income tax does he pay per month?

4 Kay has an annual salary of £23 700.
Her tax allowance is £4615 per year. She pays tax at 10p in the £ on the first £1960 of her taxable income and 22p in the £ on the remainder.
How much income tax does she pay per year?

5 Julie earns £965 per month.
Her tax allowance is £4615 per year and she pays tax at 10p in the £ on the first £1960 of her taxable income and 22p in the £ on the remainder.
How much income tax does she pay per month?

6 Jim is paid £286 per week for 52 weeks a year.
His tax allowance is £4615 per year.
He pays tax at 10p in the £ on the first £1960 of his taxable income and 22p in the £ on the remainder.
How much income tax does he pay per week?

7 Les has an annual salary of £28 600.
His tax allowance is £4615 per year.
He pays tax at 10p in the £ on the first £1960 of his taxable income and 22p in the £ on the remainder.
He is paid monthly.
How much income tax does he pay per month?

8 Alf's income is £23 850 per year.
He pays 9% of his gross income into a pension scheme on which he does not pay tax.
Alf also has a tax allowance of £4615 per year.
He pays tax at 10p in the £ on the first £1960 of his taxable income and 22p in the £ on the remainder.
Calculate how much income tax he pays per year.

9 Reg has an annual salary of £46 380.
His tax allowance is £4615 per year. He pays tax at 10p in the £ on the first £1960 of his taxable income, 22p in the £ on the next £28 540 and 40p in the £ on the remainder.
Calculate how much income tax he pays per year.

10 Alex has an annual salary of £37 240.
Her tax allowance is £4615 per year.
She pays tax at 10p in the £ on the first £1960 of her taxable income, 22p in the £ on the next £28 540 and 40p in the £ on the remainder.
She is paid monthly.
How much income tax does she pay per month?

Spending

Spending money is part of daily life. Every day people have to deal with many different situations involving money. Money is needed to buy fares for journeys, for purchases at shops, for hiring cars and equipment and for buying large items such as furniture.

When a large sum of money is needed to make a purchase, **credit** may be arranged. This involves paying for the goods over a period of time by agreeing to make a number of weekly or monthly repayments. It may also involve paying a **deposit**. The cost of credit may be more than paying cash.

EXAMPLES

1 Hamish pays £2.73 for 1 kg of pears and 2 kg of apples.
Pears cost 89p per kilogram.
How much per kilogram are apples?

2 kg of apples cost 273 − 89 = 184p
1 kg of apples costs 184 ÷ 2 = 92p
Apples cost 92p per kilogram.

Use the same units:
£2.73 is 273p

2 A motor home costs £16 450.
It can be bought on credit by paying a deposit of £3500 and 36 monthly payments of £395.
How much more is paid for the motor home when it is bought on credit?

Deposit:	£ 3 500
Payments: £395 × 36 =	£14 220
Credit Price:	£17 720

Difference: £17 720 − £16 450 = £1270
Credit price is £1270 more.

Exercise 16.5

Do not use a calculator for this exercise.

1 Esther pays £30.47 for a wheelbarrow, a fork and a spade.
The fork costs £7.49. The spade costs £6.99.
How much did the wheelbarrow cost?

2 Mr Grey pays £6 for 2 adult fares and 3 child fares on the bus. The fare for an adult is £1.65.
How much is the fare for a child?

3 Sam pays £56.40 for 200 bricks and 9 paving slabs. The bricks cost 21p each.
How much is a paving slab?

4 Mushrooms cost £2.10 per kilogram. Tomatoes cost 96p per kilogram.
James buys 200 g of mushrooms and 500 g of tomatoes.
How much does James have to pay?

5 Mr Jones pays £3.32 for 400 g of Brie and 250 g of Stilton. Stilton costs £5.60 per kilogram.
How much per kilogram is Brie?

6 A building supplier hires out cement mixers.
There is a delivery charge of £15 and a hire charge of £8 per day.
(a) How much would it cost for the delivery and hire of a cement mixer for 4 days?
(b) A builder pays £95 for the delivery and hire of a cement mixer.
For how many days did he hire it?

7 (a) Alex hires a van for one day and drives 45 miles.
How much is the total hire charge?

(b) Bob hires a van for 3 days.
The total hire charge is £114.
How many miles did Bob drive?

£30 per day
+
20p per mile driven

VAN FOR HIRE

8 The price of a pram is £299.
It can be bought on credit by paying a deposit of £50 and 10 monthly payments of £27.50.
How much more is paid for the pram when it is bought on credit?

9 A car costs £4950.
It can be bought on credit by paying a deposit of £2000 and 24 monthly payments of £149.50.
How much more is paid for the car when it is bought on credit?

10 The cash price of a settee is £900.
It can be bought on credit by paying a deposit of 10% of the cash price and 30 monthly payments of £32.50.
How much more is paid for the settee when it is bought on credit?

11 A washing machine costs £475.
It can be bought on credit by paying a deposit of 10% of the cash price and 24 monthly payments of £19.50.
How much more is paid for the washing machine when it is bought on credit?

Best buys

When shopping we often have to make choices between products which are packed in various sizes and priced differently. If we want to buy the one which gives the better value for money we must compare prices using the same units.

EXAMPLE

Peanut butter is available in small or large jars, as shown.
Which size is the better value for money?

Compare the number of grams per penny for each size.
Small: $250 \div 58 = 4.31\ldots$ grams per penny.
Large: $454 \div 106 = 4.28\ldots$ grams per penny.

The small size gives more grams per penny and is better value.

SMALL
250 g
58p

LARGE
454 g
£1.06

Exercise **16.6**   In each question you must show all your working.

1 Milk is sold in 1 pint, 2 pint and 4 pint containers.
The cost of a 1 pint container is 32p, the cost of a 2 pint container is 56p and the cost of a 4 pint container is 98p.
(a) How much per pint is saved by buying a 2 pint container instead of two 1 pint containers?
(b) How much per pint is saved by buying a 4 pint container instead of two 2 pint containers?

2 Mushroom soup is sold in two sizes.
A small tin costs 43p and weighs 224 g. A large tin costs 89p and weighs 454 g.
Which size gives more grams per penny?

3 Strawberry jam is sold in two sizes.
A small pot costs 52p and weighs 454 g. A large pot costs 97p and weighs 822 g.
Which size gives more grams per penny?

4 Jars of pickled onions are sold at the following prices: 460 g at 65p   or   700 g at 98p.
Which size is better value for money?

5 Honey is sold in two sizes.
A large pot costs £1.98 and weighs 454 g. A small pot costs 86p and weighs 185 g.
Which size is better value for money?

6 Cottage cheese costs 85p for 120 g, £1.55 for 250 g and £6 for 1 kg.
Which size is the best value for money?

7 Two bottles of sauce are shown.
Which size gives better value for money?

Small
285 g
38p

Medium
567 g
74p

1.5 litre
ACTIVE
90p

2 litre
ACTIVE
£1.30

8 Which of these two bottles of "Active" drink
is better value for money?

9 Toothpaste is sold in small, medium and large sizes.
The small size contains 75 ml and costs 85p.
The medium size contains 125 ml and costs £1.45.
The large size contains 180 ml and costs £2.05.
Which size is the best value for money?

10 Oscar wants to buy a camcorder. He looks at two different advertisements.

DAISY'S

OUR PRICE
30% OFF

Recommended
price £640

ALFIE'S

OUR PRICE
⅓ OFF

Recommended price £657

(a)   Find the actual selling price of each camcorder.
(b)   Which camcorder has the bigger discount?

Household bills

The cost of living includes many bills for services provided to our homes.
Electricity, gas and telephone charges are all examples of **quarterly bills** which are sent out four times a year. Each bill is made up of two parts:
A fixed (standing) charge, for providing the service.
A charge for the quantity of the service used (amount of gas/electricity, duration of telephone calls, etc.)

Other household bills include taxes payable to the local council, water charges and the cost of the insurance of the house (structure) and its contents.

1 Last year the Evans family received four quarterly gas bills.

March: £134.26   June: £52.00   September: £33.49   December: £80.25

(a) What was their total bill for the year?

(b) The family can pay for their gas by 12 equal monthly instalments.
How much would each instalment be?

2 Mrs Cotton uses 1064 units of electricity during one quarter.
Find the cost of her electricity bill if each unit costs 6.16 pence and the quarterly charge is £9.30.

3 Mr Jones receives an electricity bill for £59.20.
The bill includes a quarterly charge of £9.30 and the cost per unit is 6.16 pence.
Calculate to the nearest whole number, the number of units he has used.

4 Mrs Madan receives a gas bill for £179.53.
The bill includes a standing charge and the cost of the gas used.
During the quarter the gas used is equivalent to 13 377 kWh at 1.295 pence per kWh.
How much is the standing charge? Give your answer to a suitable degree of accuracy.

5 Mr Peters has an annual council tax of £1123.05.
He pays the council tax in 10 instalments. The first instalment is £115.05 and the remaining amount is payable in 9 instalments of equal value.
How much is the second instalment?

6 Mrs Dear checks her water bill. She has used 46 cubic metres of water at 77.76 pence per cubic metre and there is a standing charge of £11.
How much is her bill?

7 George insures his house valued at £184 000 and its contents valued at £27 500.
The annual premiums for the insurance are:

Buildings: £1.35 per £1000 of cover,   Contents: 56p per £100 of cover.

Calculate the total cost of the insurance premium.

8 The table shows the premiums charged by an insurance company to insure a house and its contents.

	Buildings and Contents Insurance	
	Buildings	Contents
Annual premium for each £1000 insured	£1.50 Minimum £20 per year	£5.00

(a) Mrs Adams has a flat valued at £48 000.
What premium would she pay to insure the flat?

(b) Jim has bought a house valued at £125 000.
How much would he pay to insure the house?

(c) The cost for Mr Brown to insure his house is £126.
What is the value of his house?

(d) Mrs Crow insures the contents of her house for £19 000.
What is the annual premium?

(e) Mr Rowe insures his house valued at £96 000 and its contents valued at £28 000.
What is the total cost of the insurance premium?

(f) Andy insures his flat valued at £72 000 and its contents valued at £14 000.
Calculate the total cost of the insurance premium.

9 Naomi rents a flat and pays £69.44 to insure its contents.
Contents insurance costs 56p for each £100 insured.
For how much are the contents insured?

VAT

Some goods and services are subject to a tax called **value added tax**, or **VAT**, which is calculated as a percentage of the price or bill. Total amount payable = cost of item or service + VAT

For most purchases the rate of VAT is 17.5%. For gas and electricity the rate of VAT is 5%. Some goods are exempt from VAT.

EXAMPLES

1 A bill at a restaurant is £24 + VAT at 17.5%. What is the total bill?

Remember: $17.5\% = \frac{17.5}{100} = 0.175$

VAT: £24 × 0.175 = £4.20

Total bill: £24 + £4.20 = £28.20

The total bill is £28.20.

2 An electricity bill of £49.14 includes VAT at 5%.
How much VAT is paid?

Cost = cost without VAT + 5% VAT.
£49.14 = 105% of cost without VAT.

1% of cost without VAT is given by £49.14 ÷ 105 = £0.468

VAT = 5% of cost without VAT, so VAT = £0.468 × 5 = £2.34.

Exercise 16.8

Do not use a calculator for questions 1 and 2.

1 Naomi's gas bill is £120 plus VAT at 5%. How much VAT does she have to pay?

2 Joe receives an electricity bill for £70 plus VAT at 5%.
   (a) Calculate the amount of VAT charged.
   (b) What is the total bill?

3 A washing machine costs £340 plus VAT at 17.5%.
   (a) Calculate the amount of VAT charged.
   (b) What is the total cost of the washing machine?

4 A car service costs £90 plus VAT at 17.5%.
   (a) Calculate the amount of VAT charged.
   (b) What is the total cost of the service?

5 Mrs Swan receives a gas bill for £179.53. VAT at 5% is added to the bill.
   (a) How much VAT does she have to pay?
   (b) What is the total bill?

6 A bike costs £248 plus VAT at 17.5%. What is the total cost of the bike?

7 A ladder costs £145 plus VAT at 17.5%. What is the total cost of the ladder?

8 Joyce buys a greenhouse for £184 plus VAT.
VAT is charged at 17.5%.
What is the total cost of the greenhouse?

9 James receives a telephone bill for £75.12 plus VAT at 17.5%.
How much is the total bill?

10 George buys vertical blinds for his windows. He needs three blinds at £65 each and two blinds at £85 each.
VAT at 17.5% is added to the cost of the blinds.
How much do the blinds cost altogether?

11
> **CAR HIRE CHARGES**
> £25 per day, plus 10p for every mile driven.

A car is hired for two days and driven 90 miles.
VAT at 17.5% is added to the car charges.
How much does it cost to hire the car altogether?

12 A computer costs £1233.75 including VAT at 17.5%. How much of the cost is VAT?

13 A gas bill of £67.20 includes VAT at 5%. How much VAT is paid?

14 VAT at 17.5% on a washing machine is £43.75. What is the price of the washing machine including VAT?

15 The bill for a new central heating boiler includes £436.10 VAT.
VAT is charged at 17.5%.
What is the total bill?

Money invested in a savings account or a bank or building society earns **interest**, which is usually paid once a year.

Simple Interest

With **Simple Interest**, the interest is paid out each year and not added to your account.
The amount of Simple Interest an investment earns can be calculated using:

Simple Interest = $\dfrac{\text{Amount}}{\text{invested}}$ × $\dfrac{\text{Time in}}{\text{years}}$ × $\dfrac{\text{Rate of interest}}{\text{per year}}$

Banks and building societies advertise the **yearly rates** of interest payable.

For example, 6% per year.

Interest, usually calculated annually, can also be calculated for shorter periods of time.

Compound Interest

With **Compound Interest**, the interest earned each year is added to your account and also earns interest the following year.

For example, an investment of 5% per annum means that the amount invested earns £5 for every £100 invested for one year.

So, after the first year of the investment, every £100 invested becomes £100 + 5% of £100.
£100 + 5% of £100 = £100 + £5 = £105
So, after the second year of the investment, every £100 of the original investment becomes £105 + 5% of £105.
£105 + 5% of £105 = £105 + £5.25 = £110.25

This can also be calculated as: $100 \times (1.05)^2 = £110.25$
Explain why this works.

EXAMPLES

1 Find the Simple Interest paid on £600 invested for 6 months at 8% per year.

Simple Interest
$$= 600 \times \tfrac{6}{12} \times \tfrac{8}{100}$$
$$= 600 \times 0.5 \times 0.08$$
$$= £24$$

The Simple Interest paid is £24.

Note: Interest rates are given 'per year'. The length of time for which an investment is made is also given in years.
6 months = $\tfrac{6}{12}$ years.
Explain why.

2 Find the Compound Interest paid on £600 invested for 3 years at 6% per year.

1st year	Investment	= £600
	Interest: £600 × 0.06	= £ 36
	Value of investment after one year	= £636
2nd year	Investment	= £636
	Interest: £636 × 0.06	= £ 38.16
	Value of investment after two years	= £674.16
3rd year	Investment	= £674.16
	Interest: £674.16 × 0.06	= £ 40.45
	Value of investment after three years	= £714.61

Compound Interest = Final value − Original value
$$= £714.61 - £600 = £114.61$$

This could also be calculated as follows: $600 \times (1.06)^3 - 600 = £114.61$

Exercise 16.9

Do not use a calculator for questions 1 to 8.

1 Find the simple interest paid on £200 for 1 year at 5% per year.

2 Calculate the simple interest on £500 invested at 6% per year after
(a) 1 year, (b) 6 months.

3 A school savings account pays interest at 8% per year.
Find the simple interest paid on savings of £50 after 6 months.

4 Calculate the simple interest paid on an investment of £6000 at 7.5% per year after 6 months.

5 Find the simple interest on £800 invested for 9 months at 8% per year.

6 Calculate the simple interest on £10 000 invested for 3 months at 9% per year.

7 Jenny invests £200 at 10% per annum compound interest.
What is the value of her investment after 2 years?

8 Geof invests £300 at 5% per annum compound interest.
What is the value of his investment after 2 years?

9 Which of the following investments earn more interest?
(a) £200 for 3 years at 5% compound.
(b) £300 for 2 years at 5% compound.

10 £10 000 is to be invested for 3 years.
Calculate the final value of the investment if the interest rate per annum is:
(a) 5% (b) 6% (c) 7% (d) 8%
Give your answers to a suitable degree of accuracy.

11 Interest on a loan of £2000 is charged at the rate of 21% per annum. Interest is calculated on the outstanding loan at the **start** of each year.
(a) How much is owed immediately the loan is taken out?
Repayments are £600 per year.
(b) How much is owed at the **start** of the third year of the loan?

Foreign currency

When we go abroad we have to pay for goods and services in the currency of the country we are visiting. We therefore need to change pounds (£) into other currencies. The rate of exchange varies from day to day.

The table below shows the exchange rates on one day.

EXCHANGE RATE Each £ will buy	
European currency	1.55 euros
Japan	173 yen
Malta	0.63 liri
Norway	12.48 krone
Switzerland	2.30 francs
USA	1.42 dollars

EXAMPLE

What is the value, in £s and pence, of 500 Norwegian krone?
12.48 krone = £1
500 krone = 500 ÷ 12.48
= £40.0641…
500 krone = £40.06, to the nearest penny.

Exercise 16.10

Use the table of exchange rates above to answer these questions.

1 How much will I receive if I change £200 into
(a) European euros, (b) Japanese yen, (c) Maltese liri,
(d) Norwegian krone, (e) Swiss francs, (f) United States dollars?

2 How much would each item cost in £s? Give your answers to the nearest penny.
(a) A vase in Switzerland for 90 francs. (b) A radio in Japan for 5000 yen.
(c) A pair of shoes in Italy for 75 euros. (d) A meal in Norway for 225 krone.
(e) A pair of jeans in the United States for 35 dollars.

3 (a) A tourist changes £25 into euros. How many euros does she receive?
(b) She pays 23.25 euros for a gift. What is the cost of the gift in £s?

4 Norman travels to Switzerland. He changes £120 into francs.
  (a) How many francs does he receive?
  (b) He pays 24.50 francs for a box of chocolates.
      What is the cost of the chocolates in £s?

5 Dolores travels to England from Spain. She changes 600 euros into £.
  (a) How much, in £s and pence, does she receive?
  (b) She buys a theatre ticket for £30.
      What is the cost of the theatre ticket in euros?

6 Marcel travels to England from Norway. He changes 3000 krone into £.
  (a) How much, in £s, does he receive?
  (b) He pays £45 for bed and breakfast.
      What is the cost of bed and breakfast in krone?

7 Sue changes £500 into dollars for a trip to the USA.
  (a) How many dollars does she receive?
  (b) On holiday she spends 680 dollars. She changes the remaining dollars back into £s.
      There is a £3 charge for changing the money.
      How much, in £s, will she receive?

8 Jeff has just returned from Malta. He changes 85 liri back into £s.
  There is a £3 charge for changing the money. How much, in £s, will he receive?

9 In France a car costs 9000 euros. In Japan the same car costs 1 million yen.
  In which country is the car cheaper? By how much?

What you need to know

- Time can be given using either the **12-hour clock** or the **24-hour clock**.
  When using the 12-hour clock:
      times **before** midday are given as am,
      times **after** midday are given as pm.

- **Timetables** are usually given using the 24-hour clock.
- **Hourly pay** is paid at a **basic rate** for a fixed number of hours.
  Overtime pay is usually paid at a higher rate such as time and a half,
  which means each hour's work is worth 1.5 times the basic rate.
- Everyone is allowed to earn some money which is not taxed. This is called a **tax allowance**.
- Tax is only paid on income earned in excess of the tax allowance. This is called **taxable income**.
- **Value added tax**, or **VAT**, is a tax on some goods and services and is added to the bill.
- Gas, electricity and telephone bills are paid **quarterly**. The bill consists of a standing charge plus a charge for the amount used.
- When considering a **best buy**, compare quantities by using the same units. For example, find which product gives more grams per penny.
- Money invested in a savings account at a bank or building society earns **interest**, which is usually paid once a year.
  With **Simple Interest**, the interest is paid out each year and not added to your account.

$$\text{Simple Interest} = \frac{\text{Amount}}{\text{invested}} \times \frac{\text{Time in}}{\text{years}} \times \frac{\text{Rate of interest}}{\text{per year}}$$

  With **Compound Interest**, the interest earned each year is added to your account and also earns interest the following year.

- **Exchange rates** are used to show what £1 will buy in foreign currencies.

Review Exercise 16   Do not use a calculator for questions 1 to 6.

16

1 (a) A taxi left Russell Square at 1643. It arrived at Waterloo Station 22 minutes later.
At what time did the taxi arrive at Waterloo Station?
Give your answer in 12 hour clock time.

(b) Part of a railway timetable is shown.

London Waterloo	1630	1645	1715	1745	1830	1850
Southampton	1739	1810	1825	1859	1940	2018
Bournemouth	1812	1831	1856	1929	2011	2101
Poole	1825	1905	1907	1942	2023	2116
Weymouth	1913	—	1953	2028	2111	—

George catches the 1745 from London Waterloo to Bournemouth.
How long does the journey take?

AQA

2 Mrs Wye pays 39p for 0.5 kg of carrots and 200 g of onions.
The onions cost 55p per kilogram. How much per kilogram are carrots?

3 (a) Anita hires a van for one day.
She drives 68 miles.
How much is the hire charge?

(b) John hires a van for two days.
The total hire charge is £66.
How many miles did he drive?

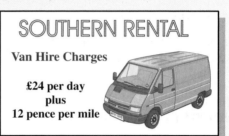

SOUTHERN RENTAL

Van Hire Charges

£24 per day
plus
12 pence per mile

AQA

4 Bernadette has to pay tax at the rate of 10p in the £ on the first £1960 of her taxable income
and 22p in the £ on the remainder. Her taxable income is £2967.
How much tax does she have to pay?

5 Gerald invests £9000 at 8% per year simple interest.
(a) How much interest does he get at the end of one year?

He has the option of taking his interest as monthly income.
(b) How much would he get each month?

6 The price of a bottle of red wine and a kilogram of
Cheddar cheese are shown.
What is the total cost of twelve bottles of red wine
and a quarter of a kilogram of Cheddar cheese?

CHEDDAR CHEESE £4.96 per kg

RED WINE £3.29

AQA

7 This appears at the top of an electricity bill.

Your bill is made up of two parts:
A service charge of £8.22
Cost of electricity used which is
9.18 pence per unit.

(a) Mrs Cooper has used 425 units.
Calculate her bill.
(b) Mrs Speed's bill is £35.76.
Calculate how many units she used.

AQA

8 Jam is sold in two sizes.
A large pot of jam costs 88p and weighs 822 g.
A small pot of jam costs 47p and weighs 454 g.
Which pot of jam is better value for money?
You must show all your working.

LARGE

SMALL

AQA

9 Mr Habib receives a gas bill for £124 + VAT. The rate of VAT is 5%.
How much VAT does he have to pay?

10 A lap top computer costs £499 + VAT at $17\frac{1}{2}$%.
What is the total cost of the computer?

11 Josie decides to buy a motorcycle on credit.
The credit terms are:

> **Cash price** **£1280,**
> **No deposit,**
> **Credit charge** **12.5% of cash price.**

The total cost is the credit charge plus the cash price.
She pays by 12 equal monthly payments.
How much does she pay each month?

AQA

12 Francis is paid £5.60 per hour for a basic 35-hour week.
One week Francis also works overtime at time and a half.
His total pay that week was £229.60.
How many hours overtime did he work that week?

13 A bottle of lemonade costs 95 pence in London. In Rome, the same size bottle costs 1.20 euros.
There are 1.60 euros to £1.
In which city does the lemonade cost more? You should show all your working.

AQA

14 In 2002 the rate of exchange was 1.56 euros to the £.
(a) A tourist changes £25 into euros.
How many euros does she receive?
(b) She pays 21.50 euros for a gift to bring home.
What is the cost of the gift in pounds and pence?

15 Sophie invests £1550 in a building society at 9% interest per year.
How much money will she have after 6 months?

AQA

16 Hannah invests £360 in a building society account at 4.8% per year.
Find the simple interest paid on her investment after 4 months.

17 Shane invests £2000 at 7% per annum compound interest.
Calculate the value of his investment after 3 years.

18 In 1982 it was estimated that there were only 20 000 Minke whales left in the world.
The hunting of Minke whales was banned in 1982.
After 1982 the population increased by 45% each year.
(a) How many Minke whales were there in 1983 (1 year after the ban)?
(b) How many Minke whales were there in 1985 (3 years after the ban)?
Give your answer to a suitable degree of accuracy.
(c) It was agreed that when the Minke whale population reached 250 000 some hunting of
Minke whales would be allowed again.
In what year did this happen?

AQA

Some faces are
SMILERS.

Some faces are
GLUMS.

In a group of 10 faces the **ratio** of SMILERS to GLUMS is 3 : 2.
This means that for every three SMILERS there are two GLUMS.

○○○○○

For the
ratio 3 : 2
say 3 to 2.

In the group there are 6 SMILERS and 4 GLUMS.

Exercise **17.1**

1 (a) Draw 10 faces where the ratio of SMILERS to GLUMS is 4 : 1.
(b) Draw 12 faces where the ratio of SMILERS to GLUMS is:
(i) 2 : 1 (ii) 1 : 3
(c) Draw 20 faces where the ratio of SMILERS to GLUMS is
(i) 4 : 1 (ii) 2 : 3

2 The ratio of GLUMS to SMILERS is 2 : 5.

(a) How many SMILERS are there when there are
(i) 30 GLUMS, (ii) 80 GLUMS?
(b) How many GLUMS are there when there are
(i) 30 SMILERS, (ii) 80 SMILERS?
(c) How many FACES are there when there are
(i) 40 SMILERS, (ii) 40 GLUMS?

3 The ratio of SMILERS to GLUMS is 4 : 3.

(a) How many SMILERS are there when there are
(i) 12 GLUMS, (ii) 60 GLUMS?
(b) How many GLUMS are there when there are
(i) 12 SMILERS, (ii) 60 SMILERS?
(c) How many FACES are there when there are
(i) 48 SMILERS, (ii) 48 GLUMS?

4 How many SMILERS and how many GLUMS are there when
(a) the ratio of SMILERS to GLUMS is 7 : 3 and there are:
(i) 20 faces, (ii) 50 faces?
(b) the ratio of SMILERS to GLUMS is 3 : 2 and there are:
(i) 15 faces, (ii) 50 faces?

Equivalent ratios

Ratios are used only to **compare** quantities.
They do not give information about actual values.

For example.
A necklace is made using red beads and white beads in
the ratio **3 : 4**.
This gives no information about the actual numbers of
beads in the necklace.
The ratio **3 : 4** means that for every 3 red beads in the
necklace there are 4 white beads.
The **possible** numbers of beads in the necklace are shown in the table.

Red beads	White beads	Total beads
3	4	7
6	8	14
9	12	21
12	16	28
18	24	42
...	...	...

*Make similar tables when the ratio of red
beads to white beads in the necklace is:*
(a) 4 : 5   (b) 2 : 3   (c) 3 : 1

The ratios 3 : 4, 6 : 8, 9 : 12, ...
are different forms of the **same** ratio.
They are called **equivalent** ratios.
They can be found by multiplying or dividing
each part of the ratio by the **same** number.

For the beads in this necklace:
The number of red beads is a **multiple** of 3.
The number of white beads is a **multiple** of 4.
The total number of beads is a **multiple** of 7.

Simplifying ratios

To simplify a ratio divide both of the numbers in the ratio by the **same** number.
A ratio with whole numbers which cannot be simplified is in its **simplest form**.

EXAMPLES

1 Find 3 ratios that are equivalent to the ratio 2 : 1.
$$2 \times 2 : 1 \times 2 = 4 : 2$$
$$2 \times 3 : 1 \times 3 = 6 : 3$$
$$2 \times 4 : 1 \times 4 = 8 : 4$$
3 ratios equivalent to the ratio 2 : 1 are 4 : 2, 6 : 3 and 8 : 4.

Finding equivalent ratios

To find equivalent ratios
multiply or divide each
number in the ratio by the
same number.

2 The ratio of boys to girls in a school is 3 : 4.
There are 72 boys. How many girls are there?

$$72 \div 3 = 24$$
To find a ratio equivalent to 3 : 4 where the first number in the ratio is 72,
multiply each number in the ratio by 24.
$$3 \times 24 : 4 \times 24 = 72 : 96$$
The number of girls = 96.

3 Write the ratio 15 : 9 in its simplest form.

15 and 9 can both be divided by 3.
$$15 \div 3 : 9 \div 3 = 5 : 3$$
5 : 3 cannot be simplified.
The ratio 15 : 9 in its simplest form is 5 : 3.

In its simplest form a ratio
contains **only** whole
numbers.
There are **no units**.
In order to simplify the ratio
both quantities in the ratio
must be in the **same units**.

4 Write the ratio 2 cm : 50 mm in its simplest form.

$$2\,cm : 50\,mm = 20\,mm : 50\,mm = 20 : 50$$
Divide both parts of the ratio by 10.
$$20 \div 10 : 50 \div 10 = 2 : 5$$
The ratio 2 cm : 50 mm in its simplest form is 2 : 5.

Do not use a calculator in this exercise.

1 Give three ratios equivalent to each ratio.   (a) 6 : 1   (b) 7 : 2   (c) 3 : 5

2 Give the simplest form of each of these ratios.
(a) 3 : 6   (b) 9 : 27   (c) 9 : 12   (d) 10 : 25   (e) 30 : 40   (f) 22 : 55
(g) 9 : 21   (h) 18 : 8   (i) 36 : 81   (j) 35 : 15

3 Each of these pairs of ratios are equivalent.
(a) 3 : 4 and 9 : *n*.   (b) 2 : 7 and 8 : *n*.   (c) 8 : *n* and 2 : 25.   (d) 25 : *n* and 5 : 4.
In each case calculate the value of *n*.

4 The heights of two friends are in the ratio 7 : 9. The shorter of the friends is 154 cm tall.
What is the height of the taller of the friends?

5 Sugar and flour are mixed in the ratio 2 : 3. How much sugar is used with 600 g of flour?

6 The ratio of boys to girls in a school is 4 : 5. There are 80 girls.
How many boys are there?

7   I earn £800 per month.   I earn £720 per month.

The amounts Jenny and James earn
is in the ratio of their ages.
Jenny is 20 years old. How old is James?

8 A necklace contains 30 black beads and 45 gold beads.
What is the simplest form of the ratio of black beads to gold beads on the necklace?

9 On Monday a hairdresser uses 800 ml of shampoo and 320 ml of conditioner.
Write in its simplest form the ratio of shampoo : conditioner used on Monday.

10 Denise draws a plan of her classroom. On her plan Denise uses 2 cm to represent 5 m.
Write the scale as a ratio in its simplest form.

11 On a map a pond is 3.5 cm long. The pond is actually 52.5 m long.
Write the scale as a ratio in its simplest form.

12 Write each of these ratios in its simplest form.
(a) £2 : 50p   (b) 20p : £2.50   (c) £2.20 : 40p   (d) 6 m : 240 cm
(e) 2 kg : 500 g   (f) 1 kg : 425 g   (g) 90 cm : 2 m   (h) 5 km : 200 m
(i) 20 seconds : 5 minutes   (j) $\frac{1}{2}$ minute : 15 seconds

13 Sam spends 90p a week on comics. Tom spends £4 a week on comics.
Write the ratio of the amounts Tom and Sam spend on comics in its simplest form.

14 The cards in a pack are marked ☒ or ◯   25% of the cards are marked ☒

What is the ratio of cards marked ☒ : ◯ in its simplest form?

15 An alloy is made of tin and zinc. 40% of the alloy is tin.
What is the ratio of tin : zinc in its simplest form?

16 A box contains blue biros and red biros. $\frac{1}{3}$ of the biros are blue.
What is the ratio of blue biros to red biros in the box?

17 A necklace is made from 40 beads. $\frac{2}{5}$ of the beads are white. The rest of the beads are red.
Find the ratio of the number of red beads to the number of white beads in its simplest form.

EXAMPLES

1 James and Sally share £20 in the ratio 3 : 2.
How much do they each get?

Add the numbers in the ratio.
3 + 2 = 5
For every £5 shared:
      James gets £3,   Sally gets £2.
20 ÷ 5 = 4
There are 4 shares of £5 in £20.
James gets £3 × 4 = £12.
Sally gets £2 × 4 = £8.
So James gets £12 and Sally gets £8.

2 A necklace is made using red beads and
gold beads in the ratio 7 : 3.
A total of 30 beads are used in the necklace.

Calculate the number of red beads and gold
beads used to make the necklace.

Add the numbers in the ratio. 7 + 3 = 10
Number of shares   30 ÷ 10 = 3
Red beads   7 × 3 = 21.
Gold beads   3 × 3 = 9.
There are 21 red beads and 9 gold beads.

Exercise 17.3

Do not use a calculator for questions 1 to 6.

1 (a)   Share 9 in the ratio 2 : 1.   (b)   Share 20 in the ratio 3 : 1.
    (c)   Share 35 in the ratio 1 : 4.   (d)   Share 100 in the ratio 9 : 1.

2 A box contains gold coins and silver coins.
The ratio of gold coins to silver coins is 1 : 9. There are 20 coins in the box.
How many silver coins are in the box?

3 Sunny and Chandni share £48 in the ratio 3 : 1. How much do they each get?

4 Copy and complete this table.

	Quantity	Shared in the ratio	
		4 : 1	3 : 2
(a)	40 marbles		
(b)	20 sweets		
(c)	80 kg		
(d)	200 g		
(e)	£1200		

5 (a)   Share £35 in the ratio 2 : 3.   (b)   Share £56 in the ratio 4 : 3.
    (c)   Share £5.50 in the ratio 7 : 4.   (d)   Share £4.80 in the ratio 3 : 5.

6 A necklace contains 72 beads. The ratio of red beads to blue beads is 5 : 3.
How many red beads are on the necklace?

7 £480 is shared in the ratio 7 : 3.
What is the difference between the larger share and the smaller share?

8 In 1901, the total population of England and Wales was 32 528 000.
The ratio of the population of England to the population of Wales was 15 : 1.
What was the population of Wales in 1901?

9 A bag contains red beads and black beads in the ratio 1 : 3.
What fraction of the beads are red?

10 A box contains red biros and black biros in the ratio 1 : 4.
What percentage of the biros are black?

11   In a school the ratio of the number of boys to the number of girls is 3 : 5.
What fraction of the pupils in the school are girls?

12   The ratio of non-fiction books to fiction books in a library is 2 : 3.
Find the percentage of fiction books in the library.

13   John is 12 years old and Sara is 13 years old. They share some money in the ratio of their ages.
What percentage of the money does John get?

14   In the UK there are 240 939 km^2 of land.
The ratio of agricultural land to non-agricultural land is approximately 7 : 3.
Estimate the area of land used for agriculture.

15   At the start of a game Jenny and Tim have 40 counters each.
At the end of the game the number of counters that Jenny and Tim each have is in the ratio 5 : 3.
(a)   How many counters do Jenny and Tim have at the end of the game?
(b)   How many counters did Jenny win from Tim in the game?

16   On a necklace, for every 10 black beads there are 4 red beads.
(a)   What is the ratio of black beads to red beads in its simplest form?
(b)   If the necklace has 15 black beads how many red beads are there?
(c)   If the necklace has a total of 77 beads how many black beads are there?
(d)   Why can't the necklace have a total of 32 beads?

17   The lengths of the sides of a triangle are in the ratio 4 : 6 : 9.
The total length of the sides is 38 cm. Calculate the length of each side.

18   To make concrete a builder mixes gravel, sand and cement in the ratio 4 : 2 : 1.
The builder wants 350 kg of concrete. How much gravel does the builder need?

19   The angles of a triangle are in the ratio 2 : 3 : 4. Calculate each angle.

20   A bag contains some red, green and black sweets. 30% of the sweets are red.
The ratio of the numbers of green sweets to black sweets is 5 to 9.
What percentage of the total number of sweets are black?

21   Alan, Beth and Catrina share some money in the ratio 1 : 3 : 4.
(a)   What percentage of the money do they each receive?
(b)   What fraction of Beth's share is Alan's share?
(c)   What fraction of Alan and Catrina's share is Beth's share?

Proportion

Some situations involve comparing **different** quantities.
For example, when a motorist buys fuel the more he buys the greater the cost.
In this situation the quantities can change but the ratio between the quantities stays the same.
When two different quantities are in the **same ratio** they are said to be in **direct proportion**.

EXAMPLE

4 cakes cost £1.20.
Find the cost of 7 cakes.

4 cakes cost £1.20
1 cake costs £1.20 ÷ 4 = 30p
7 cakes cost 30p × 7 = £2.10
So 7 cakes cost £2.10.

This is sometimes called the **unitary method**.
(a)   **Divide** by 4 to find the cost of **1** cake.
(b)   **Multiply** by 7 to find the cost of 7 cakes.

Ratio • • Ratio • • • Ratio • • • Ratio • • • Ratio • • • •

1 5 candles cost 80 pence.
   (a) What is the cost of 1 candle?
   (b) What is the cost of 8 candles?

2 Georgina works for 4 hours and earns £24.
   (a) How much does she earn in 1 hour?
   (b) How much does she earn in 10 hours?

3 Alistair pays £1.90 for 2 cups of tea.
   How much would he pay for 3 cups of tea?

4 The amount a spring stretches is proportional to the weight hung on the spring.
   A weight of 5 kg stretches the spring by 60 cm.
   (a) How much does a weight of 10 kg stretch the spring?
   (b) What weight makes the spring stretch 24 cm?

5 Jean pays £168 for 10 square metres of carpet.

   How much would 12 square metres of carpet cost?

6 These ingredients are needed to make 20 scones.

> 500 g flour,   250 g butter,
> 100 g dried fruit,   water to mix.

   (a) How much dried fruit is needed to make 50 scones?
   (b) How much butter is needed to make 12 scones?

7 Alfie is paid £48.80 for working 4 hours overtime.
   How much would he be paid for 5 hours overtime?

8 Aimee pays £1.14 for 3 kg of potatoes.

   How much would 7.5 kg of potatoes cost?

9 5 litres of petrol costs £4.10.
   How much would 18 litres of petrol cost?

10 These ingredients are needed to make an apple crumble for 6 people.

> 540 g apples
> 75 g butter
> 150 g flour
> 75 g sugar

   (a) How much sugar is needed to make an apple crumble for 4 people?
   (b) How much apple is needed to make an apple crumble for 8 people?

11 9 metres of stair carpet cost £41.85.
   How much does 9.6 metres cost?

12 29 euros is about the same as £20.
   Sue spends 47 euros.
   How many pounds is this?

13 Mary phones her uncle in New York.
   Phone calls to New York are charged at the rate of £2.20 for a 5-minute call.

   (a) How much would a 7-minute call to New York cost?
   (b) Mary's call cost £5.28. How long was her call?

14 These ingredients are needed to make macaroni cheese for 4 people.

> Macaroni   120 g
> Cheese   72 g
> Flour   30 g
> Milk   850 ml

   (a) How much cheese is needed to make macaroni cheese for 10 people?
   (b) How much milk is needed to make macaroni cheese for 3 people?
   (c) How much macaroni is needed to make macaroni cheese for 7 people?

15 A car travels 6 miles in 9 minutes.
   If the car travels at the same speed:
   (a) how long will it take to travel 8 miles,
   (b) how far will it travel in 24 minutes?

16 5 litres of paint cover an area of 30 m².
   (a) What area will 2 litres of paint cover?
   (b) How much paint is needed to cover 72 m²?

17 A school is organising three trips to the zoo.

Our trip is on Monday.
There are 45 people going.
The total cost is £468.

Our trip is on Tuesday.
25 students are going.

Our trip is on Wednesday.
The total cost is £332.80.

(a) How much does Tuesday's trip cost?
(b) How many students are going to the zoo on Wednesday?

18 A 42 litre paddling pool is filled at the rate of 12 litres of water every 5 minutes. How long will it take to fill the pool?

19 50 g of flour and 90 ml of milk are needed to make 8 biscuits.
(a) How much flour is needed to make 27 biscuits?
(b) How many biscuits can be made with 225 g of flour?
Some biscuits are made with 300 g of flour.
(c) How much milk is needed?

20 A piece of beef weighs 1.5 kg and costs £5.22. How much would a piece of beef weighing 2.4 kg cost?
Give your answer to a suitable degree of accuracy.

What you need to know

- The ratio 3 : 2 is read '3 to 2'.

- A ratio is used only to **compare** quantities.
  A ratio does not give information about the exact values of quantities being compared.

- To simplify a ratio divide both of the numbers in the ratio by the **same** number.
  A ratio with whole numbers which cannot be simplified is in its s**implest form**.
  All quantities in a ratio must have the **same units** before the ratio can be simplified.
  For example, £2.50 : 50p = 250p : 50p = 5 : 1.

- When two different quantities are in the **same ratio** the two quantities are in **direct proportion.**
  For example, the amount and cost of fuel bought by a motorist are in proportion.

Do the squares fit?
Square P has side 3 cm and square Q has side 4 cm.
Square Q is cut into four **equal** pieces, as shown, where the ratio $a : b$ on each side is 7 : 1.

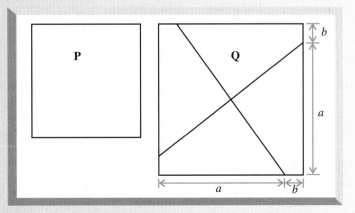

Show how square P and the four pieces of Q fit together exactly to make another square.
Repeat when square P has side 2 cm and square Q has side 6 cm.
Investigate.

Do not use a calculator for questions 1 to 10.

1 A tin contains 21 nuts and 28 bolts. What is the ratio of nuts to bolts in its simplest form?

2 A sewing box contains pins and needles in the ratio 4 : 1. There are 36 pins in the box.
How many needles are in the box?

3 In a class the ratio of students with dark hair to those with light hair is 3 : 2.
There are 18 students with dark hair.
How many students have light hair?

4 Max shares £420 with a friend in the ratio 5 : 3. How much does each receive?   AQA

5 A test is taken by 28 pupils. The ratio of the number of boys to the number of girls is 3 : 4.
How many boys take the test?   AQA

6 (a) A bag contains 3 black counters and 2 white counters.
Another bag contains 30 counters.
There is the same **ratio** of black counters to white counters.
How many black counters are in the bag?
   (b) Another bag contains black counters and white counters in the ratio 7 to 13.
What percentage of the counters are black?   AQA

7 (a) A wood contains fir trees and yew trees in the ratio 3 : 4.
There are 18 fir trees in the wood.
How many yew trees are in the wood?
   (b) Another wood contains 20 beech trees and 12 ash trees.
Write, in its simplest form, the ratio of beech trees to ash trees.

8 Alison pays £483 for a package holiday.
The cost of travel to the cost of accommodation is in the ratio 3 : 4.
What is the cost of the accommodation?   AQA

9 Fiona is given £24 for her birthday. She spends 5 times as much as she saves.
How much does she save?   AQA

10 These ingredients are needed to make 20 scones.

| 500 g flour   100 g dried fruit   250 g butter   water to mix |

   (a) How much dried fruit would you need for 5 scones?
   (b) How much flour would you need for 30 scones?   AQA

11 A recipe for 18 buns needs: 150 g flour   100 g butter   50 g sugar
   (a) Calculate the amount of flour needed for 45 buns. Give your answer in kilograms.
   (b) Lucy has plenty of flour and butter but only one kilogram of sugar.
How many buns can she make with this?   AQA

12 Two pints of milk cost 58p. What is the cost of 5 pints of milk at the same price per pint?   AQA

13 On a map the distance between two houses is 19 mm.
The actual distance between the houses is 3.8 km.
What is the scale of the map?

14 Jack is building a brick wall for a garage.
He decides to use a mortar mix given by:
1 part cement,   1 part lime,   6 parts sand.
   (a) What fraction of the mix will be sand?
   (b) What percentage of the mix will be cement?
   (c) He uses 1200 cm³ of sand for the mix.
What volume of lime will he need?   AQA

CHAPTER 18

Speed and Other Compound Measures

Speed

Speed is a measurement of how fast something is travelling.
It involves two other measures, **distance** and **time**.
Speed can be worked out using this formula.

$$\text{Speed} = \frac{\text{Distance}}{\text{Time}}$$

Speed can be thought of as the **distance** travelled in **one unit of time** (1 hour, 1 second, …)

Speed can be measured in:
kilometres per hour (km/h), metres per second (m/s), miles per hour (mph), and so on.

Average speed

When the speed of an object is **constant** it means that the object doesn't slow down or go faster.
However, in many situations, speed is not constant.
For example:
A sprinter needs time to start from the starting blocks and is well into the race before running at top speed.
A plane changes speed as it takes off and lands.

In situations like this the idea of **average speed** can be used.
The formula for average speed is:

$$\text{Average speed} = \frac{\text{Total distance travelled}}{\text{Total time taken}}$$

The formula linking speed, distance and time can be rearranged and remembered as:

(average) **speed** = (total) **distance** ÷ (total) **time**	$S = D \div T$
(total) **distance** = (average) **speed** × (total) **time**	$D = S \times T$
(total) **time** = (total) **distance** ÷ (average) **speed**	$T = D \div S$

EXAMPLES

1 A cheetah takes 4 seconds to travel 100 m.
What is the speed of the cheetah in metres per second?

$$\text{Speed} = \frac{\text{Distance}}{\text{Time}} = \frac{100}{4} = 100 \div 4 = 25 \text{ m/s}$$

2 Lisa drives at an average speed of 80 km/h on a journey that takes 3 hours.
What distance has she travelled?

Distance = Speed × Time = 80 × 3 = 240 km

So in 3 hours she travels 240 km.

3 Lucy cycles at an average speed of 7 km/h on a journey of 21 km.
How long does she take?

Time = Distance ÷ Speed = 21 ÷ 7 = 3

So her journey takes 3 hours.

4 The Scottish Pullman travels from London to York, a distance of 302.8 km in 1 hour 45 minutes.
It then travels from York to Edinburgh, a distance of 334.7 km in 2 hours 30 minutes.
Calculate the average speed of the train between London and Edinburgh.
Total distance travelled = 302.8 + 334.7 = 637.5 km
Total time taken = 1 hr 45 mins + 2 hr 30 mins = 4 hr 15 mins = 4.25 hours
Average speed = $\frac{637.5}{4.25}$ = 150 km/h

Exercise 18.1

Do not use a calculator for questions 1 to 12.

1 John cycles 16 miles in 2 hours. What is his average speed in miles per hour?

2 Calculate the average speed for each of the following journeys in kilometres per hour.

	Total distance travelled	Total time taken
(a)	60 km	3 hours
(b)	100 km	2 hours
(c)	10 km	$2\frac{1}{2}$ hours

3 Jackie runs 21 km in $1\frac{1}{2}$ hours. What is her average speed in kilometres per hour?

4 Beverley walks for 2 hours at an average speed of 4 km/h.
How many kilometres does she walk?

5 Calculate the total distance travelled on each of the following journeys.

	Total time taken	Average speed
(a)	3 hours	50 km/h
(b)	50 seconds	8 m/s
(c)	10 minutes	150 m/min

6 Aubrey runs at 6 km/h for $\frac{1}{2}$ hour. How far does he run?

7 Calculate the total time taken on each of the following journeys.

	Total distance travelled	Average speed
(a)	30 km	10 km/h
(b)	800 m	400 m/min
(c)	100 m	5 m/s

8 A train travels 75 km at an average speed of 50 km/h. How long does the journey take?

9 Ahmed drives 15 km at an average speed of 60 km/h. How long does the journey take?

10 Lauren cycles 27 km at 12 km/h. How long does she take?

11 Joe swims 100 m in 4 minutes. What is his average speed in metres per minute?

12 Penny cycles to work at 18 km/h. She takes 20 minutes. How far does she cycle to work?

13 A train travels 36 km at an average speed of 80 km/h. How long does the journey take?

14 Bristol is 40 miles from Gloucester.
(a) How long does it take to cycle from Bristol to Gloucester at 16 miles per hour?
(b) How long does it take to drive from Bristol to Gloucester at 48 miles per hour?

15 A car travels 115 km in 2 hours.
    (a)   What is its average speed in kilometres per hour?
    (b)   How many hours would the car take to travel 115 km if it had gone twice as fast?

16 The table shows details of 5 different journeys.

Journey	(a)	(b)	(c)	(d)	(e)
Total distance	200 m			200 km	250 m
Total time	25 secs	2 hours	10 min		
Average speed		50 km/h	1.2 cm/min	200 km/h	50 m/s

Copy and complete the table. State the units of each answer.

17 On the first part of a journey a car travels 140 km in 3 hours.
On the second part of the journey the car travels 160 km in 2 hours.
    (a)   What is the total distance travelled on the journey?
    (b)   What is the total time taken on the journey?
    (c)   What is the average speed of the car over the whole journey?

18 Lisa runs two laps of a 400 m running track.
The first lap takes 70 seconds. The second lap takes 90 seconds.
What is her average speed over the two laps?

19 Jenny sets out on a journey at 10.20 am.
She completes her journey at 1.05 pm. She travels a total distance of 27.5 km.
Calculate her average speed in kilometres per hour.

20 Liam drives for 40 km at an average speed of 60 km/h. He starts his journey at 9.50 am.
At what time does his journey end?

21 Sally cycles 38 km at an average speed of 23 km/h. She starts her journey at 9.30 am.
At what time does she finish? Give your answer to the nearest minute.

22 Chandni runs from Newcastle to Whitley Bay and then from Whitley Bay to Blyth.

Newcastle to Whitley Bay	Time taken:	1 hr 20 min	Distance: 20 km
Whitley Bay to Blyth	Average speed: 0.2 km/min		Distance: 12 km

    (a)   Calculate Chandni's average speed over the whole journey.
    (b)   Chandni left Newcastle at 10.50 am. At what time did she arrive in Blyth?

23 Angela, Ben and Cathy drive from London to Glasgow.
Angela takes 12 hours 30 minutes driving at an average speed of 64 km/hour.
Ben drives at an average speed of 100 km/hour.
    (a)   How long does Ben take?

Cathy takes 7 hours 12 minutes.
    (b)   What is Cathy's average speed?

24 Ron runs 400 m in 1 minute 23.2 seconds.
Calculate his average speed in   (a) metres per second,   (b) kilometres per hour.

25 A cheetah runs at a speed of 90 km/h for 4 seconds.
How many metres does the cheetah run?

26 The distance from the Sun to the Earth is about 1.5×10^8 km.
It takes light from the Sun about 500 seconds to reach the Earth.
Calculate the speed of light in metres per second.

27 A plane travels 1.65×10^3 miles at an average speed of 7.25×10^2 miles per hour.
Calculate the time taken. Give your answer in hours and minutes.

Other compound measures

Density

Density is a compound measure because it involves two other measures, **mass** and **volume**.

The formula for density is:

$$\text{Density} = \frac{\text{Mass}}{\text{Volume}}$$

The formula linking density, mass and volume can be rearranged and remembered as:

$$\text{Volume} = \frac{\text{Mass}}{\text{Density}}$$

$$\text{Mass} = \text{Density} \times \text{Volume}$$

For example, if a metal has a density of $2500\,\text{kg/m}^3$ then $1\,\text{m}^3$ of the metal weighs $2500\,\text{kg}$.

EXAMPLES

1. A block of metal has mass $500\,\text{g}$ and volume $400\,\text{cm}^3$.
   Calculate the density of the metal.

   Density $= \frac{500}{400} = 1.25\,\text{g/cm}^3$

2. The density of a certain metal is $3.5\,\text{g/cm}^3$. A block of the metal has volume $1000\,\text{cm}^3$.
   Calculate the mass of the block.

   Mass $= 3.5 \times 1000 = 3500\,\text{g}$.

Population density

Population density is a measure of how populated an area is. The formula for population density is:

$$\text{Population density} = \frac{\text{Population}}{\text{Area}}$$

EXAMPLE

Cumbria has a population of 4.897×10^5 and an area of $6824\,\text{km}^2$.
Surrey has a population of 1.036×10^6 and an area of $1677\,\text{km}^2$.
Which county has the greater population density?

The population densities are:

Cumbria $\dfrac{4.897 \times 10^5}{6824} = 71.8$ people/km^2.   Surrey $\dfrac{1.036 \times 10^6}{1677} = 617.8$ people/km^2.

Surrey has the greater population density.

Exercise 18.2

1. A metal bar has a mass of $960\,\text{g}$ and a volume of $120\,\text{cm}^3$.
   Find the density of the metal in the bar.

2. A block of copper has a mass of $2160\,\text{g}$. The block measures $4\,\text{cm}$ by $6\,\text{cm}$ by $10\,\text{cm}$.
   What is the density of copper?

3. A silver necklace has a mass of $300\,\text{g}$. The density of silver is $10.5\,\text{g/cm}^3$.
   What is the volume of the silver?

4. A rectangular can measuring $30\,\text{cm}$ by $15\,\text{cm}$ by $20\,\text{cm}$ is full of oil.
   The density of oil is $0.8\,\text{g/cm}^3$. What is the mass of the oil?

5. A rectangular pane of glass measures $60\,\text{cm}$ by $120\,\text{cm}$ by $0.5\,\text{cm}$.
   The density of glass is $2.6\,\text{g/cm}^3$. What is the mass of the glass?

6 A bag of sugar has a mass of 1 kg.
The average density of the sugar in the bag is 0.5 g/cm³.
Find the volume of sugar in the bag.

7 A block of concrete has dimensions 15 cm by 25 cm by 40 cm.
The block has a mass of 12 kg. What is the density of the concrete?

8 A bottle holds 450 cm³ of water and has a mass of 550 g when full.
The density of water is 1 g/cm³. What is the mass of the empty bottle?

9 The population of Northern Ireland is 1.595×10^6.
The area of Northern Ireland is 13 483 km².
Calculate the population density of Northern Ireland.

10 The table shows the total population, land area and the population densities for some countries in Europe.

	Country	Area km²	Population	Population density people/km²
(a)	Belgium	?	9.97×10^6	326.6
(b)	France	543 960	5.67×10^7	?
(c)	UK	244 090	?	235.2

Calculate the missing figures in the table.

What you need to know

- **Speed** is a compound measure because it involves **two** other measures.

- **Speed** is a measure of how fast something is travelling. It involves the measures **distance** and **time**.
  $$\text{Speed} = \frac{\text{Distance}}{\text{Time}}$$

- In situations where speed is not constant, **average speed** is used.
  $$\text{Average speed} = \frac{\text{Total distance travelled}}{\text{Total time taken}}$$

- The formula linking speed, distance and time can be rearranged and remembered as:
  (average) **speed** = (total) **distance** ÷ (total) **time**
  (total) **distance** = (average) **speed** × (total) **time**
  (total) **time** = (total) **distance** ÷ (average) **speed**

- Two other commonly used compound measures are **density** and **population density**.

- **Density** is a compound measure which involves the measures **mass** and **volume**.
  $$\text{Density} = \frac{\text{Mass}}{\text{Volume}}$$

- **Population density** is a measure of how populated an area is.
  $$\text{Population density} = \frac{\text{Population}}{\text{Area}}$$

Review Exercise 18

Do not use a calculator for questions 1 to 6.

1 The chart shows the distances in kilometres between some towns.
Mrs Hill drove from Manchester to Southampton.
She completed the journey in 4 hours.
What was her average speed for the journey in kilometres per hour?

London
326	Manchester
270	60	Sheffield
129	376	334	Southampton

2 Mr Mogg took 5 hours to drive from Cardiff to Leeds. His average speed was 48 miles per hour.
What is the distance from Cardiff to Leeds?

3 A train travels 120 kilometres at an average speed of 80 kilometres per hour.
How long will the journey take?

4 Selina takes $1\frac{1}{2}$ hours to cycle 12 miles.
What is her average cycling speed? *AQA*

5 (a) The train from London to Manchester takes 2 hours 30 minutes.
This train travels at an average speed of 80 miles per hour.
What is the distance from London to Manchester?

(b) The railway company is going to buy some faster trains.
These new trains will have an average speed of 100 miles per hour.
How much time will be saved on the journey from London to Manchester?
AQA

6 The distance from London to Newcastle is 285 miles.
Paul takes $4\frac{1}{2}$ hours to drive this distance.
Calculate his average speed.

7 The Grand National horse race is $4\frac{1}{2}$ miles long.
In 1839 the winning horse ran this in 15 minutes.
What was the average speed of this horse in miles per hour? *AQA*

8 (a) Nick took 20 minutes to run 3 km.
What was his average speed in km/h?
(b) Naomi cycles 12 km at an average speed of 20 km/h.
For how many minutes did she cycle?

9 Matt has to drive 18 km to work.
Calculate his average speed for the journey when he leaves home at 0750 and arrives at work at 0814.

10 Flik lives 2.4 km from school.
How many minutes does she take to walk to school if her average walking speed is 4 km/h?

11 An aeroplane flies from New York to Los Angeles, a distance of 2475 miles, at an average speed of 427 miles per hour.
How long does the flight take in hours and minutes? *AQA*

12 Jane cycles from A to B and then from B to C.
Details of each stage of her journey are given below.

A to B Distance 55 km.
Average speed 22 km per hour.
B to C Time taken 1 hour 30 minutes.
Average speed 30 km per hour.

Calculate Jane's average speed over the whole of her journey from A to C. *AQA*

13 Arnold runs 400 m in 1 minute.
What is his average speed in km/h?

14 A tiger runs at a speed of 50 kilometres per hour for 9 seconds.
How many metres does the tiger run? *AQA*

15 A gold bracelet has a mass of 84 g.
The density of gold is 19.3 g/cm³.
What is the volume of the bracelet?

16 A glass ornament has a mass of 350 g and a volume of 120 cm³.
Calculate the density of the glass.

17 Calculate the missing figures in the table.

	Materials		
	Steel	Concrete	Foam
Volume	120 cm³	?	4000 cm³
Mass	300 g	12 kg	?
Density	?	7.5 g/cm³	0.05 g/cm³

18 Which of these two continents has the larger population density?
You **must** show all your working.

	Continent	
	Europe	Asia
Population	6.82×10^8	2.96×10^9
Area (km²)	1.05×10^{10}	4.35×10^{10}

AQA

19 Light travels at 1.86284×10^5 miles per second.
The planet Jupiter is 483.6 million miles from the Sun.
Using suitable approximations, estimate the number of **minutes** light takes to travel from the Sun to Jupiter. *AQA*

Do not use a calculator for this exercise.

1 Some of the rail services from Bournemouth to Waterloo are shown.

Bournemouth	0558	0616	—	0654	0715	0754
Brockenhurst	0619	0639	—	0722	0738	0823
Southampton	0634	0655	0714	0738	0754	0838
So'ton Parkway	0642	0703	0722	0746	0802	0848
Winchester	0656	0715	0733	0759	0812	0901
Woking	0738	—	0815	0845	—	0938
Waterloo	0804	0810	0844	0901	0908	1005

(a) Tony catches the 0616 from Bournemouth to Waterloo. How long does the journey take?

(b) Mrs Harrison catches the 0738 from Southampton to Winchester.
What time does it arrive in Winchester?

(c) Kath arrives at Brockenhurst station at 0730. What is the time of the next train to Woking?

2 Steven pays 96 pence for 3 oranges and 2 grapefruit.
A grapefruit costs 27 pence.
How much is an orange?

3 (a) Work out $32.4 - 14.9$.
(b) Work out $23.6 \div 8$.

4 Raspberry jam is sold in two sizes.

Large 500 g £2.69   Standard 250 g £1.39

Which size is the better value for money?
You **must** show all your working.   AQA

5 (a) Work out. (i) $\dfrac{7 + 2 \times 4}{5}$
(ii) $15 \div (3 + 2) - 1$
(b) Write these numbers in ascending order: -3 0.6 2 -9 10
(c) Work out 0.3×0.2

6 Tickets for a concert cost £17 each.
234 people go to the concert.
How much money is paid for tickets?

7 Work out. (a) $20\,000 \times 600$
(b) $\dfrac{40\,000}{800}$ (c) $\dfrac{20 \times 90}{60^2}$
AQA

8 George needs 100 tiles.
The tiles are sold in boxes of 15.
How many boxes does he need to buy?

9 The table shows the midday temperature in two cities on one day.

London	3°C
Moscow	−8°C

(a) How much colder is Moscow than London?

(b) Paris is 5°C colder than London.
What is the temperature in Paris?

10 Paul writes down five numbers.

| 2 | 5 | 6 | 7 | 9 |

(a) (i) Which of Paul's numbers are multiples of 3?
(ii) Which of Paul's numbers are prime numbers?
(iii) Which of Paul's numbers are factors of 10?
(b) Paul uses these numbers to make the five-digit number 92576.
(i) What is the value of the 5 in Paul's number?
(ii) What is Paul's number correct to the nearest thousand?
(c) Paul uses all five numbers again.
What is the smallest **even** number that Paul can make?   AQA

11 A turkey should be cooked for 40 minutes per kilogram.
A turkey weighs 4 kilograms.
It is placed in the oven at 1030.
At what time of day will it be cooked?
AQA

12 Work out.

(a) $\sqrt{36} + \sqrt{64}$ (b) $\sqrt{36 \times 64}$

13 John pays £2.60 for 200 g of jelly babies and 300 g of toffees.
100 g of jelly babies cost 37p.
What is the cost of 100 g of toffees?

14 A crowd of 45 000 watch a football match.
(a) Two-thirds of the crowd support the home team.
How many people support the home team?
(b) 60% of the crowd are men.
How many men are in the crowd?

15 (a) Write these fractions in order of size.
$\frac{2}{5}$ $\frac{5}{8}$ $\frac{1}{3}$ $\frac{3}{10}$
(b) Write $\frac{2}{5}$ as a percentage.
(c) Calculate $\frac{5}{8}$ of 32.

16 Joyce wants to calculate $\frac{59.6}{20.2 - 4.9}$.
By writing each of the numbers in Joyce's calculation to the nearest whole number estimate the answer.

17 The number of spaces is given to the nearest ten.

> **Parking**
> **400 spaces**

What is the minimum and maximum possible number of spaces?

18 The cash price of a computer is £960.
The computer can be bought on credit by paying a deposit of 10% of the cash price and 12 monthly payments of £79.50.
How much **more** is paid when the computer is bought on credit?   AQA

19 There are 400 trees in a park.
Of these trees, $\frac{1}{4}$ are oak and $\frac{1}{10}$ are willow.
(a) How many trees are **not** oak or willow?
(b) Express the number of trees which are **not** oak or willow as a percentage of the 400 trees.   AQA

20 These are the ingredients for 12 scones.

> 300 g flour
> 150 g butter
> 90 g dried fruit

Alice has plenty of flour and dried fruit but only 500 g of butter.
What is the largest number of scones she can make?

21 Brian spends £2108 on a wedding reception for 79 guests. By rounding each of these numbers to one significant figure, estimate how much Brian spends per guest.   AQA

22 One day at St George's School:
$\frac{1}{4}$ of the pupils walked to school,
$\frac{3}{8}$ of the pupils came by bus,
the remaining 30 pupils came by car.
(a) Work out $\frac{1}{4} + \frac{3}{8}$.
Give your answer as a fraction.
(b) What fraction of pupils came by car?
(c) How many pupils are there in the school altogether?   AQA

23 Work out.   (a) $\frac{5}{6} - \frac{2}{3}$ (b) $\frac{4}{5} + \frac{3}{4}$

24 (a) Write down the value of 7^2.
(b) What is the value of $\sqrt{81}$?
(c) What is the reciprocal of $\frac{3}{2}$?

25 (a) Write down a decimal that lies between $\frac{1}{4}$ and $\frac{1}{3}$.
(b) Work out $\frac{3}{4} \times \frac{2}{3}$.

26 (a) Work out 20% of £3.60.
(b) Work out $\frac{3}{5}$ of £130.

27 (a) A tin contains 60 toffees.
Jacob eats 15% of the toffees.
How many toffees are left?
(b) A box contains milk and plain chocolates in the ratio 2 : 1.
The box contains 24 chocolates.
How many are plain?

28 (a) Work out $2^3 + \sqrt{25}$.
(b) Given that $37 \times 249 = 9213$,
find the exact value of $\frac{92.13}{3.7}$.

29 Which is bigger, 2^6 or 3^4?
Show all your working.   AQA

30 Use approximations to estimate the value of: $\frac{79.6 \times 5.01}{20.4 - 9.78}$
You must show your working.

31 An examination in history is marked out of 60 marks. Reg gets 54 marks.
What percentage of the marks does he get?

32 Use the calculation $487 \times 3.53 = 1719.11$ to find the value of:
(a) 487×0.0353
(b) 48700×0.00353 AQA

33 A cycle route is 30 miles long.
A leaflet states that this route can be covered in $2\frac{1}{2}$ hours.

(a) Calculate the average speed required to complete the route in the time stated.

(b) A cyclist completes the route in $2\frac{1}{2}$ hours.
He averages 8 miles an hour for the first $\frac{1}{2}$ hour.
Calculate his average speed for the remainder of the journey.　　AQA

34 Work out.

(a) $\frac{3}{4}$ of 5.6　(b) 0.2×0.4　(c) $3\frac{1}{4} - 1\frac{2}{5}$

35 Red tulips and yellow tulips are used for a flower display. The display uses 40 tulips. The ratio of red tulips to yellow tulips is 3 : 5. How many tulips are red?

36 A sports pitch has a length of 75 metres, correct to the nearest metre.
Write down the least and the greatest possible length of this pitch.　　AQA

37 (a) Express 72 as a product of its prime factors.

(b) Find the highest common factor of 48 and 72.

38 A racing car travels 3 miles in 45 seconds. Find the average speed of the car in miles per hour.

39 (a) Find an approximate value of
$$\frac{584 \times 4.91}{0.198}$$
You **must** show all your working.

(b) Zoe states that the product of two consecutive integers is never divisible by 50. By means of an example, show that Zoe is **not** correct.　　AQA

40 Phil has 80 birds; some are blue, and the rest are yellow. Phil sells 30% of his birds. The new ratio of blue birds to yellow birds is 4 : 3.
How many blue birds has he got left?　AQA

41 Kim invests £500 for two years, at 4% compound interest, paid yearly.
Amir says that the interest will be £40.
Is Amir correct?
Explain clearly how you obtained your answer.　　AQA

42 Jo worked for 3 hours 20 minutes.
She was paid £24.
How much was she paid per hour?

43 Andi tells Cato:
"When driving your car, if you increase your speed by 10% and then decrease your speed by 10% you will be travelling at a slower speed than you were to begin with."
Is he correct? Explain your answer.

44 (a) Use approximations to estimate the value of $\frac{9.67^2}{0.398}$.
You **must** show all your working.

(b) (i) p and q are prime numbers.
Find the values of p and q when $p^3 \times q = 24$.

(ii) Write 18 as a product of prime factors.

(iii) What is the least common multiple of 24 and 18?　AQA

45 Are these statements true or false?
A: The product of two prime numbers is always a prime number.
B: The sum of two consecutive numbers is always odd.
Explain each answer.

46 Carol is paid £6.30 per hour for a basic 30-hour week.
Overtime is paid at time and a third.
Last week Carol's total pay was £218.40.
How many hours and minutes overtime did Carol work last week?　　AQA

47 Add together 5.1×10^7 and 3.89×10^6.　　AQA

48 $A = 3 \times 10^4$　　$B = 5 \times 10^{-2}$

(a) Calculate $A \times B$.
Give your answer in standard form.

(b) Calculate $A \div B$.
Give your answer in standard form.

49 In a sale prices are reduced by 10%.
The sale price of a tennis racket is £36.
What was the original price of the tennis racket?

50 (a) Work out $4 \times 10^7 \times 6 \times 10^{-5}$, giving your answer in standard form.

(b) Work out $\frac{3.2 \times 10^8}{4 \times 10^4}$, giving your answer in standard form.

(c) Work out $(4 \times 10^5)^2$, giving your answer in standard form.　　AQA

You may use a calculator for this exercise.

1 Laura buys 18 cartons of juice.
She pays with a £10 note.
She gets £2.98 change.
How much is each carton of juice?

2 Rosie gets on a bus at 1745 and gets off the bus at 1806.
How long was she on the bus?

3 Les writes down six numbers.
4   6   7   9   10   24
(a) Which of these numbers are factors of 12?
(b) Which of these numbers is a multiple of 12?
(c) Which of these numbers is a prime number?
(d) Work out the cube of 6.

4 A caretaker is paid at a basic rate of £7.76 per hour for 36 hours a week.
Overtime is paid at one and a half times the basic rate.
One week the caretaker works 42 hours.
How much is the caretaker paid that week?

5 A gas bill is £129.26 plus VAT at 5%.
Calculate the VAT charged.

6 (a) The weights and prices of two tins of pineapple are shown.

227 g
27 pence

432 g
52 pence

Which tin of pineapple gives more grams per penny?
You **must** show all your working.
(b) A greengrocer sold 16 cauliflowers and 24 cabbages.
The total cost was £18.16.
The cost of a cauliflower was 55p.
What was the cost of a cabbage?   AQA

7 Calculate $207.9 \div 7.25$
(a) correct to one decimal place,
(b) correct to one significant figure.

8 (a) Write $2\frac{1}{4}$ as a decimal.
(b) Place the following numbers in order of size, starting with the smallest.
$2\frac{1}{4}$ 1.53^2 2.21 2.035 $\sqrt{4.78}$
   AQA

9 (a) Write $\frac{3}{7}$ as a decimal.
Give your answer correct to two decimal places.
(b) Calculate $400 \div (0.2)^3$.

10 A packet contains 15 biscuits.
(a) Harry eats 40% of the biscuits.
How many biscuits does he eat?
(b) Lauren eats 4 of the biscuits.
What percentage of the biscuits does she eat?
Give your answer to an appropriate degree of accuracy.

11 Pears cost £1.20 per kilogram.
Apples cost 30% less than pears.
What is the cost of 1.5 kg of apples?

12 Zoe chooses three consecutive numbers.
Show that the sum of the first and the last of these three numbers is always an even number.   AQA

13 The bill for an electrical repair is £48.80 plus VAT at $17\frac{1}{2}\%$.
How much is the total bill?

14

Exchange Rate
£1 = 1.48 euros

Calculate the difference is £s between 300 euros and £300.

15 Carl buys 1.2 kg of potatoes and 0.4 kg of carrots. He pays 90p in total.
The potatoes cost 70p per kilogram.
What is the cost of 1 kg of carrots?   AQA

16 Shelley drives 225 miles in 4 hours 30 minutes.
Calculate her average speed.   AQA

17 Mr Mogg earns £5690 per year.
He has a tax allowance of £4615 per year and tax is paid at 10p in the £ on his taxable income.
How much tax does he pay per year?

18

MOTOR BOAT

Cash price...£12 800

Credit terms...Deposit of 30% of cash price plus 36 monthly payments of £295

How much more is paid when the motorboat is bought on credit terms instead of cash?

19 Tom buys 200 tomato plants at a total cost of £40 to sell at a school fair.
He sells $\frac{3}{4}$ of them at 50p each.
He then reduces the price of the remaining plants to 40p.
At the end of the day there are 18 plants left which have **not** been sold.

(a) How much money does he receive from selling the tomato plants at the school fair?

(b) Find the percentage profit which Tom made on these tomato plants. AQA

20 A garden is a rectangle measuring 26 m by 11.5 m.
Grass covers 67% of the area of the garden.
Calculate the area of grass.
Give your answer to a suitable degree of accuracy.

21 (a) A kilogram of strawberries costs £1.70.
Estimate, to the nearest £, the cost of 5 lbs of strawberries.

(b) A bowl of strawberries and cream weighs 210 grams.
The ratio, by weight, of strawberries to cream is 5 : 1.
What is the weight of the cream?

22 Scooters can be hired at a cost of £21 per day plus 5.3 pence per mile.
Mustapha hires a scooter for three days and rides it 136 miles.
Find the total cost of hiring the scooter.
AQA

23 (a) Use your calculator to find the value of
$$\frac{19.8^2}{7.19 + 2.73}$$

(b) Show how you can use approximation to check your answer.

24 A geography test is marked out of 80 marks.
(a) Georgina gets 60% of the marks.
How many marks does she get?

(b) Alfie gets 36 marks.
What percentage does he get?

(c) The test is taken by a class of 28 pupils.
The ratio of the number of boys to the number of girls in the class is 3 : 4.
How many boys take the test?

The teacher said, "The class average for the test is 65.4 marks."

(d) The 28 pupils score 1832 marks altogether.
Without using a calculator, show by using approximation, that the average is about right.
You **must** show all your working.
AQA

25 A sponge cake for eight people needs 120 g of sugar.
John makes a sponge cake for five people.
(a) Calculate the weight of sugar he needs.

John cuts his cake into five equal slices.
He gives three slices to his mother.
(b) What percentage of the cake does John have left?
AQA

26 Calculate the simple interest on £480 invested at 7% for 6 months.

27 Wyn has 600 yo-yo's to sell.
He sells $\frac{3}{5}$ of them at £2 each.
He then reduces the price of the remaining yo-yo's by 40%.
In the end he is left with 24 damaged yo-yo's which he cannot sell.
Wyn paid £500 for the yo-yo's.
Find the percentages profit which he made on the sale of these yo-yo's.

28 (a) Calculate the exact value of 5^9.
(b) Find the reciprocal of 7.
Give your answer correct to 3 decimal places.

(c) Work out $\dfrac{0.36 \times 0.89}{47 - 3.9}$
Give your answer correct to 2 significant figures.

29 A film lasts 1 hour 28 minutes, correct to the nearest minute. What is the minimum possible time the film lasts?

30 The table shows the amount of foreign currency you can buy with £1.

EXCHANGE RATES
£1 will buy
France 1.56 euros   USA 1.37 dollars

An American has 400 000 dollars to spend on a holiday villa in the south of France. She sees a villa for sale for 450 000 euros. Does she have enough money to buy it? You **must** show all your working.

31 Greg drove 115 miles at an average speed of 43 mph. Calculate the time Greg took for the journey. Give your answer in hours and minutes.

AQA

32 Work out $2.37^2 - \sqrt{5.8}$
Give your answer correct to two decimal places.

33 A farm has 427 acres of land. 135 acres are used for grazing. What percentage of the land is used for grazing?

34 Three musicians received £100 between them for playing in a concert. They divided their pay in the ratio of the number of minutes for which each played. Angela played for 8 minutes, Fran played for 14 minutes and Dan played for 18 minutes. How much did each receive?

AQA

35 Nick invests £3000 at 7% per annum compound interest. Calculate the value of his investment at the end of 2 years.

36 (a) A bar of Fruit & Nut chocolate normally weighs 200 g. The ratio by weight of a special offer bar to a normal bar is 5 : 4. What is the weight of a special offer bar?

(b) The weight of a special offer bar of Milk Chocolate is 200 g. The special offer bar is 60% heavier than the usual bar. What is the weight of the usual bar?

AQA

37 Jim invests £10 000 at 5.2% per year compound interest. What is the percentage increase in the value of his investment after 3 years.

38 (a) $p = 3.7 \times 10^{-4}$.
Write p as an ordinary number.

(b) Work out each of the following. Give your answers in standard form.
(i) $5.2 \times 10^4 + 9.6 \times 10^5$
(ii) $\dfrac{8.2 \times 10^4}{2.5 \times 10^5}$

AQA

39 (a) Calculate $\dfrac{7.9 \times 8.2}{8.2 - 7.9}$
correct to two significant figures.

(b) Calculate $(4.9 \times 10^3)^2$

AQA

40 $P = 2^3 \times 3^2 \times 5$ $Q = 2 \times 3^3 \times 7$
(a) What number is the Highest Common Factor of P and Q?

(b) What number is the Least Common Multiple of P and Q?

41 Evaluate 0.9^7, giving your answer in standard form.

42 (a) Calculate $\sqrt{\dfrac{14.7}{(0.7)^3}}$
Give your answer correct to two significant figures.

(b) The distance from the Earth to the Moon is 3.81×10^5 kilometres. Light travels at a speed of 3×10^8 metres per second. How long does it take light to travel from the Earth to the Moon?

43 A gold bar has a mass of 1 kilogram. The density of gold is 19.3 g/cm^3. What is the volume of the gold?

44 Paving slabs weigh 12 kg each, correct to the nearest kilogram. Calculate the minimum possible weight of 5 paving slabs.

45 Ahmed sells silk ties at a price which is 37% more than he paid for them. The selling price of one tie is £36.99. How much did Ahmed pay for this tie?

AQA

46 In Britain there are 5.8×10^7 people. 8.8% of the people in Britain live in Scotland. How many people live in Scotland?

47 When the population of the United Kingdom was 5.8×10^7, the population of the European Community was 3.7×10^8. What percentage of the people in the European Community lived in the United Kingdom at that time? Give your answer to an appropriate degree of accuracy.

Introduction to Algebra

Algebra is sometimes called the language of Mathematics.
Algebra uses letters in place of numbers.

A class of children line up.
We cannot see how many children there are altogether because of a tree.
We can say there are n children in the line.
The letter n is used in place of an unknown number.

Three more children join the line.
There are now $n + 3$ children in the line.

This picture shows two lines of n children.
So there are $n + n$ or $2 \times n$ children altogether.
The simplest way to write this is $2n$.

Both $n + 3$ and $2n$ are examples of
algebraic expressions.

Exercise 19.1

Write algebraic expressions for each of the following questions.

1 There are n children in a queue. 4 more children join the queue.
How many children are in the queue now?

2 There are n children in a queue. 3 children leave the queue.
How many children are left in the queue?

3 There are 3 classes with n children in each class.
How many children are there altogether?

4 I have m marbles in a bag. I put in another 6 marbles.
How many marbles are now in the bag?

5 I have m marbles. I lose 12 marbles.
How many marbles do I have left?

6 I have 8 bags of marbles. Each bag contains m marbles.
How many marbles do I have altogether?

7 There are p pencils in a pencil case. I take one pencil out.
How many pencils are left in the pencil case?

8 There are p pencils in a pencil case. I put in another 5 pencils.
How many pencils are now in the pencil case?

9 I have 25 pencil cases. There are p pencils in each pencil case.
How many pencils do I have altogether?

10 I have 6 key rings. There are k keys on each key ring.
How many keys do I have altogether?

11 What is the cost of b biscuits costing 5 pence each?

12 Three cakes cost a total of c pence. What is the cost of one cake?

13 Five kilograms of apples cost a pence. What is the cost of one kilogram of apples?

14 A group of 36 students are split into g groups. How many students are in each group?

15 There are t toffees in a tin. How many toffees are there in
   (a) 2 tins,   (b) 10 tins?

Expressions and terms

Consider this situation:
    $2n$ students start a typing course.
    3 of the students leave the course.
    How many students remain on the course?
$2n - 3$ students remain.
$2n - 3$ is an **algebraic expression**, or simply an **expression**.
An expression is just an answer made up of letters and numbers.
$+2n$ and -3 are **terms** of the expression.

> **Note**
> A term includes the sign, $+$ or $-$.
> $2n$ has the same value as $+2n$.

Simplifying expressions

Addition and subtraction
You can add and subtract terms with the same letter.
This is sometimes called **simplifying an expression**.

$a + a = 2a$ $6a - 2a = 4a$
$5k + 3k = 8k$ $2d - 3d = -d$
$3p + 5 + p - 1 = 4p + 4$ $4x - 4x = 0$

$6 + a$ cannot be simplified.
$5p - 2q$ cannot be simplified.
$x^2 + x$ cannot be simplified.
$ab + ba = 2ab$

> **Note that:**
> A simpler way to write $1d$ is just d.
>
> $-1d$ can be written as $-d$.
>
> $0d$ is the same as 0.
>
> Just as with ordinary numbers you can add terms in any order.
> $a - 2a + 5a = a + 5a - 2a = 4a$

EXAMPLE

Write down an expression for the perimeter of this shape.
Give your answer in its simplest form.

Perimeter is the total distance round the outside of the shape.
$y + 2x - 1 + 2y + 2x + 3$
Imagine that each term is written on a separate card.

$\boxed{+y}$ $\boxed{+2x}$ $\boxed{-1}$ $\boxed{+2y}$ $\boxed{+2x}$ $\boxed{+3}$

The cards can be arranged in any order.

$\boxed{+2x}$ $\boxed{+2x}$ $\boxed{+y}$ $\boxed{+2y}$ $\boxed{+3}$ $\boxed{-1}$

Simplify this expression to get: $4x + 3y + 2$
The perimeter of the shape is $4x + 3y + 2$.

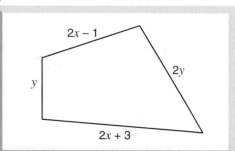

① Write simpler expressions for the following.

(a) $y + y$
(b) $c + c + c$
(c) $x + x + x + x + x$
(d) $p + p + p + p + p + p + p$
(e) $t + t + t - t$
(f) $d + d + d - d + d$
(g) $2n + n$
(h) $2y + 3y$
(i) $5g + g + 4g$
(j) $2m + 5m + m$
(k) $5z + 4z + z + 3z$
(l) $5r - 3r$
(m) $7t - 2t$
(n) $5y - y$
(o) $5j + 2j - 4j$
(p) $9c - 2c - 3c$
(q) $3x - x + 5x$
(r) $12w - 7w - 4w$
(s) $5d + 7d - 12d$
(t) $-2y - 3y$
(u) $3x - 8x$
(v) $2a - 5a - 12a + a$
(w) $3b + 5b - 4b + 2b$
(x) $m - 2m + 3m$

② Write an expression for the perimeter of each shape.
Give each answer in its simplest form.

(a)
(b)
(c)
(d)

③ Which of these expressions cannot be simplified?
Give a reason for each of your answers.

(a) $v + v$
(b) $v + 4$
(c) $2v + v + 4$
(d) $v + w$

④ Simplify where possible.

(a) $5x + 3x + y$
(b) $w + 3v - v$
(c) $2a + b - 3b$
(d) $2x + 3y + 3x$
(e) $5 + 7u - 2$
(f) $p + 3q + q$
(g) $3d - 5c - 2c$
(h) $3y + 1 - y$
(i) $-a + b + 2a$
(j) $3m + n + m$
(k) $5c + 4c - d$
(l) $2x + y - x$
(m) $-p + 4p + 3p$
(n) $5 - 9k + 4k$
(o) $2a - a + 3$

⑤ Simplify where possible.

(a) $3a + 5a + 2b + b$
(b) $p + 2q + 2p + q$
(c) $m + 2m - n + 3n$
(d) $2x + 3y - x - 5y$
(e) $3x - x + 5y - 2y$
(f) $2d + 5 - d - 2$
(g) $3a - 5a + 2b + b$
(h) $a - 2a + 7 + a$
(i) $2a - b + 3b - a$
(j) $-f + g - f - g$
(k) $2v - w - 3w - v$
(l) $7 - 2t - 9 - 3t$
(m) $-p + 3q - 3p + q$
(n) $5 - 9k - 4 + 2k$
(o) $2c + d + 4 - c - 2d + 7$

⑥ Write down an expression for the perimeter of each shape.
Give each answer in its simplest form.

(a)
(b)
(c)
(d)

⑦ Simplify.

(a) $xy + yx$
(b) $3pq - qp$
(c) $5ab - 2ba$
(d) $3x^2 - x^2$
(e) $5y^2 + 4y^2$
(f) $a^2 + 5a^2 - 2a^2$
(g) $d^2 - 2g^2 - g^2 + d^2$
(h) $3t^2 + t + 2t^2 - 2t$
(i) $3m^2 - 4m^2 + 7m - m$
(j) $p^2 - 2p + p^2 + p$

Multiplying and dividing terms

$6 \times a = 6a$ $a \times b = ab$ $x \times x = x^2$ $8a \div 2 = 4a$

$5 \times 2a = 10a$ $3x \times y = 3xy$ $5c \times 4c = 20c^2$ $6y \div 2y = 3$

                                               $b \times b \times b = b^3$ $9x \div x = 9$

EXAMPLE

Find an expression for the area of this rectangle.

Area = length $\times$ breadth
     $= 3d \times d$

The simplest way to write an expression for the area is $3d^2$.

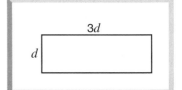

Exercise 19.3

1   Write these expressions in a simpler form.

(a) $3 \times a$ (b) $7 \times b$ (c) $2 \times 4 \times c$ (d) $3 \times 3 \times d$

(e) $e \times 4$ (f) $f \times 8$ (g) $3 \times 2p$ (h) $3q \times 5$

(i) $r \times r$ (j) $g \times g$ (k) $2g \times g$ (l) $2g \times 3g$

(m) $t \times 4t$ (n) $3t \times 4t$ (o) $5u \times 3u$ (p) $3d \times 3d$

2   Simplify.

(a) $3 \times (-y)$ (b) $y \times (-5)$

(c) $(-2) \times (-y)$ (d) $3 \times (-2y)$

(e) $t \times (-t)$ (f) $2t \times (-t)$

(g) $(-2t) \times 5t$ (h) $(-2t) \times (-5t)$

> **Remember:**
> $2 \times (-x) = -2x$
> $(-2) \times (-x) = 2x$

3   Simplify.

(a) $10a \div 2$ (b) $16b \div 4$ (c) $12x \div x$ (d) $20y \div y$

(e) $8y \div 4$ (f) $8y \div y$ (g) $8y \div 4y$ (h) $18p \div p$

(i) $18p \div 6$ (j) $18p \div 6p$ (k) $18k \div 2k$ (l) $18a \div 3a$

(m) $28g \div 7g$ (n) $10m \div 2m$ (o) $20t \div 5t$ (p) $27x \div 3x$

4   Simplify.

(a) $6y \div (-3)$ (b) $(-6y) \div 2$

(c) $(-5m) \div m$ (d) $(-5m) \div (-5)$

(e) $3a \div (-a)$ (f) $(-10d) \div 5d$

(g) $6g \div (-2g)$ (h) $(-3k) \div (-3k)$

> **Remember:**
> $2x \div (-2) = -x$
> $(-2x) \div 2 = -x$
> $(-2x) \div (-2) = x$

5   Simplify.

(a) $a \times b$ (b) $x \times y$ (c) $y \times y$ (d) $2 \times p \times q$

(e) $2 \times a \times a$ (f) $3 \times x \times y$ (g) $3 \times a \times 2 \times b$ (h) $3 \times g \times 4 \times h$

(i) $2 \times d \times 3 \times d$ (j) $3g \times g$ (k) $a \times 5b$ (l) $2g \times 3h$

(m) $a \times b \times c$ (n) $m \times m \times m$ (o) $2 \times d \times d \times d$ (p) $g \times g \times g \times 3$

(q) $2x \times 3x \times x$ (r) $5m \times m \times 2n$ (s) $3a \times b \times c$ (t) $2p \times 3q \times 3r$

6   Write an expression for the area of each shape.
Give each answer in its simplest form.

(a)   (b)   (c)   (d)

Multiplying and dividing algebraic expressions with powers

The rules for multiplying and dividing powers can be used to simplify algebraic expressions involving powers.

Remember: When multiplying or dividing expressions that include both numbers and powers:

multiply or **divide** the **numbers**, **add** or **subtract** the **powers**.

Deal with the powers of different bases **separately**.

EXAMPLES

1 Simplify.
(a) $x^3 \times x^8 = x^{3+8} = x^{11}$
(b) $2x^2 \times 5x^7 = (2 \times 5) \times (x^2 \times x^7) = 10 \times x^{2+7} = 10x^9$
(c) $x^3y^2 \times xy^4 = (x^3 \times x) \times (y^2 \times y^4) = x^{3+1} \times y^{2+4} = x^4y^6$
(d) $(x^3y^2)^2 = (x^3y^2) \times (x^3y^2) = (x^3 \times x^3) \times (y^2 \times y^2) = x^6y^4$
(e) $(3x^4)^2 = (3x^4) \times (3x^4) = (3 \times 3) \times (x^4 \times x^4) = 9x^8$

2 Simplify.
(a) $x^8 \div x^5 = x^{8-5} = x^3$
(b) $6y^6 \div 2y^4 = (6 \div 2) \times (y^6 \div y^4) = 3 \times y^{6-4} = 3y^2$

Exercise 19.4

1 Simplify.
(a) $y^2 \times y$
(b) $t^3 \times t^2$
(c) $a^3 \times a^3$
(d) $g^7 \times g^3$
(e) $a \times a \times a^2$
(f) $m \times m^3 \times m^2$
(g) $2y \times y^2$
(h) $3d^2 \times 2d^3$
(i) $4x^2 \times 2x^3$
(j) $5y^3 \times 5y^3$
(k) $2t \times t^2 \times 3t^2$
(l) $2r \times 3r^2 \times 4r^3$
(m) $mn \times m^2n$
(n) $a^2b \times ba^2$
(o) $3rs^3 \times 2r^2s$
(p) $2x^2y \times 5x^3y^2$

2 Simplify.
(a) $(t^2)^3$
(b) $(y^3)^2$
(c) $(g^3)^3$
(d) $(x^4)^2$
(e) $(3a)^2$
(f) $(2h)^3$
(g) $2 \times (m^3)^2$
(h) $(2m^3)^2$
(i) $3 \times (d^3)^2$
(j) $(3d^3)^2$
(k) $(3a^2)^3$
(l) $(2k^3)^3$
(m) $(xy)^2$
(n) $(mn^2)^3$
(o) $(2st)^3$
(p) $(3p^2q)^2$

3 Simplify.
(a) $y^3 \div y$
(b) $a^4 \div a^3$
(c) $x^5 \div x^5$
(d) $t^7 \div t^3$
(e) $g \div g^2$
(f) $h^3 \div h^5$
(g) $6b^3 \div b$
(h) $10m^3 \div 2m^2$
(i) $8x^8 \div 2x^2$
(j) $16t^3 \div 4t^2$
(k) $15y^6 \div 3y^2$
(l) $9h^2 \div 3h^3$
(m) $xy^2 \div xy$
(n) $m^3n \div mn^2$
(o) $2p^3q \div 3pq^2$
(p) $6r^2s^3 \div 2rs$

4 Simplify.
(a) $\dfrac{t^3}{t^2}$
(b) $\dfrac{g^2}{g^3}$
(c) $\dfrac{m^2 \times m}{m}$
(d) $\dfrac{y^2 \times y^3}{y^4}$
(e) $\dfrac{y \times y^3}{y^2}$
(f) $\dfrac{m^2 \times m^3}{m^6}$
(g) $\dfrac{2t^3 \times t}{t^2}$
(h) $\dfrac{6g^2 \times g}{2g^3}$

Brackets

Some expressions contain brackets.
$2(a + b)$ means $2 \times (a + b)$.

You can multiply out brackets in an expression either by using a diagram or by expanding.

Introduction to Algebra

1 Multiply out the bracket $2(x + 3)$.

Diagram method
$2(x + 3)$ means $2 \times (x + 3)$.
This can be shown using a rectangle.

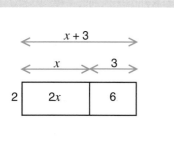

The areas of the two parts are $2x$ and 6.
The total area is $2x + 6$.
$2(x + 3) = 2x + 6$

Expanding
$2(x + 3) = 2 \times x + 2 \times 3$
$\qquad\quad = 2x + 6$

2 Multiply out the bracket $3(4a + 5)$.

Diagram method

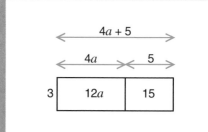

$3(4a + 5) = 12a + 15$

Expanding
$3(4a + 5) = 3 \times 4a + 3 \times 5$
$\qquad\qquad = 12a + 15$

3 Expand $x(x - 5)$.

$x \times x = x^2$ and $x \times -5 = -5x$
$x(x - 5) = x^2 - 5x$

Exercise 19.5

1 Use the diagrams to multiply out the brackets.

(a) $2(x + 5) = \ldots$

(b) $3(a + 6) = \ldots$

(c) $4(2y + 3) = \ldots$

2 Draw your own diagrams to multiply out these brackets.
(a) $3(x + 2)$ (b) $2(y + 5)$ (c) $2(2x + 1)$ (d) $3(p + q)$

3 Use the diagrams to multiply out the brackets.

(a) $a(a + 1) = \ldots$

(b) $d(2 + d) = \ldots$

(c) $x(2x + 1) = \ldots$

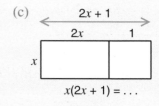

4 Multiply out the brackets by expanding.
(a) $2(x + 4)$ (b) $4(b + 1)$ (c) $4(2x + 1)$ (d) $3(t - 2)$
(e) $4(5 - a)$ (f) $3(2 - 4p)$ (g) $6(b + 2c)$ (h) $3(2m - 5n)$

5 Multiply out the brackets by expanding.
(a) $x(x + 3)$ (b) $y(2 + y)$ (c) $t(t - 5)$ (d) $g(2g + 3)$
(e) $m(2 - 3m)$ (f) $a(3a + 4)$ (g) $2p(p + 3)$ (h) $3d(2 - 3d)$
(i) $2x(x + y)$ (j) $5y(x - 2y)$

Remember:
Always remove brackets first, then simplify by collecting like terms together.

$3(t + 4) + 2$ — Remove the brackets

$= 3t + 12 + 2$ ← Simplify

$= 3t + 14$ ←

6 Multiply out the brackets and simplify.

(a) $2(x + 1) + 3$

(b) $3(a + 2) + 5$

(c) $6(w - 4) + 7$

(d) $4 + 2(p + 3)$

(e) $3 + 3(q - 1)$

(f) $1 + 3(2 - t)$

(g) $4(z + 2) + z$

(h) $5(t + 3) + 3t$

(i) $3(c - 2) - c$

(j) $2a + 3(a - 3)$

(k) $y + 2(y - 5)$

(l) $5x + 3(2 - x)$

(m) $4(2a + 5) + 3$

(n) $-2x + 4(3x - 3)$

(o) $3(p - 5) - p + 4$

(p) $3a + 2(a + b)$

(q) $3(x + y) - 2y$

(r) $2(p - q) - 3q$

(s) $2x + x(3 - x)$

(t) $a(a - 3) + a$

(u) $y(2 - y) + y^2$

7 Remove the brackets and simplify.

(a) $2(x + 1) + 3(x + 2)$

(b) $3(a + 1) + 2(a + 5)$

(c) $4(y + 2) + 5(y + 3)$

(d) $2(3a + 1) + 3(a + 1)$

(e) $3(2t + 5) + 5(4t + 3)$

(f) $3(z + 5) + 2(z - 1)$

(g) $7(q - 2) + 5(q + 6)$

(h) $5(x + 3) + 6(x - 3)$

(i) $8(2e - 1) + 4(e - 2)$

(j) $2(5d + 4) + 2(d - 1)$

(k) $m(m - 2) + m(2m - 1)$

(l) $a(3a + 2) + 2a(a - 3)$

8 Multiply out the brackets and simplify.

(a) $-3(x + 2)$

(b) $-3(x - 2)$

(c) $-2(y - 5)$

(d) $-2(3 - x)$

(e) $-3(5 - y)$

(f) $-4(1 + a)$

(g) $5 - 2(a + 1)$

(h) $5d - 3(d - 2)$

(i) $4b - 2(3 + b)$

(j) $-3(2p + 3)$

(k) $5m - 2(3 + 2m)$

(l) $2(3d - 1) - d + 3$

(m) $-a(a - 2)$

(n) $2d - d(1 + d)$

(o) $x^2 - x(1 - x) + x$

(p) $-3g(2g + 3)$

(q) $t^2 - 2t(3 - 3t)$

(r) $2m - 2m(m - 3)$

Remember:

$(-2) \times (+3) = -6$

$(-2) \times (-3) = +6$

so $-2(x + 3) = -2x - 6$

and $-2(x - 3) = -2x + 6$

Factorising

Factorising is the opposite operation to removing brackets.
For example: to remove brackets

$$2(x + 5) = 2x + 10$$

To factorise $3x + 6$ we can see that $3x$ and 6 have a **common factor** of 3 so,

$$3x + 6 = 3(x + 2)$$

A **common factor** can also be a **letter**.
Both y^2 and $5y$ can be divided by y.
To factorise $y^2 - 5y$ we take y as the common factor,
so, $y^2 - 5y = y(y - 5)$

Common factors
The **factors** of a number are all the numbers that will divide exactly into the number.
Factors of 6 are 1, 2, 3 and 6.

A **common factor** is a factor which will divide into two or more terms.

EXAMPLES

1 Factorise $4x - 6$.

Each term has a factor of 2.
So the common factor is 2.
$4x - 6 = 2(2x - 3)$

2 Factorise $x^2 + 3x$.

Each term has a factor of x.
So the common factor is x.
$x^2 + 3x = x(x + 3)$

In some instances the terms will have both a number and a letter as common factors and **both** must be taken out.

EXAMPLE

Factorise $2x^2 - 6x$.

$2x^2 - 6x = 2x(x - 3)$

Each term has a factor of 2.
Each term has a factor of x.
So the common factor is $2x$.

Exercise **19.6**

1 Copy and complete.
   (a) $2x + 2y = 2(\ldots + \ldots)$ (b) $3a - 6b = 3(\ldots - \ldots)$ (c) $6m + 8n = 2(\ldots + \ldots)$
   (d) $x^2 - 2x = x(\quad\quad)$ (e) $ab + a = a(\quad\quad)$ (f) $2x - xy = x(\quad\quad)$
   (g) $2ab - 4a = 2a(\quad\quad)$ (h) $4x^2 + 6x = 2x(\quad\quad)$ (i) $dg - dg^2 = dg(\quad\quad)$

2 Factorise.
   (a) $2a + 2b$ (b) $5x - 5y$ (c) $3d + 6e$ (d) $4m - 2n$
   (e) $6a + 9b$ (f) $6a - 8b$ (g) $8t + 12$ (h) $5a - 10$
   (i) $4d - 2$ (j) $3 - 9g$ (k) $5 - 20m$ (l) $4k + 4$

3 Factorise.
   (a) $xy - xz$ (b) $fg + gh$ (c) $ab - 2b$ (d) $3q + pq$
   (e) $a + ab$ (f) $gh - g$ (g) $a^2 + 3a$ (h) $5t - t^2$
   (i) $d - d^2$ (j) $m^2 + m$ (k) $5r^2 - 3r$ (l) $3x^2 + 2x$

4 Factorise.
   (a) $3y + 6$ (b) $t^2 - t$ (c) $2d^2 + 4d$ (d) $3m - 6mn$
   (e) $2fg + 4g^2$ (f) $4pq - 8q$ (g) $6y - 15y^2$ (h) $6x^2 + 4xy$
   (i) $6n^2 - 2n$ (j) $4ab + 6b$ (k) $\frac{1}{2}a - \frac{1}{2}a^2$ (l) $wx + 2x - x^2$

What you need to know

You should be able to:

● Write simple algebraic expressions.
● Simplify expressions and rules by collecting like terms together.
       e.g. $2d + 3d = 5d$ and $3x + 2 - x + 4 = 2x + 6$
● Multiply simple expressions together.   e.g. $2a \times a = 2a^2$ and $y \times y \times y = y^3$
● Recall and use these properties of powers:
   Powers of the same base are **added** when terms are **multiplied**.
   Powers of the same base are **subtracted** when terms are **divided**.
   Powers are **multiplied** when a power is raised to a power.

   $a^m \times a^n = a^{m+n}$
   $a^m \div a^n = a^{m-n}$
   $(a^m)^n = a^{m \times n}$

● Multiply out brackets.   e.g. $2(x - 5) = 2x - 10$ and $x(x - 5) = x^2 - 5x$
● Factorise expressions.   e.g. $3x - 6 = 3(x - 2)$ and $x^2 + 5x = x(x + 5)$

1 A lollipop costs t pence.
Write an expression for the cost of
6 lollipops.

2 Tom is x years old.
Naomi is 3 years older than Tom.
How old is Naomi in terms of x?

3 (a) Aimee is n years old.
Her brother Ben is two years younger.
Write down Ben's age in terms of n.
(b) Aimee's mother is three times as old
as Aimee.
Write down her mother's age in terms
of n.
(c) Aimee's father is four years older than
her mother.
Write down her father's age in terms
of n.
(d) Write an expression for the combined
ages of all four members of the family.
Simplify your answer.   AQA

4

Cakes cost 25 pence each.
(a) Barry buys 6 cakes for his friends.
How much do the cakes cost
altogether?
(b) Jane buys n cakes.
Write down an expression for the cost
of n cakes.
(c) Yan buys y cakes.
The total cost is x pence.
Which one of these equations shows
this?
(i) $xy = 25$ (ii) $x = 25y$
(iii) $y = 25x$ AQA

5 (a) Simplify
(i) $w + w + w$,
(ii) $2w + 5 - w - 3$,
(iii) $w \times w$.
(b) Write an expression in terms of d for
the perimeter of this shape.

6 (a) Simplify
(i) $x + 3x + x$,   (ii) $6x \div 2$,
(iii) $y \times 3y$.
(b) Multiply out
(i) $4(x + y)$,   (ii) $5(x - 2y)$.
          AQA

7 Simplify
(a) $ab + 2ba$ (b) $a^2 - a + 3a$
(c) $3(x - 2) - x$

8 Factorise
(a) $t^2 - 3t$ (b) $6a + 3ab$

9 (a) Multiply out and simplify as much as
possible $5(a - 2b) + 7b$.
(b) A loaf of bread costs y pence.
Write down an expression for the cost
of 3 loaves.   AQA

10 (a) Simplify $4x + 3x + 7y - 2x + 3y$
(b) Expand and simplify
$x(2x - 3) + 4(x^2 + 1)$ AQA

11 Simplify
(a) $p \times p \times p \times p$ (b) $2a \times 3b \times 4c$
(c) $x^3 \div x^3$ AQA

12 Simplify
(a) $t^3 \times t^5$ (b) $p^6 \div p^2$ (c) $\dfrac{a^3 \times a^2}{a}$
          AQA

13 (a) Simplify $7 - 2(x - 3)$.
(b) Factorise $6xy - 2y$.
(c) Simplify $(-5m) \times (-m)$.

14 Simplify $\dfrac{a^6c^4}{a^2c^5}$ AQA

15 Expand
(a) $2x(3 + 2y)$ (b) $4a^3(a^2 - b)$
          AQA

16 Factorise
(a) $6x - 15$,   (b) $y^2 + 7y$.

17 Multiply out the brackets and simplify.
(a) $x^2 - x(1 - x)$ (b) $4 - 3(x + 1)$

18 Simplify
(a) $3y^3 \times 2y^2$ (b) $8t^6 \div 4t^3$ (c) $(2a)^3$

19 (a) Factorise
(i) $6xy - 3y^2$,   (ii) $4m^2 + 6m$.
(b) Simplify
(i) $5y^3 \times 2y^2$,   (ii) $6x^6 \div 2x^2$.

20 Simplify $\dfrac{4a^3c \times 3ab^3}{6a^2b}$ AQA

Introduction to Algebra

CHAPTER 20

Solving Equations

Activity

Can you solve these puzzles?

● **Nueve** is a Spanish number.
  If you add 1 to **nueve** you get 10.
  What is **nueve**?

● What number must be put in each shape to make the statements correct?

$\square + 3 = 8$ $\qquad$ $\bigcirc \times 3 = 30$ $\qquad$ $2 \times \bigcirc - 3 = 7$

These are all examples of **equations.**
Equations like these can be solved using a method known as **inspection.**
Instead of words or boxes, equations are usually written using letters for the unknown numbers.
Solving an equation means finding the numerical value of the letter which fits the equation.

EXAMPLES Solve these equations by inspection.

Remember:
A letter or a symbol stands for an unknown number.

$2y$ means $2 \times y$.

1 $x - 2 = 6$

$x = 8$

Reason: $\mathbf{8} - 2 = 6$

2 $2y = 10$

$y = 5$

Reason: $2 \times \mathbf{5} = 10$

Exercise **20.1**

1 What number must be put in the box to make each of these statements true?

(a) $\square + 4 = 7$ $\qquad$ (b) $15 - \square = 11$ $\qquad$ (c) $13 = \square + 4$ $\qquad$ (d) $11 = \square - 5$

2 Solve these equations by inspection.

(a) $x + 2 = 6$ $\qquad$ (b) $a + 7 = 10$ $\qquad$ (c) $y - 4 = 4$
(d) $6 + t = 12$ $\qquad$ (e) $h - 15 = 7$ $\qquad$ (f) $d + 4 = 5$
(g) $z - 5 = 25$ $\qquad$ (h) $p + 7 = 7$ $\qquad$ (i) $c + 1 = 100$

3 What number must be put in the box to make each of these statements true?

(a) $3 \times \square = 15$ $\qquad$ (b) $\square \times 4 = 20$ $\qquad$ (c) $\square \div 2 = 9$ $\qquad$ (d) $7 = \square \div 3$

4 Solve these equations by inspection.

(a) $3a = 12$ $\qquad$ (b) $5e = 30$ $\qquad$ (c) $8 = 2p$ $\qquad$ (d) $8 = \frac{d}{2}$

5 What number must be put in the box to make each of these statements true?

(a) $2 \times \square + 3 = 5$ $\qquad$ (b) $\square \times 3 + 5 = 17$ $\qquad$ (c) $3 + \square \times 2 = 11$
(d) $5 \times \square - 1 = 9$ $\qquad$ (e) $4 \times \square - 5 = 7$ $\qquad$ (f) $\square \times 3 - 6 = 9$

6 Solve these equations by inspection.

(a) $3x + 1 = 10$ $\qquad$ (b) $5y - 2 = 8$ $\qquad$ (c) $2d + 4 = 6$ $\qquad$ (d) $4x - 7 = 13$

Solving equations by working backwards

I think of a number and then subtract 3.
The answer is 5.
What is the number I thought of?

Imagine that x is the number I thought of.
The steps of the problem can be shown in a diagram.

$x \longrightarrow$ | subtract 3 | $\longrightarrow$ Answer 5

Now work backwards, doing the opposite calculation.

$8 \longleftarrow$ | add 3 | $\longleftarrow 5$

The number I thought of is 8.

> The opposite of 'subtracting 3' is 'adding 3'.

EXAMPLES

1 Ken thinks of a number.
He multiplies it by 5.
His answer is 30.
What number did Ken think of?

$x \longrightarrow$ | multiply by 5 | $\longrightarrow 30$

$6 \longleftarrow$ | divide by 5 | $\longleftarrow 30$

Ken's number is 6.

Remember

Forwards	Backwards
add	subtract
subtract	add
multiply	divide
divide	multiply

2 I think of a number, multiply it by 3 and add 4.
The answer is 19.
What is my number?

The number I thought of is 5.

Exercise **20.2**   Solve the equations by working backwards.

1 I think of a number and then add 4. The answer is 7.
What is my number?

2 Jan thinks of a number and then subtracts 5. Her answer is 9.
What is her number?

3 I think of a number and then multiply it by 2. The answer is 10.
What is my number?

4 Lou thinks of a number. He multiplies it by 2 and then subtracts 5. The answer is 7.
What is his number?

5 I think of a number, subtract 5 and then multiply by 2. The answer is 12.
What is my number?

6 Beth thinks of a number. She multiplies it by 3 and adds 4.
If the answer is 19, what is her number?

7 I think of a number, add 4 then multiply by 3. The answer is 24.
What is my number?

8 Steve thinks of a number. He multiplies it by 5 and then adds 2. The answer is 17.
What is his number?

9 I think of a number, multiply it by 3 and then subtract 5. The answer is 7.
What is my number?

10 Solve this puzzle.

> Begin with x. Double it and then add 3. The result is equal to 17. What is the value of x?

11 Kathryn thinks of a number. She adds 3 and then doubles the result.
  (a) What number does Kathryn start with to get an answer of 10?
  (b) Kathryn starts with x. What is her answer in terms of x?

12 Sarah thinks of a number. She subtracts 2 and multiplies by 3.
  (a) What number does Sarah start with to get an answer of 21?
  (b) Sarah starts with x. What is her answer in terms of x?

13 Ali thinks of a number. He multiplies it by 2 and then adds 3.
  (a) What number does Ali start with to get an answer of 15?
  (b) Ali starts with x. What is his answer in terms of x?

The balance method

It is not always easy to solve equations by inspection.
To solve harder equations a better method has to be used.
Here is a method that works a bit like a balance.

① These scales are balanced.

② You can add the same amount to both sides and they still balance.

③ You can subtract the same amount from both sides and they still balance.

④ You can double (or halve) the amount on both sides and they still balance.

Equations work in the same way.
If you do the same to both sides of an equation, it is still true.

EXAMPLES Use the balance method to solve these equations. Explain what you are doing.

1 Solve $d - 13 = 5$.

$d - 13 = 5$
Add 13 to both sides.
$d = 18$

2 Solve $x + 7 = 16$.

$x + 7 = 16$
Subtract 7 from both sides.
$x = 9$

The aim is to find out what number the letter stands for, by ending up with **one letter** on one side of the equation and a **number** on the other side.

3 Solve $4a = 20$.

$4a = 20$
Divide both sides by 4.
$a = 5$

4 Solve $4n + 5 = 17$.

$4n + 5 = 17$
Subtract 5 from both sides.
$4n = 12$
Divide both sides by 4.
$n = 3$

Look at the examples carefully.
The steps taken to solve the equations are explained.
Notice that, doing the same to both sides means: **adding** the **same number** to both sides.
subtracting the **same number** from both sides.
dividing both sides by the **same number**.
multiplying both sides by the **same number**.

Exercise **20.3**

1 Use the balance method to solve these equations.
Write down the steps that you use to solve each equation.
(a) $y + 4 = 7$ (b) $x + 5 = 11$ (c) $a + 10 = 20$
(d) $e + 9 = 24$ (e) $d + 6 = 17$ (f) $c + 15 = 35$
(g) $9 + x = 11$ (h) $2 + y = 21$ (i) $8 + m = 15$

2 Use the balance method to solve these equations.
Explain each step of your working.
(a) $q - 5 = 2$ (b) $m - 2 = 8$ (c) $n - 7 = 9$
(d) $p - 6 = 12$ (e) $x - 11 = 20$ (f) $y - 3 = 14$
(g) $a - 1 = 1$ (h) $g - 3 = 1$ (i) $h - 5 = 7$

3 Use the balance method to solve these equations.
(a) $28 + x = 42$ (b) $t - 15 = 13$ (c) $f + 16 = 34$
(d) $y - 12 = 7$ (e) $14 + b = 21$ (f) $x - 9 = 20$
(g) $7 + m = 11$ (h) $k - 2 = 3$ (i) $5 + y = 12$

4 Use the balance method to solve these equations.
Write down the steps that you use.
(a) $3c = 12$ (b) $5a = 20$ (c) $4f = 12$
(d) $8p = 24$ (e) $6h = 30$ (f) $10u = 20$
(g) $3d = 30$ (h) $2e = 14$ (i) $3f = 27$

5 Use the balance method to solve these equations.
Show each step of your working.
(a) $2p + 1 = 9$ (b) $4t - 1 = 11$ (c) $3h - 7 = 14$
(d) $3 + 4b = 11$ (e) $5d - 8 = 42$ (f) $2x + 3 = 15$
(g) $2 + 3c = 17$ (h) $3n - 1 = 8$ (i) $4x + 3 = 11$

Solving Equations · · · Solving Equations · · ·

6 Solve these equations.
There is no need to explain your working if you are confident of what you are doing.

(a) $5c + 7 = 42$ (b) $7x = 28$ (c) $8y - 5 = 27$
(d) $3x + 5 = 11$ (e) $4b + 8 = 32$ (f) $6x - 9 = 15$
(g) $6k - 7 = 5$ (h) $7b + 4 = 25$ (i) $9c - 12 = 6$

7 Solve these equations.

(a) $6a = 18$ (b) $4x - 7 = 29$ (c) $8a + 7 = 7$
(d) $1 + 6p = 7$ (e) $8y - 14 = 26$ (f) $12 + 5p = 32$
(g) $3x - 5 = 22$ (h) $5 + 2k = 13$ (i) $5m + 3 = 18$

More equations

All the equations you have solved so far have had whole number solutions, but the solutions to equations can include negative numbers and fractions.

EXAMPLES

1 Solve $5x = 2$.

$5x = 2$
Divide both sides by 5.
$x = \frac{2}{5}$

2 Solve $-4a = 20$.

$-4a = 20$
Divide both sides by -4.
$a = -5$

3 Solve $6m - 1 = 2$.

$6m - 1 = 2$
Add 1 to both sides.
$6m = 3$
Divide both sides by 6.
$m = \frac{3}{6}$

$m = \frac{1}{2}$

4 Solve $5 - 4n = -1$.

$5 - 4n = -1$
Subtract 5 from both sides.
$-4n = -6$
Divide both sides by -4.
$n = 1.5$

Exercise 20.4

1 Solve these equations.
Explain each step of your working.

(a) $4k = 2$ (b) $2a = -6$ (c) $-3d = 12$
(d) $-8n = 4$ (e) $t + 3 = -2$ (f) $n - 3 = -2$
(g) $2m + 1 = 4$ (h) $3x - 2 = 5$ (i) $2y + 5 = 4$

2 Solve these equations.

(a) $5x = -10$ (b) $2y + 7 = 1$ (c) $4t + 10 = 2$
(d) $5 - a = 7$ (e) $2 - d = 5$ (f) $3 - 2g = 9$
(g) $4t = 2$ (h) $2x = 15$ (i) $5d = 7$
(j) $4a - 5 = 1$ (k) $3 + 5g = 4$ (l) $2b - 5 = 4$

3 Solve these equations.

(a) $x - 1 = -3$ (b) $3 + 2n = 2$ (c) $2 - x = 3$
(d) $4 - 3y = 13$ (e) $2x - 1 = -3$ (f) $3 - 5x = 18$
(g) $4x + 1 = -5$ (h) $-2 - 3x = 10$ (i) $2 - 4x = 8$

Equations with brackets

Equations can include brackets.
Before using the balance method any brackets must be simplified by multiplying out.
This is called **expanding**.
Once the brackets have been removed the balance method can be used as before.

Remember:
$2(x + 3)$ means $2 \times (x + 3)$
$2(x + 3) = 2 \times x + 2 \times 3 = 2x + 6$

$3(4a - 5) = 12a - 15$

EXAMPLES

1 Solve $3(x + 2) = 12$.

$3(x + 2) = 12$
Expand the brackets.
$3x + 6 = 12$
$3x = 6$
$x = 2$

2 Solve $5(3y - 7) + 15 = 25$.

$5(3y - 7) + 15 = 25$
Expand the brackets.
$15y - 35 + 15 = 25$
$15y = 45$
$y = 3$

Exercise 20.5

1 Solve.
  (a) $2(x + 3) = 12$
  (b) $4(a + 1) = 12$
  (c) $5(t + 4) = 30$
  (d) $2(y + 4) = 8$
  (e) $3(e + 2) = 21$
  (f) $6(3 + x) = 30$

2 Solve.
  (a) $3(p - 2) = 9$
  (b) $6(c - 2) = 24$
  (c) $2(x - 1) = 4$
  (d) $4(y - 3) = 24$
  (e) $2(g - 3) = 16$
  (f) $8(q - 3) = 40$

3 Solve.
  (a) $3(a + 1) = 15$
  (b) $2(b - 2) = 8$
  (c) $4(c + 2) = 12$
  (d) $6(d - 3) = 36$
  (e) $7(2 + e) = 49$
  (f) $5(f + 2) = 30$

4 Solve.
  (a) $3(2w + 1) = 15$
  (b) $2(4s + 5) = 34$
  (c) $4(1 + 3x) = 28$
  (d) $6(3g - 7) = 12$
  (e) $4(2q - 1) = 28$
  (f) $8(3t - 5) = 32$
  (g) $3(2w + 1) = 27$
  (h) $4(7 - 2x) = 4$
  (i) $5(3y - 10) = 25$

5 Solve these equations.
The solution will not always be a whole number.
  (a) $3(p + 2) = 3$
  (b) $2(3 - d) = 10$
  (c) $2(1 - 3g) = 14$
  (d) $2(x - 5) = 7$
  (e) $5(y + 1) = 7$
  (f) $2(1 + 3t) = 5$
  (g) $2(2t - 1) = 5$
  (h) $3(2a - 3) = 6$
  (i) $5(m - 2) = 3$

6 Solve these equations.
  (a) $2(x + 3) - 5 = 9$
  (b) $3(a - 1) + 2 = 5$
  (c) $5(3 - 2m) - 7 = 13$
  (d) $5 + 2(y - 3) = 4$
  (e) $2w + 3(1 + w) = -12$
  (f) $e + 5(2e - 4) = 2$
  (g) $3a - 7(1 - a) = 8$
  (h) $2 - 3(t + 5) = 20$
  (i) $5x - 2(3 - x) = 1$

Solving Equations ... Solving Equations ... Solving Equations ...

Equations with letters on both sides

In some questions letters appear on both sides of the equation.

EXAMPLES

1 Solve $3x + 1 = x + 7$.

$3x + 1 = x + 7$
Subtract 1 from both sides.
$\quad 3x = x + 6$
Subtract x from both sides.
$\quad 2x = 6$
Divide both sides by 2.
$\quad x = 3$

2 Solve $4(3 + 2x) = 5(x + 2)$.

$4(3 + 2x) = 5(x + 2)$
$12 + 8x = 5x + 10$
$8x = 5x - 2$
$3x = -2$
$x = -\frac{2}{3}$

Exercise 20.6

1 Solve the following equations.
(a) $3x = 20 - x$
(b) $5q = 12 - q$
(c) $2t = 15 - 3t$
(d) $5e - 9 = 2e$
(e) $3g - 8 = g$
(f) $y + 3 = 5 - y$
(g) $4x + 1 = x + 7$
(h) $7k + 3 = 3k + 7$
(i) $3a - 1 = a + 7$
(j) $3p - 1 = 2p + 5$
(k) $6m - 1 = m + 9$
(l) $3d - 5 = 5 + d$
(m) $2y + 1 = y + 6$
(n) $3 + 5u = 2u + 12$
(o) $4q + 3 = q + 3$

2 Solve.
(a) $3d = 32 - d$
(b) $3q = 12 - q$
(c) $3c + 2 = 10 - c$
(d) $4t + 2 = 17 - t$
(e) $4w + 1 = 13 - 2w$
(f) $2e - 3 = 12 - 3e$
(g) $2g + 5 = 25 - 2g$
(h) $2z - 6 = 14 - 3z$
(i) $5m + 2 = 20 + 2m$
(j) $5a - 4 = 3a + 6$
(k) $3 + 4x = 15 + x$
(l) $6y - 11 = y + 4$

3 Solve these equations.
The solution will not always be a whole number.
(a) $3m + 8 = m$
(b) $2 - 4t = 12 + t$
(c) $5p - 3 = 3p - 7$
(d) $5x - 7 = 3x$
(e) $3 + 5a = a + 5$
(f) $2b + 7 = 11 - 3b$
(g) $4 - 4y = y$
(h) $7 + 3d = 10 - d$
(i) $f - 6 = 3f + 1$

4 Solve.
(a) $4t + 3 = t - 12$
(b) $3y + 1 = 9 - y$
(c) $12s = 2s + 5$
(d) $2p + 3 = 4 + 5p$
(e) $6a - 2.5 = a + 6.5$
(f) $8c + 0.7 = 1.8 - 2c$
(g) $4 - 1\frac{1}{2}p = \frac{1}{2}p - 6$
(h) $x = \frac{1}{2}x - 3$
(i) $\frac{1}{2}x - 7 = \frac{1}{4}x + 1$

5 Solve.
(a) $3(n + 5) + n = 23$
(b) $3(2z - 5) = z + 15$
(c) $4(2w + 3) + 7 = 43$
(d) $m + 2(m + 1) = 14$
(e) $2(3h - 4) = 3(h + 1) - 5$
(f) $2(3 - 2x) = 2(6 - x)$
(g) $2(3w - 1) + 4w = 28$
(h) $2(y + 4) + 3(2y - 5) = 5$
(i) $3(2v + 3) = 5 - 4(3 - v)$
(j) $5c - 2(4c - 9) = 5 + 5(2 - c)$
(k) $5(x + 2) + 2(2x - 1) = 7(x - 4)$
(l) $3(x - 4) = 5(2x - 3) - 2(3x - 5)$

Equations with fractions

You have already met some equations with fractions.

This section deals with harder equations with fractions. For example: $\frac{3}{4}x = \frac{2}{5}$

With equations like this, it is easier to get rid of the fractions first.

To do this multiply both sides of the equation by the least common multiple of the denominators of the fractions.

Solve $\frac{3}{4}x = \frac{2}{5}$.

The multiples of 4 are: 4, 8, 12, 16, **20**, …
The multiples of 5 are: 5, 10, 15, **20**, …
The least common multiple of 4 and 5 is 20.
So, the first step is to multiply both sides of the equation by 20.

$$\frac{3}{4}x \times 20 = \frac{2}{5} \times 20$$

This is the same as: $x \times \frac{3}{4} \times 20 = \frac{2}{5} \times 20$

$$15x = 8$$

Divide both sides by 15.

$$x = \frac{8}{15}$$

Remember:

$\frac{3}{4} \times 20$ is the same as $\frac{3}{4}$ of 20.

To find $\frac{3}{4}$ of 20:

$20 \div 4 = 5$ gives $\frac{1}{4}$ of 20.

$5 \times 3 = 15$ gives $\frac{3}{4}$ of 20.

So, $\frac{3}{4} \times 20 = 15$.

EXAMPLES

1 Solve $\frac{2}{5}x = 6$.

$\frac{2}{5}x = 6$

Multiply both sides by 5.

$5 \times \frac{2}{5}x = 5 \times 6$

$2x = 30$
$x = 15$

2 Solve $\frac{2x}{4} = \frac{2}{5}$.

$\frac{2x}{4} = \frac{2}{5}$

Multiply both sides by 20.

$20 \times \frac{2x}{4} = 20 \times \frac{2}{5}$

$5 \times 2x = 4 \times 2$
$10x = 8$

$x = \frac{4}{5}$

3 Solve $\frac{x}{2} + \frac{2x}{3} = 7$.

$\frac{x}{2} + \frac{2x}{3} = 7$

Multiply both sides by 6.

$6 \times \frac{x}{2} + 6 \times \frac{2x}{3} = 6 \times 7$

$3x + 4x = 42$
$7x = 42$
$x = 6$

4 Solve $\frac{x-1}{3} = \frac{x+1}{4}$.

$\frac{x-1}{3} = \frac{x+1}{4}$

Multiply both sides by 12.

$4(x-1) = 3(x+1)$
$4x - 4 = 3x + 3$
$4x = 3x + 7$
$x = 7$

Exercise **20.7**

1 What would you multiply each of these equations by to get rid of the fractions?

(a) $\frac{2}{3}a = 5$

(b) $\frac{5}{8} = \frac{3b}{4}$

(c) $\frac{x+3}{4} = \frac{x-7}{3}$

(d) $\frac{2d}{5} + \frac{d}{3} = 3$

2 Solve these equations.

(a) $\frac{2}{3}x = 4$

(b) $\frac{3}{4}y = 6$

(c) $\frac{5a}{6} = 20$

(d) $\frac{2d}{5} = -4$

(e) $\frac{a}{8} = \frac{3}{4}$

(f) $\frac{x}{3} = \frac{3}{2}$

(g) $\frac{2m}{8} = -\frac{3}{6}$

(h) $\frac{3t}{4} = \frac{1}{3}$

Solving Equations · · · · Solving Equations · · · · Solving Equations · · ·

3 Solve.

(a) $\dfrac{h + 1}{4} = 3$

(b) $\dfrac{2x - 1}{3} = 5$

(c) $\dfrac{3a + 4}{5} = -1$

(d) $\dfrac{7 - d}{4} = \dfrac{5}{2}$

(e) $\dfrac{2x - 1}{2} = \dfrac{1}{4}$

(f) $\dfrac{2a + 1}{2} = \dfrac{3}{5}$

(g) $\dfrac{4 - d}{3} = \dfrac{1}{-2}$

(h) $\dfrac{2 - 3h}{3} = -\dfrac{5}{6}$

(i) $\dfrac{2(4x - 3)}{5} = -6$

(j) $\dfrac{x + 2}{5} = \dfrac{3 - x}{4}$

(k) $\dfrac{a - 1}{2} = \dfrac{a + 1}{3}$

(l) $\dfrac{2x - 1}{6} = \dfrac{2 - x}{3}$

4 Solve.

(a) $\dfrac{x}{2} + \dfrac{x}{4} = 1$

(b) $\dfrac{x}{2} - \dfrac{x}{3} = 2$

(c) $\dfrac{x}{4} + \dfrac{3x}{8} = -1$

(d) $\dfrac{2x}{3} - \dfrac{x}{6} = -2$

(e) $\dfrac{x + 1}{2} + \dfrac{x - 1}{3} = 1$

(f) $\dfrac{x + 2}{3} - \dfrac{x + 1}{4} = 2$

Using equations to solve problems

So far, you have been given equations and asked to solve them.
The next step is to **form an equation** first using the information given in a problem.
The equation can then be solved in the usual way.

EXAMPLE

The triangle has sides of length: x cm, $2x$ cm and 7 cm.

(a) Write an expression, in terms of x,
for the perimeter of the triangle.
Give your answer in its simplest form.

(b) The triangle has a perimeter of 19 cm.
By forming an equation find the value of x.

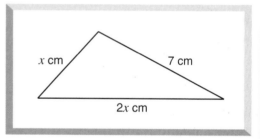

(a) The perimeter of the triangle is:
$x + 2x + 7$ cm
In its simplest form, the perimeter is:
$3x + 7$ cm

(b) The perimeter of the triangle is 19 cm,
so $3x + 7 = 19$
$3x = 12$
$x = 4$

Exercise **20.8**

1 (a) Write an expression, in terms of x,
for the sum of the angles of the triangle.
Give your answer in its simplest form.

(b) The sum of the angles is $180°$.
By forming an equation find the value of x.

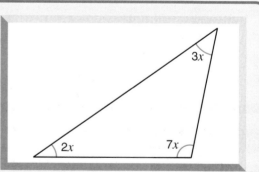

2 The weights of three packages are shown.
(a) Write an expression, in terms of k,
for the total weight of the packages.
(b) The packages weigh 15 kilograms
altogether.
By forming an equation find the
weight of the lightest package.

k kilograms $2k$ kilograms $3k$ kilograms

3 Bernadette pays 96 pence for a newspaper and a magazine.
The magazine costs twice as much as the newspaper.

   (a) The newspaper costs x pence.
Write an expression, in terms of x, for the price
of the magazine.

   (b) By forming an equation find the price of the magazine.

4 (a) Write an expression, in terms of y, for the
perimeter of this shape.
Give your answer in its simplest form.

   (b) The shape has a perimeter of 39 cm.
By forming an equation find the value of y.

5 cm
y cm
10 cm
$2y$ cm

5 A bag contains the following balls.

               a yellow balls
          $2a + 1$ red balls
          $3a + 2$ blue balls

   (a) Write an expression, in terms of a, for the total number
of balls in the bag.

   (b) The bag contains 45 balls.
How many yellow balls are in the bag?

6 Dominic is 7 years younger than Marcie.

   (a) Dominic is n years old.
Write an expression, in terms of n, for Marcie's age.

   (b) The sum of their ages is 43 years.
By forming an equation find the ages of Dominic and Marcie.

7 The diagram shows the lengths of three rods.

   (a) Write an expression, in terms of y,
for the total length of the rods.

   (b) The total length of the rods is 30 centimetres.
What is the length of the longest rod?

$y - 5$ centimetres y centimetres

$2y + 3$ centimetres

8 Grace is given a weekly allowance of £p.
Aimee is given £4 a week **more** than Grace.
Lydia is given £3 a week **less** than Grace.

   (a) Write an expression, in terms of p, for the amount given to
     (i) Aimee,   (ii) Lydia,   (iii) all three girls.

   (b) The three girls are given a total of £25 a week altogether.
By forming an equation find the weekly allowance given to each girl.

9 The cost of a pencil is x pence. The cost of a pen is 10 pence more than a pencil.

   (a) Write down, in terms of x, the cost of a pen.

   (b) Write down, in terms of x, the total cost a pencil and two pens.
Give your answer in its simplest form.

   (c) The total cost of a pencil and two pens is 65 pence.
Form an equation in x and solve it to find the cost of a pencil.

Solving Equations . . . Solving Equations . . . Solving Equations . . .

10 (a) Write down a simplified expression, in terms of x, for the perimeter of the triangle.

(b) The perimeter is 59 cm.
Write down an equation and solve it to find the value of x.

(c) Use your answer to find the length of each side of the triangle.

(2x − 5) cm   (2x − 1) cm
(3x + 2) cm

11 Geoffrey knows that the sum of the angles of this shape adds up to 540°.

(a) Write down an equation in x.

(b) Use your equation to find the size of the largest angle.

5x − 10°   6x − 30°
4x + 20°
2x + 20°   x

12 A drink costs x pence.
A cake costs 7 pence more than a drink.
The total cost of two drinks and a cake is 97 pence.
Form an equation in x and solve it to find the cost of a cake.

13 The areas of these rectangles are equal.
By forming and solving an equation in x, find the area of A.

(2x − 1) cm

3 cm   *A*

(x + 3) cm

5 cm   *B*   Not drawn accurately

14 John has x CDs in his collection.
Sarah has five times as many CDs as John.
John and Sarah each collect another 12 CDs. Now Sarah has twice as many CDs as John.

(a) Write down an expression, in terms of x, for the number of CDs Sarah has now.

(b) Form an equation and solve it to find how many CDs Sarah has now.

What you need to know

- The solution of an equation is the value of the unknown letter that fits the equation.

You should be able to:
- Solve simple equations by inspection. e.g. $x + 2 = 5$, $x − 3 = 7$, $2x = 10$, $\frac{x}{4} = 12$
- Solve simple equations by inspection by working backwards.
- Use the balance method to solve equations which are difficult to solve by inspection.
- Solve equations with brackets. e.g. $4(3 + 2x) = 36$
- Solve equations with unknowns on both sides of the equals sign. e.g. $3x + 1 = x + 7$
- Solve equations with fractions. e.g. $\frac{1}{4}x + 1 = 7$, $\frac{x + 3}{4} = 2$, $\frac{x − 1}{3} + \frac{x + 1}{2} = \frac{1}{6}$
- Write, or form, equations using the information given in a problem.
- Use equations to solve problems.

Review Exercise 20

1 What number must be put in the box to make each of these statements correct?

(a) $\boxed{} + 5 = 9$ (b) $7 − \boxed{} = 4$ (c) $3 \times \boxed{} = 18$ (d) $\boxed{} \times 2 − 3 = 5$

2 Solve these equations. (a) $x − 2 = 5$ (b) $5x = 20$

AQA

3 Jacob uses this rule.

   "**Start with a number, divide it by 2 and then add 3. Write down the result.**"

   (a) What is the result when Jacob starts with 8?

   (b) What number did Jacob start with when the result is 5?

AQA

4 What is the number Abel thinks of?

Think of a number.
Multiply it by three.
Now add seven.

Teacher

My answer is 94.

Abel

AQA

5 Solve these equations.

   (a) $y + 3 = 5$ (b) $2t + 8 = 2$ (c) $4g = 2$ (d) $5x - 1 = 2$

6 Solve the equations   (a) $2x + 3 = 11$,   (b) $3y + 7 = 1 - y$.

AQA

7 Solve these equations.   (a) $5x - 12 = 23$ (b) $3x + 4 = 5x + 8$

AQA

8 Solve these equations.

   (a) $7x = 56$ (b) $5x + 7 = 15$ (c) $8x - 1 = 4x + 19$

AQA

9 Solve the following equations.   (a) $4x + 6 = 11$ (b) $2(5 + 2x) = 16$

AQA

10 Solve the equations.

   (a) $3x - 14 = 4$ (b) $5x + 7 = x + 9$ (c) $\dfrac{x - 7}{8} = 2$

AQA

11 Solve the equations.   (a) $7x - 13 = 5(x - 3)$ (b) $\dfrac{10 - x}{4} = x - 1$

AQA

12 Solve these equations.

   (a) $3 - 4q = 11$ (b) $4(2t - 3) + 4t = 6$ (c) $\dfrac{2x + 9}{5} = 6$

13 Hassan is twice as old as Ali. Their ages add up to 39 years.
   How old is: (a) Ali,   (b) Hassan?

AQA

14 The diagram shows two cans of oil.
   The cans hold a total of 3 litres of oil.
   By forming an equation find the amount of oil in the larger can.

n litres $3n + 1$ litres

15 A drink costs x pence.
   A packet of crisps costs 15 pence **less** than a drink.

   (a) Write an expression, in terms of x, for the cost of a packet of crisps.

   (b) A drink and two packets of crisps cost 96 pence.
      By forming an equation find the cost of a drink.

16 The length of the sides of a triangle are $(x + 1)$ cm, $(x + 3)$ cm and $(x - 2)$ cm, as shown.

   (a) Write an expression, in terms of x, for the perimeter of the triangle.
      Give your answer in its simplest form.

   The perimeter is 23 cm.

   (b) Write down an equation in x
      and use it to find the value of x.

$(x + 1)$ cm

$(x - 2)$ cm

$(x + 3)$ cm

Not to scale

AQA

Solving Equations . . . Solving Equations . . .

20

CHAPTER 21

Formulae

Most people at some time make use of **formulae** to carry out routine calculations.
A **formula** represents a rule written using numbers, letters and mathematical signs.
When using a formula you will need to **substitute** your own values for the letters in order to carry out your calculation.

Substitution

Substituting whole numbers

> **EXAMPLE**
>
> Find the value of   (a) $a + 5$,   (b) $a - 3$,   (c) $3a$,   (d) $a \times a$,   when $a = 4$.
>
> (a) $a + 5$ (b) $a - 3$ (c) $3a$ (d) $a \times a$
> $= 4 + 5$ $= 4 - 3$ $= 3 \times 4$ $= 4 \times 4$
> $= 9$ $= 1$ $= 12$ $= 16$

Exercise 21.1   Do not use a calculator.

1 $m = 3$.   Find the value of   (a) $m + 2$ (b) $m - 1$ (c) $4m$ (d) $m \times m$

2 $t = 5$.   Find the value of   (a) $5 + t$ (b) $3 - t$ (c) $2t$ (d) $t \times t$

3 $x = 4$.   Find the value of   (a) $x + x$ (b) $x - 4$ (c) $3x$ (d) $x \times x \times 2$

4 $a = 6$ and $b = 3$. Find the value of
    (a) $3a + 2b$ (b) $b - a$ (c) $\frac{a}{b}$ (d) $a \times b$ (e) $2(a + b)$

5 $p = 10$ and $q = 5$. Find the value of
    (a) $p + q$ (b) $p - 2q$ (c) $\frac{p}{q}$ (d) $p \times q$ (e) $3(p - q)$

6 $x = 15$ and $y = 6$. Find the value of
    (a) $x + 2y$ (b) $x - 3y$ (c) $\frac{x}{y}$ (d) $x \times y$ (e) $6(x - y)$

Substituting negative numbers

> **EXAMPLE**
>
> Find the value of   (a) $a + 5$,   (b) $a - 3$,   (c) $3a$,   when $a = -4$.
>
> (a) $a + 5$ (b) $a - 3$ (c) $3a$
> $= -4 + 5$ $= -4 - 3$ $= 3 \times -4$
> $= 1$ $= -7$ $= -12$

Exercise 21.2

Do not use a calculator.

1 $m = -3$. Find the value of   (a) $m + 2$ (b) $m - 1$ (c) $4m$ (d) $2m + 9$

2 $t = -5$. Find the value of   (a) $5 + t$ (b) $t - 3$ (c) $2t$ (d) $3t - 1$

3 $x = -4$. Find the value of   (a) $x + x$ (b) $x - 4$ (c) $3x$ (d) $10 + 2x$

4 $a = 6$ and $b = -3$. Find the value of
     (a) $3a + 2b$ (b) $b - a$ (c) $\dfrac{a}{b}$ (d) $a \times b$ (e) $2(a + b)$

5 $p = -10$ and $q = 5$. Find the value of
     (a) $p + q$ (b) $p - 2q$ (c) $\dfrac{p}{q}$ (d) $p \times q$ (e) $3(p - q)$

6 $x = 15$ and $y = -6$. Find the value of
     (a) $x + 2y$ (b) $y - x$ (c) $\dfrac{x}{y}$ (d) $x \times y$ (e) $6(x + y)$

Writing expressions and formulae

A lollipop costs 15 pence.
How much will n lollipops cost?
Write a formula for the cost, C, in pence, of n lollipops.

Each lollipop costs 15 pence.

So, n lollipops cost $15 \times n$ pence $= 15n$ pence.

> $15n$ is an **algebraic expression**.

If the cost of n lollipops is C pence, then $C = 15n$.

> $C = 15n$ is a **formula**.

Formulae can be used in lots of situations.

The grid shows the numbers from 1 to 50.
An **L** shape has been drawn on the grid.
It is called $\mathbf{L_{14}}$ because the lowest number is 14.

What is the sum of the numbers in $\mathbf{L_{14}}$?

1	2	3	4	5	6	7	8	9	10
11	12	13	14	15	16	17	18	19	20
21	22	23	24	25	26	27	28	29	30
31	32	33	34	35	36	37	38	39	40
41	42	43	44	45	46	47	48	49	50

The **L** shape can be moved to different parts of the grid.
We can find the sum of the numbers for each shape.

A formula for the sum of the numbers, $\mathbf{S_n}$,
can be written in terms of n for shape $\mathbf{L_n}$.
$\mathbf{S_n} = n + (n + 10) + (n + 20) + (n + 21)$
$\mathbf{S_n} = 4n + 51$

n	
$n + 10$	
$n + 20$	$n + 21$

> An **expression** is just an answer using letters and numbers.
>
> A **formula** is an algebraic rule. It always has an equals sign.

EXAMPLES

1 A hedge is l metres long.
A fence is 50 metres longer than the hedge.
Write an **expression**, in terms of l, for the length of the fence.

The fence is $(l + 50)$ metres long.

2 Boxes of matches each contain 48 matches.
Write down a **formula** for the number of matches, m, in n boxes.

$m = 48 \times n$

This could be written as $m = 48n$.

1 A pencil costs *y* pence.
   (a) What is the cost of 5 pencils?
   (b) A ruler costs 8 pence more than a pencil.
       What is the cost of a ruler?

2 Egg boxes hold 12 eggs each.
   How many eggs are there in *e* boxes?

3 I am *a* years old.
   (a) How old will I be in 1 years time?
   (b) How old was I four years ago?
   (c) How old will I be in *n* years time?

4 A child is making a tower with toy bricks.
   He has *b* bricks in his tower.
   Write an expression for the number of bricks in the tower after he takes 3 bricks from the top.

5 Paul is *h* cm tall.
   Sue is 12 cm taller than Paul.
   Write down an expression for Sue's height in terms of *h*.

6 John has *d* CDs.
   (a) Carol has twice as many CDs as John.
       Write down an expression for the number of CDs that Carol has in terms of *d*.
   (b) Fred has 5 more CDs than Carol.
       Write down an expression for the number of CDs that Fred has in terms of *d*.

7 A packet of biscuits costs *y* pence.
   Write down a formula for the cost, *P* pence, of another packet which costs
   (a) five pence more than the first packet,
   (b) two pence less than the first packet,
   (c) twice the cost of the first packet.

8 David is *d* years old.
   Copy and complete this table to show the ages, *A*, of these people.

Name	Clue	Age
Alec	3 years older than David.	$A = d + 3$
Ben	2 years younger than David.	
Charlotte	Twice as old as David.	
Erica	Half David's age.	

9 Write a formula for the perimeter, *P*, for each of these shapes in terms of the letters given.

(a)

(b)

(c)

(d)

10 A caravan costs £25 per day to hire.
Write a formula for the cost, C, in £s, to hire the caravan for d days.

11 The cost of hiring a ladder is given by:

> £12 per day,
> plus a delivery charge of £8

(a) Bill hired a ladder for 3 days. How much did he pay?
(b) Sam hired a ladder for 6 days. How much did he pay?
(c) Fred hired a ladder for x days.
Write down a formula for the total cost, £C, in terms of x.

12 The grid shows the numbers from 1 to 50.
A **T** shape has been drawn on the grid.
It is called $\mathbf{T_{23}}$ because the lowest number is 23.

Calculate the sum of the numbers in:
(a) $\mathbf{T_{16}}$ (b) $\mathbf{T_{28}}$ (c) $\mathbf{T_{2}}$

1	2	3	4	5	6	7	8	9	10
11	12	13	14	15	16	17	18	19	20
21	22	23	24	25	26	27	28	29	30
31	32	33	34	35	36	37	38	39	40
41	42	43	44	45	46	47	48	49	50

(d) The diagram on the right shows $\mathbf{T_n}$.
Copy and complete the **T** shape in terms of n.

(e) Write a formula for the sum of the numbers, $\mathbf{S_n}$,
in terms of n, for shape $\mathbf{T_n}$.
Write your answer in its simplest form.

Using formulae

The formula for the perimeter of a rectangle is $P = 2L + 2W$.
By **substituting** values for the length, L, and the width, W, you can calculate the value of P.

$P = 2L + 2W$
When $L = 3$ and $W = 5$,
$P = 2 \times 3 + 2 \times 5$
$\quad = 6 + 10$
$\quad = 16$

EXAMPLES

1 $G = 4t - 1$
Find the value of G when $t = \frac{1}{2}$.

$G = 4t - 1$
$\quad = 4 \times \frac{1}{2} - 1$
$\quad = 2 - 1$
$\quad = 1$

2 $A = pq - r$
What is the value of A when
$p = 2$, $q = -2$ and $r = 3$.

$A = 2 \times (-2) - 3$
$\quad = -4 - 3$
$\quad = -7$

3 $H = 3(4x - y)$
Find the value of H when $x = 5$ and $y = 7$.

$H = 3(4x - y)$
$\quad = 3(4 \times 5 - 7)$
$\quad = 3(20 - 7)$
$\quad = 3(13)$
$\quad = 39$

4 $W = x^2 + 2$
Find the value of W when $x = 3$.

$W = x^2 + 2$
$\quad = 3 \times 3 + 2$
$\quad = 9 + 2$
$\quad = 11$

> **Remember**
> x^2 means $x \times x$.

Formulae . . . Formulae . . . Formulae . . . F

1 Find the value of $x + 3$ when
(a) $x = 7$ (b) $x = -2$

2 Find the value of $4a$ when
(a) $a = 7$ (b) $a = -3$

3 Find the value of $p - 3$ when
(a) $p = 5$ (b) $p = -3$

4 Find the value of $5 - d$ when
(a) $d = 7$ (b) $d = -3$

5 Find the value of $2x + 3$ when
(a) $x = 5$ (b) $x = -5$

6 Find the value of $4 - 2y$ when
(a) $y = 3$ (b) $y = -3$

7 Find the value of $4x$ when
(a) $x = \frac{1}{2}$ (b) $x = \frac{1}{8}$

8 Find the value of $5y$ when
(a) $y = 0.2$ (b) $y = 0.5$

9 Find the value of $2x + 5$ when
(a) $x = \frac{1}{2}$ (b) $x = 0.4$

10 Find the value of $4y - 1$ when
(a) $y = \frac{1}{4}$ (b) $y = 0.5$

11 Find the value of $5 - 3g$ when
(a) $g = 0.5$ (b) $g = \frac{1}{3}$

12 $F = 5(v + 6)$.
What is the value of F when $v = 9$?

13 $V = 2(7 + 2x)$.
What is the value of V when $x = 3$?

14 $P = 3(5 - 2d)$.
What is the value of P when $d = 4$?

15 $C = 8(p + q)$.
What is the value of C when
(a) $p = 5$ and $q = 8$,
(b) $p = 6$ and $q = -2$?

16 $T = a(x + 4)$.
What is the value of T when
(a) $a = 5$ and $x = 3$,
(b) $a = 2$ and $x = -5$,
(c) $a = -3$ and $x = 2$,
(d) $a = -3$ and $x = -6$?

17 $K = ab + c$.
Work out the value of K when
(a) $a = 3, b = -2$ and $c = 5$,
(b) $a = 5, b = 3$ and $c = -2$.

18 $L = xy - z$.
Work out the value of L when
(a) $x = 2$, $y = 3$ and $z = -4$,
(b) $x = -4$, $y = 2$ and $z = 3$.

19 The number of matches, M, needed to make a pattern of P pentagons is given by the formula: $M = 4P + 1$.
Find the number of matches needed to make 8 pentagons.

20 The distance, d metres, travelled by a lawn mower in t minutes is given by the formula: $d = 24t$.
Find the distance travelled by the lawn mower in:
(a) 4 minutes,   (b) 90 seconds.

21 Convert these temperatures from Fahrenheit to Centigrade using the formula: $C = (F - 32) \div 1.8$
(a) $14°F$ (b) $-4°F$ (c) $-40°F$

22 Convert these temperatures from Centigrade to Fahrenheit using the formula: $F = C \times 1.8 + 32$
(a) $10°C$ (b) $-10°C$ (c) $-40°C$

23 $T = 45W + 30$ is used to calculate the time in minutes needed to cook a joint of beef weighing W kilograms.
How many minutes are needed to cook a joint weighing $2.4\,kg$?

24 The voltage, V volts, in a circuit with resistance, R ohms, and current, I amps, is given by the formula: $V = IR$.
Find the voltage in a circuit when $I = 12$ and $R = 20$.

25 A simple formula for the motion of a car is $F = ma + R$.
Find F when $m = 500$, $a = 0.2$ and $R = 4000$.

26 The cost, £C, of n units of gas is calculated using the formula: $C = 0.08n + 3.5$.
Calculate the cost of 458 units of gas.

27 The formula $v = u + at$ gives the speed v of a particle, t seconds after it starts with speed u.
Calculate v when $u = 7.8$, $a = -10$ and $t = \frac{3}{4}$.

Exercise 21.5 Do not use a calculator for questions 1 to 12.

1 $S = a^2$.
Find the value of S when
(a) $a = 3$ (b) $a = -3$

2 $S = 2a^2$.
Find the value of S when
(a) $a = 3$ (b) $a = -3$

3 $S = (2a)^2$.
Find the value of S when
(a) $a = 3$ (b) $a = -3$

4 $S = \frac{1}{2}p^2$.
Find the value of S when
(a) $p = 8$ (b) $p = -8$

5 $S = \left(\frac{1}{2}p\right)^2$.
Find the value of S when
(a) $p = 8$ (b) $p = -8$

6 What is the value of $3a^2 - 9$ when
(a) $a = 4$, (b) $a = 5$,
(c) $a = -4$, (d) $a = -5$?

7 What is the value of x^3 when
(a) $x = 3$, (b) $x = -3$,
(c) $x = 5$, (d) $x = -5$?

8 What is the value of $2t^3$ when
(a) $t = 4$, (b) $t = -4$?

9 What is the value of $3x - x^3$ when
(a) $x = 2$, (b) $x = -2$?

10 $T = \sqrt{\dfrac{a}{b}}$
Work out the value of T when
(a) $a = 9$ and $b = 16$,
(b) $a = 3$ and $b = \frac{4}{3}$.

11 $S = \sqrt[3]{pq}$
Work out the value of S when
(a) $p = 2$ and $q = 32$,
(b) $p = 2\frac{1}{4}$ and $q = 1\frac{1}{2}$,
(c) $p = 54$ and $q = -0.5$.

12 $L = \sqrt{m^2 + n^2}$
Work out the value of L when
(a) $m = 6$ and $n = 8$,
(b) $m = 0.3$ and $n = 0.4$.

13 Calculate $5\sqrt{x}$ when
(a) $x = 27$ (b) $x = 0.4$
Give your answers correct to
one decimal place.

14 Calculate $\sqrt{5x}$ when
(a) $x = 27$ (b) $x = 0.4$
Give your answers correct to
two significant figures.

15 The formula $F = \frac{mv^2}{r}$
describes the motion of a cyclist
rounding a corner.
Find F when
$m = 80$, $v = 6$ and $r = 20$.

16 The height, h metres, of a bullet after
t seconds, is given by the
formula $h = ut - \frac{1}{2}gt^2$,
where $u\,\text{ms}^{-1}$ is the initial vertical
speed and $g\,\text{ms}^{-2}$ is the acceleration
due to gravity.
Find h when $u = 200$ and $t = 1\frac{3}{5}$.
Take $g = 9.8$.
Give your answer to a suitable degree
of accuracy.

17 Use the formula $R = \left(\frac{t}{s}\right)^2$
to calculate the value of R when
$t = -0.6$ and $s = \frac{2}{5}$.

18 The time T, for a pendulum to make a
complete swing is given by the
formula: $T = 2\pi\sqrt{\dfrac{l}{g}}$
(a) Calculate the value of T when
$l = 0.8$ and $g = 9.8$.
(b) Calculate the value of T when
$l = 1\frac{1}{2}$ and $g = 9.8$.
Take π to be 3.14 or use the π key on
your calculator.

19 Use the formula $v = \sqrt{u^2 + 2as}$
to calculate the value of v when
(a) $u = 2.4$, $a = 3.2$, $s = 5.25$,
(b) $u = 9.1$, $a = -4.7$, $s = 3.04$.
Give your answers correct to
one decimal place.

EXAMPLE

Birthday Party
Specials
£20, plus £8 per person

(a) Nick has a birthday party for 10 people. How much does it cost?

(b) Tony has a birthday party for x people. Write a formula for the cost £T, in terms of x.

(c) Jean pays £140 for her birthday party. How many people went to the party?

(a) Nick's party costs: £20 + 10 × £8
$$= £100$$

(b) Cost for x people in £ $= x \times 8 = 8x$
Total cost in £ $= 20 + 8x$
Total cost is £T
So formula is $T = 20 + 8x$

(c) Using the formula $T = 20 + 8x$.
Jean's party costs £140, so $T = 140$.
$$140 = 20 + 8x$$
$$8x = 120$$
$$x = 15$$

15 people went to Jean's party.

Exercise 21.6

1 The cost of a taxi journey is:

£3 plus £2 for each kilometre travelled

(a) Alex travels 5 km by taxi. How much does it cost?
(b) A taxi journey of k kilometres costs £C.
Write a formula for the cost, C, in terms of k.
(c) Adrian paid £7 for a taxi journey.
Use your formula to find the number of kilometres he travelled.

2 A rule to find the cooking time, C minutes, of a chicken which weighs k kilograms, is:

multiply the weight of the chicken by 40 and then add 20

(a) Find the cooking time for a chicken which weighs 3 kg.
(b) Write a formula for C in terms of k.
(c) Use your formula to find the weight of a chicken which has a cooking time of 100 minutes.

3 An approximate rule for changing temperatures in degrees Celsius, C, to temperatures in degrees Fahrenheit, F, is given by the rule:

double C and add on 30

(a) Find the value of F when $C = 6$.
(b) Write down a formula for F in terms of C.
(c) Use your formula to find the value of C when $F = 58$.

4 A teacher uses this rule to work out the number of exercise books he needs for Year 11 students.

3 books per student, plus 50 extra books

(a) This year there are 120 students in Year 11. How many books are needed?
(b) Using b for the number of books and n for the number of students, write down the teacher's rule for b in terms of n.
(c) For the next Year 11, he will need 470 books.
How many students will be in Year 11 next year?

5 (a) How much does it cost to hire the carpet cleaner for 3 days?

(b) Using T for the total cost in £, and d for the number of days hired, write a formula for T in terms of d.

(c) Sarah paid a total of £96 to hire the carpet cleaner.
For how many days did she hire the carpet cleaner?

CARPET CLEANER HIRE

£15
PER DAY

Plus fixed delivery charge of £6

6 Scaffolding can be hired. The hire charge is calculated using this formula:

| forty-five pounds per day plus a fixed charge of seventy pounds |

(a) How much would it cost to hire scaffolding for 5 days?

(b) Using C for the total cost in £, and n for the number of days, write a formula for C in terms of n.

(c) A builder paid £475 altogether to hire some scaffolding.
For how many days did he hire the scaffolding?

Rearranging formulae

Sometimes it is easier to use a formula if you **rearrange** it first.

EXAMPLES

1 $k = \frac{8m}{5}$

Rearrange the formula to give m in terms of k.

$k = \frac{8m}{5}$

Multiply both sides by 5.

$5k = 8m$

Divide both sides by 8.

$\frac{5k}{8} = m$

We say we have **rearranged the formula**

$k = \frac{8m}{5}$ to make m the **subject** of the formula.

2 $y = 2x + 8$

Make x the subject of the formula.

$y = 2x + 8$

Subtract 8 from both sides.

$y - 8 = 2x$

Divide both sides by 2.

$\frac{1}{2}y - 4 = x$

y is the subject of $y = 2x + 8$,
x is the subject of $x = \frac{1}{2}y - 4$.

3 $A = 3r^2$

Make r the subject of the formula.

$A = 3r^2$

Divide both sides by 3.

$\frac{A}{3} = r^2$

Take the square root of both sides.

$\pm \sqrt{\frac{A}{3}} = r$

so $r = \pm \sqrt{\frac{A}{3}}$

4 $T = a + \sqrt{b}$

Rearrange the formula to give b in terms of T and a.

$T = a + \sqrt{b}$

Take a from both sides.

$T - a = \sqrt{b}$

Square both sides.

$(T - a)^2 = b$

so $b = (T - a)^2$

1. Make m the subject of these formulae.
   (a) $a = m + 5$ (b) $a = x + m$ (c) $a = m - 2$
   (d) $a = m - b$ (e) $a = 2 - m$ (f) $a = x - m$

2. Make x the subject of these formulae.
   (a) $y = 4x$ (b) $y = ax$ (c) $y = -ax$
   (d) $y = \frac{1}{2}x$ (e) $y = \frac{x}{a}$ (f) $y = -\frac{x}{a}$
   (g) $y = \frac{2}{x}$ (h) $y = -\frac{n}{x}$

3. Make p the subject of these formulae.
   (a) $y = 2p + 6$ (b) $t = 5p + q$ (c) $m = 3p - 2$
   (d) $r = 4p - q$ (e) $a = 3 - 2p$ (f) $d = g - 3p$
   (g) $m = \frac{p}{2} + 3$ (h) $y = \frac{p}{3} + x$ (i) $t = \frac{p}{5} - 2$
   (j) $g = h - \frac{p}{2}$ (k) $s = q + \frac{3}{p}$ (l) $y = x - \frac{a}{p}$

4. A formula for changing kilograms to pounds is $P = 0.45K$.
   Rearrange the formula to give K in terms of P.

5. $F = 1.8C + 32$ changes temperatures in °C to °F.
   Rearrange the formula to give C in terms of F.

6. The cost, £C, of hiring a car for n days is given by $C = 35 + 24n$.
   Make n the subject of the formula.

7. The area of a trapezium is given by $A = \frac{1}{2}(a + b)h$.
   Make a the subject of this formula.

8. Make c the subject of these formulae.
   (a) $y = c^2$ (b) $y = \sqrt{c}$ (c) $y = dc^2$ (d) $y = \frac{\sqrt{c}}{3}$

   (e) $y = c^2 + x$ (f) $y = x + \sqrt{c}$ (g) $y = x + \frac{c^2}{d}$ (h) $y = \frac{\sqrt{c}}{a} - x$

9. Make the bold letter the subject of these formulae.
   (a) $\frac{V}{I} = R$ (b) $E = \mathbf{m}c^2$ (c) $y = a\mathbf{x}^2 + b$ (d) $e = \frac{1}{2}m\mathbf{v}^2$

10. Make a the subject of these formulae.
    (a) $b = a + c^2$ (b) $a^2 = b$ (c) $4a = 8b + c$ (d) $6a = 2b$
    (e) $3a = \frac{4b}{5}$ (f) $b = \frac{2a}{3}$ (g) $p = ma + d$ (h) $ma^2 = F$

11. $R = \left(\frac{t}{s}\right)^2$ Rearrange the formula to give t in terms of R and s.

12. $a + m = b - m$ Make m the subject of the formula.

13. Make x the subject of these formulae.
    (a) $3(x - a) = x$ (b) $2(a + x) = 3(b - x)$ (c) $2(x + a) = 5x$

14. $\frac{p + q}{3} = p - q$ Rearrange the formula to give q in terms of p.

Solve problems by rearranging formulae

EXAMPLE

A cuboid has length 7.8 cm and breadth 5 cm.
The volume of the cuboid is 136.5 cm³.
Calculate the height of the cuboid.

The formula for the volume of a cuboid is $V = lbh$,

so $h = \dfrac{V}{lb}$ (by dividing both sides of $V = lbh$ by lb)

Substitute $V = 136.5$, $l = 7.8$ and $b = 5$ in $h = \dfrac{V}{lb}$.

$$h = \frac{136.5}{7.8 \times 5} = 3.5$$

The height of the cuboid is 3.5 cm.

The values to be substituted may include whole numbers, negative numbers, decimals or fractions.

Exercise **21.8**   Do not use a calculator for questions 1 to 5.

1 The perimeter of a square is $P = 4d$.
 (a) Change the subject to d.
 (b) Find d when $P = 2.8$ cm.

2 The area of a rectangle is $A = lb$.
 (a) Change the subject to l.
 (b) Find l when
   $A = 27$ cm² and $b = 4.5$ cm.

3 The speed of a car is $S = \dfrac{D}{T}$.
 (a) (i) Change the subject to D.
   (ii) Find D when
     $S = 48$ km/h and $T = 0.5$ hours.
 (b) (i) Change the subject to T.
   (ii) Find T when
     $S = 72$ km/h and $D = 90$ km.

4 The area of a wooden shape is $A = \frac{3}{2}pq$.
 (a) Change the subject to p.
 (b) Find p when
   $A = 24$ cm² and $q = 5$ cm.

5 The perimeter of a rectangle is
 $P = 2(l + b)$.
 (a) Change the subject to b.
 (b) Find b when
   $P = 18$ cm and $l = 4.8$ cm.

6 $y = mx + c$
 (a) Rearrange the formula to give x
   in terms of y, m and c.
 (b) Calculate x when
   $y = 0.6$, $m = -0.4$ and $c = 1.8$.

7 $A = \dfrac{bh}{2}$
 (a) Rearrange the formula to give b
   in terms of A and h.
 (b) Calculate b when
   $A = 9.8$ and $h = 0.84$.

8 $I = \dfrac{C}{d^2}$
 (a) Rearrange the formula to give d
   in terms of I and C.
 (b) Calculate d when
   $I = 17.4$ and $C = 23.7$.
   Give your answer correct to 2 d.p.

9 $p^2 = q^2 + r^2$
 (a) Rearrange the formula to give q
   in terms of p and r.
 (b) Calculate q when
   $p = 7.3$ and $r = 2.7$.
   Give your answer to a suitable
   degree of accuracy.

10 $V = \frac{4}{3}\pi r^3$
 (a) Rearrange the formula to give r
   in terms of V and π.
 (b) Calculate r when
   $V = 1.6 \times 10^5$ and $\pi = 3.14$.

11 $\dfrac{x}{a} = \dfrac{b}{x}$
 (a) Make x the subject of the formula.
 (b) Calculate x when
   $a = 4.6 \times 10^3$ and $b = 3.5 \times 10^5$.
   Give your answer in standard form
   correct to two significant figures.

- A **formula** is an algebraic rule which can be rearranged to make another letter (variable) the subject.

You should be able to:
- Write simple algebraic expressions and formulae.
- Substitute positive and negative numbers in expressions and formulae.
- Substitute numbers in simple formulae to solve problems.
- Rearrange given formulae.

Review Exercise 21

1 What is the value of $2g + 3h$ when $g = 5$ and $h = -2$?

2 $V = a + bc$.
Find the value of V when $a = -5$, $b = 3$ and $c = 4$.

3 Given that $x = 3$ and $y = -2$, find the value of
(a) $x + y$, (b) $x - y$,
(c) $y - x$, (d) xy.

4 $P = 3(m + n)$.
Find the value of P when $m = 0.5$ and $n = 2$.

5 $S = pq + r$.
Find the value of S when $p = -3$, $q = 4$ and $r = -2$.

6 What is the value of $t^3 - t$ when
(a) $t = 2$, (b) $t = -2$?

7 A rectangle has a length of a cm and a width of b cm.
The perimeter of a rectangle is given by the formula $p = 2(a + b)$.
Calculate the perimeter of a rectangle when $a = 4.5$ and $b = 4.2$. AQA

8 A formula to estimate the number of rolls of wallpaper, R, for a room is

$$R = \frac{ph}{5}$$

where p is the perimeter of the room in metres and h is the height of the room in metres.
The perimeter of Carol's bedroom is 15.5 m and it is 2.25 m high.
How many rolls of wallpaper will she have to buy? AQA

9 Find the exact value of
$$\frac{1}{a} + \frac{1}{b} \text{ when } a = \frac{1}{2} \text{ and } b = \frac{1}{3}.$$
AQA

10 Segville High School has a disco for Year 7 each year. A teacher works out how many cans of drink to buy, using this rule:

> **two cans for each ticket sold, plus 20 spare cans**

(a) This year, 160 tickets have been sold. How many cans will he buy?
(b) Using N for the number of cans and T for the number of tickets, write down the teacher's formula for N in terms of T.
(c) Last year, he bought 300 cans. How many tickets were sold last year?
AQA

11 You are given the formula $v = u + at$.
(a) Work out the value of v when $u = 20$, $a = -6$ and $t = \frac{9}{5}$.
(b) Rearrange the formula to give t in terms of v, u and a. AQA

12 A formula is given as $t = 7p - 50$.
Rearrange the formula to make p the subject.
AQA

13 Rearrange the following formula to make x the subject.
$$y = mx + c$$
AQA

14 A formula is given as $V = 4h + p^2$.
Find the value of V when $h = 0.5$ and $p = 8$. AQA

15 Make p the subject of the formula
$$\frac{4(p + 3)}{7} = r.$$
AQA

16 You are given the formula $y = 3x^2$.
(a) Calculate y when $x = -3$.
(b) Find a value of x when $y = 147$.
(c) Rearrange the formula to give x in terms of y. AQA

17 You are given the formula $t = \sqrt{\frac{r}{s}}$.
Rearrange the formula to give r in terms of s and t. AQA

CHAPTER 22

Sequences ●●●●●●●●●●●●●●●

Continuing a sequence

A **sequence** is a list of numbers made according to some rule.
For example:

$$5, \quad 9, \quad 13, \quad 17, \quad 21, \quad ...$$

The first term is 5.
To find the next term in the sequence, add 4 to the last term.
The next term in this sequence is $21 + 4 = 25$.
What are the next three terms in the sequence?

> The numbers in a sequence are called **terms**.
> The start number is the **first term**, the next is the second term, and so on.

> **To continue a sequence:**
> 1. Work out the rule to get from one term to the next.
> 2. Apply the same rule to find further terms in the sequence.

EXAMPLES

Find the next three terms in each of these sequences.

1 5, 8, 11, 14, 17, ...

To find the next term in the sequence, add 3 to the last term.
$17 + 3 = 20, \qquad 20 + 3 = 23, \qquad 23 + 3 = 26.$
The next three terms in the sequence are: 20, 23, 26.

2 2, 4, 8, 16, ...

To find the next term in the sequence, multiply the last term by 2.
$16 \times 2 = 32, \qquad 32 \times 2 = 64, \qquad 64 \times 2 = 128.$
The next three terms in the sequence are: 32, 64, 128.

3 1, 1, 2, 3, 5, 8, ...

To find the next term in the sequence, add the last two terms.
$5 + 8 = 13, \qquad 8 + 13 = 21, \qquad 13 + 21 = 34.$
The next three terms in the sequence are: 13, 21, 34.
This is a special sequence called the **Fibonacci sequence**.

Exercise 22.1

1 Find the next three terms in these sequences.

(a) 1, 5, 9, 13, ...
(b) 6, 8, 10, 12, ...
(c) 28, 25, 22, 19, ...
(d) 3, 8, 13, 18, 23, ...
(e) 3, 6, 12, 24, ...
(f) $\frac{1}{4}$, $\frac{1}{2}$, $\frac{3}{4}$, 1, $1\frac{1}{4}$, ...
(g) 32, 16, 8, 4, ...
(h) 0.5, 0.6, 0.7, 0.8, ...
(i) 10, 8, 6, 4, ...
(j) 80, 40, 20, 10, ...
(k) 1, 3, 6, 10, 15,
(l) 1, 3, 4, 7, 11, 18, ...

2 Find the missing terms from these sequences.

(a) 2, 4, 6, __, 10, 12, __, 16, ...   (b) 2, 6, __, 14, 18, __, 26, ...

(c) 1, 2, 4, __, 16, __, 64, ...   (d) 28, 22, __, 10, 4, __, ...

(e) 1, 4, 9, __, 25, __, 49, ...   (f) 1, 2, 3, 5, __, 13, __, 34, ...

(g) __, 8, 14, __, __, 32, 38, ...

3 Write down the rule, in words, used to get from one term to the next for each sequence. Then use the rule to find the next two terms.

(a) 2, 9, 16, 23, 30, ...   (b) 3, 5, 7, 9, 11, ...

(c) 1, 5, 9, 13, 17, ...   (d) 31, 26, 21, 16, ...

(e) 64, 32, 16, 8, 4, ...   (f) 1, 3, 9, 27, ...

(g) −2, −4, −6, −8, ...   (h) 10, 7, 4, 1, −2, ...

4 A sequence begins 1, 4, 7, 10, ...
(a) What is the 10th number in this sequence?
(b) Explain how you found your answer.

5 A number sequence begins 1, 2, 4, ...
David says that the next number is 8.
Tony says that the next number is 7.
(a) Explain why they could both be correct.
(b) Find the 10th number in David's sequence.
(c) Find the 10th number in Tony's sequence.

6 Here is part of a number sequence: 3, 9, 15, 21, ...
Is the number 50 in this sequence?
Explain your answer.

Using rules

Sometimes you will be given a rule and asked to use it to find the terms of a sequence.
For example:
A sequence begins: 1, 4, 13, ...
The rule for the sequence is:

> Multiply the last number by 3, then add 1

The next term in the sequence is given by:
$$13 \times 3 + 1 = 39 + 1 = 40$$

The following term is given by:
$$40 \times 3 + 1 = 120 + 1 = 121$$

So the sequence can be extended to: 1, 4, 13, 40, 121, ...
Use the rule to find the next two terms in the sequence.

The **same rule** can be used to make different sequences.
For example:
Another sequence begins: 2, 7, 22, ...
Using the same rule, the next term is given by:
$$22 \times 3 + 1 = 66 + 1 = 67$$

The following term is given by:
$$67 \times 3 + 1 = 201 + 1 = 202$$

So the sequence can be extended to: 2, 7, 22, 67, 202, ...
Use the rule to find the next two terms in the sequence.

254

EXAMPLE

This rule is used to find each number in a sequence from the number before it.

Subtract 3 and then multiply by 4

Starting with 5 we get the following sequence:

5, 8, 20, 68, …

(a) Write down the next number in the sequence.
(b) Using the same rule, but a different starting number, the second number is 16.
Find the starting number.

(a) $(68 - 3) \times 4 = 65 \times 4 = 260$
Notice that, following the rule, 3 is subtracted first and the result is then multiplied by 4.
The next number in the sequence is 260.

The method of working backwards was first used in Chapter 20.

(b) Imagine the first number is x.

$x \longrightarrow$ subtract 3 $\longrightarrow$ multiply by 4 $\longrightarrow$ 16

Working backwards.

$7 \longleftarrow$ add 3 $\longleftarrow$ 4 divide by 4 $\longleftarrow$ 16

The starting number is 7.

Exercise 22.2

1 Write down the first five terms of these sequences.

(a) First term: 1
Rule: Add 4 to the last term

(b) First term: 1
Rule: Double the last term

(c) First term: 40
Rule: Subtract 5 from the last term

(d) First term: 4
Rule: Double the last term and then subtract 3

(e) First term: 47
Rule: Subtract 1 from the last term and then halve the result

(f) First term: 2   Second term: 6
Rule: Add the last two terms and then halve the result

2 This rule is used to get each number from the number before it:

Multiply by 2

Use the rule to find the next three numbers when the first number is:
(a) 1,   (b) 3,   (c) −1.

3 This rule is used to get each number from the number before it:

Add 1 and then double the result

Use the rule to find the next three numbers when the first number is:
(a) 1,   (b) 3,   (c) −3.

4 This rule is used to find each term of a sequence from the one before:

> Subtract 3 then divide by 2

(a) The first term is 45.
  (i) What is the second term?
  (ii) What is the **fourth** term?
(b) Using the same rule, but a different starting number, the second term is 17.
  What is the starting number for the sequence?

5 This rule is used to find each term of a sequence from the one before:

> Add 5 then multiply by 3

(a) The first term is 7.
  (i) What is the second term?
  (ii) What is the **third** term?
(b) Using the same rule, but a different starting number, the second term is 45.
  What is the starting number for the sequence?

6 A sequence is formed from this rule:

> Add together the last two terms to find the next term

Part of the sequence is … 5, 9, 14, 23, …
(a) Write down the next two terms after 23 in the sequence.
(b) Write down the two terms that come before 5 in the sequence.

7 A sequence begins: 1, −3, …
The sequence is continued using the rule:

> Add the previous two numbers and then multiply by 3

Use the rule to find the next two numbers in the sequence.

8 A sequence begins: 4, 7, 13, 25, …
The next number in the sequence can be found using the rule:

> "Multiply the last term by 2 then subtract 1."

(a) Write down the next **two** terms in the sequence.
(b) The 11th term in the sequence is 3073.
  Use this information to find the 10th term in the sequence.

Number sequences

A number sequence which increases (or decreases) by the same amount from one term to the next is called a **linear sequence**.
For example, terms in the sequence: 6, 11, 16, 21, …
increase by 5 from one term to the next.
We say that the sequence has a **common difference** of 5.

By comparing a sequence with multiples of the counting numbers: 1, 2, 3, 4, …
we can write a rule to find the nth term of the sequence.

Sequence: 6 11 16 21 …
Multiples of 5: 5 10 15 20 …

To get the nth term add one to the multiples of 5.
So, the nth term is $5n + 1$.

Compare the sequence with multiples of the common difference.
In this case the common difference is 5, so compare the sequence with multiples of 5.

A table can be used to find the nth term of a sequence.

The sequence 2, 8, 14, 20, … has a common difference of 6.
The common difference is used to complete the table for terms 1, 2, 3, 4 and n.

Term	Term × common difference	Sequence	Difference
1	$1 \times 6 = 6$	2	$2 - 6 = -4$
2	$2 \times 6 = 12$	8	$8 - 12 = -4$
3	$3 \times 6 = 18$	14	$14 - 18 = -4$
4	$4 \times 6 = 24$	20	$20 - 24 = -4$
n	$n \times 6 = 6n$	$6n - 4$	

The nth term of the sequence 2, 8, 14, 20, … is $6n - 4$.

The rule for the nth term can be used to find the value of
any term in the sequence.
To find the fifth term, substitute $n = 5$ into $6n - 4$.
$6 \times 5 - 4 = 30 - 4 = 26$.
The fifth term is 26.

> Term
> 1 represents the first term,
> 2 the second term, and so on.
> n represents the nth term.
>
> Common difference
> 2nd term − 1st term
> $= 8 - 2 = 6$.
>
> Differences
> Check that each pair of
> entries gives the same result.

EXAMPLE

(a) Find the nth term in the sequence 31, 28, 25, 22, …
(b) Find the value of the 10th term in the sequence.

(a) The common difference is -3.

Term	Term × common difference	Sequence	Difference
1	$1 \times (-3) = -3$	31	$31 - (-3) = 34$
2	$2 \times (-3) = -6$	28	$28 - (-6) = 34$
3	$3 \times (-3) = -9$	25	$25 - (-9) = 34$
4	$4 \times (-3) = -12$	22	$22 - (-12) = 34$
n	$n \times (-3) = -3n$	$-3n + 34$	

The nth term is $-3n + 34$.
This can also be written as $34 - 3n$.

(b) The nth term is $34 - 3n$.
Substitute $n = 10$.
$34 - 3 \times 10 = 34 - 30 = 4$
The 10th term is 4.

Exercise 22.3

① Find the common differences of the following sequences.
(a) 3, 6, 9, 12, …
(b) 2, 5, 8, 11, …
(c) 7, 13, 19, 25, …
(d) 12, 20, 28, 36, …
(e) 20, 18, 16, 14, …
(f) 7, 3, −1, −5, …

Sequences • • • Sequences • • • Sequences • • •

2 (a) The multiples of 3 are   3,   6,   9,   12,   …
What is the nth multiple of 3?
(b) What is the nth multiple of 8?
(c) What is the nth multiple of 12?
(d) What is the nth even number?

3 A sequence of numbers starts: 4,   7,   10,   13,   …
(a) What is the common difference?
(b) Copy and complete this table.

Term	Term × common difference	Sequence	Difference
1	1 × … =	4	4 − … =
2	2 × … =	7	7 − … =
3	3 × … =	10	10 − … =
4	4 × … =	13	13 − … =
n	n × … = …n	…n + …	

(c) Write down the nth term of the sequence.
(d) What is the value of the 8th term of the sequence?

4 A sequence of numbers starts: 9,   11,   13,   15,   …
(a) What is the common difference?
(b) Copy and complete this table for the first four terms of the sequence.

Term	Term × common difference	Sequence	Difference
1	2	9	7
2	4	11	…
		13	

(c) Write down the nth term of the sequence.
(d) What is the value of the 20th term of the sequence?

5 A sequence of numbers starts: 20,   16,   12,   8,   …
(a) What is the common difference?
(b) Copy and complete this table for the first four terms of the sequence.

Term	Term × common difference	Sequence	Difference
1	…	20	…
		16	

(c) Write down the nth term of the sequence.

6 Find the nth term of the following sequences.
(a)   1,   4,   7,   10,   …
(b)   19,   16,   13,   10,   …
(c)   5,   9,   13,   17,   …
(d)   4,   8,   12,   16,   …
(e)   1,   3,   5,   7,   …
(f)   7,   11,   15,   19,   …
(g)   6,   4,   2,   0,   …
(h)   5,   8,   11,   14,   …
(i)   3,   8,   13,   18,   …
(j)   40,   35,   30,   25,   …
(k)   0,   1,   2,   3,   …
(l)   −1,   1,   3,   5,   …

Activity

These patterns are made using squares.

Pattern 1
3 squares

Pattern 2
5 squares

Pattern 3
7 squares

How many squares are used to make Pattern 4?
How many squares are used to make Pattern 10?
How many squares are used to make Pattern 100?
Which pattern is made using 81 squares?

The number of squares used to make each pattern forms a **sequence**.

Pattern 4 is made using 9 squares.
You could have answered this: by drawing Pattern 4 or,
by continuing the sequence of numbers   3,   5,   7,   …
It is possible to do the same for Pattern 10, though it would involve a lot of work, but it would be unreasonable to use either method for Pattern 100.
Instead we can investigate how each pattern is made.

2 × 1 + 1 = 3 squares   2 × 2 + 1 = 5 squares   2 × 3 + 1 = 7 squares

Each pattern is made using a **rule**.
The rule can be **described in words**.
To find the number of squares used to make a pattern use the rule:

"Double the pattern number and add 1."

81 = 2 × 40 + 1,   so the 40th pattern is made using 81 squares.

The same rule can be **written using symbols**.
We can then answer a very important question:
How many squares are used to make Pattern n?

Pattern n will have   2 × n + 1 squares.
This can be written as $2n + 1$ squares.

Pattern number	Rule	Number of squares
4	2 × 4 + 1	9
10	2 × 10 + 1	21
100	2 × 100 + 1	201

Special sequences of numbers

Square numbers

   1   4   9   16

The sequence starts: 1,   4,   9,   16,   …
The numbers in this sequence are called **square numbers**.

Triangular numbers

   1   3   6   10

The sequence starts: 1,   3,   6,   10,   …
The numbers in this sequence are called **triangular numbers**.

1. A sequence of patterns is formed using equilateral triangles.

   Pattern 1   **Pattern 2**   **Pattern 3**   **Pattern 4**

   (a) How many triangles form Pattern 5?
   (b) Explain why a pattern in this sequence cannot have 27 triangles.
   (c) Write an expression, in terms of p, for the number of triangles in Pattern p.
   (d) How many triangles are used to make Pattern 120?

2. A sequence of patterns is formed using sticks.

   Pattern 1   **Pattern 2**   **Pattern 3**

   (a) How many sticks are used to make Pattern 4?
   (b) How many more sticks are used to make Pattern 5 from Pattern 4?
   (c) Write an expression, in terms of n, for the number of sticks used to make Pattern n.
   (d) How many sticks are used to make Pattern 20?

3. A sequence of patterns is made using black and white counters.

   (a) How many white counters are there in a pattern with
       (i) 5 black counters,
       (ii) 10 black counters,
       (iii) 100 black counters?

   1 black   **2 black**   **3 black**
   3 white   **6 white**   **9 white**

   (b) How many white counters are there in a pattern with n black counters?

4. These patterns are made using matches.

   (a) How many matches are used to make
       (i) Pattern 4,
       (ii) Pattern 20?

   (b) Which pattern uses 30 matches?

   (c) How many matches are used to make Pattern n?

   Pattern 1   **Pattern 2**   **Pattern 3**
   6 matches   **10 matches**   **14 matches**

5. Fences are made by placing fence posts 1m apart and using 2 horizontal bars between them.

   The fence above is 4 m long. It has 5 posts and 8 horizontal bars.
   (a) A fence is 50 m long.
       (i) How many posts does it have?
       (ii) How many horizontal bars does it have?

   (b) A fence is x metres long.
       Write down expressions for
       (i) the number of posts,
       (ii) the number of horizontal bars.

6 Linking cubes of side 1 cm are used to make rods.
This rod is made using 4 linking cubes.

The surface area of the rod is 18 square centimetres.
(4 squares on each of the long sides plus one square at each end.)
(a)   What is the surface area of a rod made using 5 linking cubes?
(b)   What is the surface area of a rod made using 10 linking cubes?
(c)   What is the surface area of a rod made using n linking cubes?

7 A sequence of patterns is made using sticks.

    Pattern 1   **Pattern 2**   **Pattern 3**   **Pattern 4**

(a)   How many sticks are used to make Pattern 5?
(b)   Pattern n uses T sticks.
     Write a formula for T in terms of n.
(c)   Use your formula to find the number of sticks used to make Pattern 10.
(d)   One pattern uses 77 sticks. What is the pattern number?

8 These patterns are made using matches.
(a)   How many matches are used to make Pattern 5?
(b)   Which pattern uses 37 matches?
(c)   Find a formula for the number of
     matches, m, in Pattern p.

     Pattern 1   **Pattern 2**   **Pattern 3**

9 These are the first four **square numbers**.   1,   4,   9,   16, …
(a)   What is the next square number?
(b)   Copy and complete this list for the first 5 square numbers.
$$1^2 = 1, \quad 2^2 = 4, \quad 3^2 = 9, \quad \ldots = 16, \quad 5^2 = \ldots$$
(c)   Write an expression for the nth square number.
(d)   Find the 15th square number.

10 (a)   Find the next term in each of these sequences.
     Explain how you found your answers.
     (i)   2,   5,   10,   17,   26,   …
     (ii)   0,   3,   8,   15,   24,   …
     (iii) 4,   7,   12,   19,   28,   …
     (iv)   2,   8,   18,   32,   50,   …
     (v)   2,   6,   12,   20,   30,   …
(b)   By comparing each of these sequences to the sequence of square numbers write an
     expression for the nth term of each sequence.

11 A sequence of shapes is made using small squares

    Shape 1   **Shape 2**   **Shape 3**   **Shape 4**

(a)   Shape n uses T small squares.
     Write a formula for T in terms of n.
(b)   Use your formula to find the number of small squares in Shape 10.

12 These are the first four **triangular numbers**: 1, 3, 6, 10, ...
  (a) What is the next triangular number?
  (b) Copy and complete this list for the first 5 triangular numbers.
  $$\frac{1 \times 2}{2} = 1, \qquad \frac{2 \times 3}{2} = 3, \qquad \frac{3 \times 4}{2} = 6, \qquad \frac{}{2} = 10, \qquad ... = ...$$
  (c) Write an expression for the nth triangular number.
  (d) Find the 10th triangular number.

13 These are the first four **powers of 2**: 2, 4, 8, 16, ...
  (a) What is the next power of 2?
  (b) Copy and complete this list for the first 5 powers of 2.
  $$2^1 = 2, \qquad 2^2 = 4, \qquad 2^3 = 8, \qquad ... = 16, \qquad ... = ...$$
  (c) Write an expression for the nth power of 2.
  (d) Find the 10th power of 2.
  (e) What power of 2 is equal to 256?

14 (a) Write down the first 5 powers of 10.
  (b) Write an expression for the nth power of 10.
  (c) What power of 10 is equal to one million?

15 (a) Write an expression for the nth term of this sequence: 3, 9, 27, 81, ...
  (b) Use your expression to find the 10th term of the sequence.

What you need to know

- A **sequence** is a list of numbers made according to some rule.
  The numbers in a sequence are called **terms**.
- **To continue a sequence:** 1. Work out the rule to get from one term to the next.
  2. Apply the same rule to find further terms in the sequence.
- A number sequence which increases (or decreases) by the same amount from one term to the next is called a **linear sequence**.
  The sequence: 2, 8, 14, 20, 26, ... has a **common difference** of 6.
- Special sequences **Square numbers:** 1, 4, 9, 16, 25, ...
  Triangular numbers: 1, 3, 6, 10, 15, ...
- Patterns of shapes can be drawn to represent a number sequence.
  For example, this pattern represents the sequence 3, 5, 7, ...

You should be able to:

- Draw patterns of shapes which represent number sequences.
- Continue a given number sequence.
- Find the expression for the nth term of a sequence.

Review Exercise 22

1 What is the next number in each of these sequences?
  (a) 3, 6, 11, 18, 27, ...   (b) 8, 4, 2, 1, $\frac{1}{2}$, ...   AQA

2 Look at this number sequence: 16, 25, 36, 49, 64, ...
  (a) Write down the next term in this sequence.
  (b) Will the number 196 be in this sequence?
  Give a reason for your answer.   AQA

3 The first two terms of a sequence are: 4, 8.

   (a) Using the rule:

> ADD THE TWO PREVIOUS NUMBERS AND DIVIDE BY TWO

      write down the third and fourth terms of the sequence.

   (b) If the sequence had begun 8, 4 instead of 4, 8 would the third and fourth terms be the same as those in part (a)?

      Give a reason for your answer.   AQA

4 Here are the rules for a sequence: *If a number is even, halve it;*
                                         If a number is odd, multiply by 3 and add 1.

   Here are the first four terms for a sequence using these rules.   12, 6, 3, 10,

   Write down the next three terms.   AQA

5 (a) What is the next number in this sequence? 3, 7, 11, 15, …

   One number in the sequence is x.

   (b) (i) Write, in terms of x, the next number in the sequence.

        (ii) Write, in terms of x, the number in the sequence before x.   AQA

6 A sequence of numbers begins: 2, 5, 8, 11, …

   (a) Write down the next number in this sequence.

   (b) Work out the 20th number in this sequence.

   (c) Find the nth term of this sequence.   AQA

7 (a) Write down the next two terms in the sequence: 3, 5, 9, 15, 23, …

   (b) (i) Write down the next term in the sequence: 3, 5, 9, 17, 33, …, …

        (ii) Explain how you got your answer.

   (c) Write down the nth term for the sequence: 3, 5, 7, 9, 11, …   AQA

8 Write down the nth term for each of the following sequences.

   (a) 3, 6, 9, 12, …   (b) 1, 4, 7, 10, …   (c) 1, 4, 9, 16, …   AQA

9 A sequence of patterns is formed using equilateral triangles.

       Pattern 1   **Pattern 2**   **Pattern 3**

   (a) How many triangles are in Pattern 10?

   (b) Explain why a pattern in this sequence cannot have 40 triangles.

   (c) Write an expression, in terms of p, for the number of triangles in Pattern p.   AQA

10 A sequence of patterns is shown.

      Pattern 1   **Pattern 2**   **Pattern 3**

   Write an expression, in terms of n, for the number of white squares in the nth pattern of the sequence.   AQA

11 A sequence of numbers begins: 1, 3, 6, 10, 15, 21, …, ….

   (a) Write down the next number in the sequence.

   (b) Explain how you worked out your answer.

   (c) What type of numbers form this sequence?   AQA

Graphs ●●●●●●●●●●●●●●●

Coordinates

Coordinates are used to describe the position of a point.

Two lines are drawn at right angles to each other.
The horizontal line is called the **x axis**.
The vertical line is called the **y axis**.
The plural of axis is **axes**.
The two axes cross at the point called the **origin**.

On the diagram, the coordinates of point A are (3, 2).
The coordinates of point B are $(-2, 3)$.

What are the coordinates of the points C and D?

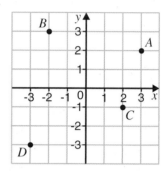

Linear functions

Look at these coordinates (0, 1), (1, 2), (2, 3), (3, 4).
Can you see any number patterns?

The same coordinates can be shown in a **table**.

x	0	1	2	3
y	1	2	3	4

The diagram shows the coordinates plotted on a **graph**.
The points all lie on a **straight line**.

A **rule** connects the x coordinate with the y coordinate.
All points on the line obey the rule $y = x + 1$.

$y = x + 1$ is an example of a **linear function**.
The graph of a linear function is a **straight line**.

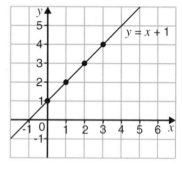

EXAMPLE

Draw the graph of the equation $y = 2x - 3$.

If values for x are not given in the question you must choose your own.

When $x = 0$, $y = 2 \times 0 - 3 = -3$.

When $x = 1$, $y = 2 \times 1 - 3 = -1$.

When $x = 3$, $y = 2 \times 3 - 3 = 3$.

Plot the points $(0, -3)$, $(1, -1)$ and $(3, 3)$.

The straight line which passes through these points is the graph of the equation $y = 2x - 3$.

Special graphs

This diagram shows the graphs: $x = 4$ $y = 1$
$x = -2$ $y = -5$

Notice that:
The graph of $x = 4$ is a **vertical** line.
All points on the line have x coordinate 4.

The graph of $y = 1$ is a **horizontal** line.
All points on the line have y coordinate 1.

$x = 0$ is the y axis.
$y = 0$ is the x axis.

Exercise **23.1**

 1

(a)   Write down the equations of the
lines labelled on this graph.

(b)   What are the coordinates of the points
where lines (1) and (3) cross?

(c)   What are the coordinates of the points
where lines (2) and (4) cross?

2   Copy the coordinate grid given in question 1.
Draw and label the lines:
(a) $x = 3$,   (b) $y = 2$,   (c) $x = -2$,   (d) $y = -1$.

3   (a)   Copy and complete a table, like the one shown,
for each of these equations.

x	0	1	2	3
y				

(i) $y = x + 2$ (ii) $y = 2x$
(iii) $y = -x$ (iv) $y = 2 - x$
(b)   Draw graphs for each of the equations in part (a).

4   Draw tables of values and use them to draw graphs of:
(a) $y = x - 1$ (b) $y = 3x + 1$
Draw and label the x axis from -1 to 3 and the y axis from -2 to 10.

5   (a)   Draw the graph of $y = 3x - 2$ for values of x from -1 to 2.
(b)   What are the coordinates of the point where the graph crosses the y axis?

6   (a)   Draw these graphs **on the same diagram**:
(i) $y = x + 2$ (ii) $y = x + 1$ (iii) $y = x$ (iv) $y = x - 1$
Draw and label the x axis from 0 to 3 and the y axis from -1 to 5.
(b)   What do they all have in common? What is different?

7   (a)   Draw these graphs **on the same diagram**:
(i) $y = 2x + 2$ (ii) $y = 2x + 1$ (iii) $y = 2x$ (iv) $y = 2x - 1$
Draw and label the x axis from 0 to 3 and the y axis from -1 to 8.
(b)   What do they all have in common? What is different?

8   (a)   Draw these graphs **on the same diagram**:
(i) $y = 3x + 3$ (ii) $y = 2x + 3$ (iii) $y = x + 3$ (iv) $y = \frac{1}{2}x + 3$
Draw and label the x axis from -2 to 2 and the y axis from -3 to 9.
(b)   What do they all have in common? What is different?

9   Draw graphs of:
(a) $y = x - 2$ (b) $y = 3x - 1$ (c) $y = 5 - x$ (d) $y = 6 - 2x$

10 (a) Draw the graph of $y = 2x - 1$ for values of x from -2 to 3.
  (b) Use your graph to find the value of x when $y = 0$.

11 (a) Copy and complete this table and use it to draw the straight line graph of $y = 4 - x$.
    Draw and label the x axis from -3 to 3 and the y axis from -1 to 6.

x	-2	-1	0	1	2
y		5			2

  (b) Use your graph to find the value of:
    (i) y when $x = 1.5$,   (ii) y when $x = -0.5$.

12 (a) Draw the graph of $y = 2x + 1$ for values of x from -2 to 3.
  (b) Use your graph to find the value of:
    (i) y when $x = -1.5$,   (ii) x when $y = 2$.

13 (a) Draw the graphs of $y = 2x - 3$ and $y = 3 - x$ on the same axes.
  (b) Write down the coordinates of the point where the lines cross.

Gradient and intercept

Lines that are **parallel** have the same **slope** or **gradient**.

$$\text{Gradient} = \frac{\text{distance up}}{\text{distance along}}$$

The gradient of a straight line graph is found by drawing a right-angled triangle.

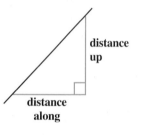

The gradient of a line can be positive, zero or negative.

Positive gradients go "uphill".   **Zero gradients are "flat".**   **Negative gradients go "downhill".**

The graphs of:
$y = 2x + 2$, $y = 2x + 1$, $y = 2x$, $y = 2x - 1$,
go 2 squares up for every 1 square along.
The graphs are all parallel and have a gradient of 2.

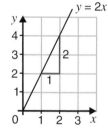

The point where a graph crosses the y axis is called the **y-intercept**.

The graphs of:
$y = 3x + 3$, $y = 2x + 3$, $y = x + 3$, $y = \frac{1}{2}x + 3$,
all cross the y axis at the point $(0, 3)$.
The graphs each have the same y-intercept of 3.

In general, the equation of any straight line can be written in the form

$$y = mx + c$$

where m is the **gradient** of the line
and c is the **y-intercept**.

EXAMPLES

1 Write down the gradient and y-intercept for each of the following graphs.
(a) $y = 3x + 5$
(b) $y = 4x - 1$
(c) $y = 6 - x$

(a) Gradient = 3, y-intercept = 5.
(b) Gradient = 4, y-intercept = -1.
(c) Gradient = -1, y-intercept = 6.

2 Write down the equation of the straight line which has gradient -7 and cuts the y axis at the point $(0, 4)$.

The general form for the equation of a straight line is $y = mx + c$.
The gradient, $m = -7$,
and the y-intercept, $c = 4$.
Substitute these values into the general equation.
The equation of the line is
$y = -7x + 4$.
This can be written as
$y = 4 - 7x$.

3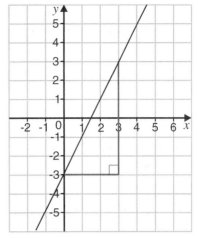

Find the equation of the line shown on this graph.

First, work out the gradient of the line.
Draw a right-angled triangle.

$$\text{Gradient} = \frac{\text{distance up}}{\text{distance along}}$$

$$= \frac{6}{3}$$

$$= 2$$

The graph crosses the y axis at the point $(0, -3)$, so the y-intercept is -3.
The equation of the line is $y = 2x - 3$.

Exercise 23.2

1 (a) Write down the gradient and y-intercept of $y = 3x - 1$.
(b) Draw the graph of $y = 3x - 1$ to check your answer.

2 Which of the following graphs are parallel?

| $y = 3x$ | | $y = x + 2$ | | $y = 2x + 3$ | | $y = 3x + 2$ |

3 Copy and complete this table.

Graph	gradient	y-intercept
$y = 4x + 3$	4	3
$y = 3x + 5$	3	
$y = 2x - 3$		
$y = 4 - 2x$		4
$y = \frac{1}{2}x + 3$		
$y = 2x$		
$y = 3$		
$y = 4 - \frac{1}{2}x$		

4 (a) Write down the equation of the straight line which has gradient 5 and crosses the y axis at the point $(0, -4)$.
(b) Write down the equation of the straight line which has gradient $-\frac{1}{2}$ and cuts the y axis at the point $(0, 6)$.

5 Match the following equations to their graphs.

(1) $y = x - 6$

(2) $y = 6 - x$

(3) $y = 2x + 1$

(4) $y = 2x - 1$

A   B   C   D

6 Find the equations of the lines shown on the following graphs.

(a)

(b)

(c)

7 (a) Draw x and y axes from -8 to 8.
  (b) Plot the points $A(-2, -6)$ and $B(8, 4)$.
  (c) Find the gradient of the line which passes through the points A and B.
  (d) Write down the coordinates of the point where the line crosses the y axis.
  (e) Find the equation of the line which passes through the points A and B.

8 (a) Draw x and y axes from -8 to 8.
  (b) Plot the points $P(-2, 3)$ and $Q(3, -7)$.
  (c) Find the equation of the line which passes through the points P and Q.

9 What can you say about the slope of a line if the gradient is
  (a) 5,   (b) -5,   (c) 0?

10 A line, with a gradient of 3, passes through the origin.
What is the equation of the line?

11 A line, with a gradient of 3, passes through the point $P(-1, 5)$.
What is the equation of the line?

12 A plumber charges a fixed call-out charge and an hourly rate.
The graph shows the charges made for jobs
up to 4 hours.

(a) What is the fixed call-out charge?

(b) What is the hourly rate?

(c) Find the equation of the line in the
form $y = mx + c$.

(d) Use your equation to calculate the
total charge for a job which takes 8 hours.

13 A line, with a gradient of -3, passes through the point $Q(2, 7)$.
What is the equation of the line?

14 The graph shows the taxi fare for journeys up to 3 km.

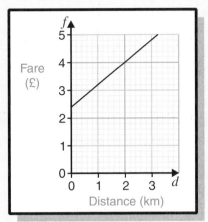

(a) Find the equation of the line, in the form $f = md + c$.
(b) Use your equation to calculate the taxi fare for a journey of 5 km.

15 In an experiment, weights are added to a spring and the length of the spring is measured.
The graph shows the results.

 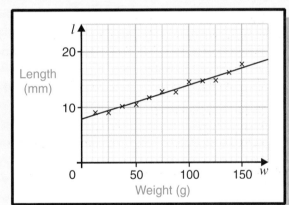

A line of best fit has been drawn.
(a) Find the equation of the line in the form $l = mw + c$.
(b) Use your equation to estimate the length of the spring for a weight of 300 g.

Rearranging equations

The general equation for a straight line graph is $y = mx + c$.
When an equation is in this form the gradient and y-intercept are given by the values of m and c.

The equation for a straight line can also be written in the form $px + qy = r$.
To find the gradient and y-intercept of this line we must first **rearrange** the equation.

For example, the graph of a straight line is given as $2y - 6x = 5$.
To rearrange: $2y - 6x = 5$

> Add $6x$ to both sides.

$$2y = 6x + 5$$

> Divide both sides by 2.

$$y = 3x + 2.5$$

Hence, the line has gradient 3 and y-intercept 2.5.

EXAMPLES

1 The graph of a straight line is given by the equation $4y - 3x = 8$.
   (a) Write this equation in the form $y = mx + c$.
   (b) Write down the gradient and the y-intercept of the line.

   (a) $4y - 3x = 8$
        Add $3x$ to both sides.
          $4y = 3x + 8$
        Divide both sides by 4.
          $y = \frac{3}{4}x + 2$

   (b) The line has gradient $\frac{3}{4}$ and y-intercept 2.

2 The equation of a straight line is $6x + 3y = 2$.
   Write down the equation of another line which is parallel to this line.

   Write the equation in the form $y = mx + c$.
   $6x + 3y = 2$
   Subtract $6x$ from both sides.
          $3y = -6x + 2$
   Divide both sides by 3.
          $y = -2x + \frac{2}{3}$
   The gradient of the line is -2.
   To write an equation of a parallel line keep the same gradient and change the value of the y-intercept.
   For example: $y = -2x + 5$

   Write the equations for two different lines which are parallel to this line.

3 Sketch the graph of the line given by the equation $4y - 3x = 12$.

   Substitute $x = 0$ into the equation.
   $4y = 12$
    $y = 3$
   The line crosses the y axis at (0, 3).

   Substitute $y = 0$ into the equation.
   $-3x = 12$
   Divide both sides by -3.
      $x = -4$

   The line crosses the x axis at $(-4, 0)$.

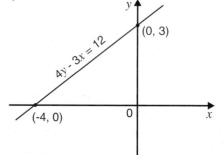

Exercise 23.3

1 The graph of a straight line is given by the equation $2y - 3x = 6$.
   Write this equation in the form $y = mx + c$.

2 Write the equations of the following lines in the form $y = mx + c$.
   (a) $2y + x = 4$ (b) $5y + 4x = 20$ (c) $4 - 3y = 2x$ (d) $2x - 7y = 14$

3 Find the gradients of these lines.
   (a) $2y = x$ (b) $x - y = 0$ (c) $2x - y = 0$
   (d) $3y + x = 0$ (e) $4y - 3x = 0$ (f) $2x + 5y = 0$

4 These lines cross the y axis at the point $(0, a)$. Find the value of a for each line.
   (a) $y = x$ (b) $2y = x + 1$ (c) $3y + 6 = x$
   (d) $2y - 5 = x$ (e) $4y - 3x = 8$ (f) $x + 5y = 2$

5 Write down an equation which is parallel to each of these lines.

(a) $y = x$ (b) $y = 2x - 3$ (c) $2y = x - 4$

6 The equation of a straight line is $2y + 3x = 4$.
Write down the equation of another line which is parallel to this line.

7 The equation of a line is given by $5y - 4x = 10$.

(a) Find the gradient of the line.
(b) Find the y-intercept of the line.
(c) Write down an equation of another line which has the **same** y-intercept but a **different** gradient.

8 A straight line has equation $3y + 5x = 15$.

(a) By substituting $x = 0$ find the coordinates of the point where the line crosses the y axis.
(b) By substituting $y = 0$ find the coordinates of the point where the line crosses the x axis.
(c) **Sketch** the graph of the line $3y + 5x = 15$.

9 Sketch the graphs of lines with the following equations, marking clearly the coordinates of the points where the lines cross the axes.

(a) $5y + 4x = 20$ (b) $4x - y = 2$ (c) $3y + 2x = 15$

10 The diagram shows a sketch of the line $2y = x + 4$.

(a) Find the coordinates of points A and B.
(b) What is the gradient of the line?
(c) (i) Copy the diagram and draw the sketch of another line that has the same gradient as $2y = x + 4$.
  (ii) What is the equation of the line you have drawn?

11 The diagram shows a sketch of the line $2y = 6 - x$.

(a) Find the coordinates of points P and Q.
(b) What is the gradient of the line?
(c) (i) Copy the diagram and draw the sketch of another line that has the same gradient as $2y = 6 - x$.
  (ii) What is the equation of the line you have drawn?

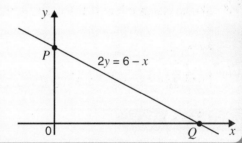

Using graphs to solve equations

The equation $2x - 3 = 2$ can be solved algebraically.

$2x - 3 = 2$
Add 3 to both sides.
$2x = 5$
Divide both sides by 2.
$x = 2.5$

Equations can also be solved using graphs.
The diagram shows two graphs:
$y = 2x - 3$
$y = 2$

At the point where the lines cross,
both $y = 2x - 3$ and $y = 2$ are true.
The value of x at this point is the solution
to the equation $2x - 3 = 2$.
Reading from the graph, $x = 2.5$.

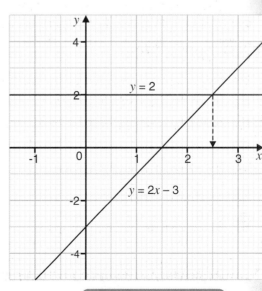

(a) Complete the tables for $y = x + 6$ and $y = 13 - x$.

x	1	2	3
$y = x + 6$			

x	1	2	3
$y = 13 - x$			

(b) Draw the graphs of $y = x + 6$ and $y = 13 - x$ on the same diagram.
(c) Use your graph to solve the equation $13 - x = x + 6$.

(a)

x	1	2	3
$y = x + 6$	7	8	9

x	1	2	3
$y = 13 - x$	12	11	10

(b)

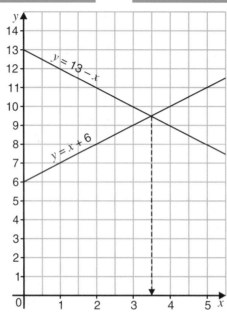

(c) Reading from the graph.
$x = 3.5$

Check the graphical solution of the equation by solving $13 - x = x + 6$ algebraically.

Exercise 23.4

1 (a) Copy and complete the tables for $y = x + 2$ and $y = 5 - x$.

x	1	2	3
$y = x + 2$			

x	1	2	3
$y = 5 - x$			

(b) Draw the graphs of $y = x + 2$ and $y = 5 - x$ on the same diagram.
(c) Use your graphs to solve $x + 2 = 5 - x$.

2 (a) Draw the graphs of $y = 3x + 1$ and $y = x + 6$.
(b) Use your graphs to solve the equation $3x + 1 = x + 6$.

3 (a) Draw the graphs of $y = x$ and $y = 3x - 1$.
(b) Use your graphs to solve the equation $x = 3x - 1$.

4 By drawing the graphs of $y = \frac{1}{2}x$ and $y = 3 - 2x$, solve the equation $\frac{1}{2}x = 3 - 2x$.

5 (a) Draw the graph of $y = 3 + 2x$.
(b) What graph should be drawn to solve the equation $3 + 2x = 9$?
(c) Draw the graph and use it to solve the equation $3 + 2x = 9$.

Using graphs

Graphs are sometimes drawn to show real-life situations.
In most cases a quantity is measured over a period of time.

EXAMPLE

Craig drew a graph to show the amount of fuel in the family car as they travelled to their holiday destination.
He also made some notes:

Part of Graph	Event
A	Leave home.
A to B	Motorway.
B to C	Car breaks down.
C to D	On our way again.
D to E	Stop for lunch.
E to F	Fill tank with fuel.
F to G	Country roads.
G	Arrive, at last!

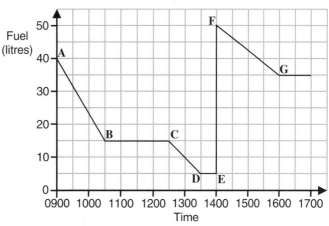

(a) How much fuel was in the tank at the start of the journey?
(b) At what time did the car break down?
(c) How long did the family stop for lunch?
(d) How much fuel was put into the tank at the garage?
(e) At what time did the journey end?

(a) 40 litres   (b) 1030   (c) $\frac{1}{2}$ hour   (d) 45 litres   (e) 1600

Use the graph to work out how many litres of fuel were used for the journey.

Notice that in this example and others involving graphs against time:

A quantity increasing with time.   **A quantity decreasing with time.**   **A quantity not changing, i.e. constant.**   **A quantity changing instantly.**

Exercise 23.5

1 A climber pulls a rucksack up a vertical cliff face using a rope.
Which of the graphs below could represent the motion of the rucksack against time?

2 Match the graphs to the situations. In each graph, the horizontal axis represents time and the vertical axis represents speed.

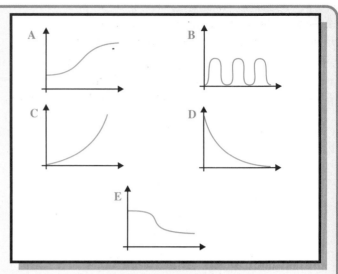

1 A runner starts from rest and begins to pick up speed.

2 A runner keeps having to stop and start.

3 A runner gets tired and has to slow down.

4 A runner sees the finish, builds up speed and sprints to the line.

3 Cans of drink can be bought from a vending machine in the school canteen.
At 0900 one day the machine is three-quarters full.
During break, from 1045 to 1100, drinks are bought from the machine at a steady rate.
By the end of the break the machine is one-quarter full. At 1200 the machine is filled.
The lunch break is from 1230 to 1330. Someone complains at 1315 that the machine is empty.
The machine is filled at 1400, ready for the afternoon break from 1445 to 1500.
At 1600 the machine is three-quarters full.
Sketch a graph to show the number of drinks in the machine from 0900 to 1600.

4 Two companies each use a formula to calculate the charge made for hiring out scaffolding.
Company A uses the formula $c = 20 + 5d$,
Company B uses the formula $c = 8d + 2$,
where c is the total charge, in pounds,
d is the length of the hire period, in days.
(a) Draw the horizontal axis for d from 0 to 8 and the vertical axis for c from 0 to 60.
(b) Draw the graph of $c = 20 + 5d$.
(c) Draw the graph of $c = 8d + 2$.

Use your graph to answer the following.
(d) From which company is it cheaper to hire scaffolding for 2 days?
(e) From which company is it cheaper to hire scaffolding for 8 days?
(f) For what number of days do both companies make the same charge?

5 Water is poured into some containers at a constant rate.
Copy the axes given and sketch the graph of the depth of the water against time for each container as it is filled.

Distance-time graphs

Distance-time graphs are used to illustrate journeys.

Speed is given by the gradient, or slope, of the line.
The faster the speed the steeper the gradient.
Zero gradient (horizontal line) means zero speed (not moving).

> **Calculations** involving speed, distance and time are covered in Chapter 18.

EXAMPLES

1 The graph shows a bus journey.
   (a) How many times does the bus stop?
   (b) On which part of the journey does the bus travel fastest?

   (a) At zero speed the distance-time graph is horizontal.
       So the bus stops 3 times.
   (b) The bus travels fastest when the gradient of the distance-time graph is steepest.
       So the bus travels fastest between the second and third stops.

2 The graph represents a train journey from Woking.

   (a) At what time did the train leave Woking?
   (b) How far did the train travel?

   (a) 0924
   (b) 12 miles

3 What speed is shown by this distance-time graph?
Give your answer in metres per second.

A distance of 30 metres is travelled in a time of 6 seconds.
Using Speed = Distance ÷ Time
       Speed = 30 ÷ 6
            = 5 metres per second

Exercise 23.6

1 The graph represents a bus journey from Poole.

   (a) At what time did the bus leave Poole?
   (b) How far did the bus travel?
   (c) How many times did the bus stop on the journey?

2 The graph represents the journey of a cyclist from Hambone to Boneham.

(a) What time did the cyclist leave Hambone?

(b) The cyclist arrived in Boneham at 1200. How far is Boneham from Hambone?

(c) The cyclist made one stop on his journey.
  (i) At what time did the cyclist stop?
  (ii) How far was the cyclist from Boneham when he stopped?

3 (a) The graph represents the journey of a car.
What is the speed of the car in kilometres per hour?

(b) The graph represents the journey of a train.
What is the speed of the train in metres per second?

(c) The graph represents the speed of a cyclist.
What is the speed of the cyclist in miles per hour?

4 This graph shows the progress made by a runner during the first 20 km of a marathon race.

Find the average speed of the runner:
(a) during the first 10 km of the race,
(b) during the second 10 km of the race,
(c) during the first 20 km of the race.

5 Selby is 20 miles from York.

(a) Kathryn leaves Selby at 1030 and drives to York.
She travels at an average speed of 20 miles per hour.
Draw a distance-time graph to represent her journey.

(b) At 1030 Matt leaves York and drives to Selby.
He travels at an average speed of 30 miles per hour.
  (i) On the same diagram draw a distance-time graph to represent his journey.
  (ii) At what time does Matt arrive in Selby?

6 Dan walks around Bolam Lake. He starts and finishes his walk at the car park beside the lake. The distance-time graph shows his journey.

(a) At what time did Dan start his walk?
(b) At what time did Dan reach the furthest distance from the car park?
(c) How many times did Dan stop during his walk?
(d) Dan stopped for lunch at 1330.
For how many minutes did he stop for lunch?
(e) Between what times did Dan walk the fastest?
(f) At what speed did Dan walk between 1530 and 1600?

7 The graph represents the journey of a cyclist from Bournemouth to the New Forest.
(a) What is the average speed of the cyclist in miles per hour?
(b) Another cyclist is travelling from the New Forest to Bournemouth at an average speed of 12 miles per hour. At 1300 the cyclist is 15 miles from Bournemouth.
(i) Copy the graph and on the same diagram draw a graph to show the journey of the cyclist to Bournemouth.
(ii) At what time does the cyclist arrive in Bournemouth?

8 Billy has a 10 km journey to school.
He leaves home at 8.05 am and takes 10 minutes to walk 1 km to Jane's house.
Billy gets a lift with Jane's mum at 8.20 am. Billy arrives at school at 8.45 am.
(a) Using 1 cm for 5 minutes on the time axis and 1 cm for 1 km on the distance axis draw a distance-time graph for Billy's journey.
(b) Find Billy's average speed for his whole journey in km/hour.

9 Emby and Ashwood are two towns 14 km apart.
Kim leaves Emby at 1000 and walks at a steady pace of 6 km/hour towards Ashwood.
Ray leaves Ashwood at 1040 and cycles towards Emby.
Ray travels at a steady speed of 21 km/hour for the first 20 minutes and then at a slower steady speed for the rest of his journey.
Ray arrives at Emby at 1130.
(a) On the same diagram and using a scale of 1 cm for 10 minutes on the time axis and 1 cm for 1 km on the distance axis, draw a distance-time graph to show both journeys.
(b) Use your diagram to find:
(i) the time that Kim arrives at Ashwood,
(ii) the time that Kim and Ray pass each other,
(iii) Ray's speed for the slower part of his journey.

- **Coordinates** (involving positive and negative numbers) are used to describe the position of a point on a graph.
  For example, $A(-3, 2)$ is the point where the lines $x = -3$ and $y = 2$ cross.

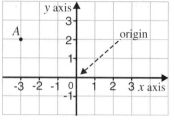

- The graph of a **linear function** is a **straight line**.

- The **gradient** of a line can be found by drawing a right-angled triangle.

  Gradient $= \dfrac{\text{distance up}}{\text{distance along}}$

  Gradient can be positive, zero or negative.

> In general, the equation of any straight line can be written in the form
>
> $$y = mx + c$$
>
> where m is the **gradient** of the line and c is the **y-intercept**.

- The points where a line crosses the axes can be found:
  by reading the coordinates from a graph,
  by substituting $x = 0$ and $y = 0$ into the equation of the line.

- Equations of the form $px + qy = r$ can be **rearranged** to the form $y = mx + c$.

- **Distance-time graphs** are used to illustrate journeys.
  On a distance-time graph: speed can be calculated from the gradient of a line,
  the faster the speed the steeper the gradient,
  zero gradient (horizontal line) means zero speed (not moving).

- You should be able to construct and interpret graphs arising from real-life situations.

Review Exercise 23

1 (a) Write the coordinates of a point that is on the line $y = x + 1$.
   (b) Draw the line $y = x + 1$ on graph paper.
      Label the x and y axes from -3 to 6.

      AQA

2 Draw and label the lines $y = x + 2$ and $y = 4 - x$ for values of x from -2 to 4.

   AQA

3 (a) Copy and complete the table of values for the equation $y = 2x - 1$.

x	-1	1	3
y			

   (b) Draw the graph of $y = 2x - 1$.
   (c) **Use your graph** to estimate the value of x when $y = 2.5$.

   AQA

4 The points $(1, 3)$ and $(4, 6)$ have been plotted and joined with a straight line.

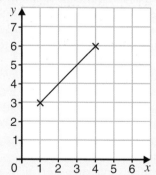

Copy the diagram onto squared paper.
   (a) On the same axes draw the graph of $y = 6 - x$.
   (b) Solve the equation $x + 2 = 6 - x$.

   AQA

5 (a) On the same diagram draw and label the lines: $y = 2x$ and $x + y = 6$
(b) Write down the coordinates of the point where the lines cross.

6 (a) Sketch the graph of the line given by the equation $4y - 3x = 12$.
(b) Write down the coordinates of the point where the line crosses the y axis.

7 In an experiment, different weights are attached to a spring and the length of the spring is measured each time.
The graph shows the result obtained.

(a) Estimate the length of the spring when no weight is attached.

(b) Calculate the gradient of the line.

(c) Estimate the weight needed to **stretch** the spring by 20 cm.

AQA

8

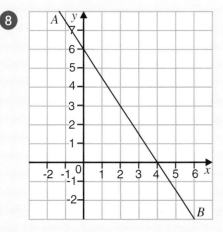

The graph shows the line AB.
Work out the equation of the line AB.

AQA

9 The graph illustrates a 1000 metre race between Nina and Polly.

(a) Who was in the lead 10 seconds after the start of the race?

(b) Describe what happened 20 seconds after the start of the race.

(c) Describe what happened to Nina 90 seconds after the start of the race.

(d) Who won the race?

10 (a) The graph of a straight line is given by the equation $y - 3x = 2$.
Write down the equation of a line parallel to this line which passes through the point $(0, 5)$.
(b) The graph of a different line is given by the equation $3y - 2x = -6$.
(i) What is the gradient of this line?
(ii) Find the coordinates of the point where this line crosses the y axis.

11 Decide which graph matches each relationship.

Graph **W**   Graph **X**   Graph **Y**   Graph **Z**

Relationships

A: The area of a circle plotted against its radius.

B: The circumference of a circle plotted against its radius.

C: The length of a rectangle of area 24 cm² plotted against its width.

AQA

12 Water flows into some containers at a constant rate.

(a) Sketch the graphs of the depths of the water against time.

(i)   (ii)

(b) Sketch the cross-section of the container that generated this graph.

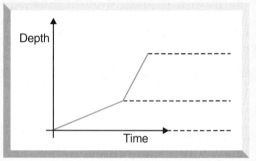

AQA

13 Jenny cycles to school.
The graph shows her journey from home to school.
On the way she stops to talk to her friends.

(a) How many times does she stop to talk to her friends?

(b) (i) How far does she travel in the first stage from home to *A*?

   (ii) What is her average speed over the first ten minutes? Give your answer in kilometres per hour.

(c) On which stage of the journey is her average speed the fastest?

AQA

14 The distance from Ashby to Banborough is 16 km.
The distance from Banborough to Calby is 8 km.
John leaves Ashby at noon. He walks towards Banborough for 1 hour at an average speed of 6 km/h and then rests for 20 minutes. John then runs the remaining distance to Banborough at an average speed of 10 km/h. At Banborough John talks to a friend for 20 minutes and borrows his bicycle. He then cycles to Calby at an average speed of 16 km/h.
John leaves Calby at 1600. He cycles back over the same route, arriving in Ashby at 1650.

Using a scale of 1 cm for 20 minutes and 1 cm for 2 km draw a distance-time graph for John's journey.

$x + y = 10$ is an equation with two unknown quantities x and y.
Many pairs of values of x and y fit this equation.

For example.
$x = 1$ and $y = 9$, $x = 4$ and $y = 6$, $x = 2.9$ and $y = 7.1$, $x = 1.005$ and $y = 8.995$, …
$x - y = 2$ is another equation with the **same** two unknown quantities x and y.
Again, many pairs of values of x and y fit this equation.

For example.
$x = 4$ and $y = 2$, $x = 7$ and $y = 5$, $x = 2.9$ and $y = 0.9$, $x = -1$ and $y = -3$, …

There is only **one** pair of values of x and y which fit **both** of these equations ($x = 6$ and $y = 4$).
Pairs of equations like $x + y = 10$ and $x - y = 2$ are called **simultaneous equations**.

To solve simultaneous equations you need to find values which fit **both** equations simultaneously.
Simultaneous equations can be solved using different methods.

Using graphs to solve simultaneous equations

Consider the simultaneous equations $x + 2y = 5$ and $x - 2y = 1$.

Draw the graphs of $x + 2y = 5$ and $x - 2y = 1$.

For $x + 2y = 5$:
When $x = 1$, $y = 2$.
This gives the point $(1, 2)$.

When $x = 5$, $y = 0$.
This gives the point $(5, 0)$.

To draw the graph of $x + 2y = 5$
draw a line through the points
$(1, 2)$ and $(5, 0)$.

For $x - 2y = 1$:
When $x = 1$, $y = 0$.
This gives the point $(1, 0)$.

When $x = 5$, $y = 2$.
This gives the point $(5, 2)$.

To draw the graph of $x - 2y = 1$
draw a line through the points
$(1, 0)$ and $(5, 2)$.

> Drawing straight
> line graphs was
> first covered in
> Chapter 23.

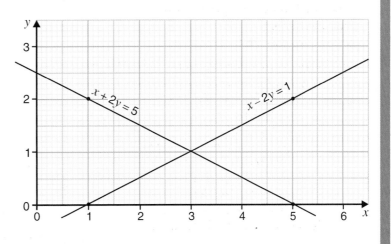

The values of x and y at the point where the lines cross give the solution to the
simultaneous equations.

The lines cross at the point $(3, 1)$.

This gives the solution $x = 3$ and $y = 1$.

To solve a pair of simultaneous equations plot the graph of each of the equations on the same diagram.
The coordinates of the point where the two lines cross:

- fit **both equations** simultaneously,
- give the **graphical solution** of the equations.

Use a graphical method to solve this
pair of simultaneous equations:
$$5x + 2y = 20$$
$$y = 2x + 1$$

Find the points that fit the equations
$5x + 2y = 20$ and $y = 2x + 1$.

For $5x + 2y = 20$:

When $x = 0$, $y = 10$.
This gives the point $(0, 10)$.

When $y = 0$, $x = 4$.
This gives the point $(4, 0)$.

Draw a line through the points $(0, 10)$ and $(4, 0)$.

For $y = 2x + 1$:

When $x = 0$, $y = 1$.
This gives the point $(0, 1)$.

When $x = 4$, $y = 9$.
This gives the point $(4, 9)$.

Draw a line through the points $(0, 1)$ and $(4, 9)$.

The lines cross at the point $(2, 5)$.
This gives the solution
$x = 2$ and $y = 5$.

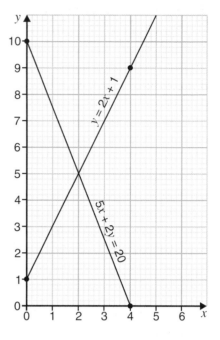

Check
You can check a graphical solution by
substituting the values of x and y into
the original equations.
When $x = 2$ and $y = 5$
$$5x + 2y = 5 \times 2 + 2 \times 5 = 20$$
$$y = 2x + 1 = 2 \times 2 + 1 = 5$$

Exercise 24.1

Use a graphical method to solve each of these pairs of simultaneous equations.
For each question use the sizes of axes given.
For example, $0 \leq x \leq 8$ means draw and label the x axis from 0 to 8 inclusive.

1 $x + y = 6$
$y = x - 2$
Axes $0 \leq x \leq 8$, $-3 \leq y \leq 7$

2 $x + y = 8$
$y - x = 2$
Axes $0 \leq x \leq 10$, $-3 \leq y \leq 10$

3 $x + 2y = 8$
$2x + y = 7$
Axes $0 \leq x \leq 10$, $0 \leq y \leq 8$

4 $3x + 2y = 12$
$y = x + 1$
Axes $0 \leq x \leq 5$, $0 \leq y \leq 8$

5 $x + 3y = 6$
$y = 2x - 5$
Axes $0 \leq x \leq 10$, $-6 \leq y \leq 4$

6 $3x + 4y = 24$
$2y = x + 2$
Axes $-4 \leq x \leq 10$, $-2 \leq y \leq 8$

7 $2x + y = -1$
$x + 2y = 4$
Axes $-3 \leq x \leq 5$, $-2 \leq y \leq 4$

8 $x + 2y = 6$
$x - 2y = 4$
Axes $0 \leq x \leq 6$, $-2 \leq y \leq 3$

Simultaneous equations with no solution

Some pairs of simultaneous equations do not have a solution.

EXAMPLE

Show that this pair of simultaneous equations do not have a solution.

$$y - 2x = 4$$
$$2y = 4x - 1$$

Method 1
Draw the graph of each equation.

$y - 2x = 4$
When $x = 0$, $y = 4$.
When $y = 0$, $x = -2$.
Plot and draw a line through the points $(0, 4)$ and $(-2, 0)$.

$2y = 4x - 1$
When $x = 0$, $y = -0.5$.
When $x = 2$, $y = 3.5$.
Plot and draw a line through the points $(0, -0.5)$ and $(2, 3.5)$.

The two lines are **parallel**.
This means they never cross and there are no values of x and y which fit both equations.
So the simultaneous equations have no solution.

Method 2
Rearrange each equation to the form $y = mx + c$.

$y - 2x = 4$
Add $2x$ to both sides.
$y = 2x + 4$
The graph of this equation has a gradient (m) of 2 and a y-intercept (c) of 4.

$2y = 4x - 1$
Divide both sides by 2.
$y = 2x - 0.5$
The graph of this equation has a gradient (m) of 2 and a y-intercept (c) of -0.5.

Both lines have the same gradient (2) and different y-intercepts which shows that the lines are parallel.

Exercise 24.2

1 Draw graphs to show that each of these pairs of simultaneous equations have no solution.

(a) $x + y = 6$
$y = 2 - x$

(b) $y - 4x = 8$
$y = 4x + 2$

(c) $3x + 4y = 12$
$8y = 24 - 6x$

(d) $5y - 2x = 10$
$5y = 2x + 20$

2 By rearranging each of these pairs of simultaneous equations to the form $y = mx + c$ show that they do not have a solution.

(a) $2x + y = 6$
$y = 3 - 2x$

(b) $2y - 4x = 7$
$y - 2 = 2x$

(c) $5x - 2y = 8$
$4y = 10x + 7$

(d) $4y + 12x = 5$
$1 - 2y = 6x$

3 Two of these pairs of simultaneous equations have no solution.

(a) $5x + y = 6$
$y - 5x = 2$

(b) $5x = 8 + y$
$y - 5x = 2$

(c) $2y - 10x = 5$
$4y + 20x = 5$

(d) $y + 1 = -5x$
$2y + 10x = 5$

Use an appropriate method to find which ones.
Use a graphical method to solve the other two.

Simultaneous Equations

The elimination method

The graphical method of solving simultaneous equations can be quite time consuming.
Sometimes, due to the equations involved, the coordinates of the points where the lines intersect can be difficult to read accurately.
For these reasons, other methods of solving simultaneous equations are often used.

Consider again the simultaneous equations $x + 2y = 5$ and $x - 2y = 1$.
Both equations have the same number of x's and the same number of y's.
If the two equations are added together the y's will be **eliminated** as shown.

$$x + 2y = 5$$
$$x - 2y = 1$$

Adding gives $\quad 2x \quad = 6$
So $\quad x \quad = 3$

Remember
$+ 2y + -2y$
$= 2y - 2y = 0$

By **substituting** the value of this letter (x) into one of the original equations we can find the value of the other letter (y).

$$x + 2y = 5$$
$$3 + 2y = 5$$
$$2y = 2$$
$$y = 1$$

This gives the solution $x = 3$ and $y = 1$.

Remember:
If you do the same to both sides of an equation it is still true.

EXAMPLES

1 Use the elimination method to solve this pair of simultaneous equations:
$$2x - y = 1$$
$$3x + y = 9$$

Each equation has the **same number** of y's but the **signs** are **different**.
To eliminate the y's the equations must be **added**.

$$5x = 10$$
$$x = 2$$

Substitute $x = 2$ into $3x + y = 9$.
$$3 \times 2 + y = 9$$
$$6 + y = 9$$
$$y = 3$$

The solution is $x = 2$ and $y = 3$.

Check
Substitute $x = 2$ and $y = 3$ into
$$2x - y = 1$$
$$2 \times 2 - 3 = 1$$
$$4 - 3 = 1$$
$$1 = 1$$
The equation is true, so the solution $x = 2$ and $y = 3$ is correct.

2 Use the elimination method to solve this pair of simultaneous equations:
$$2x + 3y = 9$$
$$2x + y = 7$$

Each equation has the **same number** of x's and the **signs** are the **same**.
To eliminate the x's one equation must be **subtracted** from the other.

Subtract $2x + y = 7$ from $2x + 3y = 9$.
$$2y = 2$$
$$y = 1$$

Substitute $y = 1$ into $2x + y = 7$.
$$2x + 1 = 7$$
$$2x = 6$$
$$x = 3$$

The solution is $x = 3$ and $y = 1$.

Check
Substitute $x = 3$ and $y = 1$ into $2x + 3y = 9$.
Do this and make sure the solution is correct.

Exercise 24.3

Use the elimination method to solve each of these pairs of simultaneous equations.

1 $3x - y = 1$
$x + y = 3$

2 $2x - y = 2$
$x + y = 7$

3 $4x + y = 9$
$2x - y = 3$

4 $-x + 2y = 13$
$x + y = 8$

5 $2x + y = 7$
$x + y = 4$

6 $3x + y = 9$
$2x + y = 7$

7 $2x + y = 12$
$x + y = 7$

8 $x + 5y = 14$
$x + 2y = 8$

9 $x + 2y = 13$
$x + 4y = 21$

10 $x + 4y = 11$
$x + y = 5$

11 $2x + 5y = 13$
$2x + y = 9$

12 $5x + 3y = 26$
$2x + 3y = 14$

13 $5x + 4y = 22$
$5x + y = 13$

14 $2x - y = 10$
$3x + y = 10$

15 $5x - 2y = 13$
$3x + 2y = 3$

16 $x + 5y = 14$
$-x + 2y = 7$

17 $2x + 3y = 8$
$2x + y = -4$

18 $2x + y = 4$
$4x - y = 11$

19 $3x + 4y = -8$
$x + 4y = 4$

20 $3x + 2y = 6$
$x - 2y = 6$

21 $x - 3y = 8$
$x + 2y = -7$

22 $2x - 2y = 9$
$4x - 2y = 16$

23 $3x - y = 5$
$3x + y = 4$

24 $5x - 3y = 5$
$5x + y = -5$

Further use of the elimination method

Look at this pair of simultaneous equations:
$$5x + 2y = 11$$
$$3x - 4y = 4$$

A useful technique is to use capital letters to label the equations.

$5x + 2y = 11$ Equation A
$3x - 4y = 4$ Equation B

These equations do not have the same number of x's or the same number of y's.

To make the number of y's the same we can multiply equation A by 2.

A × 2 gives $10x + 4y = 22$ Equation C
B × 1 gives $3x - 4y = 4$ Equation D

C + D gives $13x = 26$
$x = 2$

The number of y's in equations C and D is the **same** but the **signs** are **different**. To eliminate the y's the equations must be **added**.

Substitute $x = 2$ into $5x + 2y = 11$.
$$5 \times 2 + 2y = 11$$
$$10 + 2y = 11$$
$$2y = 1$$
$$y = 0.5$$

The solution is $x = 2$ and $y = 0.5$.

In this example eliminating the y's rather than the x's is less likely to produce an error.
Try to solve the equations by eliminating the x's.

Check the solution by substituting $x = 2$ and $y = 0.5$ into $3x - 4y = 4$.

Solve this pair of simultaneous equations:
$$3x + 7y = -2$$
$$4x + 9 = -3y$$

Rearrange and label the equations.
$$3x + 7y = -2 \quad \text{A}$$
$$4x + 3y = -9 \quad \text{B}$$
These equations do not have the same number of x's or the same number of y's. So the multiplying method can be used.

> Both equations must be in the form $px + qy = r$ before the elimination method can be used.
> You may have to **rearrange** the equations you are given.
> $4x + 9 = -3y$ can be rearranged as $4x + 3y = -9$.

Method 1
Eliminating the x's.

A × 4 gives $\quad 12x + 28y = -8 \quad \text{C}$
B × 3 gives $\quad 12x + 9y = -27 \quad \text{D}$

C − D gives $\quad\quad 19y = -8 - -27$
$$19y = -8 + 27$$
$$19y = 19$$
$$y = 1$$
Substitute $y = 1$ into $3x + 7y = -2$.
$$3x + 7 \times 1 = -2$$
$$3x + 7 = -2$$
$$3x = -9$$
$$x = -3$$

The solution is $x = -3$ and $y = 1$.

Method 2
Eliminating the y's.

A × 3 gives $\quad 9x + 21y = -6 \quad \text{C}$
B × 7 gives $\quad 28x + 21y = -63 \quad \text{D}$

D − C gives $\quad\quad 19x = -63 - -6$
$$19x = -63 + 6$$
$$19x = -57$$
$$x = -3$$
Substitute $x = -3$ into $3x + 7y = -2$.
$$3 \times -3 + 7y = -2$$
$$-9 + 7y = -2$$
$$7y = 7$$
$$y = 1$$

Check the solution by substituting $x = -3$ and $y = 1$ into $4x + 9 = -3y$.

Exercise 24.4

Solve each of these pairs of simultaneous equations.

1 $\quad 3x + 2y = 8$
$\quad\quad 2x - y = 3$

2 $\quad x + y = 5$
$\quad\quad 5x - 3y = 1$

3 $\quad 2x + 3y = 9$
$\quad\quad x + 4y = 7$

4 $\quad x + 3y = 10$
$\quad\quad 2x + 5y = 18$

5 $\quad 5x + 2y = 8$
$\quad\quad 2x - y = 5$

6 $\quad 3x + y = 9$
$\quad\quad x - 2y = 10$

7 $\quad 3x - 4y = 10$
$\quad\quad x + 2y = 5$

8 $\quad x + 6y = 0$
$\quad\quad 3x - 2y = -10$

9 $\quad 2x + 3y = 11$
$\quad\quad 3x + y = 13$

10 $\quad 2x + y = 10$
$\quad\quad -x + 2y = 9$

11 $\quad 2x + 3y = 9$
$\quad\quad 4x - y = 4$

12 $\quad 2x + 3y = 8$
$\quad\quad 3x + 2y = 7$

13 $\quad 3x + 4y = 23$
$\quad\quad 2x + 5y = 20$

14 $\quad 2x - 3y = 8$
$\quad\quad x - 5y = 11$

15 $\quad 3x + 4y = 5$
$\quad\quad -2x + 5y = 12$

16 $\quad 3x - 2y = 4$
$\quad\quad x + 4y = 6$

17 $\quad -3x + 2y = 5$
$\quad\quad 4x + 3y = -1$

18 $\quad 3x + 4y = 6$
$\quad\quad 3y = 7 - x$

19 $\quad 5x + 3y = 16$
$\quad\quad 2y = 13 - x$

20 $\quad 5x - 4y = 24$
$\quad\quad 2x = y + 9$

21 $\quad 2x + 3y = 14$
$\quad\quad 8x - 5y = 5$

22 $\quad 4x - 7y = 15$
$\quad\quad 5x - 12 = 2y$

23 $\quad 8x + 3y = 2$
$\quad\quad 5x = 1 - 2y$

24 $\quad 9x = 4y - 20$
$\quad\quad 5x = 6y - 13$

The substitution method

For some pairs of simultaneous equations a method using **substitution** is sometimes more convenient.

> ### EXAMPLE
>
> Solve this pair of simultaneous equations: $5x + y = 9$
> $$y = 4x$$
>
> $5x + y = 9$ Equation A
> $y = 4x$ Equation B
> Substitute $y = 4x$ into Equation A
> $$5x + 4x = 9$$
> $$9x = 9$$
> $$x = 1$$
>
> Substitute $x = 1$ into $y = 4x$.
> $$y = 4 \times 1$$
> $$y = 4$$
>
> The solution is $x = 1$ and $y = 4$.
>
> *Check the solution by substituting*
> $x = 1$ and $y = 4$ *into* $5x + y = 9$.

Exercise 24.5

Use the substitution method to solve these pairs of simultaneous equations.

1. $2x + y = 10$
   $y = 3x$

2. $3x - y = 9$
   $y = 2x$

3. $x + 5y = 18$
   $x = 4y$

4. $x + 2y = 15$
   $y = 2x$

5. $2x + y = 17$
   $y = 6x + 1$

6. $3x + 2y = 4$
   $x = y - 2$

7. $5x + 6y = 34$
   $y = x + 2$

8. $5x - 2y = 23$
   $x = y + 1$

9. $5x - y = 12$
   $y = 32 - 6x$

10. $x + 5y = 13$
   $x = 3y + 9$

11. $5x - 3y = 26$
   $y = 2x + 14$

12. $x + 4y = 32$
   $x = 2y - 4$

Solving problems using simultaneous equations

> ### EXAMPLE
>
> Billy buys 5 first class stamps and 3 second class stamps at a cost of £2.
> Jane buys 3 first class stamps and 5 second class stamps at a cost of £1.84.
> Calculate the cost of a first class stamp and the cost of a second class stamp.
>
> Let x pence be the cost of a first class stamp, and let y pence be the cost of a second class stamp.
>
> Billy's purchase of the stamps gives this equation. $5x + 3y = 200$ Equation A
> Jane's purchase of the stamps gives this equation. $3x + 5y = 184$ Equation B
>
> This gives a pair of simultaneous equations which can be solved using the elimination method.
> $$5x + 3y = 200 \quad \text{A}$$
> $$3x + 5y = 184 \quad \text{B}$$
>
> A × 5 gives $25x + 15y = 1000$ C
> B × 3 gives $9x + 15y = 552$ D
>
> C − D gives $16x = 448$
> $$x = 28$$
>
> Substitute $x = 28$ into $5x + 3y = 200$.
> $$5 \times 28 + 3y = 200$$
> $$3y = 60$$
> $$y = 20$$
>
> So the cost of a first class stamp is 28 pence and the cost of a second class stamp is 20 pence.
>
> *Check the solution by substituting the values for x and y into the original problem.*

1 Pencils cost x pence each and pens cost y pence each.
Pam buys 6 pencils and 3 pens for 93 pence.
Ray buys 2 pencils and 5 pens for 91 pence.
(a)   Write down two equations connecting x and y.
(b)   By solving these simultaneous equations find the cost of a pencil and the cost of a pen.

2 Apples are x pence per kg. Oranges are y pence each.
5 kg of apples and 30 oranges cost £9.00.
10 kg of apples and 15 oranges cost £12.60.
(a)   Write down two equations connecting x and y.
(b)   By solving these simultaneous equations find the cost of a kilogram of apples and the cost of an orange.

3 Standard eggs cost x pence per dozen.
Small eggs cost y pence per dozen.
10 dozen standard eggs and 5 dozen small eggs cost £13.60.
5 dozen standard eggs and 8 dozen small eggs cost £11.31.
By forming two simultaneous equations find the values of x and y.

4 A group of children and adults went on a coach trip to a theme park.
Ticket prices for the theme park were £20 for adults and £10 for children.
Ticket prices for the coach were £10 for adults and £4 for children.
The total cost of the tickets for the theme park was £380.
The total cost of the coach tickets was £158.
How many children and adults went on the trip?

5 Jenny types at x words per minute.
Stuart types at y words per minute.
When Jenny and Stuart both type for 1 minute they type a total of 170 words.
When Jenny types for 5 minutes and Stuart types for 3 minutes they type a total of 710 words.
Calculate x and y.

6 At a café, John buys 3 coffees and 2 teas for £3.80 and Susan buys 2 coffees and 3 teas for £3.70.
Calculate the price of a coffee and the price of a tea.

7 Standard coaches hold x passengers and first class coaches hold y passengers.
A train with 5 standard coaches and 2 first class coaches carries a total of 1040 passengers.
A train with 7 standard coaches and 3 first class coaches carries a total of 1480 passengers.
By forming two simultaneous equations find the values of x and y.

What you need to know

- A pair of **simultaneous equations** are linked equations with the same unknown letters in each equation.
- To solve a pair of simultaneous equations find values for the unknown letters that fit **both** equations.
- Simultaneous equations can be solved either **graphically** or **algebraically**.
- Solving simultaneous equations **graphically** involves:
    drawing the graph of both equations,
    finding the point where the graphs cross.
  When the graphs of both equations are parallel, the equations have no solution.
- Solving simultaneous equations **algebraically** involves using either:
    the **elimination** method, or
    the **substitution** method (if it is more convenient).

1 Use a graphical method to solve each of these simultaneous equations.
For each question use the size of axes given.

(a) $x + y = 10$
$y = 2x + 1$
Axes $0 \le x \le 11, \ 0 \le y \le 11$

(b) $5x + 6y = 30$
$2y = x - 2$
Axes $0 \le x \le 8, \ -3 \le y \le 8$

2 Use an algebraic method to solve each of these simultaneous equations.
You must show all your working.

(a) $2x + y = 8$
$x + y = 5$

(b) $3x + y = 10$
$x - 2y = 8$

(c) $3y - 5x = 1$
$5y - 3x = 7$

(d) $x + 5y = 3$
$y = 3x + 7$

3 Solve the simultaneous equations: $x - 3y = 7$
$2x + y = 0$

AQA

4 Solve the simultaneous equations: $4x + 5y = 5$
$2x - y = 6$

AQA

5 Solve the simultaneous equations: $3x + y = -5$
$x - 4y = 7$

AQA

6 (a) Show that the simultaneous equations $y = 2x - 2$ and $2y - 4x = 3$ have no solution.
(b) Show that the simultaneous equations $4y = x + 1$ and $8y - 2x = 3$ have no solution.
(c) The simultaneous equations $y = 3x + 2$ and $y = ax + b$ have no solution.
What can you say about the values of a and b?
(d) The simultaneous equations $y = 3x + 2$ and $py + qx = r$ have no solution.
Find some possible values for p, q and r.

7 This graph shows the line $y - 2x = -1$.

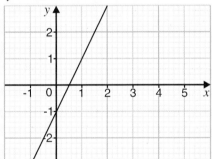

Copy the graph.
By drawing another line, use the graph to solve the simultaneous equations:
$y - 2x = -1$ and $x + 2y = 4$

AQA

8 **Use a graphical method** to solve the simultaneous equations:
$y = x + 7$ and $y + 3x = 5$

AQA

9 In a competition, a win scores x points and a draw scores y points.
Nayeem has won one game, drawn three games and has 16 points.
Freda has won two games, drawn one game and has 17 points.
Find x and y, by solving the simultaneous equations: $x + 3y = 16$
$2x + y = 17$

AQA

10 Peaches cost x pence each and oranges cost y pence each.
4 peaches and one orange cost 58p.
6 peaches and 2 oranges cost 92p.
(a) Write down two equations connecting x and y.
(b) Solve these simultaneous equations to find the values of x and y.

CHAPTER 25

More or Less

Activity

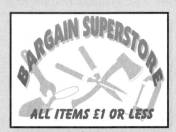

For all children who enter the competition we can say that
Age < 16 years

For anyone riding the Big Dipper we can say that
Height $\geqslant 1.2$ m

For all items sold in the store we can say that
Cost $\leqslant$ £1

These are examples of inequalities.
Can you think of other situations where inequalities are used?

Inequalities

An **inequality** is a mathematical statement, such as $x > 1$, $a \leqslant 2$ or $-3 \leqslant n < 2$.

In the following, x is an integer.

Sign	Meaning	Example	Possible values of x
$<$	is less than	$x < 4$	$3, 2, 1, 0, -1, -2, -3, \ldots$
$\leqslant$	is less than or equal to	$x \leqslant 4$	$4, 3, 2, 1, 0, -1, -2, -3, \ldots$
$>$	is greater than	$x > 6$	$7, 8, 9, 10, \ldots$
$\geqslant$	is greater than or equal to	$x \geqslant 2$	$2, 3, 4, 5, \ldots$

> An **integer** is a positive or negative whole number or zero.

Explain the difference between the meanings of the signs $<$ and $\leqslant$.
Explain the difference between the meanings of the signs $>$ and $\geqslant$.

Number lines

Inequalities can be shown on a **number line**.

As you move to the right, numbers get bigger.
As you move to the left, numbers get smaller.

The number line below shows the inequality $-2 < x \leqslant 3$.

The circle at 3 is **filled** to show that 3 is **included**.
The circle at -2 is **not filled** to show that -2 is **not included**.

EXAMPLES

1 Draw number lines to show these inequalities:
(a) $x < 1.5$ (b) $x \geqslant -2$ (c) $x \leqslant 4$ and $x > -1$

The circle is:
filled if the inequality is **included**,
not filled if the inequality is **not included**.

(a) $x < 1.5$

(b) $x \geqslant -2$

(c) $x \leqslant 4$ and $x > -1$.

x has to satisfy two inequalities.

2 (a)   Draw a number line to show the inequality $3 \leqslant x < 8$.
(b) x is an integer.
Write down the values of x which satisfy the inequality.

$3 \leqslant x < 8$
is a shorthand method
of writing
$3 \leqslant x$ **and** $x < 8$.

(a)

(b)   The values of x which satisfy the inequality
$3 \leqslant x < 8$ are: 3, 4, 5, 6, 7.

Exercise 25.1

1 Write down the following mathematical statements and say whether each is true or false.
(a) $4 < 7$ (b) $3 > -3$ (c) $4 \geqslant 4$ (d) $-2 > -1$
(e) $-8 \leqslant -8$ (f) $1.5 \geqslant 2.1$ (g) $3 \times 5 \leqslant 7 \times 2$ (h) $-4 \times (-2) > -4 - 4$

2 Write down an integer which could replace the letter.
(a) $x < 6$ (b) $a \geqslant -2$ (c) $c + 2 < 8$ (d) $2d \leqslant 14$
(e) $f - 3 > 7$ (f) $-2 < h < 0$ (g) $t \leqslant 5$ **and** $t > 4$ (h) $r \geqslant -6$ **and** $r < -1$

3 In this question x is an integer. Write down all the values of x which satisfy these inequalities.
(a) $1 < x < 5$ (b) $-2 < x \leqslant 3$ (c) $-4 \leqslant x \leqslant -1$ (d) $-1 \leqslant x < 3$

4 Write down a mathematical statement, using inequalities, for each of these diagrams.

5 Draw number lines to show the following inequalities.
For each part, draw and label a number line from -5 to 5.
(a) $-2 \leqslant x < 3$ (b) $x > -4$ (c) $x < -3$ and $x \geqslant 1$

Solving inequalities

Solve means to find the values of x which make the inequality true.
The aim is to end up with **one letter** on one side of the inequality
and a **number** on the other side of the inequality.

Solving inequalities is similar
to solving equations.

1 Solve the inequality $5x - 3 < 27$ and show the solution on a number line.

$5x - 3 < 27$
Add 3 to both sides.
$5x < 30$
Divide both sides by 5.
$x < 6$

The solution is shown on a number line as:

This means that the inequality is **true** for all values of x which are less than 6.

2 Solve the inequality $7a \geqslant a + 9$.

$7a \geqslant a + 9$
Subtract a from both sides.
$6a \geqslant 9$
Divide both sides by 6.
$a \geqslant 1.5$

This means that the inequality is true for all values of a which are equal to 1.5, or greater.

Substitute $a = 1.5$, $a = 2$ and $a = 1$ into the original inequality. What do you notice?

Exercise 25.2

1 Solve each of the following inequalities and show the solution on a number line.
  (a) $3n > 6$
  (b) $a + 1 < 5$
  (c) $2d - 5 \leqslant 1$
  (d) $t + 2 < -1$
  (e) $5 + 2g > 1$
  (f) $4 + 3y \geqslant 4$

2 Solve the following inequalities. Show your working clearly.
  (a) $a + 3 < 7$
  (b) $b - 3 \geqslant -2$
  (c) $-2 + b \leqslant -1$
  (d) $3c > 15$
  (e) $2d < -6$
  (f) $\frac{1}{2} a \geqslant 3$
  (g) $\frac{1}{3} b < 5$
  (h) $2c + 5 \leqslant 11$
  (i) $3d - 4 > 8$
  (j) $4 + 3f < -2$
  (k) $8g - 1 \leqslant 3$
  (l) $5h < h + 8$
  (m) $6j \geqslant 2j + 10$
  (n) $7k > 3k - 16$
  (o) $4m + 2 > 2m - 11$
  (p) $7n - 3 \leqslant 13 - n$
  (q) $3p - 2 > 6 + 2p$
  (r) $4q + 5 > 12 - 3q$
  (s) $6r + 1 \geqslant 4r - 2$
  (t) $2t - 10 > t + 3$
  (u) $2(u - 5) \leqslant 8$
  (v) $3(4v + 1) < -15$
  (w) $\frac{1}{2} w + 3 > 7$
  (x) $\frac{1}{2}(5x - 1) < 3$

Multiplying (or dividing) an inequality by a negative number

Activity

$-2 < 3$

Multiply both sides by -1.
$-2 \times (-1) = 2$ and $3 \times (-1) = -3$

$2 > -3$

To keep the statement true we have to reverse the inequality sign.

Multiply both sides of these inequalities by -1.

1 $3 > 2$

2 $3 > -2$

3 $-3 < -1$

4 $5 \geqslant 4$

5 $-4 \leqslant 5$

6 $-4 \geqslant -5$

The same rules for equations can be applied to inequalities, with one exception:
When you **multiply** (or **divide**) both sides of an inequality by a negative number the inequality is reversed.

EXAMPLES

1 Solve $-3x < 6$.

Divide both sides by -3.
Because we are dividing by a negative number the inequality is reversed.
$x > -2$

2 Solve $3a - 2 \geqslant 5a - 9$.

Subtract $5a$ from both sides.
$-2a - 2 \geqslant -9$
Add 2 to both sides.
$\quad -2a \geqslant -7$
Divide both sides by -2.
$\quad\quad a \leqslant 3.5$

Exercise 25.3

Solve the following inequalities. Show your working clearly.

1 $-4a > 8$

2 $-5b \leqslant -15$

3 $-3c \geqslant 12$

4 $3 - 2d < 5$

5 $14 - 3e \leqslant 4e$

6 $-5f > 4f - 9$

7 $4g < 7g + 12$

8 $5 - 3h \leqslant h - 3$

9 $-5 - j \geqslant 12j - 18$

10 $3 - 5k < 2(3 + 2k)$

11 $3(m - 2) > 5m$

12 $3(2n - 1) < 8n + 5$

13 $3p \geqslant 5 - 6p$

14 $2(q - 3) < 5 + 7q$

15 $n - 5 > 2(n - 7)$

Double inequalities

EXAMPLE

Find the values of x such that $-8 < 4x - 2 \leqslant 10$.

$-8 < 4x - 2 \leqslant 10$
Add 2 to each part of the inequality.
$-6 < 4x \leqslant 12$
Divide each part of the inequality by 4.
$-1.5 < x \leqslant 3$

Alternative method
Write the **double inequality** as two separate inequalities.
$\quad -8 < 4x - 2 \quad\quad$ and $\quad\quad 4x - 2 \leqslant 10$
Solve each inequality.

$-8 < 4x - 2$	$4x - 2 \leqslant 10$
Add 2 to both sides.	Add 2 to both sides.
$-6 < 4x$	$4x \leqslant 12$
Divide both sides by 4.	Divide both sides by 4.
$-1.5 < x$	$x \leqslant 3$

So $-1.5 < x \leqslant 3$

The double inequality $-1.5 < x \leqslant 3$ gives **all** the possible values of x.
This means that the inequality $-8 < 4x - 2 \leqslant 10$ is true for all the values of x from -1.5 (not included) up to 3 (included).

More or Less . . . More or Less . . .

EXAMPLE

Find the integer values of n for which $-1 \leqslant 2n + 3 < 7$.

$-1 \leqslant 2n + 3 < 7$
Subtract 3 from each part.
$-4 \leqslant 2n < 4$
Divide each part by 2.
$-2 \leqslant n < 2$

Integer values which satisfy the inequality $-1 \leqslant 2n + 3 < 7$ are: $-2, -1, 0, 1$.

Exercise 25.4

1 Solve each of the following inequalities and show the solution on a number line.
   (a) $5 < x + 4 \leqslant 9$
   (b) $-3 \leqslant x - 2 < 7$
   (c) $2 < 9 + x \leqslant 13$

2 Find the values of x such that:
   (a) $2 < 2x \leqslant 6$
   (b) $-6 \leqslant 3x < 12$
   (c) $5 < 2x - 1 < 8$
   (d) $-2 \leqslant 3x - 1 \leqslant 11$
   (e) $12 < 5x + 2 \leqslant 27$
   (f) $-9 \leqslant 4x + 3 < 27$
   (g) $-16 < 7x - 2 < 12$
   (h) $-1 \leqslant 3x - 10 < 8$
   (i) $-4 \leqslant 5 + 2x \leqslant 3$

3 Find the integer values of n for which:
   (a) $3 < n - 2 < 7$
   (b) $-2 < n + 1 \leqslant 5$
   (c) $-2 < 2n \leqslant 4$
   (d) $5 \leqslant 2n - 3 < 13$
   (e) $0 < 2n - 8 < 3$
   (f) $5 < 4n + 1 \leqslant 13$
   (g) $-4 \leqslant 5n + 6 < 11$
   (h) $-4 < 3n + 2 \leqslant 11$
   (i) $-5 \leqslant \frac{1}{2}n - 3 \leqslant 0$
   (j) $-12 < 5 - n \leqslant -3$
   (k) $-3 \leqslant 4 - 2n \leqslant 12$
   (l) $-5 < 3(n + 5) < 0$

Graphs of inequalities

Activity

Line A has equation $y = 2$.

Describe the y coordinates of points **on** line A.
Describe the y coordinates of points **below** line A.
Describe the y coordinates of points **above** line A.

Above the line is the region $y > 2$.
Below the line is the region $y < 2$.

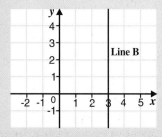

Line B has equation $x = 3$.

Use an inequality to describe the region to the right of line B.
Use an inequality to describe the region to the left of line B.

Regions

A line divides the graph into two **regions**.
The region $x \leqslant 2$ is to the **left** of the line $x = 2$,
including the line itself.
The region $x \geqslant 2$ is to the **right** of the line $x = 2$,
including the line itself.

The region $y < -3$ is **below** the line $y = -3$.
The region $y > -3$ is **above** the line $y = -3$.

A **solid line** is used when the points on the line are included.
A **broken line** is used when the points on the line are
not included.

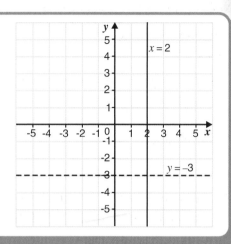

EXAMPLE

On a sketch, show the region where the inequalities $x > -2$ and $y \leqslant 1$ are both true.
Label the region R.

To do this:
1 Draw the x and y axes.
2 Draw and label the line $x = -2$, using a broken line.
3 Show the region $x > -2$ by shading out the
   unwanted region.

4 Draw and label the line $y = 1$ using a solid line.
5 Show the region $y \leqslant 1$ by shading out the
   unwanted region.

6 Label the region, R, where $x > -2$ **and** $y \leqslant 1$.
   Note that the region R extends for ever to the
   right and downwards.

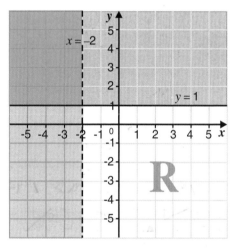

Shading regions on a graph
Unless you are told to do otherwise, always shade out the **unwanted** region.

Exercise 25.5

For each question, draw and label axes for x and y from -5 to 5.
Shade the unwanted regions. Leave the given region unshaded and label it R.

1 $x > 2$ and $y \geqslant 1$

2 $x \geqslant -3$ and $y < 4$

3 $x \geqslant -2$, $x < 1$ and $y > 2$

4 $x < 5$, $x \geqslant -1$ and $y \leqslant 3$

5 $x \leqslant 2$, $x > -2$, $y < 3$ and $y \geqslant 1$

6 $x \geqslant -2$, $x \leqslant 0$, $y \geqslant 1$ and $y \leqslant 4$

7 $x \leqslant 1.5$, $y > -1$ and $y \leqslant 2.5$

8 $x > -2.5$, $x \leqslant 1.5$ and $y \leqslant 2.5$

EXAMPLES

1. Show the region defined by the inequality $y \geqslant 2x - 3$.

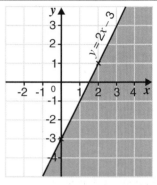

First draw the line with equation $y = 2x - 3$.
When $x = 0$, $y = -3$. Plot the point $(0, -3)$.
When $x = 2$, $y = 1$. Plot the point $(2, 1)$.

Next, draw the line through the two points.
Use a solid line because the inequality sign is $\geqslant$.

Now test a point above the line and a point below the line.

Point	Coordinates	Value of y	Value of $2x - 3$	Is $y \geqslant 2x - 3$?
Above	$(1, 3)$	3	-1	Yes
Below	$(4, -2)$	-2	5	No

The inequality $y \geqslant 2x - 3$ is true **above** the line, so we shade the unwanted region, below the line.

2. Show the region where the inequality $2x + 3y < 12$ is true.

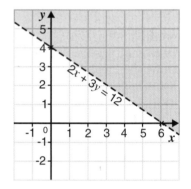

First draw the line with equation $2x + 3y = 12$.
When $x = 0$, $y = 4$. Plot the point $(0, 4)$.
When $y = 0$, $x = 6$. Plot the point $(6, 0)$.

Next, draw the line through the two points.
Use a broken line because the inequality sign is $<$.

Point	Coordinates	Is $2x + 3y < 12$?
Above	$(3, 4)$	No
Below	$(2, 1)$	Yes

The inequality $2x + 3y < 12$ is true **below** the line, so we shade the unwanted region, above the line.

Exercise 25.6

1. Draw graphs to show the following. Leave unshaded the regions where the inequalities are true.
   (a) $y \geqslant x$ (b) $y < 2x$ (c) $y < x + 1$ (d) $y \geqslant 2x - 1$
   (e) $x + y \leqslant 3$ (f) $x + y > 2$ (g) $2x + y \geqslant 4$ (h) $x + 4y < 6$

2. Draw graphs to show the following. Label with the letter R the region defined by the inequalities.
   (a) $y < 3x$, $x < 2$ and $y > 0$ (b) $2x + 5y \leqslant 10$, $x \geqslant 0$ and $y \geqslant 0$
   (c) $3x + 4y \geqslant 12$, $x < 3$ and $y < 4$ (d) $x + 3y < 6$, $x > -1$ and $y > 1$
   (e) $2x + 3y \geqslant 6$, $1 < x \leqslant 3$ and $y < 4$

3. Copy the diagram and shade the region which satisfies all of these inequalities:
   $y \geqslant 2$, $y \leqslant 2x$, $x > 0$, $x + y \leqslant 4$.

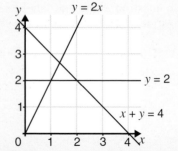

4 Match each of these inequalities to its **unshaded** region.

  A $2y < x + 2$ **B** $y > x$ **C** $2y < 4 - x$ **D** $y < 4 - x$

   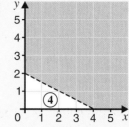

5 The shaded area can be described by three inequalities, one for each side of the shape.
One of the inequalities is $x < 3$.
Write down the other two inequalities.

6 Use inequalities to describe the shaded region in these diagrams.

(a)

(b)

(c)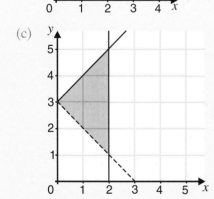

(d)

7 A point P has whole number coordinates and lies in the region
  $y < 3$, $1 < x < 4$ and $2y > x$.

(a) Copy the diagram and show the region which satisfies these inequalities.

(b) Write down the coordinates of all the possible positions of P.

What you need to know

- Inequalities can be described using words or numbers and symbols.

Sign	Meaning
$<$	is less than
$\leqslant$	is less than or equal to
$>$	is greater than
$\geqslant$	is greater than or equal to

- Inequalities can be shown on a **number line**.

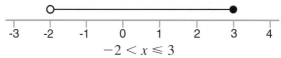

$$-2 < x \leqslant 3$$

The circle is:
   filled if the inequality is **included** (i.e. $\leqslant$ or $\geqslant$),
   not filled if the inequality is **not included** (i.e. $<$ or $>$).

- Solving inequalities.
  Solve means find the values of x which make the inequality true.
  The same rules for equations can be applied to inequalities, with one exception:
   When you **multiply** (or **divide**) both sides of an inequality by a negative number the inequality is reversed. For example,   if $-3x < 6$ then $x > -2$.

- Inequalities can be shown on a graph. Replace the inequality sign by '=' and draw the line.
  For $>$ and $<$ the line is **broken**. For $\geqslant$ and $\leqslant$ the line is **solid**.
  Test a point on each side of the line to see whether its coordinates satisfy the inequality.
  Shade the **unwanted** region.

Review Exercise 25

1 Solve these inequalities.
   (a) $3x \geqslant -15$ (b) $3x < x + 6$ (c) $5x - 4 \leqslant 2x + 14$ (d) $5 - 3x < 11$

2 Draw number lines to show each of these inequalities.
   (a) $x \leqslant -1$ (b) $4 < x \leqslant 9$ (c) $x < -2$ **and** $x > 5$

3 List the values of x, where x is an integer number, such that $-3 \leqslant x < 5$.   AQA

4 List the values of n, where n is an integer, such that $3 \leqslant n + 4 < 6$.   AQA

5 Solve these inequalities and show the solution on a number line.
   (a) $x - 3 < 1$ (b) $-2 < 2x \leqslant 4$ (c) $-1 \leqslant 3x + 2 < 5$ (d) $-1 < 2x + 5 < 3$

6 Find the integer values of n such that:
   (a) $-4 < 2n \leqslant 8$ (b) $-3 \leqslant 3n + 6 < 12$ (c) $-4 \leqslant 5n + 6 \leqslant 1$

7 (a) List all the possible values of x, where x is an integer, such that $-4 \leqslant x < 2$.
   (b) Solve $4x - 5 < -3$.   AQA

8 Solve the inequality $-1 \leqslant 3x + 2 < 5$.   AQA

9 Solve the inequality $3x - 7 > x - 3$.   AQA

10 Solve the inequality $5(a - 3) > 3a - 5$.   AQA

11 Solve the following inequalities.
   (a) $2 > x - 4$ (b) $2(x + 3) > 3(2 - x)$ AQA

12 (a) Solve the inequality $3x + 4 \leqslant 7$.

(b) (i) Solve the inequality $3x + 11 \geqslant 4 - 2x$.

(ii) If x is an integer what is the smallest possible value of x?

AQA

13 Copy the grids and shade the region where

(a) $x \geqslant 2$,

(b) $y \leqslant 4$,

(c) $x + y \leqslant 4$.

AQA

14 Match each of these inequalities to its **unshaded** region.

A $2x + y < 4$ **B** $2x - y > 4$ **C** $y > 4 - 2x$ **D** $x + 2y < 4$

AQA

15 This graph shows the lines $y = x + 4$ and $y = 9 - x$.
Two points, with whole number coordinates, satisfy the inequalities

$y < x + 4$,
$y < 9 - x$,
$y > 4$.

Write down the coordinates of these two points.

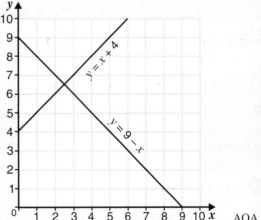

AQA

16 Draw and label axes for x from -3 to 8 and for y from 0 to 7.

(a) On your diagram draw and label the lines
$y = 3$ and $x + y = 5$.

(b) Show clearly on your diagram the single region that is satisfied by all of these inequalities.
$x \geqslant 0$, $y \geqslant 3$ and $x + y \leqslant 5$.
Label this region R.

17 Show, on a graph, the region where the following inequalities are true.

(a) $x \leqslant 2$, $y > -3$ and $y < 1$.   (b) $2x + 3y < 6$, $x > -1$ and $y \geqslant 0$.

(c) $3x + 4y \leqslant 12$, $3x + y > 3$ and $y > -1$.

CHAPTER 26

Quadratic and Other Equations

Brackets

You can multiply out brackets, either by using a diagram or by expanding.

○○○○○○○○○○○○○○
Removing brackets was first covered in Chapter 19.

EXAMPLES

1 Multiply out $2(x + 3)$.
Diagram method

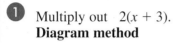

The areas of the two parts are $2x$ and 6.
The total area is $2x + 6$.
$2(x + 3) = 2x + 6$

Expanding
$2(x + 3) = 2 \times x + 2 \times 3$
$= 2x + 6$

2 Multiply out $x(x + 3)$.

The areas of the two parts are x^2 and $3x$.
$x(x + 3) = x^2 + 3x$

More brackets

This method can be extended to multiply out $(x + 2)(x + 3)$.

The areas of the four parts are:
x^2, $3x$, $2x$ and 6.

$(x + 2)(x + 3) = x^2 + 3x + 2x + 6$
Collect like terms and simplify   (i.e. $3x + 2x = 5x$)
$= x^2 + 5x + 6$

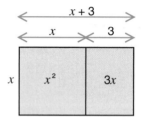

EXAMPLES

1 Expand $(2x + 3)(x + 4)$.

$(2x + 3)(x + 4) = 2x^2 + 8x + 3x + 12$
$= 2x^2 + 11x + 12$

2 Expand $(x + 3)(x - 5)$.

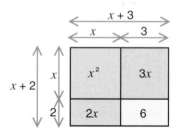

The diagram method works with negative numbers.
$(x + 3)(x - 5) = x^2 - 5x + 3x - 15$
$= x^2 - 2x - 15$

EXAMPLES

3 Expand $(2x - 5)^2$.

	$2x$	-5
$2x$	$4x^2$	$-10x$
-5	$-10x$	25

$$(2x - 5)^2 = (2x - 5)(2x - 5)$$
$$= 4x^2 - 10x - 10x + 25$$
$$= 4x^2 - 20x + 25$$

4 Expand $(x - 1)(2x + 3)$.
As you become more confident you may not need a diagram to expand the brackets.

1   $x \times 2x = 2x^2$
2   $x \times 3 = 3x$
3   $-1 \times 2x = -2x$
4   $-1 \times 3 = -3$

$$(x - 1)(2x + 3) = 2x^2 + 3x - 2x - 3$$
$$= 2x^2 + x - 3$$

Exercise 26.1

Questions 1 to 6. Use diagrams to multiply out the brackets.

1 $(x + 3)(x + 4)$

2 $(x + 1)(x + 5)$

3 $(x - 5)(x + 2)$

4 $(2x + 1)(x - 2)$

5 $(3x - 2)(x - 6)$

6 $(2x + 1)(3x + 2)$

Questions 7 to 24. Expand the following brackets. Only draw a diagram if necessary.

7 $(x + 8)(x - 2)$

8 $(x + 5)(x - 2)$

9 $(x - 1)(x + 3)$

10 $(x - 3)(x - 2)$

11 $(x - 4)(x - 1)$

12 $(x - 7)(x + 2)$

13 $(2x + 3)(x - 1)$

14 $(3x - 1)(x + 5)$

15 $(4x - 2)(3x + 5)$

16 $(x + 3)(x - 3)$

17 $(x + 5)(x - 5)$

18 $(x + 7)(x - 7)$

19 $(x - 10)(x + 10)$

20 $(x + 3)^2$

21 $(x + 5)^2$

22 $(x - 3)^2$

23 $(x - 7)^2$

24 $(2x - 3)^2$

Factorising

Factorising is the opposite operation to removing brackets.
For example, $x^2 + 4x = x(x + 4)$
and $3x^2 + 6 = 3(x^2 + 2)$.
You can check that you have factorised an expression correctly by multiplying out the brackets.

Factorising was first covered in Chapter 19.

Factorising quadratic expressions

$x^2 + 8x + 15$, $x^2 - 4$ and $x^2 + 7x$
are examples of **quadratic expressions**.
You will need to be able to factorise such
expressions in order to solve quadratic equations
in the next section of this chapter.

The general form of a quadratic expression is
$ax^2 + bx + c$, where a cannot be equal to 0.

Common factors

A **common factor** is a factor which will divide into each term of an expression.
For example, $x^2 + 7x$ has a common factor of x.
$$x^2 + 7x = x(x + 7)$$

Difference of two squares

In the expression $x^2 - 4$,
$x^2 = x \times x$ and $4 = 2^2 = 2 \times 2$.

$x^2 - 4 = (x + 2)(x - 2)$
This result is called the **difference of two squares**.
In general: $a^2 - b^2 = (a + b)(a - b)$

Checking your work
To check your work, expand the brackets and simplify, where necessary.
The result should be the same as the original expression.

EXAMPLES   Factorise the following.

1 $x^2 - 100$
$= x^2 - 10^2$
$= (x + 10)(x - 10)$

2 $25 - x^2$
$= 5^2 - x^2$
$= (5 + x)(5 - x)$

3 $s^2 - t^2$
$= (s + t)(s - t)$

Quadratics of the form $x^2 + bx + c$

The expression $x^2 + 8x + 15$ can be factorised.

From experience, we know that the answer is likely to be of the form:
$x^2 + 8x + 15 = (x + ?)(x + ?)$,
where the question marks represent numbers.
Replacing the question marks with letters, p and q, we get:
$x^2 + 8x + 15 = (x + p)(x + q)$

Multiply the brackets out, using either the diagram method or by expanding, and compare the results with the original expression.

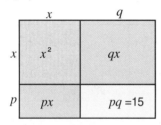

$px + qx = x(p + q) = 8x$
    and $p \times q = 15$

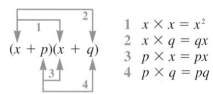

1   $x \times x = x^2$
2   $x \times q = qx$
3   $p \times x = px$
4   $p \times q = pq$

$(x + p)(x + q) = x^2 + qx + px + pq$
$= x^2 + (q + p)x + pq$
$= x^2 + 8x + 15$

Two numbers are required which: when multiplied give $+15$, **and** when added give $+8$.
    $+5$ and $+3$ satisfy **both** conditions.
    $x^2 + 8x + 15 = (x + 5)(x + 3)$

EXAMPLES

1   Factorise $x^2 + 6x + 9$.

    $x^2 + 6x + 9 = (x + 3)(x + 3)$
               $= (x + 3)^2$

    Because $3 \times 3 = 9$
    and $3 + 3 = 6$.

2   Factorise $x^2 - 8x + 12$.

    $x^2 - 8x + 12 = (x - 6)(x - 2)$

    Because $-6 \times -2 = 12$
    and $-6 + -2 = -8$.

3   Factorise $x^2 + 2x - 15$.

    $x^2 + 2x - 15 = (x + 5)(x - 3)$

    Because $+5 \times -3 = -15$
    and $+5 + -3 = +2$.

4   Factorise $x^2 - 2x - 8$.

    $x^2 - 2x - 8 = (x + 2)(x - 4)$

    Because $+2 \times -4 = -8$
    and $+2 + -4 = -2$.

1 Factorise these expressions.

(a) $x^2 + 5x$ (b) $x^2 - 7x$ (c) $y^2 - 6y$ (d) $2y^2 - 12y$

(e) $5t - t^2$ (f) $8y + y^2$ (g) $x^2 - 20x$ (h) $3x^2 - 60x$

2 Factorise.

(a) $x^2 - 9$ (b) $x^2 - 81$ (c) $y^2 - 25$ (d) $y^2 - 1$

(e) $x^2 - 64$ (f) $100 - x^2$ (g) $36 - x^2$ (h) $x^2 - a^2$

3 Copy and complete the following.

(a) $x^2 + 6x + 5 = (x + 5)(x + \ldots)$ (b) $x^2 + 9x + 14 = (x + 7)(x + \ldots)$

(c) $x^2 + 6x + 8 = (x + \ldots)(x + 4)$ (d) $x^2 + 9x + 18 = (x + \ldots)(x + 6)$

(e) $x^2 - 6x + 5 = (x - 5)(x - \ldots)$ (f) $x^2 - 7x + 10 = (x - 5)(x - \ldots)$

(g) $x^2 - 7x + 12 = (x - \ldots)(x - 3)$ (h) $x^2 + 3x - 4 = (x + 4)(x - \ldots)$

(i) $x^2 + 5x - 14 = (x + 7)(x - \ldots)$ (j) $x^2 - 4x - 5 = (x - 5)(x + \ldots)$

4 Factorise.

(a) $x^2 + 3x + 2$ (b) $x^2 + 8x + 7$ (c) $x^2 + 8x + 15$ (d) $x^2 + 8x + 12$

(e) $x^2 + 12x + 11$ (f) $x^2 + 9x + 20$ (g) $x^2 + 10x + 24$ (h) $x^2 + 13x + 36$

5 Factorise.

(a) $x^2 - 6x + 9$ (b) $x^2 - 6x + 8$ (c) $x^2 - 11x + 10$ (d) $x^2 - 16x + 15$

(e) $x^2 - 8x + 15$ (f) $x^2 - 10x + 16$ (g) $x^2 - 12x + 20$ (h) $x^2 - 11x + 24$

6 Factorise.

(a) $x^2 - x - 6$ (b) $x^2 - 5x - 6$ (c) $x^2 + 2x - 24$ (d) $x^2 + 5x - 24$

(e) $x^2 - 2x - 15$ (f) $x^2 + 3x - 18$ (g) $x^2 - 3x - 40$ (h) $x^2 - 4x - 12$

7 Factorise.

(a) $x^2 - 4x + 4$ (b) $x^2 + 11x + 30$ (c) $x^2 + 2x - 8$ (d) $x^2 - 4x - 21$

(e) $x^2 + x - 20$ (f) $x^2 + 7x + 12$ (g) $x^2 + 8x + 16$ (h) $x^2 - 2x + 1$

(i) $x^2 - 49$ (j) $t^2 + 12t$ (k) $x^2 - 9x + 14$ (l) $x^2 - 7x + 6$

(m) $x^2 + 11x + 18$ (n) $x^2 + 11x + 24$ (o) $x^2 + 19x + 18$ (p) $x^2 - y^2$

(q) $x^2 + x - 6$ (r) $y^2 + 4y$ (s) $y^2 - 10y + 25$ (t) $x^2 - 12x + 36$

Further factorising

When factorising, work logically.   Does the expression have a common factor?

Is the expression a difference of two squares?

Will the expression factorise into two brackets?

EXAMPLES

1 Factorise $2x^2 - 14x$.

Common factor $2x$.

$2x^2 - 14x = 2x(x - 7)$

2 Factorise $25 - 4y^2$.

Difference of two squares.

$25 - 4y^2 = 5^2 - (2y)^2$

$\qquad\quad = (5 + 2y)(5 - 2y)$

3 Factorise $2x^2 - 18$.

Common factor 2.

$2x^2 - 18 = 2(x^2 - 9)$

Difference of two squares.

$\qquad\quad = 2(x + 3)(x - 3)$

4 Factorise $x^2 - 6x + 8$.

$x^2 - 6x + 8 = (x - 2)(x - 4)$

Because $-2 \times -4 = 8$

and $\qquad -2 + -4 = -6$.

Factorise.

1 $3x + 12y$ | **2** $t^2 - 16$ | **3** $x^2 + 4x + 3$ | **4** $y^2 - y$

5 $2d^2 - 6$ | **6** $p^2 - q^2$ | **7** $a^2 - 2a$ | **8** $x^2 - 2x + 1$

9 $2y^2 - 8y$ | **10** $a^2 - 6a + 9$ | **11** $3m^2 - 12$ | **12** $v^2 - v - 6$

13 $ax^2 - ay^2$ | **14** $-8 - 2x$ | **15** $4 - 4k + k^2$ | **16** $18 - 2x^2$

17 $50 - 2x^2$ | **18** $12x^2 - 27y^2$ | **19** $6a^2 - 3a$ | **20** $x^2 - 15x + 56$

Algebraic fractions

Algebraic fractions have a numerator and a denominator (just as an ordinary fraction) but at least one of them is an expression involving an unknown.

e.g $\dfrac{1}{x}$ $\dfrac{x}{2}$ $\dfrac{2}{x - 5}$ $\dfrac{x + 1}{x - 6}$ $\dfrac{3}{x + 7}$ $\dfrac{x^2 + 2x + 1}{x^2 - 1}$

Algebraic fractions can be simplified, added, subtracted, multiplied, divided and used in equations in the same way as numerical fractions.

Simplifying algebraic fractions

Fractions can be simplified if the numerator and the denominator have a common factor.
In its **simplest form**, the numerator and denominator of an algebraic fraction have no common factor other than 1.

The numerator and denominator of $\frac{15}{25}$ have a highest common factor of 5.

$$\frac{15}{25} = \frac{15 \div 5}{25 \div 5} = \frac{3}{5}$$

3 and 5 have no common factors, other than 1.

$\frac{15}{25} = \frac{3}{5}$ in its simplest form.

Algebraic fractions work in a similar way.

To write an algebraic fraction in its simplest form:
- factorise the numerator and denominator of the fraction,
- divide the numerator and denominator by their highest common factor.

This is sometimes called **cancelling** a fraction.

EXAMPLES

Write the following in their simplest form.

1 $\dfrac{3x - 6}{3}$

$= \dfrac{3(x - 2)}{3}$

$= x - 2$

2 $\dfrac{3x + 9}{4x + 12}$

$= \dfrac{3(x + 3)}{4(x + 3)}$

$= \dfrac{3}{4}$

3 $\dfrac{9 - 3y}{y - 3}$

$= \dfrac{3(3 - y)}{y - 3}$

$= \dfrac{-3(y - 3)}{(y - 3)} = -3$

Exercise **26.4**

1 Simplify these algebraic fractions.

(a) $\dfrac{4d + 6}{2}$

(b) $\dfrac{9x + 6}{3}$

(c) $\dfrac{8a + 10b}{2}$

(d) $\dfrac{15m - 10n}{5}$

(e) $\dfrac{8x - 4y}{2}$

(f) $\dfrac{ax + bx}{x}$

(g) $\dfrac{x^2 - x}{x}$

(h) $\dfrac{2x^2 - 4}{2}$

(i) $\dfrac{2x}{6x - 4}$

(j) $\dfrac{3x}{6x^2 - 3}$

(k) $\dfrac{3x}{6x^2 - 3x}$

(l) $\dfrac{2x - 1}{6x^2 - 3x}$

(m) $\dfrac{3m - 6}{2m - 4}$

(n) $\dfrac{m^2 + 3m}{3m + 9}$

(o) $\dfrac{x^2 - 3x}{x^2 + 2x}$

(p) $\dfrac{2x^2 + 4x}{x + 2}$

(q) $\dfrac{8x - 4}{4x^2 - 2x}$

(r) $\dfrac{5x - 10}{6 - 3x}$

2 Match the algebraic fractions with the values **A** to **E**.

(a) $\dfrac{3x + 6}{4x + 8}$

(b) $\dfrac{5x - 15}{2x - 6}$

(c) $\dfrac{8 - 4y}{6 - 3y}$

(d) $\dfrac{8x + 10}{4x + 5}$

(e) $\dfrac{-2x - 4}{-4x - 8}$

A 2   **B** $\frac{4}{3}$ **C** $2\frac{1}{2}$ **D** $\frac{1}{2}$ **E** $\frac{3}{4}$

3 Simplify these algebraic fractions.

(a) $\dfrac{x^2 + 3x}{x^2 + 4x + 3}$

(b) $\dfrac{x^2 + 3x + 2}{x^2 + 4x + 3}$

(c) $\dfrac{x^2 - 2x}{x^2 + x - 6}$

(d) $\dfrac{x^2 - x - 20}{x^2 + 7x + 12}$

(e) $\dfrac{x^2 - 4x + 4}{x^2 - 5x + 6}$

(f) $\dfrac{x^2 - 5x}{x^2 + 4x}$

(g) $\dfrac{x^2 - 1}{x + 1}$

(h) $\dfrac{x - 2}{x^2 - 4}$

(i) $\dfrac{x^2 - 2x - 3}{2x - 6}$

Solving quadratic equations

Activity

> I am thinking of two numbers.
> I multiply them together.
> The answer is zero.

Write down 2 numbers which could be Jim's numbers.
Now write down **four** more pairs.
What can you say about Jim's numbers?

You should have discovered that at least one of Jim's numbers must be **zero**.
We can use this fact to solve **quadratic equations**.

1 Find x if:

(a) $x(x - 2) = 0$
Either $x = 0$ or $x - 2 = 0$
Because one of them must be zero.
$x = 0$ or $x = 2$

(b) $(x - 3)(x + 2) = 0$
$x - 3 = 0$ or $x + 2 = 0$
Because one of them must be zero.
$x = 3$ or $x = -2$

2 Factorise the quadratic expression and so solve the equation.

(a) $x^2 - 5x + 6 = 0$
$(x - 2)(x - 3) = 0$
$x = 2$ or $x = 3$

Check: Does $(2)^2 - 5 \times (2) + 6 = 0$
and $(3)^2 - 5 \times (3) + 6 = 0$?

(b) $x^2 - 9 = 0$
$(x - 3)(x + 3) = 0$
$x = 3$ or $x = -3$

(c) $y^2 + 7y = 0$
$y(y + 7) = 0$
$y = 0$ or $y + 7 = 0$
$y = 0$ or $y = -7$

(d) $a^2 + 4a - 5 = 0$
$(a - 1)(a + 5) = 0$
$a = 1$ or $a = -5$

Exercise 26.5

1 Solve these equations.
(a) $(x - 2)(x - 3) = 0$
(b) $(x + 4)(x + 6) = 0$
(c) $(x - 3)(x + 1) = 0$
(d) $(x - 5)(x + 2) = 0$
(e) $x(x - 4) = 0$
(f) $3x(x + 2) = 0$

2 Solve.
(a) $x^2 - 3x + 2 = 0$
(b) $y^2 + 7y + 12 = 0$
(c) $m^2 - 2m - 8 = 0$
(d) $a^2 + a - 12 = 0$
(e) $n^2 - 5n - 36 = 0$
(f) $z^2 - 9z + 18 = 0$
(g) $k^2 + 8k + 15 = 0$
(h) $c^2 + 15c + 56 = 0$
(i) $b^2 + b - 20 = 0$
(j) $v^2 - 7v - 60 = 0$
(k) $w^2 + 8w - 48 = 0$
(l) $p^2 - p - 72 = 0$

3 Solve.
(a) $x^2 - 5x = 0$
(b) $y^2 + y = 0$
(c) $p^2 + 3p = 0$
(d) $4a - a^2 = 0$
(e) $t^2 - 6t = 0$
(f) $g^2 - 4g = 0$

4 Solve.
(a) $x^2 - 4 = 0$
(b) $y^2 - 144 = 0$
(c) $9 - a^2 = 0$
(d) $d^2 - 16 = 0$
(e) $x^2 - 100 = 0$
(f) $36 - x^2 = 0$
(g) $x^2 - 49 = 0$
(h) $2.25 - x^2 = 0$

5 Rearrange these equations and then solve them.
(a) $y^2 = 4y + 5$
(b) $x^2 = x$
(c) $x^2 = 8x - 16$
(d) $x^2 = 2x + 15$
(e) $n^2 - 10n = 24$
(f) $7 = 8m - m^2$
(g) $a(a - 5) = 24$
(h) $x^2 - 5x + 6 = 3 - x$

6 This rectangle has an area of 21 cm².
(a) Form an equation in x.
(b) By solving your equation, find the value of x.

x cm

$(x - 4)$ cm

7 The product of x and $(x - 2)$ is 63.
By forming an equation, find the value of x.

8 The sum of two numbers is 15.
Their product is 56.
By forming an equation, find the two numbers.

Solving quadratic equations graphically

The graph of a **quadratic function** is always a smooth curve and is called a **parabola**. The general equation of a quadratic function is $y = ax^2 + bx + c$, where a cannot be equal to zero.

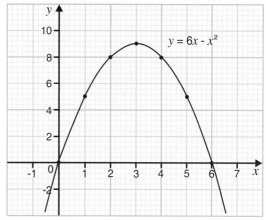

The graph of $y = x^2 - 4$ has a **minimum value** at the point $(0, -4)$.

The graph of $y = 6x - x^2$ has a **maximum value** at the point $(3, 9)$.

The values of x where the graphs of quadratic functions cross (or touch) the x axis give the **solutions to quadratic equations**.

At the point where the graph $y = x^2 - 4$ crosses the x axis the value of $y = 0$.
$x^2 - 4 = 0$
The solutions of this quadratic equation can be read from the graph $x = -2$ and $x = 2$.

Remember:
● Your graphs should never be flat or pointed.
● Quadratic graphs are always symmetrical.
● Join plotted points using smooth curves and not a series of straight lines.

Find the solutions of the equation $6x - x^2 = 0$ from the graph of $y = 6x - x^2$. Check the graphical solutions using the factorising method.

EXAMPLE

Draw the graph of
$y = x^2 + 3x - 2$ for values of x from -5 to 2.
Use the graph to find the solutions of the equation
$x^2 + 3x - 2 = 0$.

First make a table of values for $y = x^2 + 3x - 2$.

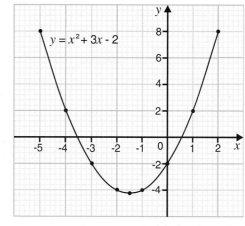

x	-5	-4	-3	-2	-1	0	1	2
y	8	2	-2	-4	-4	-2	2	8

The graph has a **minimum value** between
$x = -2$ and $x = -1$.
To find this value substitute $x = -1.5$ into the equation.
$y = (-1.5 \times -1.5) + (3 \times -1.5) - 2$
$= 2.25 - 4.5 - 2 = -4.25$
Plot the point $(-1.5, -4.25)$.

$x^2 + 3x - 2 = 0$
To solve this equation, read the values of x where the graph of $y = x^2 + 3x - 2$ crosses the x axis.
$x = -3.6$ and $x = 0.6$, correct to 1 d.p.

Cubic graphs

The general form of a **cubic function** is $y = ax^3 + bx^2 + cx + d$, where a cannot be equal to zero. As for quadratic graphs, the solutions of cubic equations can be found in a similar way.

Quadratic and Other Equations

1 (a) Copy and complete this table of values for $y = x^2$.

x	-3	-2	-1	0	1	2	3
y	9		1			4	

(b) Draw the graph of $y = x^2$.
    Label the x axis from -3 to 3 and the y axis from 0 to 10.
(c) Use your graph to find the value of y when $x = 1.5$.

2 (a) Copy and complete this table of values for $y = x^2 - 2$.

x	-3	-2	-1	0	1	2	3
y		2			-1		7

(b) Draw the graph of $y = x^2 - 2$.
    Label the x axis from -3 to 3 and the y axis from -3 to 8.
(c) Use your graph to find the value of y when $x = -1.5$.
(d) Write down the coordinates of the points where the graph of $y = x^2 - 2$
    crosses the x axis.

3 (a) Draw the graph of $y = x^2 - 4$ for values of x from -3 to 3.
(b) Use your graph to find the value of y when $x = -1.5$.
(c) Use your graph to find the values of x when $y = 0$.

4 Draw the graphs of $y = x^2 + 2$ and $y = x^2 - 2$ on the same diagram.
Draw the x axis from -2 to 2 and the y axis from -2 to 6.
What do you notice about the two graphs?

5 (a) Draw the graph of $y = x^2 + 1$ for values of x from -2 to 4.
(b) Use your graph to find the value of y when $x = 2.5$.
(c) Use your graph to find the values of x when $y = 4$.

6 (a) Draw the graph of $y = 2x^2$ for values of x from -2 to 2.
(b) Use your graph to solve the equation $2x^2 = 5$.

7 (a) Copy and complete this table of values for $y = x^2 + x$.

x	-3	-2	-1	0	1	2
y						

(b) Draw axes marked from -3 to 2 for x and from -2 to 6 for y.
    Draw the graph of $y = x^2 + x$ on your axes.
(c) Use your graph to solve the equation $x^2 + x = 0$.
(d) Find the coordinates of the point at which the graph has a minimum value.

8 (a) Copy and complete this table of values for $y = x^2 - x - 1$.

x	-2	-1	0	1	2	3
y						

(b) Draw axes marked from -2 to 3 for x and from -2 to 6 for y.
    Draw the graph of $y = x^2 - x - 1$ on your axes.
(c) Use your graph to solve the equation $x^2 - x - 1 = 0$.

9 (a) Copy and complete this table of values for $y = 15 - 2x^2$.

x	-3	-2	-1	0	1	2	3
y							

(b) Draw axes marked from -3 to 3 for x and from -4 to 16 for y.
Draw the graph of $y = 15 - 2x^2$ on your axes.

(c) Use your graph to solve the equation $15 - 2x^2 = 0$.

10 (a) Draw the graph of $y = x^2 + 2x - 3$ for values of x from -5 to 3.

(b) Use your graph to solve the equation $x^2 + 2x - 3 = 0$.

11 (a) Draw the graph of $y = 10 - x^2$ for values of x from -4 to 4.

(b) Use your graph to solve the equation $10 - x^2 = 0$.

(c) Find the coordinates of the point at which the graph has a maximum value.

12 Draw suitable graphs to solve the following equations.

(a) $x^2 - 8 = 0$ (b) $5 - x^2 = 0$ (c) $3x^2 = 0$ (d) $12 - 2x^2 = 0$

13 (a) Draw the graph of $y = x^3 - 3$ for values of x from -3 to 3.

(b) Draw the graph of $y = x^3 + x$ for values of x from -3 to 3.

(c) Draw the graph of $y = \frac{1}{x}$ for values of x from -4 to 4.

14 (a) Copy and complete this table of values for $y = x^3 + x^2 - 6x$.

x	-4	-3	-2	-1	0	1	2	3
y								

(b) Draw axes marked from -4 to 3 for x and from -25 to 20 for y.
Draw the graph of $y = x^3 + x^2 - 6x$ on your axes.

(c) Use your graph to solve the equation $x^3 + x^2 - 6x = 0$.

15 (a) Draw the graph of $y = x^3 - 5x + 6$ for values of x from -3 to 3.

(b) Use your graph to solve the equation $x^3 - 5x + 6 = 0$.

Trial and improvement

Some equations cannot be solved directly (as quadratics can be).
Numerical solutions can be found by making a guess and improving the accuracy of the guess by
trial and improvement.
This can be a time consuming method of solving equations and is
often used only as a last resort for solving equations which cannot
be easily solved by algebraic or graphical methods.

A solution to the equation $x^3 - 4x = 7$ lies between 2 and 3.
Find this solution to 1 decimal place.

First guess: $x = 2.5$ $2.5^3 - 4(2.5) = 5.625$ Too small
Second guess: $x = 2.6$ $2.6^3 - 4(2.6) = 7.176$ Too big

The solution lies between 2.5 and 2.6, but 2.6 gives an answer closer to 7.
The answer is probably 2.6, correct to 1 d.p.
To be certain, try $x = 2.55$. $2.55^3 - 4(2.55) = 6.381375$ Too small

The solution lies between 2.55 and 2.6.
2.6 is the solution, correct to 1 d.p.

Because the solution lies
between 2 and 3, notice that:
when $x = 2$
$2^3 - 4(2) = 0$
Less than 7

when $x = 3$
$3^3 - 4(3) = 15$
Greater than 7

We are trying to find a value
for x which produces the
answer 7.

You will need a calculator for this exercise.

1 Use trial and improvement to solve $x^3 = 54$, correct to one decimal place.
The working can be shown in a table.

x	x^3	
3	27	Too small
4	64	Too big
3.5		

2 Use trial and improvement to solve these equations.
(a) $w^3 = 72$ (b) $4x^3 = 51$

3 A solution to the equation $x^3 + 2x = 40$ lies between 3 and 4.
Find this solution to 1 decimal place.

x	$x^3 + 2x$	
3	33	Too small
3.5	49.875	Too big

4 A solution to the equation $x^3 + 5x = 880$ lies between 9 and 10.
Use trial and improvement to find this solution to 1 decimal place. Show your trials.

5 Show that a solution to $x^3 - 5x^2 = 47$ lies between 6 and 7.
Use trial and improvement to find this solution, showing your trials,
(a) to 1 decimal place,   (b) to 2 decimal places.

6 This cuboid has dimensions: x, $x + 2$ and $2x$.
(a) Write down an expression, in terms of x,
for the volume of the cuboid.
(b) The volume of the cuboid is $400\,\text{cm}^3$.
Form an equation and use trial and improvement
to find x, correct to 1 d.p.

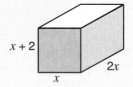

7 A solution to $x^4 + 5x - 20 = 0$ lies between 1 and 2.
Use trial and improvement to find this solution correct to 2 decimal places. Show your trials.

What you need to know

● Brackets, such as $(x + 2)(x + 5)$ can be multiplied out using:
the **diagram method**, or by **expanding**.

● **Factorising** is the opposite operation to removing brackets.

● A **common factor** is a factor which divides into two, or more,
numbers (or terms).
For example: $8ab + 12bc = 4b(2a + 3c)$
where $4b$ is a common factor of $8ab$ and $12bc$.

● **Difference of two squares** $a^2 - b^2 = (a - b)(a + b)$

● **Algebraic fractions** have a numerator and a denominator (just as an ordinary fraction) but at
least one of them is an expression involving an unknown.

● To write an algebraic fraction in its **simplest form**:
factorise the numerator and denominator of the fraction,
divide the numerator and denominator by their highest common factor.
This is sometimes called **cancelling** a fraction.

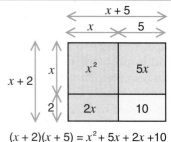

$(x + 2)(x + 5) = x^2 + 5x + 2x + 10$
$= x^2 + 7x + 10$

- **Quadratic equations** can be solved: by factorising or graphically.
- The general equation for a **quadratic function** is
  $y = ax^2 + bx + c$, where a cannot be zero.
  The graph of a quadratic function is symmetrical
  and has a **maximum** or **minimum** value.

- The general form of a **cubic function** is $y = ax^3 + bx^2 + cx + d$, where a cannot be zero.
  Cubic equations can be solved graphically or by trial and improvement.

- **Trial and improvement** is a method used to solve equations. The accuracy of the value of the
  unknown letter is improved until the required degree of accuracy is obtained.

maximum value / minimum value

Review Exercise 26

1 Expand and simplify $(x + 5)(x - 2)$.

    AQA

2 (a) Factorise $x^2 - 3x - 10$.
   (b) Hence, or otherwise, solve the
      equation $x^2 - 3x - 10 = 0$.   AQA

3 Multiply out the brackets and simplify
your answer: $(2x - 3)(x + 4)$ AQA

4 Solve the equations:
  (a) $2x + 3 = 15 - x$,
  (b) $(x + 3)(x - 4) = 0$.   AQA

5 Solve $x^2 + 8x + 12 = 0$.   AQA

6 (a) Factorise $x^2 - 2x - 8$.
  (b) Solve $a^2 + 4a = 0$.

7 These two rectangles have the same area.

Not drawn accurately

  (a) Form an equation in x and show
     that it can be simplified to
     $x^2 + x - 2 = 0$.
  (b) Solve the equation $x^2 + x - 2 = 0$
     to find the length of BC.   AQA

8 Draw the graph of $y = x^2 - 3$
for values of x from 0 to 4.
Draw axes marked from 0 to 4 for x and
from -4 to 14 for y.   AQA

9 (a) Draw the graph of $y = 5 - x$
     for values of x from -2 to 5.
  (b) Copy and complete the table of
     values for $y = 2x^2$.

x	-2	-1	0	1	2
y				2	

  (c) On the same grid, draw the graph of
     $y = 2x^2$ for $-2 \leq x \leq 2$.
  (d) Write down the coordinates of the
     points where your graphs cross.

    AQA

10 (a) Copy and complete the table of
     values for $y = x^2 - 2x - 2$.

x	-2	-1	0	1	2	3	4
y	6		-2			1	

  (b) Draw the graph of $y = x^2 - 2x - 2$.
     Draw axes marked from -2 to 4
     for x and from -4 to 6 for y.
  (c) Use your graph to solve the
     equation $x^2 - 2x - 2 = 0$.   AQA

11 Use a trial and improvement method to
solve the equation $x^3 - x = 300$.
Give your answer to one decimal place.
Show all your trials in a table, as shown.

Trial x	$x^3 - x$	Too high/too low
8	504	Too high

    AQA

12 The equation $x^3 + x = 20$
has a solution between 2 and 3.
Use a trial and improvement method
to find the solution correct to
two decimal places.
Show all your working.

26

Quadratic and Other Equations

Section Review - Algebra ●●●●●●●●●●●●●

1 (a) On graph paper, plot the points $A(1, 3)$ and $B(-3, -1)$.
  (b) M is the midpoint of AB. What are the coordinates of M?

2 A building supplier hires out cement mixers. He calculates the hire charge using this formula.

> **Five pounds per day plus a fixed charge of seven pounds.**

  (a) How much would it cost to hire the cement mixer for 3 days?
  (b) A builder paid £52 altogether to hire a cement mixer.
     For how many days did he hire it?

AQA

3 A rule is used to produce lists of numbers. The rule is shown below.

> **Add 3 to the last number and then double the result.**

  (a) A list starts 1, 8, 22, …. What is the next number in the list?
  (b) A different list starts with the number -1. What is the second number in the list?
  (c) The second number in another list is 16. What is the first number in this list?

AQA

4 Simplify $3m + 4m + 5m$.

5 (a) Pens cost x pence each. Write an expression for the cost of 3 pens.
  (b) A ruler costs 7 pence more than a pen. Write an expression for the cost of a ruler.

6 Solve the equations. (a) $y + 3 = 11$ (b) $4a = 32$

7 If $a = 3$, $b = 4$ and $c = \frac{1}{2}$, work out the value of: (a) $2a + 3b$,   (b) $a - b + 3c$.

AQA

8 (a) A sequence begins: 8, 5, 2, -1, …
     What is the next term in the sequence?
  (b) A different sequence begins: 0, 6, 24, …
     The nth term is $n(n^2 - 1)$.
     What is the 5th term of the sequence?

AQA

9 If $x = -5$ and $y = 4$, find the value of: (a) $2x - 3y$,   (b) $\dfrac{y(x + 8)}{6}$.

AQA

10 Kim thinks of a number. She doubles it and adds 3. The answer is 16.
What is her number?

11 (a) Simplify $a + 3 - 2a$.
  (b) Solve the equation $5t - 3 = 17$.
  (c) Find the value of $3x + y^3$ when $x = -2$ and $y = 2$.

AQA

12 n represents any whole number.
  (a) What type of whole number is $2n$?
  (b) Which of the statements below describes the number $3n + 1$? Explain your answer.
     always even   always odd   could be even or odd

AQA

13 There is a rule in the box below.

> To change temperatures from Centigrade to Fahrenheit,
> "Double the Centigrade and add 30"

  (a) Use this rule to change 20° Centigrade to Fahrenheit.
  (b) C is the temperature in °Centigrade. F is the temperature in °Fahrenheit.
     Write the rule as an equation using C and F.
  (c) Use your equation to calculate C when $F = 100$.

AQA

14 (a) On the same diagram, draw and label the lines $y = x$ and $y = 6 - x$.
   (b) What are the coordinates of the point where the two lines cross?

15 Solve the equations. (a) $5x - 3 = 7$ (b) $5x + 5 = 7 + x$ AQA

16 Rowena and Hugh are following these instructions:

| Choose any starting number. | → | Halve it. | → | Halve the result. | → | Final answer. |

   (a) Rowena chooses 32.   What final answer will she get?
   (b) Hugh chooses 30.   What final answer will he get?
   (c) Rowena's final answer is a whole number, but Hugh's is not.
      Find two more numbers that will give final answers which are whole numbers.
   (d) What do you notice about the starting numbers that give whole number answers?   AQA

17 Match the equations to the graphs.

   A: $x = 3$ **B:** $y = 3$ **C:** $y = x + 3$ **D:** $y + x = 3$

P

Q

R

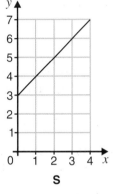

S

18 The graph shows the journey made by a cyclist from Guildford to Brighton.

   (a) (i)   How far is Brighton from Guildford?
      (ii) Describe what happened between 1200 and 1300 hours.
      (iii) Find the average speed of the cyclist between 1000 and 1200.
   (b) The cyclist later cycled back to Guildford at an average speed of 16 miles per hour.
      How long did it take the cyclist to get back to Guildford?

19 (a) Solve the equation $5x - 7 = 3x + 5$.
   (b) Expand and simplify $2x + 3(x - 4)$.   AQA

20 (a) Write, as simply as possible, an expression
      for the total length of these rods.
   (b) The total length of the rods is 23 cm.
      By forming an equation find the value of a.

2a cm   3 cm   3a cm

21 (a) Buns cost x pence each.
      How much will 2 buns cost?
   (b) A doughnut costs 5 pence more than a bun.
      How much will 3 doughnuts cost?
   (c) The cost of buying 2 buns and 3 doughnuts is 95 pence.
      By forming an equation find the cost of a bun.

22 Factorise (a) $4a + 2b$,   (b) $3t - t^2$.

23 (a) Write down the next term in the sequence: 2, 6, 10, 14, ...
    (b) Write an expression, in terms of n, for the nth term of the sequence.

24 (a) On the same diagram, draw and label the lines
        $y = x$ and $x + y = 3$ for values of x from 0 to 3.
    (b) Shade the region that is satisfied by all of the inequalities
        $y \geqslant x$, $x + y \leqslant 3$ and $x \geqslant 0$.

25 (a) Solve the equation $3(x + 2) = 4 - x$.
    (b) Factorise $m^2 - 7m$.
    (c) List the values of n, where n is an integer, such that $1 \leqslant n - 5 < 4$.
    (d) Solve the simultaneous equations: $3x + 4y = \quad 0$
                                              $4x - 2y = -11$.

AQA

26 The diagram shows a sketch of the line $2y + x = 10$.
    (a) Find the coordinates of points G and H.

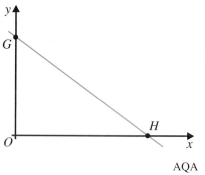

Copy the diagram.
    (b) (i) On your diagram, sketch the graph of $y = 2x$.
        (ii) Solve the simultaneous equations:
              $2y + x = 10$ and $y = 2x$.

    (c) The equation of a straight line is $y = ax + b$.
        Rearrange the equation to give x
        in terms of y, a and b.

AQA

27 (a) Copy and complete the table for the equation $y = x^2 - 2x + 2$.

x	-1	0	1	2	3
y					

    (b) Draw the graph of $y = x^2 - 2x + 2$ for $-1 \leqslant x \leqslant 3$.
    (c) Use your graph to find the values of x when $y = 3$.

AQA

28 The graph shows the cost of printing wedding invitation cards.

    (a) Find the equation of the line in the form $y = mx + c$.
    (b) For her wedding Charlotte needs 100 cards to be printed.
        How much will they cost?

AQA

29 (a) Expand and simplify. (i) $3(x + 2) + 5(2x - 1)$ (ii) $(x + 4)(x - 2)$
(b) (i) Factorise the expression $x^2 + 8x + 15$.
(ii) Hence solve the equation $x^2 + 8x + 15 = 0$.

30 Draw and label axes for x from 0 to 20 and for y from 0 to 30.
On your diagram draw the appropriate boundary lines and carefully shade the area that contains all the points satisfying the inequalities: $x > 5$, $y > 8$ and $y < 30 - 2x$.

31 Simplify. (a) $2y^3 \times 3y^2$ (b) $6y^6 \div 3y^2$ (c) $(3y^2)^3$

32 (a) Solve the equation $\frac{1}{3}x = 2$.
(b) Solve the simultaneous equations $x + 3y = 5$ and $x - y = 3$.
(c) List the values of n, where n is an integer, such that $1 \le 2n - 3 < 5$.
(d) Solve the equation $x^2 - 5x + 6 = 0$.

33 $V = \frac{4}{3}\pi r^3$.
(a) Rearrange the formula to give r in terms of V.
(b) Calculate the value of r when $V = 905$.

34 Using trial and improvement copy and continue the table to find a solution to the equation $x^3 + x = 20$.

x	$x^3 + x$	Comment
2	10	Too low

Give your answer correct to 1 decimal place.

35 (a) Expand and simplify $(2x + 5)(3x - 4)$
(b) Factorise completely $5x^2y + 15xy^3$

36 The diagram shows a square $ABCD$ and a rectangle $RBPQ$.
$CP = 2\,\text{cm}$ and $RA = 3\,\text{cm}$.
The length of the side of square $ABCD$ is $x\,\text{cm}$.
The rectangle $RBPQ$ has an area of $42\,\text{cm}^2$.

(a) Form an equation, in terms of x, for the area of the rectangle.
Show that it can be written in the form $x^2 + 5x - 36 = 0$.
(b) Solve $x^2 + 5x - 36 = 0$, and hence calculate the area of the square $ABCD$.

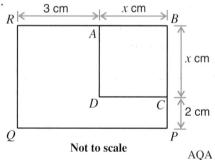

Not to scale

37 Solve the equations (a) $y^2 + 5y = 0$ (b) $m^2 - 7m + 12 = 0$

38 The sum of two numbers is 15.
The product of the numbers is 54.
If one of the numbers is x, show that $x^2 - 15x + 54 = 0$.

39 (a) Simplify $\dfrac{a^2 + 2a}{5a + 10}$
(b) Factorise $2x^2 - 18$

40 A rectangle has length $(x + 2)\,\text{cm}$ and width $(x + 1)\,\text{cm}$.
The rectangle has an area of $6\,\text{cm}^2$.
Form an equation and show that it can be simplified to $x^2 + 3x - 4 = 0$.

CHAPTER 27

Angles

The diagram shows a stopwatch with a second hand.
Every minute the second hand will make one complete turn.
An **angle** is a measure of turn.
Angles are measured in **degrees**.
In one minute the second hand will turn through an angle of 360°.

Types and names of angles

Each of these diagrams shows a quarter-turn.

A quarter-turn is called a **right angle**.
A right angle is 90°.

An angle less than 90° is called an **acute** angle.
An angle between 90° and 180° is called an **obtuse** angle.
An angle greater than 180° is called a **reflex** angle.

Exercise **27.1**

1 Through what angle will a second hand turn in:
  (a) half a minute,   (b) quarter of a minute,
  (c) three-quarters of a minute,   (d) 15 seconds,
  (e) 20 seconds,   (f) 1 second,
  (g) 7 seconds,   (h) 2 minutes,
  (i) $1\frac{1}{2}$ minutes,   (j) 135 seconds?

2 This clock shows 4.30.
  (a) What size is the acute angle between the hands of the clock?
  (b) What is the size of the reflex angle between the hands?

3 Through what angle will the hour hand of the clock turn between:
  (a) 10.00 am and 11.30 am,
  (b) 10.00 am and 10.00 pm?

4 Say whether each of the marked angles is acute, obtuse, reflex or a right angle.

Measuring angles

To measure an angle accurately we need to use a **protractor**.

Some protractors have two scales. Look at the type of angle (acute/obtuse) you are measuring and use the correct scale.

To measure an angle, the protractor is placed so that its centre point is on the corner (vertex) of the angle, with the base along one of the arms of the angle as shown.

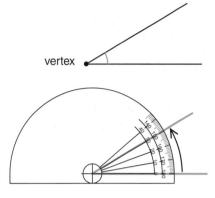

This angle measures 30°.

How can you measure the size of a reflex angle?

Drawing angles

Draw an angle of 74°.

Draw a line.
Mark the vertex of the angle.

Position the protractor as if you were measuring an angle.
Mark a dot at 74°.

Draw a line from the vertex through the dot.

Exercise **27.2**

1 Use a protractor to measure these angles.

(a)

(b)

(c)

2 Draw these angles accurately.

(a) 20° (b) 85° (c) 165° (d) 64° (e) 128°

3 Use a protractor to measure these angles.

(a)

(b)

4 Draw these angles accurately.

(a) 190°   (b) 280°   (c) 205°   (d) 324°

Angle properties

Complementary angles

When two angles add up to 90°, the angles are called **complementary**.

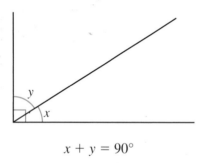

$$x + y = 90°$$

x and y are complementary angles.

Supplementary angles

Angles which can be placed together on a straight line add up to 180°.
When two angles add up to 180°, the angles are called **supplementary**.

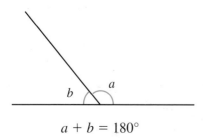

$$a + b = 180°$$

a and b are supplementary angles.

Angles at a point

When angles meet at a point, the sum of all the angles is 360°.

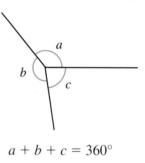

$$a + b + c = 360°$$

Vertically opposite angles

When two lines cross each other the angles between the lines make two pairs of equal angles.

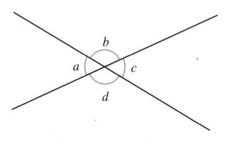

$$a = c \text{ and } b = d$$

a and c are vertically opposite angles.
b and d are vertically opposite angles.

318

Angles · · · Angles · · · Angles · · ·

EXAMPLES

1 Without measuring, work out the size of the angle marked a.

Angles at a point add up to 360°.

$a + 95° + 120° = 360°$
$\qquad a = 360° - 95° - 120°$
$\qquad a = 145°$

2 Calculate the size of the angles marked with letters.

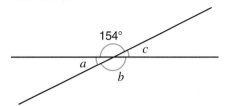

$b = 154°$ (vertically opposite angles)

$a + 154° = 180°$ (supplementary angles)
$\qquad a = 180° - 154°$
$\qquad a = 26°$

$c = 26°$

$a = 26°, b = 154°, c = 26°$

Exercise **27.3**

1 Without measuring, work out the size of the angles marked with letters.

(a)

(b)

(c)

(d)

(e)

(f)

(g)

(h)

(i)

(j)

(k)

2 These diagrams are not drawn accurately.
Without measuring, work out the value of x in each diagram.

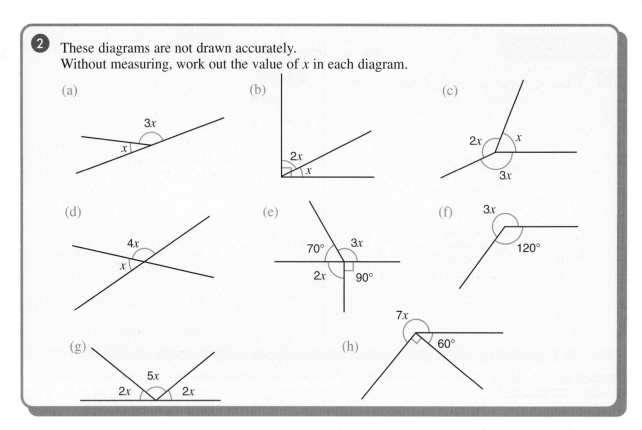

(a)   3x   x

(b)   2x   x

(c)   2x   x   3x

(d)   4x   x

(e)   70°   3x   2x   90°

(f)   3x   120°

(g)   5x   2x   2x

(h)   7x   60°

Perpendicular lines
Lines which meet at right angles are **perpendicular** to each other.

Parallel lines
Parallel lines are lines which never meet.
Which of the following pairs of lines are parallel?

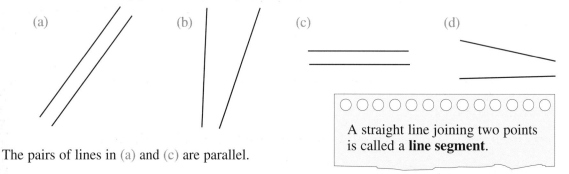

(a)   (b)   (c)   (d)

> A straight line joining two points is called a **line segment**.

The pairs of lines in (a) and (c) are parallel.

Activity
The diagram shows two parallel lines crossed by another straight line called a **transversal**.

> Arrowheads are used to show that lines are parallel.

Measure the marked angles.
What do you notice?

Corresponding angles

Angles a and c are equal. They are called **corresponding** angles.
Corresponding angles are always equal.
Here are some examples of corresponding angles.

Corresponding angles are always on the same side of the transversal.

Alternate angles

Angles b and c are equal. They are called **alternate** angles.
Alternate angles are always equal.
Here are some examples of alternate angles.

Alternate angles are always on opposite sides of the transversal.

Allied angles

Angles b and d add up to $180°$. They are called **allied** angles.
Allied angles are supplementary, they always add up to $180°$.
Here are some examples of allied angles.

Allied angles are always between parallels on the same side of the transversal.

$b + d = 180°$

EXAMPLES

1 Work out the size of the angles marked with letters. Give a reason for each answer.

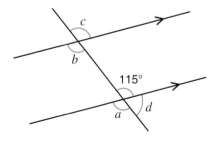

$a = 115°$ (vertically opposite angles)

$b = 115°$ (alternate angles)

$c = 115°$ (corresponding angles)

$d + 115° = 180°$ (supplementary angles)
$\quad\quad d = 180° - 115°$
$\quad\quad d = 65°$

2 Show that angle x is $104°$.

$x + 76° = 180°$ (allied angles)
$\quad\quad x = 180° - 76°$
$\quad\quad x = 104°$

The diagrams in this exercise have **not** been drawn accurately.

1. Work out the size of the angles marked with letters.
   Give a reason for each answer.

   (a)

   65° a

   (b)

   115° b

   (c)

   c 75°

   (d)

   100° d

2. Work out the size of the angles marked with letters.

   (a)

   b a 130°

   (b)

   60° c d

   (c)

   40° f e

   (d)

   h g 65°

3. Calculate the size of the angles marked with letters.

   (a)

   117° a

   (b)

   c 68° b

   (c)

   87° d

   (d)

   56° e

   (e)

   f 115°

   (f)

   126° g

   (g)

   h 67°

   (h)

   56° i

4. Calculate the size of the angles marked with letters.

   (a)

   a 55° b

   (b)

   c 118° e d

   (c)

   74° f g

   (d)

   128° h i

5. Calculate the size of the angles marked with letters.

   (a)

   96° n m 64°

   (b)

   q p 124° 116°

   (c)

   28° r 33°

   (d)

   s 50° 40°

Naming angles

Up to now we have used small letters to name angles. This is not always convenient.
Another method is to use three capital letters.

angle *ABC*
∠*ABC*

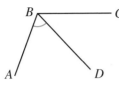

angle *ABD*
∠*ABD*

○○○○○○○○○○○○○○○○○○○○○○○

∠ means 'angle'.

∠*CBA* is the same as ∠*ABC*.
We usually write the letters either side of the
vertex (shown by the middle letter) in
alphabetical order.

Notice that the middle letter is where the angle is made.

Exercise **27.5**

1 Use three letters to name the marked angles in each of these diagrams.

(a)

(b)

(c)

2 Use three letters to name the angles marked with small letters in this diagram.

3 Use your protractor to measure accurately the size of these angles.

(a) ∠*ABH*

(b) ∠*HGF*

(c) ∠*BCD*

(d) ∠*AJE*

(e) ∠*GFJ*

(f) reflex ∠*GFJ*

(g) reflex ∠*BHG*

(h) reflex ∠*DEJ*

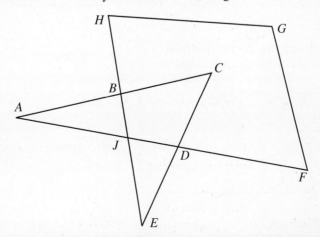

4 These diagrams have not been drawn accurately.
   (i)   Work out the size of the required angles.
   (ii) Give a reason for each of your answers.

(a) *PQ* is a straight line.
     Find ∠*QOR*.

(b) *AB* and *CD* are straight lines.
     Find ∠*AOD*.

(c) *PQ* and *RT* are parallel.
     Find ∠*XOQ*.

5 These diagrams are not drawn accurately.
Work out the size of the required angles.

(a)

Find ∠*ABC*.

(b)

Find ∠*QRS*.

(c)

Find ∠*ZYV*.

(d)

Find ∠*LMN*.

(e)

Find ∠*ABC*.

(f)

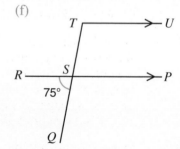

Find ∠*QSP* and ∠*STU*.

6 These diagrams are not drawn accurately.
Work out the size of the required angles.

(a)

Find ∠*AOB* and ∠*COD*.

(b)

Find ∠*QTU* and ∠*QTS*.

(c)

Find reflex angle *TUV*.

Direction and distance

Journeys are often described in terms of **direction** and **distance**.
When planning journeys we often use **maps**.
To interpret maps we need to understand:

     angles in order to describe **direction**,
     scales in order to find **distances**.

Compass points and **three-figure bearings** are used to describe direction.

Compass points

The diagram shows the points of the compass.

The angle between North and East is 90°.

The angle between North and North-East is 45°.

Do you know the names of any other compass points?

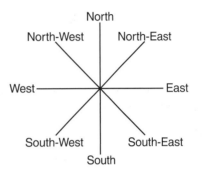

Exercise 27.6

1 (a) What is the angle between North and North-West?
   (b) What is the angle between South and North-West?
   (c) What is the angle between South-West and South-East?
   (d) What is the angle between North-West and South-West?
   (e) What is the angle between South-East and North-West?

2 (a) Lyn is facing North.
     She turns through an angle of 180°.
     In which direction is she now facing?
   (b) Tony is facing West.
     He turns through an angle of 90° clockwise.
     In which direction is he now facing?

3 (a) Claire is facing South.
     In which direction will she face after turning clockwise through an angle of 135°?
   (b) Kevin turned anticlockwise through an angle of 270°.
     He is now facing South-East.
     In which direction was he facing?

4 Copy and complete this table.
The first line has been done for you.

Start facing	Amount of turn	Finish facing
South	135° clockwise	North-West
North-East	90° clockwise	
West	135° anticlockwise	
	270° clockwise	East
	45° anticlockwise	West

Three-figure bearings

Bearings are used to describe the direction in which you must travel to get from one place to another.

A bearing is an angle measured from the North line in a clockwise direction.

The angle, which can be from 0° to 360°, is written as a three-figure number.

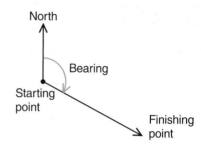

Bearings which are less than 100° include noughts to make up the three figures, e.g. 005°, 087°.

To show the direction given by a bearing

Example

The bearing of *C* from *D* is 153°. Draw a diagram to show this information.

The bearing of *C* **from** *D* tells you that *D* is the starting point.
- Draw a North line. Mark and label point *D* on the North line.
- Using your protractor, centred on point *D*, mark an angle of 153° measured in a clockwise direction from the North line.
- Draw a line from *D* through the marked point.
  An arrow is drawn on the line to show the direction in which you must travel to get to *C*.

This diagram shows the positions of Bath and Poole.

The bearing of Poole from Bath is 162°.

If you are at Bath, facing North, and turn through 162° in a clockwise direction you will be facing in the direction of Poole.

Back bearings

The return bearing of Bath from Poole is called a **back bearing**. Back bearings can be found by using parallel lines and alternate angles.

The bearing of Poole from Bath is 162°.

a = 162° (alternate angles)

Required angle = 180° + 162° = 342°.
The bearing of Bath from Poole (the back bearing) is 342°.

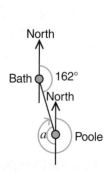

1 Use your protractor to find the three-figure bearings of *A* from *B* in each of the following.

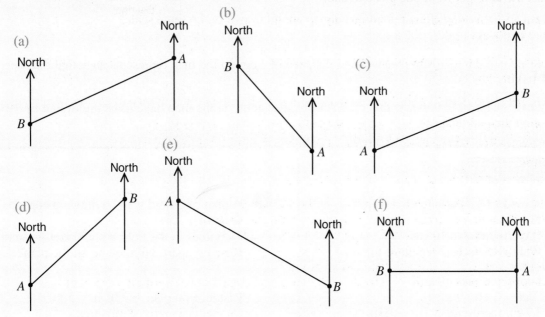

2 (a) Draw sketches to show the following information.
   (i)   The bearing of *F* from *E* is 050°.
   (ii) The bearing of *C* from *H* is 125°.
   (iii) The bearing of *K* from *Q* is 195°.
   (iv) The bearing of *L* from *B* is 260°.
   (v) The bearing of *A* from *J* is 305°.
   (vi) The bearing of *X* from *T* is 175°.
   (b) Use your sketches to give the back bearings for each of the directions in part (a).

3 Copy the diagram.

   R is on a bearing of 100° from *P*.
   R is on a bearing of 060° from *Q*.
   Mark the position of *R* on your diagram.

4 The diagram shows the positions of
   three oil rigs at *A*, *B* and *C*.

   (a) What is the bearing of *A* from *B*?
   (b) What is the bearing of *B* from *A*?
   (c) What is the bearing of *C* from *B*?
   (d) What is the bearing of *B* from *C*?
   (e) What is the bearing of *C* from *A*?
   (f) What is the bearing of *A* from *C*?

Scale drawing

Maps and plans are scaled down representations of real-life situations.
The **scale** used in drawing a map or plan determines the amount of detail that can be shown.

The distances between different points on a map are all drawn to the same scale.
There are two ways to describe a scale.

1 A scale of 1 cm to 10 km means that a distance of 1 cm on the map represents an actual distance of 10 km.

2 A scale of 1 : 10 000 means that all distances measured on the map have to be multiplied by 10 000 to find the real distance.

EXAMPLES

1 A road is 3.7 cm long on a map.
The scale given on the map is
'1 cm represents 10 km'.
What is the actual length of the road?

1 cm represents 10 km.
Scale up, so multiply.
3.7 cm represents 3.7 × 10 km
    = 37 km
The road is 37 km long.

2 A plan of a field is to be drawn using a scale of 1 : 500.
Two trees in the field are 350 metres apart.
How far apart will they be on the plan?

Scale down, so divide.
Distance on plan = 350 m ÷ 500
Change 350 m to centimetres.
    = 35 000 cm ÷ 500
    = 70 cm
The trees will be 70 cm apart on the plan.

Exercise 27.8

1 A forest walk measures 8.4 cm on a map.
The scale given on the map is "1 cm represents 2 km".
What is the actual length of the walk in kilometres?

2 A motor-racing circuit is 9.6 km in length.
A plan of the circuit has been drawn to a scale of 1 cm to 3 km.
What is the length of the circuit on the plan?

3 The scale of a map is 1 : 200.
(a) On the map a house is 3.5 cm long. How long is the actual house?
(b) A field is 60 m wide. How wide is the field on the map?

4 Roy draws a plan of a boat using a scale of 2 : 125.
On Roy's plan the width of the boat is 20 cm.
What is the actual width of the boat?

5 Claire draws a diagram for a printed circuit board in the ratio 20 : 1.
On Claire's diagram the distance between two components is 35 mm.
What is the actual distance between the components?

6 Helen drew a plan of her classroom using a scale of 5 cm to represent 1 m.
(a) Write the scale Helen used in the form 1 : n.
(b) On the plan, the length of the classroom is 29 cm.
What is the actual length of the classroom?
(c) The actual width of the classroom is 4.5 m.
What is the width of the classroom on the plan?

7 Here is a map of an island.

(a) Use your protractor to find:
   (i)   the bearing of Q from P,
   (ii) the bearing of P from Q.

(b) (i)   Measure the distance
         between P and Q on the map.
   (ii) What is the actual distance
         between P and Q?

Scale: 1cm to 10 km

8

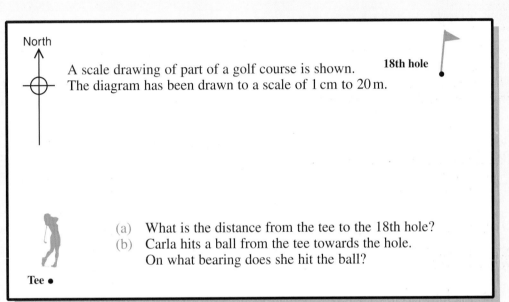

North

A scale drawing of part of a golf course is shown.   18th hole
The diagram has been drawn to a scale of 1 cm to 20 m.

(a) What is the distance from the tee to the 18th hole?
(b) Carla hits a ball from the tee towards the hole.
    On what bearing does she hit the ball?

Tee •

9 The sketch shows the positions of Ayton, Boulder, Carey and Dole.

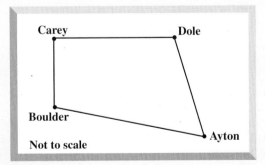

Carey   Dole

Boulder

Ayton

Not to scale

Carey is 12 km due West of Dole.
Carey is 8 km due North of Boulder.
Ayton is on a bearing 100° from Boulder and 160° from Dole.
By using a scale of 1 cm to 2 km, find by scale drawing the distance of Ayton from Carey.

10 A boat leaves port and sails on a bearing of 144° for 4 km.
It then changes course and sails due East for 5 km to reach an island.
Find by scale drawing:
(a) the distance of the island from the port,
(b) the bearing of the island from the port,
(c) the bearing on which the boat must sail to return directly to the port.

11 A yacht sails on a bearing of 040° for 5000 m and then a further 3000 m on a bearing of 120°. Find by scale drawing:
   (a) the distance of the yacht from its starting position,
   (b) the bearing on which it must sail to return directly to its starting position.

12 An aircraft leaves an airport, at *A*, and flies on a bearing of 035° for 50 km and then on a bearing of 280° for a further 40 km before landing at an airport, at *B*. Find by scale drawing:
   (a) the distance between the airports,
   (b) the bearing of *B* from *A*,
   (c) the bearing of *A* from *B*.

What you need to know

- An angle of 90° is called a **right angle**.
  An angle less than 90° is called an **acute angle**.
  An angle between 90° and 180° is called an **obtuse angle**.
  An angle greater than 180° is called a **reflex angle**.

- The sum of the angles at a point is 360°.

- Angles on a straight line add up to 180°.
  Angles which add up to 180° are called **supplementary angles**.
  Angles which add up to 90° are called **complementary angles**.

- When two lines cross, the opposite angles formed are equal and are called **vertically opposite angles**.

- Lines which meet at right angles are **perpendicular** to each other.

- A straight line joining two points is called a **line segment**.

- Lines which never meet and are always the same distance apart are **parallel**.

- When two parallel lines are crossed by a transversal the following pairs of angles are formed.

Corresponding angles	**Alternate angles**	**Allied angles**

$$a + b = 180°$$

- **Bearings** are used to describe the direction in which you must travel to get from one place to another. A bearing is an angle measured from the North line in a clockwise direction. A bearing can be any angle from 0° to 360° and is written as a three-figure number.

- To find a bearing:
      measure angle *a* to find the bearing of *Y* from *X*,
      measure angle *b* to find the bearing of *X* from *Y*.

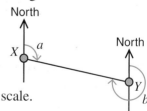

- **Scales**
  The distances between points on a map are all drawn to the same scale.
  There are two ways to describe a scale.
  1. A scale of 1 cm to 10 km means that a distance of 1 cm on the map represents an actual distance of 10 km.
  2. A scale of 1 : 10 000 means that all distances measured on the map have to be multiplied by 10 000 to find the real distance.

1 (a) What is the size of angle *a*?
Give a reason for your answer.

123° *a*

(b) What is the size of angle *x*?

x 5*x*

2 (a) Find the values of angles *p* and *q*.

55° *p*
q

(b) Calculate the value of angle *y*.

78°
55° *y*
142°

AQA

3 Find the size of (a) angle *a*, (b) angle *b*, (c) angle *c*.

63° *b*
c 71°
a

AQA

4 The lines *AB* and *CD* are parallel.

B
30° *x*
A *z*
y *D*
Not drawn
accurately 110°
C

(a) Work out the size of angle *x*.
(b) Work out the size of angle *y*.
(c) Work out the size of angle *z*.

AQA

5 In the diagram *AOB* and *POQ* are straight lines.
Angle *ROB* = 90°.
Angle *AOP* = 27°.

Q
A *O*
27° *B*
P
R

(a) (i) Work out the size of angle *AOQ*.
(ii) Work out the size of angle *POR*.

(b) What angle is the same size as angle *AOP*?

6 The diagram shows the plan of a sailboard race.
The sailboards have to go round buoys at *A*, *B* and *C*.
Buoy *B* is on a bearing of 050° from buoy *A*.
Angle *ABC* is 90°.

(a) What is the bearing of *A* from *B*?
(b) What is the bearing of *C* from *B*?

The plan has been drawn to a scale of 1 : 20 000.
(c) (i) Measure *AB*.
(ii) What is the distance from *A* to *B* in metres?

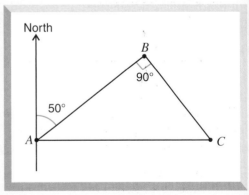

North
B
90°
50°
A *C*

7 Axford is 70 km from Moxley on a bearing of 065°.
Parley is 55 km from Moxley on a bearing of 125°.
(a) By using a scale of 1 cm to 10 km, draw an accurate diagram to show the positions of
Axford, Parley and Moxley.
(b) What is the bearing of Moxley from Axford?
(c) By taking measurements from your diagram work out
(i) the distance of Parley from Axford,
(ii) the bearing of Parley from Axford.

A **triangle** is a shape made by three straight lines.

The smallest number of straight lines needed to make a shape is 3.
Can you explain why?

Types of triangle

Measure the angles in each of these triangles.
What do you notice?

  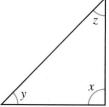

Angles *d*, *e* and *f* are all acute angles.
Triangles with three acute angles are called **acute-angled** triangles.

Angle *p* is an obtuse angle.
Triangles with an obtuse angle are called **obtuse-angled** triangles.

Angle *x* is a right angle.
Triangles with a right angle are called **right-angled** triangles.

The sum of the angles in a triangle

The sum of the three angles in a triangle is 180°.

$a + b + c = 180°$

Add up the three angles d, e and f
in the triangle above.
Do the same for the other
two triangles.
You may not always get 180°.
Can you explain why?

This result can easily be proved.

Draw a line which is parallel to
one side of the triangle, as shown.

$p + a + q = 180°$ (supplementary angles)
$p = b$ (alternate angles)
$q = c$ (alternate angles)

Alternate angles and
supplementary angles
were covered in Chapter 27.

Substitute $p = b$ and $q = c$ into $p + a + q = 180°$.
So $b + a + c = 180°$, which can be written as $a + b + c = 180°$.

EXAMPLE

Without measuring, work out the size of the angle marked a.

The sum of the angles in a triangle is $180°$.

$$a + 102° + 37° = 180°$$
$$a + 139° = 180°$$
$$a = 180° - 139°$$
$$a = 41°$$

Exercise 28.1

1 Is it possible to draw triangles with the following types of angles?
Give a reason for each of your answers.

(a) three acute angles,
(b) one obtuse angle and two acute angles,
(c) two obtuse angles and one acute angle,
(d) three obtuse angles,
(e) one right angle and two acute angles,
(f) two right angles and one acute angle.

2 Is it possible to draw a triangle with these angles?
If a triangle can be drawn, what type of triangle is it?
Give a reason for each of your answers.

(a) $95°$, $78°$, $7°$
(b) $48°$, $62°$, $90°$
(c) $48°$, $62°$, $70°$
(d) $90°$, $38°$, $52°$
(e) $130°$, $35°$, $15°$
(f) $27°$, $100°$, $63°$

3 Without measuring, work out the size of the third angle in each of these triangles.

(a) (b) (c) (d)

Exterior angle of a triangle

When one side of a triangle is extended, as shown, the angle formed is called an **exterior angle**.

$$a + b = d$$

In any triangle the exterior angle is always equal to the sum of the two opposite interior angles.
Check this by measuring the angles a, b and d in the diagram.

This result can be easily proved.
$a + b + c = 180°$
(sum of angles in a triangle)
$\quad c + d = 180°$
(supplementary angles)
$a + b + c = c + d$
$\quad a + b = d$

Triangles . . . Triangles . . . Triangles . . .

EXAMPLE

Find the size of the angles marked *a* and *b*.

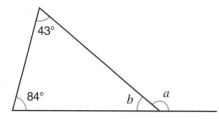

$a = 84° + 43°$ (ext. ∠ of a Δ)
$a = 127°$

$b + 127° = 180°$ (supp. ∠'s)
$b = 180° - 127°$
$b = 53°$

○○○○○○○○○○○○○○○○○○○○

Short but fully accurate
In geometry we often abbreviate words and
use symbols to provide the reader with full
details using the minimum amount of writing.

Δ is short for triangle.
ext. ∠ of a Δ means exterior angle of a triangle.
supp. ∠'s means supplementary angles.

Exercise 28.2

The diagrams in this exercise have not been drawn accurately.

1. The diagram shows a triangle with one side extended.
Explain why angle *x* is 35°.

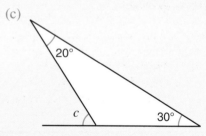

2. Work out the size of the marked angles.

(a)   (b)   (c)

(d)   (e)   (f)

3. Work out the size of the marked angles.

(a)   (b)   (c)

334

Naming parts of a triangle

Triangles are named by labelling each vertex with a capital letter.
Triangle *ABC* can be written as Δ*ABC*.

Triangle *ABC* is formed by the sides *AB*, *BC* and *AC*.
Triangles and lines are often named in alphabetical order.
Δ*ABC* is the same as Δ*BCA*.

The angles of a triangle are also described in terms of the vertices.
For example, the angle marked on the diagram is angle *ACB* or ∠*ACB*.
The middle letter is the vertex where the angle is made.

Special triangles

scalene triangle	**isosceles triangle**	**equilateral triangle**
Sides have different lengths.	Two equal sides.	Three equal sides.
Angles are all different.	Two angles equal.	All angles are 60°.

A sketch is used when an accurate drawing is not required.
Dashes across lines show sides that are equal in length.
Equal angles are marked using arcs.

Exercise 28.3

1 (a) What special name is given to Δ*ABE*?
(b) What special name is given to Δ*BDE*?
(c) Triangle *BDC* is scalene.
Give the three-letter name of another
scalene triangle in the diagram.

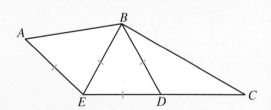

2 (a) On squared paper, draw triangles with the following coordinates:
(i) (1, 1), (6, 1), (3, 5) (ii) (1, 1), (5, 1), (1, 4)
(iii) (1, 1), (5, 1), (3, 4) (iv) (1, 1), (6, 1), (9, 5)

(b) Which of the following words could be used to describe each of the triangles you
have drawn?
Acute-angled, Obtuse-angled or Right-angled.
Scalene, Equilateral or Isosceles.

3 On squared paper, draw an isosceles triangle with coordinates:
A (3, 3), *B* (9, 3) and *C* (6, 10).
Which two sides are equal?
Which two angles are equal?

4 Triangle *PQR* is isosceles with angle *RPQ* = angle *QRP*.
P is the point (3, 5) and *R* is the point (9, 5).
Give the coordinates of the two possible positions of *Q* so that angle *PQR* is a right angle.

Triangles . . . Triangles . . . Triangles . . .

5 These triangles have not been drawn accurately.
Work out the size of angle *a* in each triangle.

(a)

(b)

(c)

(d)

6 The following diagrams have not been drawn accurately.
Work out the size of the angles marked with letters.

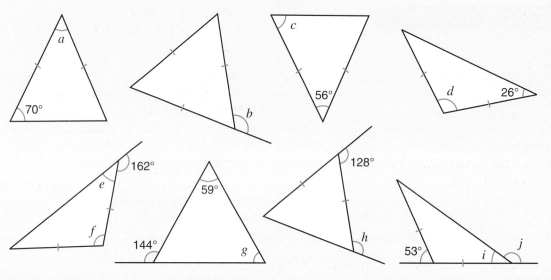

7 In the diagram $AB = BD = DA$ and $BC = CD$.

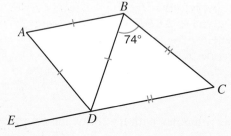

Not drawn accurately

(a) What type of triangle is *BCD*?
(b) What is the size of angle *BDC*?
(c) Work out the size of angle *ADE*.

8 These diagrams have not been drawn accurately.
Work out the size of the required angles.

(a)

Find ∠*BCD*.

(b)

Find ∠*PRQ* and ∠*QRS*.

(c)

Find ∠*MNX*.

336

Your ruler, compasses and protractor can be used to draw triangles accurately.
Drawings can be made from written information or sketch diagrams.
Follow the instructions below to accurately draw two triangles.

Sketch diagram

Information given:
Lengths of three sides of the triangle.

Step 1
Start by drawing the longest side, *AB*.
Draw a line 6 cm long.

A ———————————— *B*

Step 2
Set your compasses to a radius of 4 cm.
Draw an arc from *B*.

A ———————————— *B*

Step 3
Set your compasses to a radius of 3 cm.
Draw an arc from *A* to intersect (cross) the
arc drawn in step 2. Label the point *C*.

A ———————————— *B*

Step 4
Draw the sides *AC* and *BC*.
Add labels.

Sketch diagram

Information given:
Lengths of two sides of the triangle and the
size of the angle between the two sides.

Step 1
Start by drawing the longest side, *PR*.
Draw a line 5 cm long.

P ———————————— *R*

Step 2
∠*QPR* = 47° (acute angle)
Use your protractor to measure 47°.

Step 3
Using the dot as a guide, draw a line,
4 cm long, from *P*. Label point *Q*.

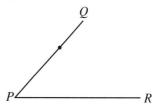

Step 4
Draw the line *QR* to complete the triangle.
Add labels.

If you are given written information draw a sketch diagram first.

For example, information for triangle *ABC* could be given as:

Draw accurately triangle *ABC* with sides   *AB* = 6 cm,   *BC* = 4 cm   and   *AC* = 3 cm.

Activity

Write instructions which someone could follow to draw the following triangles accurately.

(a)

(b)

Exercise 28.4

1 Use a ruler and compasses to draw accurately triangles with the following sides.
(a) 4 cm, 5 cm, 6 cm.
(b) 3.5 cm, 4.5 cm, 5 cm.
(c) $AB = 4.8$ cm, $BC = 3.6$ cm, $AC = 6.2$ cm.
(d) $PQ = 6$ cm, $QR = 6.5$ cm, $PR = 2.5$ cm.

2 Use a ruler and compasses to construct an equilateral triangle of side 5 cm.

3 Accurately draw the triangles using the information shown in the sketch diagrams below.

(a)

(b)

(c)

4 Use a ruler and protractor to draw the following triangles.
(a) $AB = 4$ cm, $BC = 4$ cm, $\angle ABC = 40°$.
(b) $PQ = 3.5$ cm, $PR = 5$ cm, $\angle QPR = 100°$.
(c) $XY = YZ = ZX = 4$ cm.
(d) $FG = 5$ cm, $FH = 5$ cm, $\angle FGH = 40°$.

5 A sketch of triangle PQR is shown.
(a) Make an accurate drawing of triangle PQR.
(b) Measure and write down the length of PR.
(c) Measure and write down the size of angle QPR.

Perimeter of a triangle

The **perimeter** is the distance round the outside of a shape. The perimeter of a triangle is the sum of the lengths of its three sides.

Measure the sides of this triangle.
What is the perimeter?

You should find:
$AB = 4$ cm, $BC = 5$ cm and $AC = 6$ cm.
Perimeter = $4 + 5 + 6 = 15$ cm.

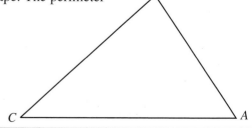

Area of a triangle

The area of a triangle is given by: Area $= \frac{1}{2} \times$ base $\times$ perpendicular height.

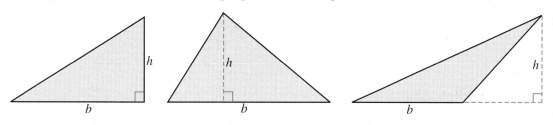

Imagine a rectangle with a diagonal drawn.
Area of a triangle can be remembered as:

Area $= \dfrac{\text{base} \times \text{perpendicular height}}{2}$

In these triangles b is the base and h is the **perpendicular height**.

The area, A, can be found using the formula: $A = \frac{1}{2} \times b \times h$

EXAMPLES

1 Calculate the area of this triangle.

$A = \frac{1}{2} \times b \times h$

$\quad = \frac{1}{2} \times 12 \times 7 \, \text{cm}^2$

$\quad = 42 \, \text{cm}^2$

7 cm

12 cm

2 This triangle has area $36 \, \text{cm}^2$.
Find the height of the triangle.

$A = \frac{1}{2} \times b \times h$

$36 = \frac{1}{2} \times 16 \times h$

$36 = 8h$

$h = \frac{36}{8}$

$h = 4.5 \, \text{cm}$

h

16 cm

Exercise 28.5

Do not use a calculator for questions 1 to 5.

1 Work out the lengths of the perimeters of these triangles.

(a)

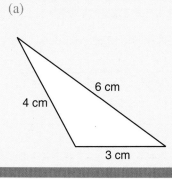

4 cm

6 cm

3 cm

(b)

4.6 cm

3.5 cm

5.2 cm

(c)

3.2 cm

7.6 cm

9.1 cm

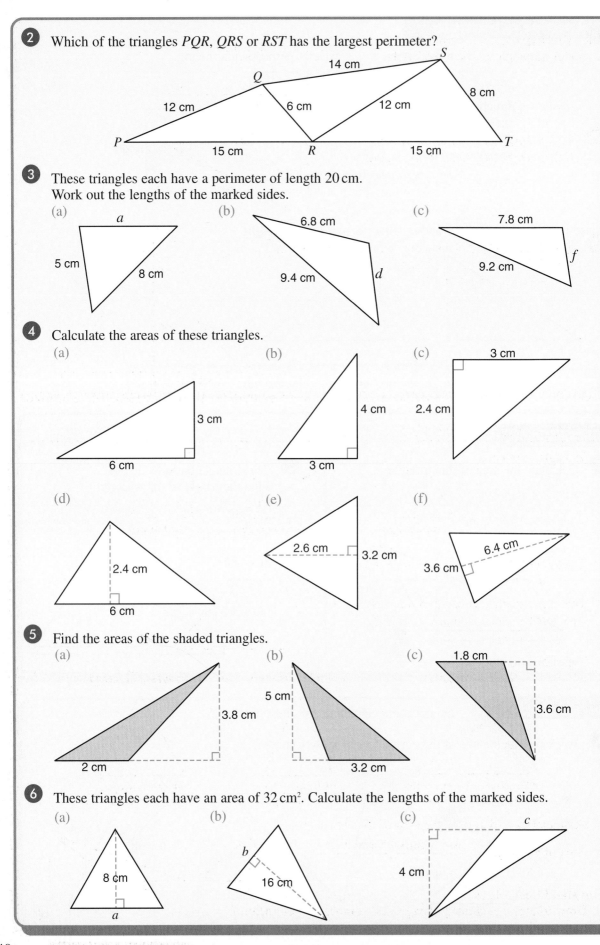

2 Which of the triangles *PQR*, *QRS* or *RST* has the largest perimeter?

3 These triangles each have a perimeter of length 20 cm.
Work out the lengths of the marked sides.

(a)

(b)

(c)

4 Calculate the areas of these triangles.

(a)

(b)

(c)

(d)

(e)

(f)

5 Find the areas of the shaded triangles.

(a)

(b)

(c)

6 These triangles each have an area of 32 cm². Calculate the lengths of the marked sides.

(a)

(b)

(c)

7 This triangle has a perimeter of 45 cm.
Calculate the area of the triangle.

19.5 cm

18 cm

8 This triangle has an area of 37.5 cm².
Calculate the perimeter of the triangle.

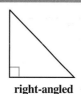

10 cm

12.5 cm

9 The shape *ABCDE* is made of two right-angled triangles.
ABCDE has an area of 28.5 cm².
Calculate the length of *ED*.

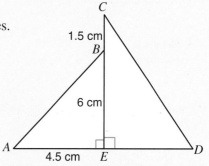

C

1.5 cm

B

6 cm

A

4.5 cm *E* *D*

What you need to know

- Triangles can be:

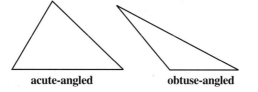

acute-angled **obtuse-angled** **right-angled**

- The sum of the angles in a triangle is 180°.
  $$a + b + c = 180°$$

- The exterior angle is equal to the sum of the two opposite interior angles.
  $$a + b = d$$

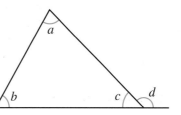

a

b *c* *d*

- Types of triangle:

Scalene triangle **Isosceles triangle** **Equilateral triangle**

Sides have different lengths. Two equal sides. Three equal sides.
Angles are all different. Two equal angles. Three equal angles, 60°.

- Perimeter of a triangle is the sum of its three sides.

- Area of a triangle = $\dfrac{\text{base} \times \text{perpendicular height}}{2}$

  $$A = \tfrac{1}{2} \times b \times h$$

  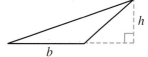

h *b* *b* *h*

You should be able to:
- Draw triangles accurately using ruler, compasses, protractor.

1 (a) Plot the points $P(2, 1)$, $Q(4, 5)$, $R(6, 1)$.
Join the points to form triangle PQR.
  (b) (i) What special name is given to triangle PQR?
  (ii) What is the area of the triangle?
  (c) On the same diagram draw another triangle PRS, which has the same area as triangle PQR.

2 ABC is an isosceles triangle.
BCD is a straight line.

Not drawn accurately

  (a) Work out the size of angle x.
  (b) $AB = AC$.
Work out the size of angle y. **AQA**

3 In the diagram, triangle ABC is isosceles with $BA = AC$, and triangle ACD is right-angled with angle $CAD = 90°$.

The diagram has not been drawn accurately.
  (a) Angle $ADC = 37°$.
Work out the size of angle DCA.
  (b) Angle $ACB = 65°$.
Work out the size of angle BAC.

4 ABC is an equilateral triangle.
ACD is an isosceles triangle. $\angle BCD = 40°$.

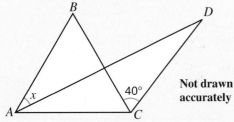

Not drawn accurately

Work out the size of angle x, giving a reason for your answer. **AQA**

5 A sketch of triangle LMN is shown.
$LM = 13.5$ cm. $LN = 8$ cm.
Angle $MLN = 42°$.

  (a) Make an accurate drawing of triangle LMN.
  (b) Measure and write down the size of angle LNM. **AQA**

6 Calculate the area of triangle ABC.

7 The diagram shows a sketch of triangle PQR.

  (a) Make an accurate drawing of the triangle.
  (b) By measuring the height of your triangle calculate the area of triangle PQR.

8 The diagram shows three triangles, BAE, BED and BDC.

  (a) Calculate the perimeter of triangle BAE.
  (b) Calculate the area of triangle BED.
  (c) The areas of triangles BED and BDC are equal.
Calculate the length of DC.

CHAPTER 29

Symmetry and Congruence

Lines of symmetry

These shapes are **symmetrical**.

When each shape is folded along the dashed line one side will fit exactly over the other side.
The dashed line is called a **line of symmetry**.

Some shapes have more than one line of symmetry.

Rectangle
2 lines of symmetry.

Square
4 lines of symmetry.

Circle
Infinite number of
lines of symmetry.
Each diameter is a
line of symmetry.

Shape with no lines of
symmetry.

Rotational symmetry

Is this shape symmetrical?

The shape does not have line symmetry.

*Try placing a copy of the shape over the original
and rotating it about the centre of the circle.*

After 180° (a half-turn) the shape fits into its own outline.
The shape has **rotational symmetry**.
The point about which the shape is rotated is called the **centre of rotation**.
The **order of rotational symmetry** is 2. When rotating the shape through 360° it fits into its own outline
twice (once after a half-turn and again after a full-turn).
A shape is only described as having rotational symmetry if the order of rotational symmetry is 2 or more.

A shape can have both line symmetry and rotational symmetry.

EXAMPLES

Order of rotational symmetry 5.

Order of rotational symmetry 4.
4 lines of symmetry.

Order of rotational symmetry 1.
The shape is **not** described as
having rotational symmetry.

516 answers

1 These shapes have **line symmetry**.
Copy each shape and draw the line of symmetry.

(a)   (b) (c) (d)

2 The following diagrams show half a shape.
The dashed line is the line of symmetry for the complete shape.
Copy the diagrams and complete each shape.

(a)   (b)   (c)   (d)

3 These shapes have been drawn accurately.
How many lines of symmetry has each shape?

(a)   (b)   (c)

4 How many lines of symmetry has each of these letters?

A C E H K

5 What is the order of rotational symmetry for each of these shapes?

(a)   (b)   (c)

(d)   (e)   (f)

6 Look at these letters of the alphabet.

J M N O P X Y Z

    (a)   Which two letters have only line symmetry?
    (b)   Which two letters have only rotational symmetry?
    (c)   Which letters have rotational symmetry of order 2?
    (d)   Which letters have neither rotational nor line symmetry?

7 Make a copy of this shape.

    (a)   How many lines of symmetry does the shape have?
    (b) (i)   Colour one more square so that your shape
              has rotational symmetry of order 2.
       (ii)   Mark the centre of rotational symmetry on your shape.

8

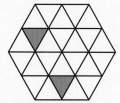

    Make a copy of this shape.

    (a)   How many lines of symmetry does the shape have?
    (b) (i)   Colour one more triangle so that your shape
              has rotational symmetry of order 3.
       (ii)   How many lines of symmetry does your shape have?

9 For each shape state
    (i)   the number of lines of symmetry,
    (ii)   the order of rotational symmetry.

    (a)   (b)   (c)   (d)   (e)

Symmetry in three-dimensions

Planes of symmetry

So far we have looked at two-dimensional (flat) shapes.
Two-dimensional shapes can have line symmetry.
Three-dimensional objects can have **plane symmetry**.
A **plane of symmetry** slices through an object so that one half is the mirror image of the other half.

A cuboid has three planes of symmetry as shown.

  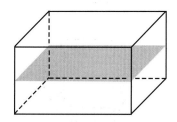

Axes of symmetry

A wall is built using cuboids.

In how many different ways can the next cuboid be placed in position?

If the cuboid can be placed in more than one way, it must have rotational symmetry about one or more **axes**.

A cuboid has three axes of symmetry.
The diagram shows one **axis of symmetry**.
The order of rotational symmetry about this axis is two.

Exercise 29.2

1 How many planes of symmetry has a cube?

2 State the order of rotational symmetry about the axis shown in each of the following.

    (a) Cube   (b) Square-based pyramid   (c) Cylinder   (d) Cone

3 Each end of this cuboid is a square.
The axes of symmetry are labelled *a*, *b* and *c*.
What is the order of rotational symmetry about
  (a) axis *a*,
  (b) axis *b*,
  (c) axis *c*?

4 The diagram shows a cuboid, with a square base.
On top of the cuboid is a square-based pyramid with vertex *A* above the centre of the top of the cuboid.

  (a) How many planes of symmetry has the figure?
  (b) How many axes of symmetry has the figure?
       Give the order of rotational symmetry about each axis.

5

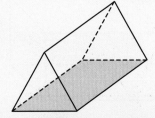

The diagram shows a triangular prism.
The ends of the prism are equilateral triangles.

  (a) How many axes of symmetry has the prism?
  (b) How many planes of symmetry has the prism?

Congruent shapes

When two shapes are the same shape and size they are said to be **congruent**.
A copy of one shape would fit exactly over the second shape.
Sometimes it is necessary to turn the copy over to get an exact fit.
These shapes are all congruent.

Exercise 29.3

1 Look at the shapes below. List five **pairs** of congruent shapes.

2 Which of these shapes are congruent to each other?

3 The diagram shows a rectangle that has been divided into five triangles.
  (a) Which triangle is congruent to triangle *AFG*?
  (b) Which quadrilateral is congruent to quadrilateral *ABEF*?

4 Triangle *ABC* has been divided into four smaller triangles as shown.

Name two pairs of congruent triangles.

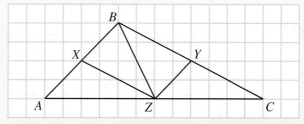

Symmetry and Congruence

Congruent triangles

There are four ways to show that a pair of triangles are congruent.

1 Three sides. SSS

2 Two sides and the included angle. SAS

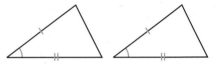

The included angle is the angle between the two sides.

3 Two angles and a corresponding side. ASA

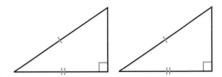

This can be written as AAS if the corresponding side is not between the angles.

4 Right angle, hypotenuse and one side. RHS

The hypotenuse is the side opposite the right angle and is the longest side in a right-angled triangle.

To show that two triangles are congruent you will need to state which pairs of sides and/or angles are equal, to match one of the four conditions for congruency given above.

EXAMPLE

Show that triangles *ABC* and *PQR* are congruent.

$AB = PQ$ (equal lengths, given)
$AC = PR$ (equal lengths, given)
$\angle BAC = \angle QPR$ (equal angles, given)

So triangles *ABC* and *PQR* are congruent.
Reason: SAS (Two sides and the included angle.)

Since the triangles are congruent we also know that
$BC = QR$, $\angle ABC = \angle PQR$ and $\angle ACB = \angle PRQ$.

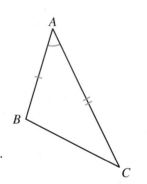

Exercise **29.4**

1 The following triangles have not been drawn accurately.
Which two of these triangles are congruent to each other?
Give a reason for your answer.

2 The following triangles have not been drawn accurately.
Which two of these triangles are congruent to each other?
Give a reason for your answer.

3 The following triangles have not been drawn accurately.
State whether each pair of triangles is congruent or not.
Where triangles are congruent give the reason.

(a)

(b)

(c)

(d)

(e)

(f)

(g)

(h)

(i)

4 For each of the following, is it possible to draw a congruent triangle without taking any other measurements from the original triangle?
If a triangle can be drawn give the reason for congruence which applies.

(a)

(b)

(c)

(d)

(e)

(f)

(g)

(h)

(i)

Symmetry and Congruence

5 Triangle *ABC* has angles 90°, 50° and 40°.
Triangle *XYZ* also has angles 90°, 50° and 40°.
The triangles are not congruent.
Can you explain why?

6 Show that triangles *DEF* and *PQR* are congruent.

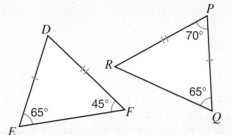

7 In the diagram *AB* is parallel to *CD*.
AB = *CD* = 7 cm and ∠*ABD* = 25°.

(a) What is the size of ∠*BDC*?
(b) Show that triangles *ABD* and *BCD* are congruent.
(c) Name an angle which is the same size as ∠*CBD*.

What you need to know

- A two-dimensional shape has **line symmetry** if the line divides the shape so that one side fits exactly over the other.

- A two-dimensional shape has **rotational symmetry** if it fits into a copy of its outline as it is rotated through 360°.

- A shape is only described as having rotational symmetry if the order of rotational symmetry is 2 or more.

- The number of times a shape fits into its outline in a single turn is the **order of rotational symmetry**.

- A **plane of symmetry** slices through a three-dimensional object so that one half is the mirror image of the other half.

- Three-dimensional objects can have **axes of symmetry**.

- When two shapes are the same shape and size they are said to be **congruent**.

- There are four ways to show that a pair of triangles are congruent:
  - SSS   Three equal sides.
  - SAS   Two sides and the included angle.
  - ASA   Two angles and a corresponding side.
  - RHS   Right angle, hypotenuse and one other side.

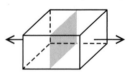

Order of rotational symmetry 5

Review Exercise 29

1 Half of a shape is drawn on squared paper.
AB is a line of symmetry for the complete shape.
Copy the diagram and complete the shape.

2 Consider the letters

X Y Z

(a) Which of these letters has line symmetry only?
(b) Which of these letters has rotational symmetry but not line symmetry?

3 All these patterns have five sides.

A   B   C   D

(a) Which pattern has more than one line of symmetry?
(b) Which pattern does not have rotational symmetry?

AQA

4 The diagram shows a five-pointed star.
(a) Write down the order of rotational symmetry of the star.
(b) (i) Draw a shape that has rotational symmetry of order 3.
    (ii) On your drawing mark the centre of rotational symmetry with an X.

AQA

5 Copy the diagram and shade two more squares so that the final pattern has line symmetry **and** rotational symmetry.

AQA

6 This diagram has been drawn accurately.
(a) Which triangle is congruent to triangle *ABC*?
(b) Which triangle is congruent to triangle *ACF*?
(c) Which quadrilateral is congruent to quadrilateral *ABCF*?

7 These triangles are congruent.
What is the size of (a) *x*, (b) *y*?

Not drawn accurately

AQA

8 These triangles have not been drawn accurately.
Which two triangles are congruent to each other? Give a reason for your answer.

9 A teacher sketches five triangles.

Which two of these triangles are congruent? Give a reason for your answer.

AQA

CHAPTER 30

Quadrilaterals

A **quadrilateral** is a shape made by four straight lines.

Special quadrilaterals

Parallelogram

Opposite sides equal and parallel.
Opposite angles equal.
Diagonals bisect each other.

Rhombus

Four equal sides.
Opposite sides parallel.
Opposite angles equal.
Diagonals bisect each other at 90°.

Trapezium

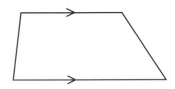

One pair of parallel sides.

Rectangle

Opposite sides equal and parallel.
Angles of 90°.
Diagonals bisect each other.

Kite

Two pairs of adjacent sides equal.
One pair of opposite angles equal.
One diagonal bisects the other at 90°.

Isosceles trapezium

One pair of parallel sides.
Non-parallel sides equal.
Two pairs of equal angles.
Diagonals equal.

Square

Four equal sides.
Opposite sides parallel.
Angles of 90°.
Diagonals bisect each other at 90°.

Remember:
Sides of equal length are marked with the same number of **dashes**.
Lines which are parallel are marked with the same number of **arrowheads**.
Angles of equal size are marked with the same number of **arcs**.

Sum of the angles of a quadrilateral

The sum of the four angles of a quadrilateral is 360°.

Measure the angles of this quadrilateral.
Do the angles add up to 360°?

You may not always get 360°.
Can you explain why?

$$a + b + c + d = 360°$$

This result can easily be proved.

Split the quadrilateral into two triangles *A* and *B*, as shown.

In triangle *A*:
$$p + q + r = 180°$$ (sum of angles in a triangle)
In triangle *B*:
$$w + x + y = 180°$$ (sum of angles in a triangle)

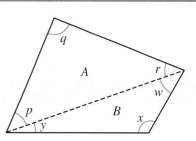

The sum of the angles of the quadrilateral is given by:
$$p + q + r + w + x + y$$
$$= 180° + 180°$$
$$= 360°$$

The sum of the angles in a triangle is 180°.
This was covered in Chapter 28.

EXAMPLE

PQRS is a parallelogram. Work out the size of the angle marked *x*.

The opposite angles of a parallelogram are equal.

$$55° + 55° + x + x = 360°$$
$$110° + 2x = 360°$$
$$2x = 360° - 110°$$
$$2x = 250°$$
$$x = 125°$$

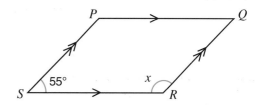

Exercise 30.1

Use squared paper to answer questions 1 to 8.

1 (a) Draw quadrilaterals with the following coordinates.
  (i)   *A* (3, 1), *B* (1, 3), *C* (2, 6), *D* (6, 2)
  (ii) *E* (1, 0), *F* (6, 2), *G* (8, 9), *H* (3, 7)
  (iii) *J* (3, 0), *K* (0, 4), *L* (3, 8), *M* (6, 4)
  (iv) *P* (1, 1), *Q* (2, 4), *R* (4, 4), *S* (4, 2)
  (v)   *W* (3, 1), *X* (1, 3), *Y* (3, 5), *Z* (5, 3)
  (b) What special name is given to each of these quadrilaterals?

2 *JKLM* is a square. *J* is the point (1, 1), *K* (4, 1), *L* (4, 4).
  Find the coordinates of *M*.

3 *PQRS* is a rectangle. *P* is the point (1, 3), *Q* (4, 6), *R* (6, 4).
  Find the coordinates of *S*.

4 *ABCD* is a rhombus. *A* is the point (3, 0), *B* (0, 4) and *D* (8, 0).
  Find the coordinates of *C*.

5 *WXYZ* is a parallelogram. *W* is the point (1, 0), *X* (4, 1), *Z* (3, 3).
Find the coordinates of *Y*.

6 *OABC* is a kite. *O* is the point (0, 0), *B* (5, 5), *C* (3, 1).
Find the coordinates of *A*.

7 *KLMN* is an isosceles trapezium with *K* at (1, 1), *M* (4, 3) and *N* (5, 1).
Find the coordinates of *L*.

8 *STUV* is a square with *S* at (1, 3) and *U* at (5, 3).
Find the coordinates of *T* and *V*.

9 Work out the size of angle *a* in each of these quadrilaterals.

(a)   (b)   (c)   (d)

10 Work out the size of the angles marked with letters in each of these rectangles.

(a)   (b)   (c)   (d)

11 Work out the size of the angles marked with letters in each of these parallelograms.

(a)   (b)   (c)   (d)

12 Work out the size of the angles marked with letters in each of these kites.

(a)   (b)   (c)   (d)

13 The diagram shows a trapezium.
Find the size of angle *a* and angle *b*.

14 *WXYZ* is an isosceles trapezium.
Work out the size of angle *WXY* and angle *XYZ*.

354

15 The following diagrams have not been drawn accurately.
Work out the size of the angles marked with letters.

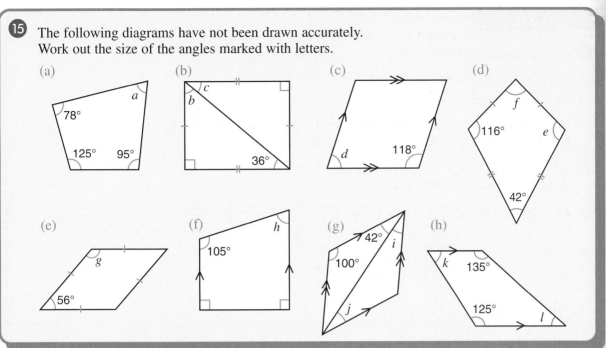

(a)   (b)   (c)   (d)

(e)   (f)   (g)   (h)

Symmetry of quadrilaterals

Remember:

A two-dimensional shape has line symmetry if the line divides the shape so that one side fits exactly over the other.

A two-dimensional shape has rotational symmetry if it fits into a copy of its own outline as it is rotated through 360°.

Parallelogram	**Isosceles trapezium**	**Rectangle**
0 lines of symmetry. Order of rotational symmetry 2.	1 line of symmetry.	2 lines of symmetry. Order of rotational symmetry 2.

Square	**Rhombus**	**Kite**
4 lines of symmetry. Order of rotational symmetry 4.	2 lines of symmetry. Order of rotational symmetry 2.	1 line of symmetry.

1 These quadrilaterals have been drawn on squared paper.

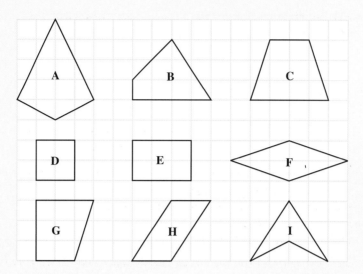

Copy and complete the table for each shape.

Shape	A	B	C	D	E	F	G	H	I
Number of lines of symmetry									
Order of rotational symmetry									

2 How many lines of symmetry has each of these quadrilaterals?

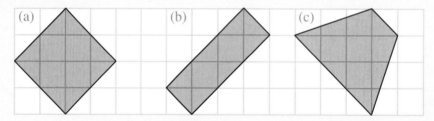

3 What is the order of rotational symmetry for each of these quadrilaterals?

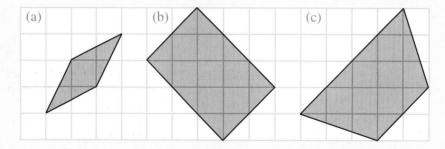

4 (a) Draw a rhombus of side 4 cm, with angles of 80° and 100°.
(b) Mark on your diagram any lines of symmetry.
(c) What order of rotational symmetry has the rhombus?

Perimeters of rectangles and squares

The **perimeter** is the distance round the outside of a shape.
The perimeter of a rectangle (or square) is the sum of the lengths of its four sides.

Measure the sides of this rectangle.
What is the perimeter of the rectangle?

You should find:
$AB = 3\,\text{cm}, \quad BC = 4\,\text{cm},$
$CD = 3\,\text{cm}, \quad DA = 4\,\text{cm}.$
Perimeter $= 3 + 4 + 3 + 4$
$\qquad\qquad = 14\,\text{cm}$

Area

Area is the amount of surface covered by a shape.
The standard unit for measuring area is the square centimetre, cm^2.
Small areas are measured using square millimetres, mm^2.
Large areas are measured using square metres, m^2, or square kilometres, km^2.

Area formulae

Rectangle

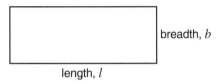

Area = length × breadth
$\quad A = lb$

Square

Area = length × breadth
In a square, length = breadth
Area = (length)^2
$\quad A = l^2$

Parallelogram

Area = base × height
$\quad A = bh$

Rhombus

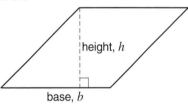

Area = base × height
$\quad A = bh$

Base and perpendicular height
The **base** is the side of the shape from which the height is measured.
The base does not have to be at the bottom of the shape.
The height of a shape, measured at right angles to the base, is called the **perpendicular height**.

Trapezium

Area = half the sum of the parallel sides × perpendicular height

$\quad A = \frac{1}{2}(a + b)\,h$

EXAMPLES

1 Find the area of this trapezium.

$A = \frac{1}{2}(a + b)h$

$= \frac{1}{2}(5 + 9)6$

$= \frac{1}{2} \times 14 \times 6$

$= 42\,cm^2$

2 The area of a rectangular room is $17.5\,m^2$. The room is 5 m long. Find the width of the room.

$A = lb$

$17.5 = 5 \times b$

$b = \frac{17.5}{5}$

$b = 3.5\,m$

Area = 17.5 m² b

5 m

Exercise 30.3   You should be able to do questions 1 and 2 without using a calculator.

1 Four rectangles are shown.

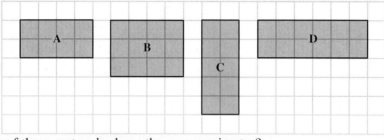

(a) Which of these rectangles have the same perimeter?

(b) Which of these rectangles have the same area?

2 These shapes have been drawn on 1 cm squared paper. Find the area of each shape.

3 Calculate the perimeters and areas of these rectangles and squares.

(a)   (b)   (c)   (d)

2.5 cm

1.5 cm

3.1 cm

0.9 cm

2.8 cm

2.8 cm

1.4 cm

1.4 cm

4 Calculate the areas of these shapes.

(a)

3.5 cm

(b)

2.8 cm

1.4 cm

(c)

1.8 cm

2.6 cm

(d)

3.6 cm

6.8 cm

(e)

2 cm

1.5 cm

3.8 cm

(f)

3.6 cm   2.3 cm

1.4 cm

5 A carpet measuring 4 m by 4 m is placed on a rectangular floor measuring 5 m by 6 m. What area of floor is not carpeted?

6 The diagram shows a picture in a frame. The outer dimensions of the frame are 18 cm by 10 cm. The frame is 2 cm wide. What is the area of the picture?

7 A rectangle has an area of 36 cm². The length of the rectangle is 9 cm. What is the breadth?

8 The diagram shows a square drawn inside a rectangle.

Calculate the shaded area.

9 A rhombus of side 6 cm has an area of 48 cm². What is the perpendicular height of the rhombus?

10 A trapezium has an area of 30 cm². The two parallel sides are 7 cm and 8 cm. What is the perpendicular distance between the sides?

11 These shapes all have the same area. Calculate the values of h and l.

12 Each of these shapes has an area of 24 cm². Calculate the lengths marked with letters.

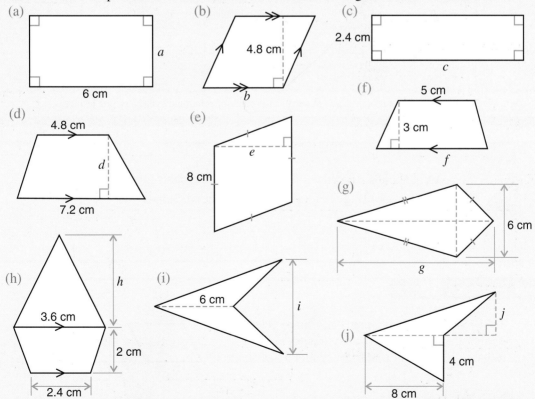

- A **quadrilateral** is a shape made by four straight lines.
- The sum of the angles in a quadrilateral is 360°.
- The **perimeter** of a quadrilateral is the sum of the lengths of its four sides.

$$a + b + c + d = 360°$$

- Facts about these special quadrilaterals:

parallelogram   rectangle   square   rhombus   trapezium   isosceles trapezium   kite

Quadrilateral	Sides	Angles	Diagonals	Line symmetry	Order of rotational symmetry	Area formula
Parallelogram	Opposite sides equal and parallel	Opposite angles equal	Bisect each other	0	2	$A = bh$
Rectangle	Opposite sides equal and parallel	All 90°	Bisect each other	2	2	$A = bh$
Rhombus	4 equal sides, opposite sides parallel	Opposite angles equal	Bisect each other at 90°	2	2	$A = bh$
Square	4 equal sides, opposite sides parallel	All 90°	Bisect each other at 90°	4	4	$A = l^2$
Trapezium	1 pair of parallel sides					$A = \frac{1}{2}(a + b)h$
Isosceles trapezium	1 pair of parallel sides, non-parallel sides equal	2 pairs of equal angles	Equal in length	1	1*	$A = \frac{1}{2}(a + b)h$
Kite	2 pairs of adjacent sides equal	1 pair of opposite angles equal	One bisects the other at 90°	1	1*	

*A shape is only described as having rotational symmetry if the order of rotational symmetry is 2 or more.

IDEAS FOR INVESTIGATION

The area of a quadrilateral in which the diagonals intersect at 90° can be worked out using, area = $\frac{1}{2}$ product of the diagonals.

Investigate.

Review Exercise 30

 (a) How many lines of symmetry has shape **B**?
    (b) Which shape has no lines of symmetry?
    (c) What is the order of rotational symmetry of shape **C**?

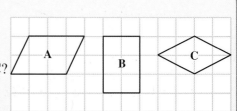

2 *PQRS* is a parallelogram with vertices at
P (1, 1), *R* (7, 8) and *S* (5, 3).
Write down the coordinates of *Q*.

Not drawn accurately

AQA

3

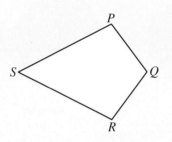

ABCD is a parallelogram.
Angle *DAC* = 87° and angle *ACD* = 44°.
Calculate angle *ABC*,
giving reasons for each step of your working.

AQA

4 The diagram shows a rectangle with its diagonals drawn.
Work out the size of angle *x* and the size of angle *y*.

AQA

5

The diagram shows a kite *PQRS*.
(a) How many lines of symmetry has *PQRS*?

Angle *QRS* = 93° and angle *PQR* = 118°.
(b) Work out the size of angle *PSR*.

AQA

6 The diagram shows a trapezium.
Find the size of angle *a* and angle *b*.

7

8 cm

The diagram shows the dimensions of a kite.
What is the area of the kite?

8 A square has a perimeter of 20 cm. Calculate the area of the square.

9 The rectangle has an area of 54 cm².
The length of the rectangle is 7.5 cm.
Calculate the perimeter of the rectangle.

7.5 cm

10

The plan of a bedroom floor is shown.
(a) What is the area of the bedroom floor?
(b) What area of floor is **not** covered by the carpet? AQA

11 *ABCD* is a trapezium.
(a) Find the area of *ABCD*.
(b) Find the area of triangle *BCD*.

AQA

CHAPTER 31

Polygons

A **polygon** is a shape made by straight lines.
A three-sided polygon is a **triangle**.

A four-sided polygon is called a **quadrilateral**.

A polygon is a many-sided shape.
Look at these polygons.

Pentagon	**Hexagon**	**Heptagon**	**Octagon**
5 sides	6 sides	7 sides	8 sides

Interior and exterior angles of a polygon

Angles formed by sides inside a polygon are called **interior angles**.

When a side of a polygon is extended, as shown, the angle formed
is called an **exterior angle**.

At each vertex of the polygon:
  interior angle + exterior angle = 180°

interior angle   exterior angle

Sum of the interior angles of a polygon

The diagram shows polygons with the diagonals from one vertex drawn.

P   Q   R   S

The diagonals divide the polygons into triangles.

Shape	Number of sides	Number of triangles	Sum of interior angles
P	3	1	1 × 180° = 180°
Q	4	2	2 × 180° = 360°
R	5	3	3 × 180° = 540°
S	6	4	4 × 180° = 720°

In general, for any n-sided polygon, the sum of the interior angles is $(n - 2) \times 180°$.

The sum of the exterior angles of **any** polygon is 360°.

$$a + b + c + d + e = 360°$$

EXAMPLE

Find the size of the angles marked a and b.

$155° + a = 180°$ (int. angle + ext. angle = 180°)
$a = 180° - 155°$
$a = 25°$

The sum of the interior angles of a pentagon is 540°.
$b + 140° + 155° + 125° + 65° = 540°$
$b + 485° = 540°$
$\quad\quad b = 540° - 485°$
$\quad\quad b = 55°$

To find the sum of the interior
angles of a pentagon substitute
$n = 5$ into $(n - 2) \times 180°$.
$\quad (5 - 2) \times 180°$
$\quad = 3 \times 180°$
$\quad = 540°$

Exercise 31.1

The diagrams in this exercise have not been drawn accurately.

1 In the diagram, ABC is a straight line.
  (a) Explain why angle $x = 50°$.
  (b) Show that angle $y = 60°$.

2 Work out the size of the angles marked with letters.
  (a)   (b)   (c)

3 Work out the size of the angles marked with letters.
  (a)   (b)   (c)   (d)

Polygons . . . Polygons . . . Polygons . . .

4 Work out the size of the angles marked with letters.

(a)

140°   100°   *a*

(b)

115°   55°   *b*   128°

(c)

67°   60°   *c*   85°   72°

(d)

90°   25°   60°   *d*   65°   *e*   70°

5 Work out the sum of the interior angles of these polygons.

(a)

(b)

(c)

(d)

6 Work out the size of the angles marked with letters.

(a)

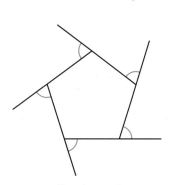

70°   *d*   *d*   90°   80°

(b)

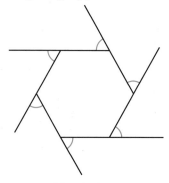

e   *e*   *e*   95°   85°

(c)

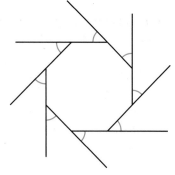

100°   *f*   100°   *f*   *f*   *f*

Regular polygons

A polygon with all sides equal and all angles equal is called a **regular polygon**.

A regular triangle is usually called an **equilateral triangle**.
A regular quadrilateral is usually called a **square**.

Regular hexagon   Regular octagon

Exterior angles of regular polygons

Measure the exterior angles of these regular polygons. *What do you find?*

Regular pentagon   Regular hexagon   Regular octagon

You should find the exterior angles of a regular polygon are equal.

In general, for any regular *n*-sided polygon: exterior angle $= \frac{360°}{n}$

By rearranging the formula we can find the number of sides, *n*, of a regular polygon when we know the exterior angle. $n = \dfrac{360°}{\text{exterior angle}}$

EXAMPLE

A regular polygon has an exterior angle of 30°.
(a)   How many sides has the polygon?
(b)   What is the size of an interior angle of the polygon?

Remember:
It is a good idea to write down the formula you are using.

(a) $n = \dfrac{360°}{\text{exterior angle}}$

$n = \dfrac{360°}{30°} = 12$

The polygon has 12 sides.

(b)   interior angle + exterior angle = 180°
int. ∠ + 30° = 180°
int. ∠ = 180° − 30°
interior angle = 150°

Exercise 31.2

1   Calculate (a) the exterior angle and (b) the interior angle of these regular polygons.

(i)   (ii)   (iii)   (iv)

2   A regular polygon has an exterior angle of 18°.
How many sides has the polygon?

3   Calculate the number of sides of regular polygons with an exterior angle of:
(a)   9°   (b)   24°   (c)   40°   (d)   60°

4   A regular polygon has an interior angle of 135°.
How many sides has the polygon?

5   Calculate the number of sides of regular polygons with an interior angle of:
(a)   108°   (b)   162°   (c)   171°   (d)   90°

6   (a)   Calculate the size of an exterior angle of a regular pentagon.
(b)   What is the size of an interior angle of a regular pentagon?
(c)   What is the sum of the interior angles of a pentagon?

7   The following diagrams are drawn using regular polygons.
Work out the values of the marked angles.

(a)   (b)   (c)   (d)

(e)   (f)   (g)   (h)

8 The following diagrams are drawn using regular polygons.
Work out the values of the marked angles.

(a) (b) (c)

9 Find the sum of the interior angles of these regular polygons.
(a) A hexagon.   (b) An octagon.

10 A regular polygon has *x* sides. Each of its interior angles is *y*°.
Find a formula for *y* in terms of *x*.

11 A footpath is made in the shape of a regular hexagon *ABCDEF*.
The point *B* is due east of point *A*.
What is the bearing of
(a) *A* from *F*,   (b) *B* from *C*,   (c) *A* from *C*,
(d) *A* from *D*,   (e) *E* from *B*?

12 Find the number of lines of symmetry and the order of rotational symmetry for
(a) a regular pentagon,   (b) a regular hexagon.

Tessellations

Covering a surface with identical shapes produces
a pattern called a **tessellation**.

To tessellate the shape must not overlap and there
must be no gaps.

Regular tessellations

This pattern shows a tessellation of regular hexagons.
This pattern is called a **regular tessellation** because
it is made by using a single regular polygon.

Exercise 31.3

1 Draw diagrams to show tessellations of these shapes.
(a)   (b)   (c)

2 Copy these regular tessellations.
Continue the tessellation by drawing four more shapes.

(a)

(b)

3 (a) The diagram shows part of a tessellation.
Copy the diagram.
Continue the tessellation by drawing four more quadrilaterals.

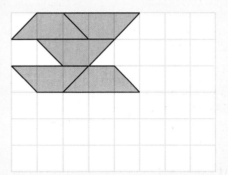

(b) Copy this quadrilateral onto card.
Use the quadrilateral to make a tessellation.

(c) All quadrilaterals tessellate.
Draw a quadrilateral of your own, make copies, and show that it will tessellate.

4 Explain why regular pentagons will not tessellate.

What you need to know

- A **polygon** is a many-sided shape made by straight lines.
- A polygon with all sides equal and all angles equal is called a **regular polygon**.
- Shapes you need to know: A 5-sided polygon is called a **pentagon**.
  A 6-sided polygon is called a **hexagon**.
  An 8-sided polygon is called an **octagon**.
- The sum of the exterior angles of any polygon is 360°.
- At each vertex of a polygon: interior angle + exterior angle = 180°
- The sum of the interior angles of an n-sided polygon is given by:
  $(n - 2) \times 180°$

interior angle / exterior angle

- For a regular n-sided polygon: exterior angle $= \dfrac{360°}{n}$
- A shape will **tessellate** if it covers a surface without overlapping and leaves no gaps.
- All triangles tessellate.
- All quadrilaterals tessellate.
- Equilateral triangles, squares and hexagons can be used to make **regular tessellations**.
- A regular pentagon cannot be used to make a regular tessellation.

Inscribed regular polygons

Inscribed regular polygons can be constructed by equal divisions of a circle.
To draw an inscribed regular polygon follow these steps.

Step 1 Find the exterior angle of the polygon.

$$\text{Exterior angle} = \frac{360°}{\text{number of sides}}$$

Step 2 Draw a circle.
Divide the circle into equal sectors, where the sector angles are equal to the exterior angle of the polygon.

Step 3 Join the divisions on the circumference of the circle to form the polygon.

Example Draw an inscribed regular hexagon.

Step 1

A hexagon has 6 sides.

$$\text{Exterior angle} = \frac{360°}{6} = 60°$$

Step 2

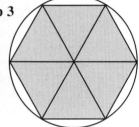

Step 3

(a) Draw an inscribed equilateral triangle.
(b) Draw an inscribed square.
(c) Draw other inscribed regular polygons.
Which regular polygons are difficult to draw accurately? Explain why.

Review Exercise 31

1 A regular polygon is shown.
   (a) What special name is given to this type of polygon?
   (b) Copy the diagram and draw all the lines of symmetry.
   (c) What is the order of rotational symmetry of this polygon?

AQA

2 (a) Explain why equilateral triangles tessellate.
   (b) On dotty paper draw at least five regular hexagons in the form of a tessellation.
   (c) This tessellation is formed from regular octagons and squares.
   Calculate the size of angle $x°$.
   Show all your working.

AQA

3

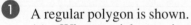

168° q

Part of a regular polygon is shown.
(a) What is the size of angle q?
(b) How many sides has the polygon?

4 Copy each of the following diagrams onto squared paper and draw six more shapes to form a tessellation.

   (a)

   (b)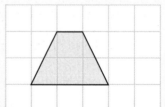

368

5 *ABCDE* is a regular pentagon.
Given that ∠*BAC* = 36°, explain why *AC* is parallel to *ED*.

6

Not drawn accurately

The diagram shows a shape which consists of two regular polygons.
Work out the size of angle *x*. AQA

7 The diagram shows a pentagon with just one line of symmetry.
(a) Explain why angle *x* is 90°.
(b) Calculate the size of angle *y*.
(c) Write down the size of angle *z*.

Not drawn accurately

AQA

8

Not drawn accurately

The diagram shows a regular octagon.
(a) Work out the size of angle *x*, giving a reason for your answer.
(b) What name is given to the quadrilateral *ABCD*? AQA

9 A regular octagon has eight sides.
One side of the octagon has been extended to form angle *p*.
(a) Work out the size of angle *p*.
(b) Work out the size of angle *q*.

10

ABCDEF is a regular polygon.
(a) What name is given to this polygon?
(b) What is the size of the exterior angle marked *x*?
(c) What is the sum of the interior angles?

11 *ABCDEFGHIJ* is a regular decagon.
(a) (i) Calculate the size of the angle marked *x*.
(ii) Calculate the size of the angle marked *y*.
(b) (i) What can you say about the lines *GH* and *FI*?
(ii) Calculate the size of the angle marked *z*.

Circle Properties

Circles

A **circle** is the shape drawn by keeping a pencil the same distance from a fixed point on a piece of paper. Compasses can be used to draw circles accurately.

It is important that you understand the meaning of the following words:

Circumference – special name used for the perimeter of a circle.

Radius – distance from the centre of the circle to any point on the circumference.

Diameter – distance right across the circle, passing through the centre point.
Notice that the diameter is twice as long as the radius.

Chord – a line joining two points on the circumference. The longest chord of a circle is the diameter.

Tangent – a line which touches the circumference of a circle at one point only.

Arc – part of the circumference of a circle.

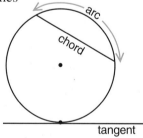

Segment – a chord divides a circle into two segments.

Sector – two radii divide a circle into two sectors.

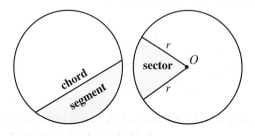

Activity

Measure the marked angles in these diagrams. *What do you notice?*

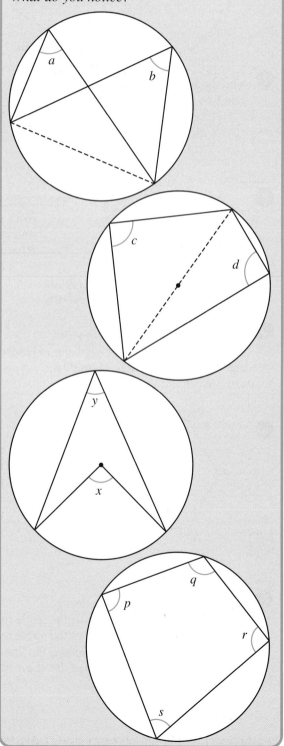

Circle properties

The angle in a semi-circle is a right angle

Angles which are:
    at the circumference,
    standing on a diameter,
are equal to 90°.

 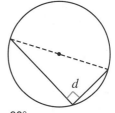

$$c = d = 90°$$

The angle at the centre is twice the angle at the circumference

If two angles are standing on the same chord,
the angle at the centre of the circle is twice
the angle at the circumference.

$$x = 2y$$

Angles in the same segment are equal

Angles which are:
    at the circumference,
    standing on the same chord,
    in the same segment,
are equal.

$$a = b$$

Opposite angles of a cyclic quadrilateral are supplementary

A quadrilateral whose vertices lie on the circumference
of a circle is called a **cyclic quadrilateral**.

The opposite angles of a cyclic quadrilateral are
supplementary (add up to 180°).

$$p + r = 180°$$
and
$$q + s = 180°$$

EXAMPLE

The diagram has not been drawn accurately.
O is the centre of the circle.
Find the marked angles.

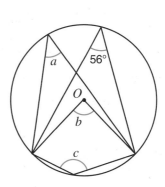

$a = 56°$ (angles in the same segment)

$b = 2 × 56°$ (∠ at centre = twice ∠ at circum.)
$b = 112°$

$c = 180° - 56°$ (opp. ∠'s of a cyclic quad.)
$c = 124°$

Circle Properties . . . Circle Properties . . . Circle Properties . . .

The diagrams in this exercise have not been drawn accurately.

1 The following diagrams show triangles drawn in semi-circles.
Work out the size of the marked angles.

(a)

(b)

(c)

(d)

2 *O* is the centre of the circle.
Work out the size of the marked angles.

(a)

(b)

(c)

(d)

(e)

(f)

(g)

(h)

3 *O* is the centre of the circle.
Work out the size of the marked angles.

(a)

(b)

(c)

(d)

(e)

(f)

(g)

(h)

4 In the diagram BD is a diameter.
Angle $ACD = 43°$.
Calculate angle x.

5 $ABCD$ is a cyclic quadrilateral, with
BA produced (extended) to E.
Angle $EAD = 70°$ and angle $CDB = 34°$.
Calculate angles BCD and CAD.

6 PQ is a diameter.
Angle $RPQ = 29°$.
Calculate angle PSR.

7 In the diagram, O is the centre of the circle.
Angle $PSQ = 28°$ and angle $QSR = 47°$.
Calculate angle PQR
and angle QRS.

8 P, Q, R, S and T are points on a circle.
$\angle QRS = 105°$, $\angle PTS = 140°$,
$\angle PQR = 135°$ and $PT = TS$.
Calculate $\angle PSR$ and $\angle TPQ$.

9 In the figure, O is the centre of the circle.
Angle $ORP = 20°$.
Calculate   (a) angle POR,   (b) angle PQR.

10 In the figure, O is the centre of the circle.
$AC = CB$.
Calculate the angles
(a) DOE,   (b) ABD,   (c) DBE.

11 The centre of the circle is O.
Calculate the value of x.

12 In the circle, centre O, QR is a diameter.
The line QS is a common chord of the
two circles.
TR is a straight line.
Find angle QPT.

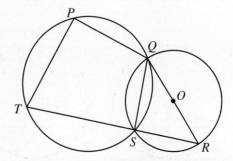

Circle Properties . . . Circle Properties . . .

Tangents

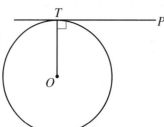

The diagram shows a tangent drawn from a point P to touch the circle, centre O, at T.

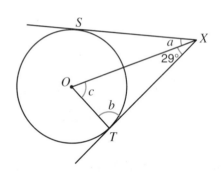

This diagram shows two tangents drawn from a point P to touch the circle, centre O, at points A and B.

Tangents drawn to a circle from the same point are equal.
$PA = PB$
OP bisects angle APB.

What is the name given to the shape OAPB?

EXAMPLE

The diagram has not been drawn accurately.
O is the centre of the circle. Find the marked angles.

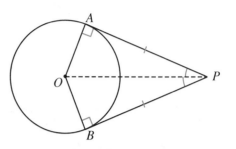

$a = 29°$ (SX and TX are tangents from X, so $\angle TXO = \angle SXO$.)

$b = 90°$ (Tangent perpendicular to radius at T.)

$c = 180° - 90° - 29°$
$c = 61°$

Exercise 32.2

The diagrams in this exercise have not been drawn accurately.

1 O is the centre of the circle. Work out the size of the marked angles.

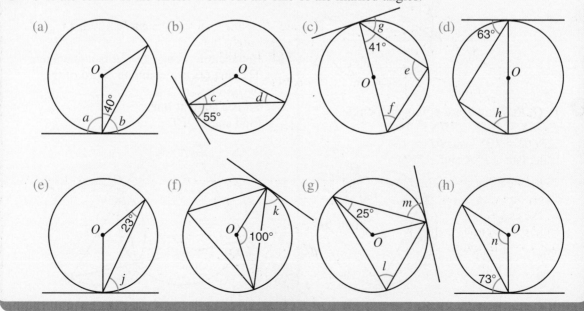

2 *O* is the centre of the circle. Work out the size of the marked angles.

(a)

(b)

(c)

3 *AB* and *AD* are tangents to the circle centre *O*.
COD is a diameter and angle *CBO* = 48°.

Calculate (a) angle *BOC*,
               (b) angle *BDO*,
               (c) angle *BAD*.

4

In the diagram, *O* is the centre of the circle.
TP is a tangent.
Angle *TPA* = 42° and angle *ABP* = 42°.

Calculate (a) angle *PAB*,
               (b) angle *PTA*.

5 In the diagram, *PQ* and *PS* are tangents to the circle centre *O*.
POR is a straight line.
Angle *SRQ* = 50°.

Calculate (a) ∠*SOQ*,
               (b) ∠*SPO*,
               (c) ∠*RSO*.

6

PQ and *PS* are tangents to the circle centre *O*.
POR is a straight line.
Angle *SPO* = 18°.

Calculate (a) ∠*POS*,
               (b) ∠*OSR*,
               (c) ∠*SQR*.

7 The line *XY* is a tangent to the
circle and *O* is the centre
of the circle.
Find the size of the angles
marked *p*, *q*, *r* and *s*.

What you need to know

- A **circle** is the shape drawn by keeping a pencil the same distance from a fixed point on a piece of paper.
- The meaning of the following words:

  Circumference – special name used for the perimeter of a circle.

  Radius – distance from the centre of the circle to any point on the circumference. The plural of radius is **radii**.

  Diameter – distance right across the circle, passing through the centre point. The diameter is twice as long as the radius.

  Chord – a line joining two points on the circumference. The longest chord is the diameter.

  Tangent – a line which touches the circumference of a circle at one point only.

  Arc – part of the circumference of a circle.

  Segment – a chord divides a circle into two segments.

  Sector – two radii divide a circle into two sectors.

- The vertices of a **cyclic quadrilateral** lie on the circumference of a circle.

- **Circle properties**

The angle in a semi-circle is a right angle.

Angles in the same segment are equal.

$x = 2y$
The angle at the centre is twice the angle at the circumference.

$p + r = 180°$ and $q + s = 180°$
Opposite angles of a cyclic quadrilateral are supplementary.

- A tangent is perpendicular to the radius at the point of contact.

- Tangents drawn to a circle from the same point are equal in length.

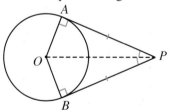

Review Exercise 32

The diagrams in this exercise have not been drawn accurately.

1 O is the centre of the circle. Work out the size of the marked angles.

(a)   (b)   (c)   (d)

376

2 P, Q, R and S are four points on the circumference of a circle.
PR is a diameter of the circle and PQ is parallel to SR.
Angle $QPR = 37°$.
Calculate the size of the angles marked x, y and z.

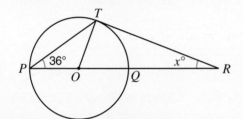

3 In the diagram, O is the centre of the circle.
Find x.

4 O is the centre of the circle.
Tangents are drawn from T to touch the circle at A and B.
Angle $OBA = 35°$.

Explain why angle $ATB = 70°$.

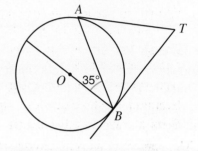

5 In the diagram, O is the centre of the circle and TR is the tangent to the circle at T. Calculate x.

6 RP is the diameter of the circle O.
Work out the size of angles PQS, QRP, QSP and QOP.

7 In the diagram, O is the centre of the circle and PQR is a tangent to the circle.
Find the values of the angles marked x, y and z.

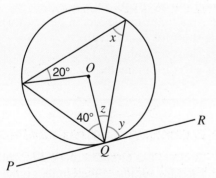

8 O is the centre of the circle.
ABC is a tangent to the circle at B.
Work out the size of angles x, y and z.

CHAPTER 33

Circles and Other Shapes

Activity

Draw a circle with radius 2 cm.
Use thread or the edge of a strip of paper to measure the circumference of your circle.
Draw circles with radii 3 cm, 4 cm and so on.
Measure the circumference of each circle and write your results in a table.
What do you notice?

Radius (cm)	2	3	4	5	6	7	8
Diameter (cm)							
Circumference (cm)							

The Greek letter π

The circumference of any circle is just a bit bigger than three times the diameter of the circle.
The Greek letter π is used to represent this number.

We use an approximate value for π, such as 3, $3\frac{1}{7}$, 3.14, or the π key on a calculator, depending on the accuracy we require.

Circumference of a circle

The diagram shows a circle with radius r and diameter d.

The **circumference** of a circle can be found using the formulae:

$$C = \pi \times d$$

$$\text{or} \quad C = 2 \times \pi \times r$$

Remember: $\quad d = 2 \times r$

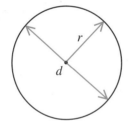

These formulae can be rearranged to find the radius, or diameter, when given the circumference.

For $C = 2\pi r$

$$r = \frac{C}{2\pi}$$

For $C = \pi d$

$$d = \frac{C}{\pi}$$

Chapter 32 looked at angle properties of circles.
In this chapter we look at various calculations involving lengths and areas associated with circles.

Short but accurate
We sometimes use letters in place of words.
C is short for circumference.
r is short for radius.
d is short for diameter.

EXAMPLES

1 Find the circumference of a circle with diameter 80 cm.
Take π to be 3.14.
Give your answer to the nearest centimetre.

$C = \pi \times d$
$\quad = 3.14 \times 80 \, \text{cm}$
$\quad = 251.2 \, \text{cm}$
Circumference is 251 cm to the nearest centimetre.

2 A circle has circumference 37.2 cm.
Find the radius of the circle, giving your answer to the nearest millimetre.
Take $\pi = 3.14$.

$C = 2 \times \pi \times r$
$37.2 = 2 \times 3.14 \times r$
$37.2 = 6.28 \times r$
$\quad r = \frac{37.2}{6.28}$
$\quad r = 5.923\ldots$
$\quad r = 5.9 \, \text{cm}$, to the nearest millimetre.

Do not use a calculator for questions 1 to 3.   (33)

① Estimate the circumference of these circles.
Use the approximate rule: Circumference = 3 × diameter.

(a)

4 cm

(b)

8 cm

(c)

13 cm

② Use the approximate rule to estimate the circumference of these circles.

| Remember: diameter = 2 × radius |

(a)

2.5 cm

(b)

5 cm

(c)

6.4 cm

③ The diagram shows the actual size of a 1p coin and a 2p coin.

1p   **2p**

(a) Find, by measurement, the diameter of each coin.
(b) Use the approximate rule: Circumference = 3 × diameter
                to estimate the circumference of each coin.

In questions 4 to 16, take π to be 3.14 or use the π key on your calculator.

④ Calculate the circumference of these circles.   Use the formula $C = \pi \times d$.

(a)

12 cm

(b)

7 cm

(c)

15 cm

⑤ Calculate the circumference of these circles.   Use the formula $C = 2 \times \pi \times r$.

(a)

4.5 cm

(b)

5.6 cm

(c)

16 cm

Circles and Other Shapes

6 A circle has a diameter of 9 cm. Calculate the circumference of the circle.
Give your answer correct to the nearest whole number.

7 A circular biscuit tin has a diameter of 24 cm. What is the circumference of the tin?

8 A dinner plate has a radius of 13 cm. Calculate the circumference of the plate.
Give your answer to an appropriate degree of accuracy.

9 A circle has a radius of 6.5 cm. Calculate the circumference of the circle.
Give your answer correct to one decimal place.

10 Stan marks the centre circle of a football pitch.
The circle has a radius of 9.15 m.
What is the circumference of the circle?

11 The radius of a tractor wheel is 0.8 m.
Calculate the circumference of the wheel.

12 Two cyclists go once round a circular track.
Eddy cycles on the inside of the track which has a radius of 20 m.
Reg cycles on the outside of the track which has a radius of 25 m.
How much further does Reg cycle?

13 A circular mug has a circumference of 24 cm.
Find the radius of the mug, giving your answer to the nearest millimetre.

14 The circumference of a copper pipe is 94 mm.
Find, to the nearest millimetre, the diameter of the pipe.

15 The circumference of a bicycle wheel is 190 cm.
Find the diameter of the wheel,
giving your answer to the nearest centimetre.

16 The circumference of the London Eye is approximately 420 metres.
What is the radius? Give your answer correct to the nearest metre.

Area of a circle

Activity

Cut out the 20 sectors.
Arrange them like this.

Draw a circle.
Divide it into 20 equal **sectors**.
Colour the sectors using two colours.

$\pi \times r$

The circumference of a circle is given by $2 \times \pi \times r$.
Half of the circumference is $\pi \times r$.
So the length of the rectangle is $\pi \times r$.
The width of the rectangle is the same as the radius of the circle, r.

Using area of a rectangle = length × breadth
area of a circle = $\pi \times r \times r$
area of a circle = $\pi \times r^2$

$\pi \times r$

Take the end sector and cut it in half.
Place one piece at each end of the pattern

Area of a circle

The area of a circle can be found using the formula: $A = \pi \times r^2$

This formula can be rearranged to find the radius when given the area of the circle.

For $A = \pi r^2$

$$r^2 = \frac{A}{\pi}$$

$$r = \sqrt{\frac{A}{\pi}}$$

radius

EXAMPLES

1 Estimate the area of a circle with radius of 6 cm.
Take π to be 3.

$A = \pi \times r \times r$
$ = 3 \times 6 \times 6$
$ = 108 \text{ cm}^2$
Area is approximately 108 cm².

2 Calculate the area of a circle with diameter 9 cm.
Give your answer correct to the nearest whole number.

> **Remember** $r = \frac{d}{2}$

$A = \pi \times r \times r$
$ = \pi \times 4.5 \times 4.5$
$ = 63.617... \text{ cm}^2$
Area is 64 cm² to the nearest whole number.

3 The top of a tin of cat food has an area of 78.5 cm².
What is the radius of the tin?
Take $\pi = 3.14$.

$A = \pi \times r^2$
Substitute values for A and π.
$ 78.5 = 3.14 \times r^2$
Solve this equation to find r.
Divide both sides of the equation by 3.14.
$$\frac{78.5}{3.14} = r^2$$
$$r^2 = 25$$
Take the square root of both sides.
$$r = 5$$
The radius of the tin is 5 cm.

Exercise 33.2   Do not use a calculator for questions 1 and 2.

1 Estimate the areas of these circles. Use the approximate rule: Area = 3 × (radius)².

(a)

5 cm

(b)

7 cm

(c)

9 cm

2 Estimate the areas of these circles.
Take π to be 3.

> **Remember** Radius = $\frac{\text{diameter}}{2}$

(a)

6 cm

(b)

10 cm

(c)

16 cm

In questions 3 to 14, take π to be 3.14 or use the π key on your calculator.

3 Calculate the areas of these circles. Give your answers to the nearest whole number.

(a)

4 cm

(b)

6.5 cm

(c)

12 cm

4 Calculate the areas of these circles. Give your answers correct to one decimal place.

(a)

6.4 cm

(b)

7.6 cm

(c)

26 cm

5 The base of a paddling pool is a circle with radius 84 cm.
Find the area of the base.

6 The lid on a tin of paint is a circle of radius 72 mm.
Calculate the area of the lid.

7 The diameter of a bicycle wheel is 66 cm.
A plastic spoke cover is made for the wheel.
What is the area of the spoke cover?

66 cm

8 A dinner plate has a diameter of 25 cm.
Find the area of the plate.
Give your answer correct to the nearest whole number.

9

A circular table has a diameter of 1.2 m.
Calculate the area of the table.
Give your answer correct to one decimal place.

10 A circular rug has a radius of 0.5 m.
Calculate the area of the rug.
Give your answer correct to two decimal places.

11 A mug has a diameter of 8 cm.
Calculate the area of the base of the mug.
Give your answer to an appropriate degree of accuracy.

12 A circle has an area of 50 cm².
Calculate the radius of the circle.

13

A circular flower bed has an area of 40 m².
Calculate the diameter of the flower bed.
Give your answer to a suitable degree of accuracy.

14 The face of a circular disc has an area of 5.3 cm².
Calculate the radius of the disc.
Give your answer to the nearest millimetre.

Some questions will involve finding the area and some the circumference of a circle.

Remember: Choose the correct formula for area or circumference.
You need to think about whether to use the radius or the diameter.

EXAMPLES

1 Gina's bicycle wheel has a radius of 24 cm.
How many complete rotations of the wheel are needed to cycle 500 cm?
Take π = 3.14.

Find the circumference of the wheel.
$C = 2 \times \pi \times r$
$\quad = 2 \times 3.14 \times 24$ cm
$\quad = 150.72$ cm

Number of rotations
$\quad = 500$ cm $\div$ circumference
$\quad = 500$ cm $\div 150.72$ cm
$\quad = 3.317...$

So 4 complete rotations of the wheel are needed.

2 Find the area of a semi-circle with radius 4 cm.
Take π = 3.14.
Give your answer to the nearest whole number.

Begin by finding the area of a circle with radius 4 cm.

$A = \pi \times r^2$
$\quad = 3.14 \times 4 \times 4$ cm^2
$\quad = 50.24$ cm^2

Area of semi-circle
$= \frac{1}{2} \times$ area of circle

$= \frac{1}{2} \times 50.24$ cm^2

$= 25.12$ cm^2

Area of semi-circle is 25 cm^2, to the nearest whole number.

Exercise **33.3**

In this exercise take π to be 3.14 or use the π key on your calculator.

1 A tea plate has a radius of 9 cm.
 (a) What is the circumference of the plate?
 (b) What is the area of the plate?

2 The top of a tin of cat food is a circle of diameter 8.4 cm.
 (a) Calculate the circumference of the tin.
 Give your answer correct to the nearest whole number.
 (b) Calculate the area of the top of the tin.
 Give your answer correct to one decimal place.

3 The front wheel on Nick's tricycle has a diameter of 18 cm.
 (a) Calculate the circumference of the front wheel.
 (b) How far does Nick have to cycle for the front wheel to make 20 complete turns?

4 The letter O is cut from card.
The inside radius of the letter is 3 cm.
The outside radius of the letter is 4 cm.
Calculate the area of the letter.

5 A circle is drawn inside a square, as shown.
The square has sides of length 10 cm.
Calculate the area of the shaded region.

6 Which has the greater area:

      a circle with radius 4 cm, or a semi-circle with diameter 11 cm?

You must show all your working.

7 Thirty students join hands to form a circle.

The diameter of the circle is 8.5 m.
- (a) Find the circumference of the circle.
  Give your answer to the nearest metre.
- (b) What area is enclosed by the circle?

8 A semi-circle has a radius of 6 cm. Find the perimeter of the semi-circle.
Give your answer to the nearest whole number.

9 The radius of a circular plate is 15 cm.
- (a) What is its area?
- (b) What is its circumference?

Give your answers in terms of π.

10 A cotton reel is a cylinder with radius 1.3 cm. 200 cm of cotton is wrapped round the reel.
How many times does it wrap round?

11 A circular flower bed has diameter 12 m.
- (a) How much edging is needed to go right round the bed?
- (b) The gardener needs one bag of fertiliser for each 7 m².
  How many bags of fertiliser are needed for this bed?

12 The wheel of a wheelbarrow rotates 60 times
when it is pushed a distance of 50 m.
Calculate the radius of the wheel.

13 Calculate the area of a semi-circle with a diameter of 6.8 cm.

14 Calculate the perimeter of a semi-circle with a radius of 7.5 cm.

15 A pastry cutter is in the shape of a semi-circle.
The straight side of the semi-circle is 12 cm long.
How long is the curved side?

16 A circle has a circumference of 64 cm. Calculate the area of the circle.

17 A circle has an area of 128 cm². Calculate the circumference of the circle.

18 A circle has a circumference of 14π cm. Calculate the area of the circle in terms of π.

19 A circle has an area of 144π cm². Calculate the circumference of the circle in terms of π.

20 The diagram shows a small circle drawn inside a larger circle.
The shaded area is 55π cm².
The small circle has a radius of 3 cm.
Calculate the radius of the larger circle.

21 The diagram shows a small circle drawn inside a larger circle.
The small circle has an area of 16π cm².
The larger circle has a circumference of 18π cm.
Calculate the shaded area.
Give your answer in terms of π.

Areas of shapes

Here is a reminder of the formulae used to find the areas of other shapes.

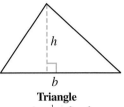

Triangle
$A = \frac{1}{2} \times b \times h$

Rectangle
$A = lb$

Parallelogram
$A = bh$

Trapezium
$A = \frac{1}{2}(a+b)h$

Compound shapes

Shapes formed by joining different shapes together are called **compound shapes**.
To find the area of a compound shape we must first divide the shape up into rectangles, triangles, circles, etc and find the area of each part.
Shapes can be divided in different ways, but they should all give the same answer.

EXAMPLES

1

Area of shape is given by:
Area A + Area B
= (45 × 30) + (120 × 40)
= 1350 + 4800
= 6150 m²

Area of shape is given by:
Area C + Area D
= (45 × 70) + (75 × 40)
= 3150 + 3000
= 6150 m²

Area of shape is given by:
Area (E + F) − Area F
= (120 × 70) − (75 × 30)
= 8400 − 2250
= 6150 m²

All the methods give the same answer so use the method you find easiest.

2 Find the area of this metal plate.

The plate can be split into a rectangle, A, and two triangles, B and C.

Area A = 2 × 1.8 = 3.6 cm²

Area B = $\frac{2 \times 1.8}{2}$ = 1.8 cm²

Area C = $\frac{0.5 \times 1.8}{2}$ = 0.45 cm²

Total area = 3.6 + 1.8 + 0.45 = 5.85 cm²

Note: There are other methods. Try one!

Circles and Other Shapes

1 Find the areas of these shapes which are made up of rectangles.

(a)

(b)

(c)

2 Find the areas of these shapes.

(a)

(b)

(c)

3 Find the areas of these shapes.

(a)

(b)

(c)

4 Calculate the shaded areas in each of these shapes.

(a)

(b)

(c)

5 A rectangle measures 8 cm by 32 cm.
Four circles are drawn inside the rectangle, as shown.
What area of the rectangle is not shaded?

6 Find the area of the shaded square.

10 cm

7 cm

10 cm

3 cm

7 cm   3 cm

7 A window is made in the shape of a semi-circle of radius 0.2 m on top of a rectangle of height 0.8 m.

(a) What is the area of glass in the window?

0.2 m

0.8 m

(b) A plastic strip is made to go right round the edge of the window. How long is the strip?

8 Find the area and perimeter of the shaded shape.

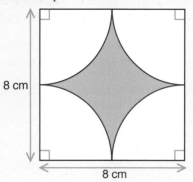

8 cm

8 cm

9 A right-angled triangle has sides 6 cm, 8 cm and 10 cm. Semi-circles are drawn on each side.

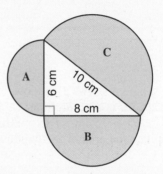

C

A

6 cm

10 cm

8 cm

B

Find the areas of A, B and C. What do you notice about the areas of the three semi-circles?

What you need to know

- A **circle** is the shape drawn by keeping a pencil the same distance from a fixed point on a piece of paper.

- Diameter = 2 × radius

- The **circumference** of a circle is given by:
  $C = \pi \times d$ or $C = 2 \times \pi \times r$

- The **area** of a circle is given by:
  $A = \pi \times r^2$

circumference

radius

diameter

- Shapes formed by joining different shapes together are called **compound shapes**.
  To find the area of a compound shape we must first divide the shape up into rectangles, triangles, circles, etc and find the area of each part.
  Here is a reminder of the formulae used to find the areas of other shapes.

h	b	h	a, h
b	l	b	b
Triangle	**Rectangle**	**Parallelogram**	**Trapezium**
$A = \frac{1}{2} \times b \times h$	$A = lb$	$A = bh$	$A = \frac{1}{2}(a+b)h$

Take π to be 3.14 or use the π key on your calculator.

1   (a)   Calculate the area of a circle of radius 1.2 cm.
   (b)   Calculate the circumference of a circle of diameter 3.5 cm.   AQA

2   Calculate the area of a circle with a diameter of 15 cm.
Give your answer to an appropriate degree of accuracy.   AQA

3   A circular flower bed has an area of 84 m².
Explain why the radius of the flower bed must be bigger than 5 m.   AQA

4   The diagram shows a car park.
Calculate the area of the car park.

5   Calculate the area of a semi-circle, radius 10 cm.   AQA

6   The diagram shows a window.
The arc AB is a semi-circle.
$BC = AD = 75$ cm, $DC = 80$ cm.
Calculate the area of the window.

Not drawn accurately

AQA

7   Andre is rolling a hoop along the ground.
The hoop has a diameter of 90 cm.
What is the minimum number of complete turns the hoop must make to cover a distance of 5 m?   AQA

8   The Smith family has a circular dining table.
The circumference of the dining table is 320 centimetres.
   (a)   Calculate its radius.

The family uses circular table mats each of radius 11 centimetres.
   (b)   Work out the area covered by one of these mats.   AQA

9
   (a)   Calculate the area of a circle of radius 4 cm.
      Give your answer in terms of π.
   (b)   A square is drawn inside the circle, as shown in the diagram.
      (i)   Calculate the area of the square.
      (ii)   Calculate the area of the shaded segment.
         Give your answer in terms of π.   AQA

Not drawn accurately

10   A circle has a circumference of 42 cm.
Calculate the area of the circle.
Give your answer correct to two significant figures.

Loci and Constructions

Following rules

Three students are given rules to follow.

John
Walk so that you are always 2 metres from the lamp post.

His path is a circle, radius 2 metres.

Hanif
Walk along a straight road.
You must keep 30 cm from the edge of the road and stay on the pavement.

His path is a straight line.

Sarah
Start from the corner of the lawn.
Walk across the lawn so that you are always the same distance from two sides.

Her path is a straight line.
The line cuts the angle in two.

Locus

The path of a point which moves according to a rule is called a **locus**.
If we talk about more than one locus we call them **loci**.

EXAMPLES   Draw sketches to show the loci of John, Hanif and Sarah.

John

Hanif

Sarah

1. Adam goes down this slide.
   Make a sketch of the slide as viewed from the side and show the locus of Adam's head as he goes down the slide.

2. The diagram shows part of a rectangular lawn.
   Starting from the wall, Sally walks across the lawn so that she is always the same distance from both hedges.
   Draw a sketch to show the locus of Sally's path.

3. *PQRS* is a square of side 8 cm.
   A point *X* is inside the square.

   X is less than 8 cm from *P*.
   X is nearer to *PQ* than to *SR*.

   Make a sketch showing where *X* could be.

4. A ball is rolled down a step.
   Copy the diagram, and sketch the locus of *P*, the centre of the ball, as it rolls from *X* to *Y*.

5. A wire is stretched between two posts.
   A ring slides along the wire and a dog is attached to the ring by a rope.
   Make a sketch to show where the dog can go.

6. A point *P* is 1 cm from this shape.
   Copy the diagram, and draw an accurate locus of **all** the positions of *P*.

Sometimes it is necessary to construct loci accurately.
You are expected to use only a ruler and compasses.
Here are the methods for two constructions.

To draw the perpendicular bisector of a line

This means to draw a line at right angles to a given line dividing it into two equal parts.

1 Draw line *AB*.

2 Open your compasses to just over half the distance *AB*. Mark two arcs which cross at *C* and *D*.

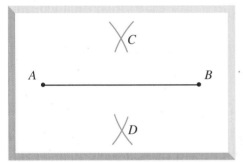

3 Draw a line which passes through the points *C* and *D*.

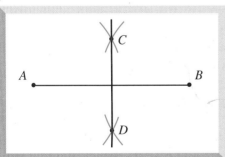

This line is the locus of a point which is the same distance from *A* and *B*.
Points on the line *CD* are **equidistant** (the same distance) from points *A* and *B*.
The line *CD* is at right angles to *AB*.
CD is sometimes called the **perpendicular bisector** of *AB*.

To draw the bisector of an angle

This means to draw a line which divides an angle into two equal parts.

1 Draw the angle *A*.
Use your compasses, centre *A*, to mark points *B* and *C* which are the same distance from *A*.

2 Use points *B* and *C* to draw equal arcs which cross at *D*.

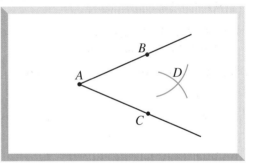

3 Draw a line which passes through the points *A* and *D*.

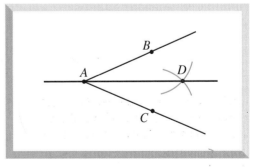

This line is the locus of a point which is the same distance from *AB* and *AC*.
Points on the line *AD* are **equidistant** from the lines through *AB* and *AC*.
The line *AD* cuts angle *BAC* in half.
AD is sometimes called the **bisector** of angle *BAC*.

Loci and Constructions

1 Mark two points, *A* and *B*, 10 cm apart. Construct the perpendicular bisector of *AB*.

2 Use a protractor to draw an angle of 60°. Construct the bisector of the angle.
Check that both angles are 30°.

3 Draw a triangle in the middle of a new page.
Construct the perpendicular bisectors of
all three sides.
They should meet at a point, *Y*.

Put the point of your compasses on *Y* and
draw the circle which goes through
all three vertices of the triangle.
This construction is sometimes called the
circumscribed circle of a triangle.

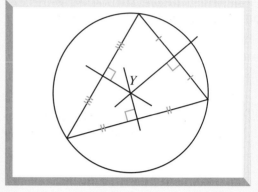

4 Draw another triangle on a new page.
Bisect each angle of the triangle.
The bisectors should meet at a point, *X*.

Put the point of your compasses on point *X*
and draw the circle which just touches
each side of the triangle.
This construction is sometimes called the
inscribed circle of a triangle.

5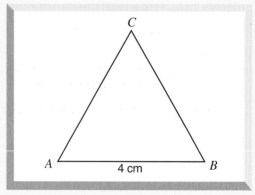

Using a circle of radius 4 cm, copy the diagram.
Draw the perpendicular bisectors of the chords *WX* and *YZ*.
What do you notice about the perpendicular bisectors?

> The perpendicular bisector of a chord always
> passes through the centre of a circle.

6 Two trees are 6 metres apart. Alan walks so that he is always an equal distance from each tree.
Draw a scale diagram to show his path.

7 *ABC* is an equilateral triangle with sides 4 cm.

A point *X* is inside the triangle.
It is nearer to *AB* than to *BC*.
It is less than 3 cm from *A*.
It is less than 2 cm from *BC*.
Shade the region in which *X* could lie.

8 Draw a rectangle *ABCD* with *AB* = 6 cm and *AD* = 4 cm.
  (a) Mark, with a thin line, the locus of a point which is 1 cm from *AB*.
  (b) Mark, with a dotted line, the locus of a point which is the same distance from *A* and *B*.
  (c) Mark, with a dashed line, the locus of a point which is 3 cm from *A*.

9 Draw a right-angled triangle with sides of 6 cm, 8 cm and 10 cm.

A point X is in the triangle.
It is 4 cm from B.
It is the same distance from A and B.

Mark accurately, the position of X.

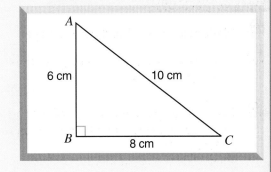

10 Copy the diagram and draw the locus of a point which is the same distance from PQ and RS.

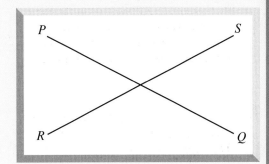

11 Triangle ABC is isosceles with $AB = BC = 7$ cm and $AC = 6$ cm.
  (a) Construct triangle ABC.
  (b) Point X is equidistant from A, B and C. Mark accurately the position of X.

12 (a) The diagram shows the sketch of a field. Make a scale drawing of the field using 1 cm to represent 100 m.
  (b) A tree is 400 m from corner D and 350 m from corner C.
      Mark the position of the tree on your drawing.
  (c) John walks across the field from corner D, keeping the same distance from AD and CD. Show his path on your diagram.
  (d) Does John walk within 100 m of the tree in crossing the field?

13 Part of a coastline is shown.

A boat is:
  (i) equidistant from X and Z, and
  (ii) equidistant from XY and YZ.

Copy the diagram and mark the position of the boat.

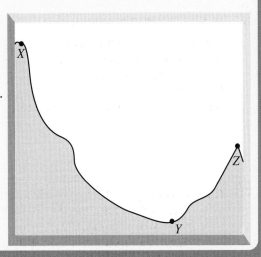

More constructions

To draw the perpendicular from a point to a line

This means to draw a line at right angles to a given line, from a point that **is not on the line**.

1 Open your compasses so that from point A you can mark two arcs on the line PQ.

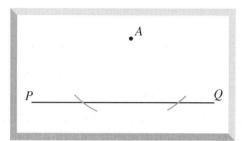

2 Use points B and C to draw equal arcs which cross at D.

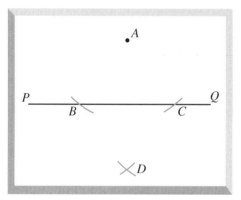

3 Draw a line from A to D.

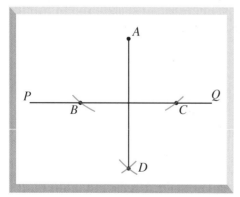

The line AD is perpendicular (at right angles) to the line PQ.

To draw the perpendicular from a point on a line

This means to draw a line at right angles to a given line, from a point that **is on the line**.

Keep your compasses at the same setting whilst doing this construction.

1 From A, draw an arc which cuts the line PQ.

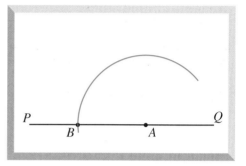

2 From B, draw an arc to cut the first arc at C. Then from C, draw an arc to cut the first arc at D.

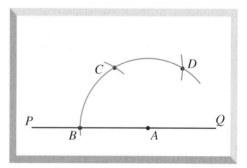

3 From C and D, draw arcs to meet at E. Draw the line AE.

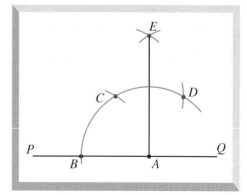

The line AE is perpendicular (at right angles) to the line PQ.

① Draw a line *PQ*, 8 cm long.
Mark a point *A*, about 5 cm above the line.
Draw the line which passes through *A* and is perpendicular to line *PQ*.

② Draw a line *PQ*, 8 cm long.
Mark a point *A*, somewhere on the line.

(a) Using your compasses, mark points *B* and *C*,
which are 3 cm from *A* on the line *PQ*.

(b) Set your compasses to 5 cm.
Draw arcs from *B* and *C* which intersect at *D*.

(c) Draw the line *AD*.

This is another method of constructing a
perpendicular from a given point on a line.

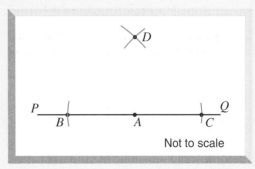

Not to scale

③ Using ruler and compasses only, make an accurate drawing of the triangle shown in this sketch.

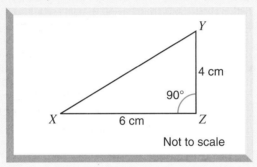

Not to scale

④ (a) Make an accurate drawing of this triangle.

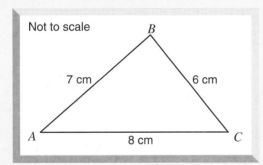

(b) The **altitude** of the triangle is a line perpendicular to a side which passes through the
opposite corner of the triangle.
Draw the altitude of the triangle *ABC* which passes through point *B*.

⑤ (a) Copy the diagram.

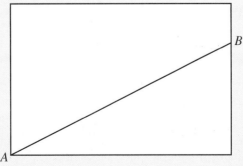

(b) Mark all points inside the rectangle that are less than 2 cm from the line *AB*.

Loci and Constructions

6 Draw a line PQ, 5 cm long.

Using compasses, draw an arc centre P to cut PQ at X.

With your compasses at the same setting draw another arc, centre X, to cut the first arc at Y.

Draw a line through PY.

Measure angle XPY. What do you find?

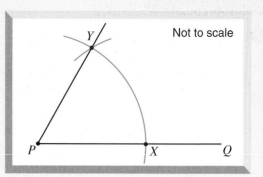

Not to scale

Show how you can use this construction to draw angles of 30° and 120°.

What you need to know

- The path of a point which moves according to a rule is called a **locus**.
- The word **loci** is used when we talk about more than one locus.

Using a ruler and compasses you should be able to:

- Construct the **perpendicular bisector of a line**.

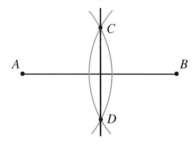

Points on the line CD are **equidistant** from the points A and B.

- Construct the **bisector of an angle**.

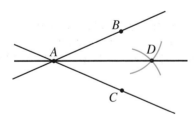

Points on the line AD are **equidistant** from the lines AB and AC.

- Construct the **perpendicular from a point to a line**.

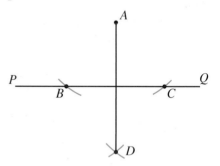

- Construct the **perpendicular from a point on a line**.

A coin is rolled along a line.
Sketch the locus of a point which starts off at the bottom.

What is the locus of the point if the coin rolls around another coin, or if the coins are not round, or … ?

Investigate.

1 The diagram shows part of a building site.
The scale is 1 cm to 1 m.
People are not allowed to walk anywhere within 2 m of the site.

Building Site

Copy the diagram.
Draw accurately the edge of the region
where people may **not** walk.

AQA

2 (a) Use ruler and compasses only to construct an equilateral triangle of side 4 cm.
(b) A point P is 1 cm from the edge of the triangle.
Draw an accurate locus of **all** the possible positions of P.

3 PQRS shows a sketch of a park.
(a) Use ruler and compasses only to construct a plan of the park using a scale of 1 cm to
represent 100 m.

P   300 m   Q

400 m   120°   500 m

S   600 m   R

A fountain is:
    (i)   equidistant from P and Q,
    (ii)   equidistant from PS and SR.
(b) Draw the locus for (i) and (ii) on your plan, and hence find the position of the fountain.
Label it with the letter F.
(c) Find the distance, in metres, of the fountain from R.

4 Ceri and Diane want to find how far away a tower, T, is on the other side of a river.
To do this they mark a base line, AB, 100 metres long as shown on the diagram.
Next they measure the angles at the ends A and B between the base line and the lines of sight
of the tower. These angles are 30° and 60°.

Not to scale

T

30°   60°

A   100 m   B

(a) Use ruler and compasses only to make a scale drawing of the situation.
Use a scale of 1 cm to represent 10 m.
Show clearly all your construction lines.
(b) Find the shortest distance of the tower, T, from the base line AB.

AQA

The movement of a shape from one position to another is called a **transformation**.
The change in position of the shape can be described in terms of a **reflection**, a **rotation** or a **translation**.
Later in the chapter you will meet another transformation, called an **enlargement**.

Reflection

Look at this diagram.
It shows a **reflection** of a shape in the line PQ.
The line PQ is sometimes called a **mirror line**.
Place a mirror on the line PQ and look at the reflection.
You should see that the image of the shape is the
same distance from the mirror as the original.

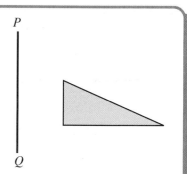

In this diagram the shape $WXYZ$ has been reflected in the line AB to $W_1X_1Y_1Z_1$.

If you join the points W and W_1:

the distance from W to the mirror line is the same as the distance from the mirror line to W_1,
the line WW_1 is at right angles to the mirror line.

Notation

$W_1X_1Y_1Z_1$ is the **image** of $WXYZ$.
We can also say that $WXYZ$ is **mapped** onto $W_1X_1Y_1Z_1$.

When a shape is reflected it stays the same shape and size but it is turned over.

For a reflection we need:
a mirror line.

EXAMPLE

Copy the shape P onto squared paper.
Draw the reflection of shape P in the y axis.

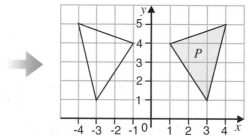

Notice that:
$(1, 4) \rightarrow (-1, 4)$
$(4, 5) \rightarrow (-4, 5)$
$(3, 1) \rightarrow (-3, 1)$
Can you see a pattern?

① Copy each of the following shapes and draw the reflection of the shape in the line *AB*.

(a)

(b)

(c)

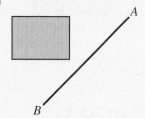

② Copy each of the following shapes onto squared paper and draw the image of the shape after reflection in the line *AB*.

(a)

(b)

(c)

(d)

(e)

(f)

③ Copy each of the following diagrams onto squared paper and draw the reflection of each shape in the line given.

(a)

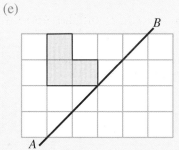

Reflect in the *y* axis.

(b)

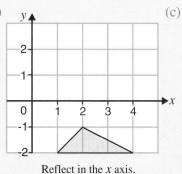

Reflect in the *x* axis.

(c)

Reflect in *y* = 2.

(d)

Reflect in *x* = 3.

(e)

Reflect in *y* = −1.

(f)

Reflect in *y* = *x*.

Transformations · · · Transformations · · ·

35

4 Copy the diagram onto squared paper.
Draw the image of the shape after:
(a) a reflection in the x axis,
(b) a reflection in the y axis,
(c) a reflection in the line $x = 3$,
(d) a reflection in the line $x = -1$,
(e) a reflection in the line $y = x$.

5

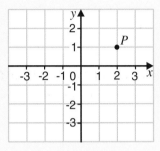

In the diagram, P is the point (2, 1).
Find the coordinates of the image of P under a reflection in:
(a) the x axis,
(b) the y axis,
(c) the line $x = 1$,
(d) the line $y = -1$,
(e) the line $y = x$.

6 The diagram shows a quadrilateral $ABCD$.
Give the coordinates of B after:
(a) a reflection in the x axis,
(b) a reflection in the y axis,
(c) a reflection in the line $x = 4$,
(d) a reflection in the line $x = -1$,
(e) a reflection in the line $y = x$.

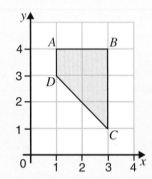

Rotation

Look at this diagram.
It shows the **rotation** of a shape P through 90° anticlockwise about O (the origin).

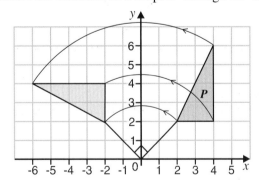

When describing rotations the direction of turn can be **clockwise** or **anticlockwise**.

Remember: clockwise

anticlockwise

All points on shape P are turned through the same angle about the same point.
This point is called the **centre of rotation**.

When a shape is rotated it stays the same shape and size but its **position** on the page changes.

For a rotation we need: a centre of rotation, an amount of turn, a direction of turn.

EXAMPLE

Copy triangle ABC onto squared paper.
Draw the image of triangle ABC after it has been rotated through
$90°$ clockwise about the point $P\,(1,\,1)$.
Label the image $A_1B_1C_1$.

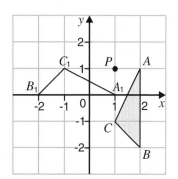

Exercise 35.2

1 Copy each of these shapes onto squared paper.
Draw the new position of each shape after the rotation given.

(a)

$\frac{1}{4}$ turn clockwise about centre X.

(b)

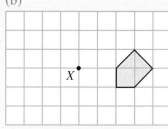

$\frac{1}{2}$ turn clockwise about centre X.

(c)

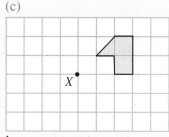

$\frac{1}{4}$ turn anticlockwise about centre X.

(d)

$\frac{1}{2}$ turn about centre X.

(e)

$\frac{3}{4}$ turn clockwise about centre X.

(f)

$\frac{3}{4}$ turn anticlockwise about centre X.

2 Copy each of the following shapes onto squared paper.
Draw the new position of the shape after it has been rotated through $90°$ clockwise about the
origin $(0,\,0)$.

(a)

(b)

(c)

Module 5   401

3 Copy each of the following shapes onto squared paper and then draw the new position of the shape after it has been rotated through 180°, about the point X.

(a)

(b)

(c)

4 The diagram shows a quadrilateral *ABCD*.

Give the coordinates of *B* after:
(a) a rotation through 90°, clockwise about (0, 0),
(b) a rotation through 90°, anticlockwise about (0, 0),
(c) a rotation through 180°, about (0, 0),
(d) a rotation through 90°, clockwise about (3, 1),
(e) a rotation through 90°, anticlockwise about (3, 1),
(f) a rotation through 180°, about (3, 1).

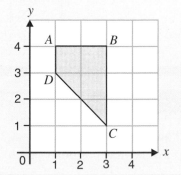

Translation

Look at this diagram.
It shows a **translation** of a shape *P* with vector $\begin{pmatrix} 2 \\ -1 \end{pmatrix}$.

P is mapped onto P_1.
All points on the shape *P* are moved the same distance in the same direction without turning.
A translation can be given:

- in terms of a **distance** and a **direction**,
  e.g. 2 units to the right and 1 unit down.

- with a vector, e.g. $\begin{pmatrix} 2 \\ -1 \end{pmatrix}$.

When a **vector** is used to describe a translation:
the top number describes the **horizontal** part of the movement:
  $+$ = to the right, $-$ = to the left

the bottom number describes the **vertical** part of the movement:
  $+$ = upwards, $-$ = downwards

When a shape is translated it stays the same shape and size and has the same orientation.

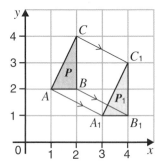

$A(1, 2) \rightarrow A_1(3, 1)$
$B(2, 2) \rightarrow B_1(4, 1)$
$C(2, 4) \rightarrow C_1(4, 3)$
Can you see a pattern?

EXAMPLE Copy triangle *P* onto squared paper. The translation $\begin{pmatrix} -3 \\ 2 \end{pmatrix}$ maps *P* onto P_1.
Draw and label P_1.

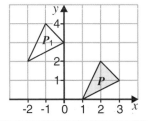

○ ○ ○ ○ ○ ○ ○ ○ ○ ○

Vector notation

$\begin{pmatrix} -3 \\ 2 \end{pmatrix}$ means move triangle *P*
3 units to the left and
2 units up.

① Copy the shape onto squared paper.

Draw the new position of the shape after each of the following translations:
(a) 2 units to the right and 3 units up,
(b) 1 unit to the right and 2 units down,
(c) 3 units to the left and 2 units up,
(d) 1 unit to the left and 3 units down.

② Copy the shape onto squared paper.

Draw the new position of the shape after each of the following translations.

(a) $\begin{pmatrix} 3 \\ 2 \end{pmatrix}$ (b) $\begin{pmatrix} 2 \\ -3 \end{pmatrix}$ (c) $\begin{pmatrix} -2 \\ 3 \end{pmatrix}$ (d) $\begin{pmatrix} -2 \\ -3 \end{pmatrix}$

③ The diagram shows a quadrilateral *ABCD*.

Give the coordinates of *B* after the shape has been translated with vector:

(a) $\begin{pmatrix} 2 \\ 1 \end{pmatrix}$ (b) $\begin{pmatrix} -2 \\ 2 \end{pmatrix}$ (c) $\begin{pmatrix} 1 \\ -3 \end{pmatrix}$ (d) $\begin{pmatrix} -2 \\ -3 \end{pmatrix}$

④ The translation $\begin{pmatrix} 2 \\ -1 \end{pmatrix}$ maps *S*(5, 3) onto *T*.

What are the coordinates of *T*?

⑤ Write down the translation which maps:
(a) *X*(1, 1) onto *P*(3, 2),   (b) *X*(1, 1) onto *Q*(2, –1),
(c) *X*(1, 1) onto *R*(–2, 2),   (d) *X*(1, 1) onto *S*(–2, –1).

⑥ The diagram shows quadrilateral *S*.
Copy *S* onto squared paper.

(a) The translation $\begin{pmatrix} 3 \\ 2 \end{pmatrix}$ maps *S* onto *T*.

   Draw and label *T*.
(b) Write down the translation which maps *T* onto *S*.

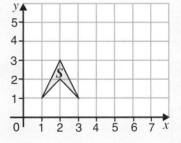

⑦ The translation $\begin{pmatrix} 2 \\ -1 \end{pmatrix}$ maps *P*(3, 2) onto *Q*.

The translation $\begin{pmatrix} -3 \\ 2 \end{pmatrix}$ maps *Q* onto *R*.

(a) What are the coordinates of *R*?
(b) Write down the translation which maps *R* onto *P*.

⑧ The translation $\begin{pmatrix} -2 \\ -3 \end{pmatrix}$ maps *A* onto *B* and the translation $\begin{pmatrix} -1 \\ 2 \end{pmatrix}$ maps *C* onto *B*.

(a) *B* has coordinates (−1, 2).
   What are the coordinates of *A*?
(b) Write down the translation which maps *A* onto *C*.

This diagram shows another transformation, called an **enlargement**.
It shows an enlargement of a shape P with scale factor 2 and centre O.

P is mapped onto P_1.

When a shape is enlarged:
    angles remain unchanged,
    all **lengths** are multiplied by a **scale factor**.

$$\text{Scale factor} = \frac{\text{new length}}{\text{original length}}$$

For an enlargement we need:
    a centre of enlargement,
    a scale factor.

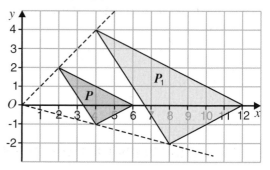

Using a centre of enlargement

A slide projector makes an enlargement of a picture.
The light bulb is the **centre of enlargement.**

Screen
Slide
Bulb

To enlarge a shape using a centre of enlargement:
Draw a line from the centre of enlargement, P, to one corner, A.
Extend this line to A' so that the length of PA' = the scale factor $\times$ the length of PA.
Do the same for other corners of the shape.
Join up the corners to make the enlarged shape.
Label the diagram.

EXAMPLES

 Draw an enlargement of triangle ABC,
centre $P(0, 1)$ and scale factor 3.

 Use centre $P(3, 2)$ and a scale factor
of 2 to enlarge triangle ABC.

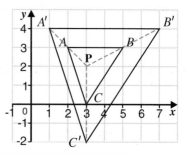

To find the centre and scale factor of an enlargement:
Join pairs of corresponding points.
Extend the lines until they meet. This point is the centre of enlargement.
Measure a pair of corresponding lengths.

$$\text{Scale factor} = \frac{\text{new length}}{\text{original length}}$$

EXAMPLE

Find the centre of enlargement and the scale factor when triangle *XYZ* is mapped onto triangle *X'Y'Z'*.

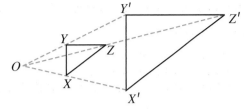

Scale factor $= \dfrac{X'Y'}{XY} = \dfrac{2.0}{0.8} = 2.5$

The centre of enlargement is the point *O*.

Exercise 35.4

1 Copy each diagram onto squared paper and enlarge it using the centre and scale factor given. You will need longer axes than those shown below.

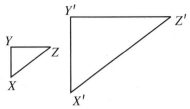

(a) **Centre (0, 0), scale factor 2.**

(b) **Centre (0, 2), scale factor 3.**

(c) **Centre (3, 2), scale factor 2.**

(d) **Centre (5, 2), scale factor 2.5.**

2 The diagram shows a quadrilateral *ABCD*. Give the coordinates of *B* after an enlargement:
(a) scale factor 2, centre (0, 0),
(b) scale factor 3, centre (0, 0),
(c) scale factor 2, centre (0, 2),
(d) scale factor 3, centre *C* (3, 1),
(e) scale factor 2, centre *D* (1, 3),
(f) scale factor 2, centre *A* (1, 4).

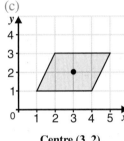

3 For each of the following diagrams find the scale factor and the coordinates of the centre of enlargement.

(a)

(b)

(c)

Using a scale factor which is a fraction

When the scale factor is a value between 0 and 1, such as 0.5 or $\frac{1}{3}$, the new shape is smaller than the original shape. Even though the shape gets smaller it is still called an enlargement.

EXAMPLE　　　Draw an enlargement of this shape with centre (0, 1) and scale factor $\frac{1}{3}$.

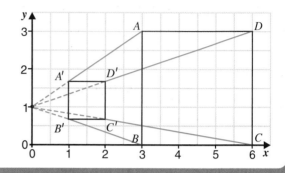

Exercise 35.5

1　Copy the following shapes onto squared paper and draw the enlargement given.

(a)　Scale factor $\frac{1}{2}$, centre (1, 2).

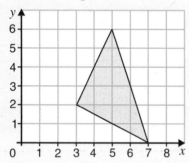

(b)　Scale factor $\frac{1}{3}$, centre (0, 0).

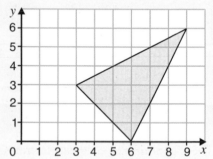

2　For each of the following diagrams give the centre of enlargement and the scale factor.

(a)　(b)　(c)

(d)　(e)　(f)

406

Describing transformations

Look at the shapes in this diagram.

We can describe the single transformation which maps A onto B as a **reflection** in the line $x = 3$.

We can describe the single transformation which maps A onto C as a **rotation** of 180° about (2, 1).

We can describe the single transformation which maps A onto D as a **translation** with vector $\begin{pmatrix} 2 \\ -3 \end{pmatrix}$.

We can describe the single transformation which maps D onto E as an **enlargement**, scale factor 2, centre (2, 0).

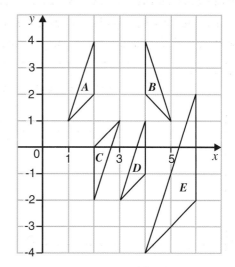

The flow chart below can be used to decide what type of transformation has taken place. The details required to fully describe each type of transformation are also given.

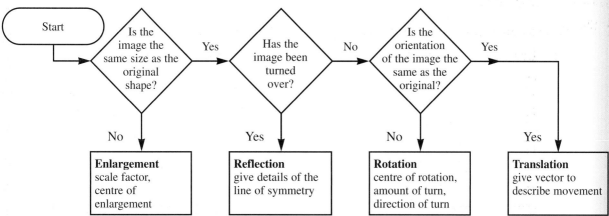

Try following the flow chart for the diagram above.

To find a line of reflection

1 Join each point to its image point.
2 Put a mark halfway along each line.
3 Use a ruler to join the marks.

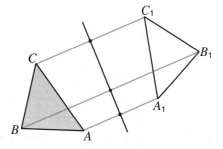

To find the centre and angle of rotation

1 Join each point to its image point.
2 Put a mark halfway along each line.
3 Use a set-square to draw a line at right angles to each line.
   The point where the lines cross is the centre of rotation, R.
4 Join one point and its image to the centre of rotation.
5 The angle of rotation is given by the size of the angle ARA_1.

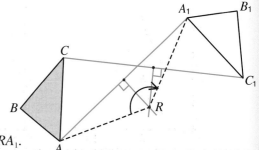

1 Describe fully the single transformation which takes **L₁** onto **L₂**, **L₃**, **L₄**, **L₅** and **L₆**.

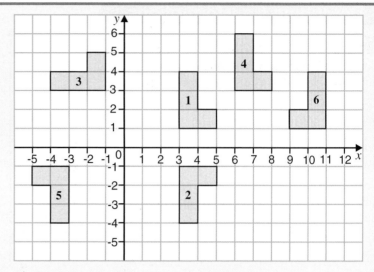

2 Describe fully the single transformation which maps
  (a) *T* onto *U*,
  (b) *T* onto *V*,
  (c) *T* onto *W*.

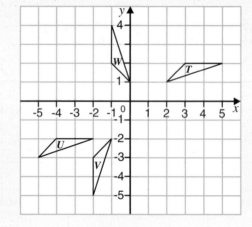

3 Describe fully the single transformation which maps
  (a) *A* onto *B*,
  (b) *A* onto *C*,
  (c) *A* onto *D*.

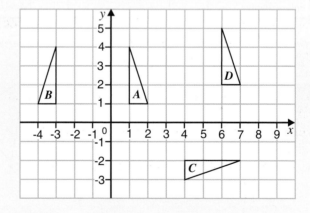

4 Describe the single transformation which maps *ABCD* onto *PQRS*.

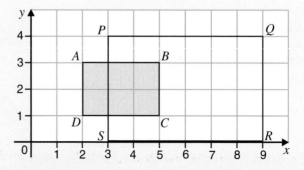

5 Describe fully the single transformation which maps *ABC* onto *XYZ*.

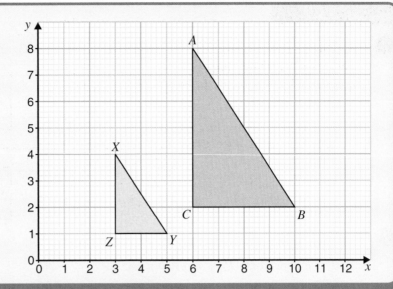

Combinations of transformations

Look at this diagram.

P has been mapped onto P_1 by a reflection in the *x* axis.

Then P_1 has been mapped onto P_2 by a reflection in the *y* axis.

Describe the single transformation which maps P onto P_2.

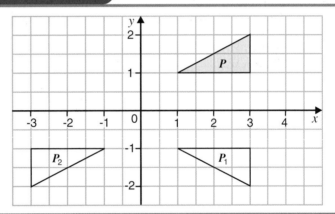

EXAMPLE   Copy triangle *Q* onto squared paper.

(a) *Q* is mapped onto Q_1 by a rotation through 90°, clockwise about (0, 0). Draw and label Q_1.

(b) Q_1 is mapped onto Q_2 by a reflection in the line $y = 0$. Draw and label Q_2.

(c) Describe the single transformation which maps *Q* onto Q_2.

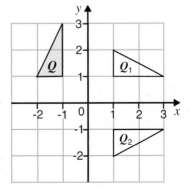

(c) The single transformation which maps *Q* onto Q_2 is a reflection in the line $y = x$.

1 The diagram shows a quadrilateral labelled A.   Copy the diagram onto squared paper.

(a) A is mapped onto A_1 by a reflection in the line $x = 0$.
Draw and label A_1.

(b) A_1 is mapped onto A_2 by a reflection in the line $x = 4$.
Draw and label A_2.

(c) Describe fully the single transformation which maps A onto A_2.

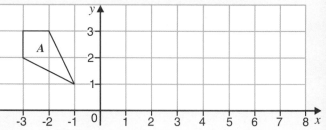

2 The diagram shows a triangle labelled P.   Copy the diagram onto squared paper.

(a) P is mapped onto P_1 by a reflection in the line $y = x$.
Draw and label P_1.

(b) P_1 is mapped onto P_2 by a reflection in the line $x = 5$.
Draw and label P_2.

(c) Describe fully the single transformation which maps P onto P_2.

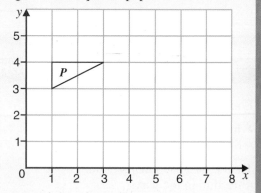

3 The diagram shows a triangle labelled T.   Copy the diagram onto squared paper.

(a) Rotate T through 90° clockwise about (0, 0) to T_1.
Draw and label T_1.

(b) Reflect T_1 in the line $y = 0$ to T_2.
Draw and label T_2.

(c) Reflect T_2 in the line $x = 0$ to T_3.
Draw and label T_3.

(d) Describe fully the single transformation which maps T onto T_3.

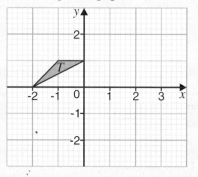

4 The diagram shows a quadrilateral labelled Q.   Copy the diagram onto squared paper.

(a) Q is mapped onto Q_1 by a rotation through 90°, anticlockwise about (0, 0).
Draw and label Q_1.

(b) Q_1 is mapped onto Q_2 by a rotation through 90°, anticlockwise about (2, 0).
Draw and label Q_2.

(c) Describe fully the single transformation which maps Q onto Q_2.

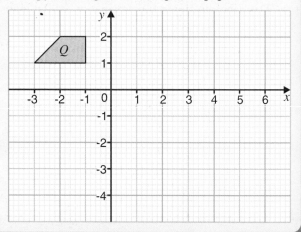

5 The diagram shows a shape labelled S. Copy the diagram onto squared paper.

(a) The translation $\begin{pmatrix} 4 \\ 2 \end{pmatrix}$ maps S onto S_1.

Draw and label S_1.

(b) The translation $\begin{pmatrix} -8 \\ 1 \end{pmatrix}$ maps S_1 onto S_2.

Draw and label S_2.

(c) Describe fully the single transformation which maps S onto S_2.

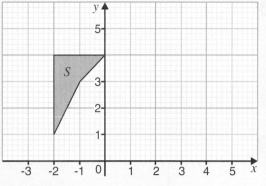

6 The diagram shows a triangle labelled R. Copy the diagram onto squared paper.

(a) R is mapped onto R_1 by a rotation through $90°$, anticlockwise about $(0, 0)$. Draw and label R_1.

(b) R_1 is mapped onto R_2 by a reflection in the line $y = -x$. Draw and label R_2.

(c) R_2 is mapped onto R_3 by a reflection in the line $x = 3$. Draw and label R_3.

(d) Describe fully the single transformation which maps R onto R_3.

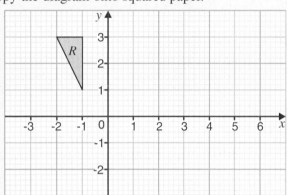

What you need to know

- The movement of a shape from one position to another is called a **transformation**.
- **Single transformations** can be described in terms of a reflection, a rotation, a translation or an enlargement.
- **Reflection**: The image of the shape is the same distance from the mirror line as the original.
- **Rotation**: All points are turned through the same angle about the same point, called a centre of rotation.
- **Translation**: All points are moved the same distance in the same direction without turning.
- **Enlargement**: All lengths are multiplied by a scale factor.

  Scale factor $= \dfrac{\text{new length}}{\text{original length}}$ New length = scale factor $\times$ original length

  The size of the original shape is:
  increased by using a scale factor greater than 1,
  reduced by using a scale factor which is a fraction, i.e. between 0 and 1.
- How to fully describe a transformation.

Transformation	Image same shape and size?	Details needed to describe the transformation
Reflection	Yes	Mirror line, sometimes given as an equation.
Rotation	Yes	Centre of rotation, amount of turn, direction of turn.
Translation	Yes	Horizontal movement and vertical movement. Vector: top number = horizontal movement, bottom number = vertical movement.
Enlargement	No	Centre of enlargement, scale factor.

Transformations . . . Transformations . . . Transformations . . .

1 Copy the diagram.
Shape P is reflected in the line $y = -1$.
Draw the new position of P on your diagram.

2

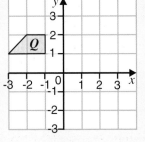

Copy the diagram.
Shape Q is rotated 90° anticlockwise about centre (0, 0).
Draw the new position of Q on your diagram.

3 Copy the diagram.
Shape T is translated 3 units to the right and 2 units up.
Draw the new position of T on your diagram.

4

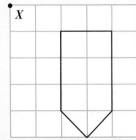

The diagram shows the position of X and a pentagon.
Copy the diagram onto squared paper.
Draw an enlargement of the pentagon, scale factor 2, centre X.

AQA

5 (a) Give the letter of the finishing position:
(i) after the shaded shape is reflected in the x axis,
(ii) after the shaded shape is rotated $\frac{1}{2}$ turn about (0, 0),
(iii) after the shaded shape is translated 3 units right and 4 units down.
(b) Describe fully the single transformation which will map shape **G** onto shape **H**.

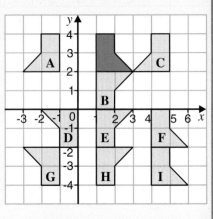

AQA

6 The diagram shows two transformations of the shaded rectangle $PQRS$.

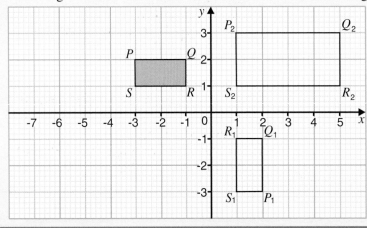

Describe fully the single transformation which takes:
(a) $PQRS$ onto $P_1 Q_1 R_1 S_1$,
(b) $PQRS$ onto $P_2 Q_2 R_2 S_2$.

AQA

7 The diagram shows triangles P, Q, R, S and T.
Describe fully the single transformation which maps
   (a) P onto Q,   (b) T onto Q,
   (c) R onto S,   (d) S onto R,
   (e) R onto T,   (f) T onto R.

8

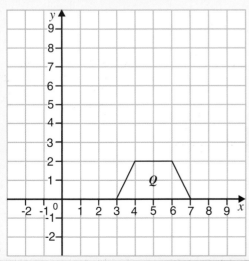

Copy the diagram onto squared paper and enlarge the triangle with scale factor $\frac{1}{3}$, centre P.

AQA

9 (a) Describe the single transformation that will transform shape C to shape B.
   (b) Describe the single transformation that will transform shape A to shape C.

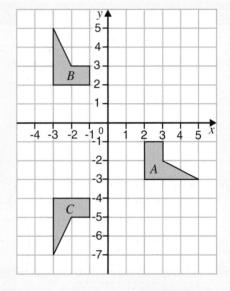

AQA

10 The diagram shows a trapezium labelled Q.
Copy the diagram onto squared paper.

(a) Q is mapped onto Q_1 by a reflection in the x axis.
   Draw and label Q_1.
(b) Q_1 is mapped onto Q_2 by a translation with vector $\begin{pmatrix} 2 \\ 4 \end{pmatrix}$.
   Draw and label Q_2.
(c) Q_2 is mapped onto Q_3 by a reflection in the line $y = x$.
   Draw and label Q_3.
(d) Describe fully the single transformation which maps Q onto Q_3.

Transformations . . . Transformations . . .

CHAPTER 36

Volumes and Surface Areas

3-dimensional shapes (or solids)

These are all examples of 3-dimensional shapes.

Cuboid

Cylinder

Sphere

Pyramid with square base

Cone

What other 3-dimensional shapes do you know?

Making and drawing 3-dimensional shapes

Nets

3-dimensional shapes can be made using **nets**.

This is the net of a cube.

The net can be folded to make a cube.

There are 12 different nets which can be used to make a cube. See how many of them you can draw.

2-dimensional drawings of 3-dimensional shapes

Isometric drawings are used to draw 3-dimensional shapes.
Here are two isometric drawings of a cube of side 2 cm.

Naming parts of a solid shape

Each flat surface is called a **face**.
Two faces meet at an **edge**.
Edges of a shape meet at a corner, or point, called a **vertex**.
The plural of vertex is **vertices**.

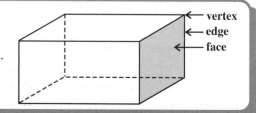

← vertex
← edge
← face

1   A cube has edges of length 2 cm.
    Use squared paper to draw an accurate net of the cube.

2   The diagram shows part of a net of a cube.

(a) In how many different ways can
     you complete the net?
     Draw each of your nets.

(b) Explain why the diagram above
     is **not** the net of a cube.

3   Use squared paper to draw an accurate net of this cuboid.

2 cm   3 cm   1 cm

4   Draw an accurate net for each of these 3-dimensional shapes.

(a)   (b)   (c)

1 cm
1 cm
2 cm
5 cm
2 cm

4 cm
4 cm
6 cm
4 cm

4 cm   4 cm
4 cm
4 cm

5   The diagram shows a pyramid.
    A model of the pyramid is to be made using straws.
    The straws are each 10 cm long and are joined using pipe cleaners.

(a) How many edges does the pyramid have?
(b) How many vertices does the pyramid have?
(c) How many straws are needed to make the pyramid?
(d) What is the total length of the edges of the pyramid?

20 cm
10 cm
10 cm

6

    The diagram shows a cuboid measuring 2 cm × 1 cm × 1 cm
    drawn on isometric paper.
    Draw a net of the cuboid.

7   Draw these 3-dimensional shapes on isometric paper.
    (a) A cube of side 3 cm.
    (b) A 3 cm by 2 cm by 1 cm cuboid.
    (c) A 3 cm by 4 cm by 5 cm cuboid.

8   There are 8 different 3-dimensional shapes which
    can be made using 4 linking cubes.
    One of them is shown.

    (a) Make all the 3-dimensional shapes using linking cubes.
    (b) Draw the 3-dimensional shapes on isometric paper.

Plans and Elevations

When an architect designs a building he has to draw diagrams to show what the building will look like from different directions.
These diagrams are called **plans and elevations**.

The view of a building looking from above is called the **plan**.
The views of a building from the front or sides are called **elevations**.

To show all the information about a 3-dimensional shape we often need to draw several diagrams.

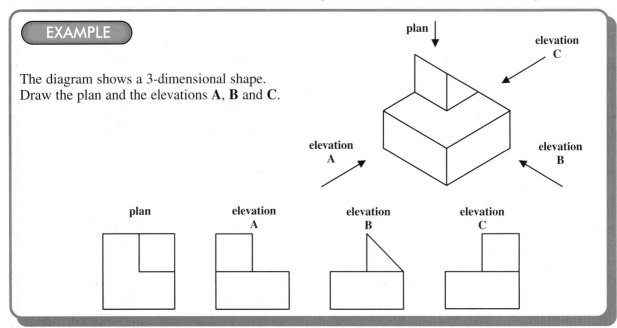

EXAMPLE

The diagram shows a 3-dimensional shape.
Draw the plan and the elevations **A**, **B** and **C**.

plan   elevation A   elevation B   elevation C

Exercise 36.2

1 Draw a sketch to show the plan view of each of these 3-dimensional shapes.

(a) **a staircase**
(b) **a pyramid**
(c) **a cup**

2 Each of these 3-dimensional shapes has been made using 5 linking cubes of side 1 cm.
On squared paper, draw diagrams to show the plan and the elevations **A**, **B** and **C** of each shape.

(a)
(b)
(c)

3 The diagram shows a plastic cylinder of height 3 cm and radius 2 cm with a hole of radius 1 cm drilled through the centre.
Draw the plan and a side elevation of the cylinder.

3 cm

4 The diagram shows an open box containing 3 balls of radius 2 cm.

(a) Draw a plan of the box.
(b) Draw an elevation of the box from the direction marked **A**.

5 The plans and elevations of 3-dimensional shapes made from linking cubes of side 1 cm are shown.
Draw each of the 3-dimensional shapes on isometric paper.

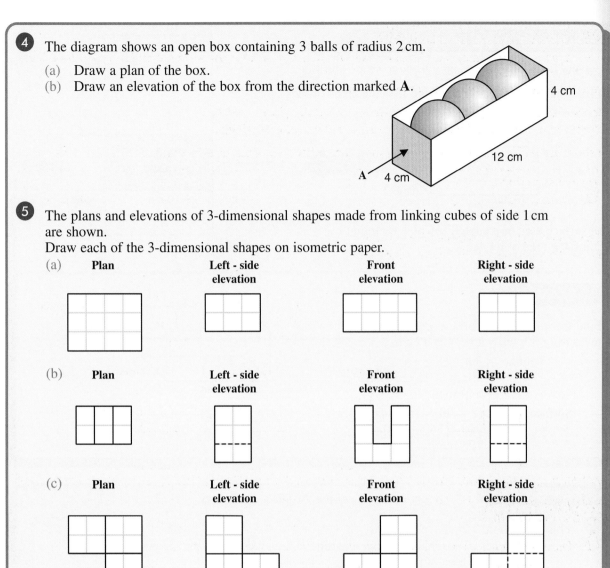

(a) Plan   Left - side   Front   Right - side
                   elevation   elevation   elevation

(b) Plan   Left - side   Front   Right - side
                   elevation   elevation   elevation

(c) Plan   Left - side   Front   Right - side
                   elevation   elevation   elevation

Volume

Volume is the amount of space occupied by a three-dimensional shape.

This **cube** is 1 cm long, 1 cm wide and 1 cm high.
It has a volume of **1 cubic centimetre**.
The volume of this cube can be written as 1 cm^3.

Small volumes can be measured using cubic millimetres (mm^3).
Large volumes can be measured using cubic metres (m^3).

Volume = 1 cm^3

Volume of a cuboid

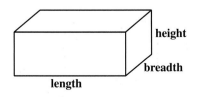

Volume of a cube
A cube is a special cuboid in which the length, breadth and height all have the same measurement.
Volume = length × length × length
$$V = l^3$$

The formula for the volume of a cuboid is: Volume = length × breadth × height

This formula can be written using letters as: $V = lbh$

Surface area of a cuboid

Opposite faces of a cuboid are the same shape and size.

To find the surface area of a cuboid find the areas of the six rectangular faces and add the answers.

The surface area of a cuboid can also be found by finding the area of its net.

EXAMPLE

Find the volume and surface area of a cuboid measuring 30 cm by 15 cm by 12 cm.

$$\begin{aligned} \text{Volume} &= lbh \\ &= 30\,\text{cm} \times 15\,\text{cm} \times 12\,\text{cm} \\ &= 5400\,\text{cm}^3 \end{aligned}$$

$$\begin{aligned} \text{Surface area} &= (2 \times 30 \times 15) + (2 \times 15 \times 12) + (2 \times 30 \times 12) \\ &= 900 + 360 + 720 \\ &= 1980\,\text{cm}^2 \end{aligned}$$

Exercise 36.3

Do not use a calculator for questions 1 to 5.

1 This is a cuboid.
  (a) Draw a net of the cuboid on one-centimetre squared paper.
  (b) Calculate the area of the net.
  (c) What is the surface area of the cuboid?

2 Large cubes are made from small cubes of edge 1 cm.
  (a) How many small cubes are in each of the large cubes?
  (b) What is the surface area of each large cube?

(i)   (ii)   (iii)   (iv)

3 Calculate the volumes and surface areas of these cubes and cuboids.

(a)   (b)   (c)

4 This **cuboid** is made using 24 one-centimetre cubes.

A cuboid made from 24 one-centimetre cubes has a volume of 24 cm³.
(a) What other different cuboids can you make with 24 cubes?
There are 5 others. Which cuboid has the smallest surface area?
(b) How many different cuboids can you make with 36 cubes?
What are the dimensions of the cuboid with the largest surface area?

5 Shapes are made using one-centimetre cubes. Find the volume and surface area of each shape.

  (a)   (b)   (c)   (d)   (e)   (f)

6 Calculate the volumes and surface areas of these cuboids.
Where necessary give your answer to an appropriate degree of accuracy.
(a) 3 cm by 5 cm by 10 cm.   (b) 2.4 cm by 3.6 cm by 6 cm.
(c) 18 cm by 24 cm by 45 cm.   (d) 3.2 cm by 4.8 cm by 6.3 cm.
(e) 5.8 cm by 10.6 cm by 14.9 cm.

7 A cuboid has a volume of 76.8 cm³.
The length of the cuboid is 3.2 cm. The breadth of the cuboid is 2.4 cm.
What is the height of the cuboid?

8 A cuboid has a square base of side 3.6 cm. The volume of the cuboid is 58.32 cm³.
Calculate the height of the cuboid.

9 A cuboid has a volume of 2250 cm³.
The length of the cuboid is 25 cm. The height of the cuboid is 12 cm.
Calculate the surface area of the cuboid.

10 The surface area of this cuboid is 197 cm².
Calculate the volume of the cuboid.

8 cm

5 cm

Prisms

These shapes are all **prisms**.

What do these 3-dimensional shapes have in common?
Draw a different 3-dimensional shape which is a prism.

Explain why these shapes are not prisms.

Volumes and Surface Areas

Volume of a prism

The formula for the volume of a prism is:
Volume = area of cross-section × length.

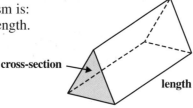

cross-section

length

Volume of a cylinder

A **cylinder** is a prism.
The **volume of a cylinder** can be written as:
Volume = area of cross-section × height
$$V = \pi r^2 h$$

Notice that length has been replaced by height.

EXAMPLES — Find the volumes of these prisms.

(a)

Area 18 cm²

10 cm

Volume = area of cross-
  section × length
= 18 × 10
= 180 cm³

(b)

3 cm

8 cm A

2 cm

B

5 cm

6 cm

Area A = 8 × 3 = 24 cm²
Area B = 3 × 2 = 6 cm²
Total area = 30 cm²
Volume = 30 × 5 = 150 cm³

(c)

5 cm

6 cm

$V = \pi r^2 h$
$= \pi \times 5^2 \times 6$
$= 471.238...$
$= 471$ cm³, correct to 3 s.f.

Exercise 36.4

You should be able to do questions 1 to 3 without using a calculator.
Having completed them you can use your calculator to check your answers.

1 Find the volumes of these prisms.

(a)

Area = 20 cm²

2 cm

(b)

Area 28 cm²

5 cm

(c)

Area 9.6 cm²

10 cm

2 Calculate the shaded areas and the volumes of these prisms.

(a)

1.5 cm

2 cm

4cm

1.4 cm

4cm

(b)

4 cm

3 cm

2.5 cm

(c)

2.4 cm

6 cm

3 cm

3 Calculate the shaded areas and the volumes of these prisms.

(a)

2 cm
1.6 cm
2 cm
5 cm

(b)

10 cm
20 cm

Take π to be 3.14

(c)

5 cm
2 cm

Take π to be 3.14

4 Find the volumes of these prisms.
Where necessary take π to be 3.14 or use the π key on your calculator.

(a)

3 cm   3 cm
2 cm
1 cm   1 cm

(b)

8 cm²   7 cm

(c)

10 cm
6 cm   5 cm
12 cm

(d)

3 cm
4 cm

(e)

20 cm
5 cm

(f)

3 cm
4 cm   6 cm
7 cm

(g)

15 cm
12 cm
Semi-circular
cross-section

(h)

3 cm   4 cm
3 cm

5 Which tin holds more cat food?
Show your working.

3 cm,
4 cm
4 cm   P
Q   7 cm

6 Sylvia says, "A cylinder with a radius of 5 cm and a height of 10 cm has the same volume as a cylinder with a radius of 10 cm and a height of 5 cm."
Is she right? Explain your answer.

7 The radius of a cylinder is 5 cm.
It has a volume of 900 cm³.
Calculate the height of the cylinder, giving your answer correct to 1 decimal place.

8 A cylinder is 8 cm high.
It has a volume of 183 cm³.
Calculate the radius of the cylinder correct to 1 decimal place.

9 A cylinder has a diameter of 10.6 cm.
The volume of the cylinder is 1060 cm³.
Calculate the height of the cylinder.
Give your answer to an appropriate degree of accuracy.

10 A cylinder with a radius of 3 cm and a height of 8 cm is full of water.
The water is poured into another cylinder with a diameter of 8 cm.
Calculate the height of the water.

Surface area of a cylinder

The top and bottom of a cylinder are circles.
The curved surface of a cylinder is a rectangle.

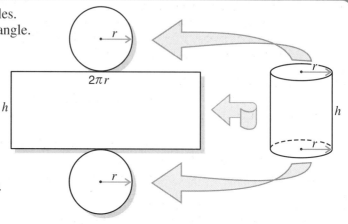

The rectangle has the same height, h,
as the cylinder.
The length of the rectangle must be
just long enough to "wrap around"
the circle.
The lid of the cylinder has radius r and
circumference $2\pi r$.
So the length of the rectangle is also $2\pi r$.

Area of lid $= \pi r^2$ Area of rectangle $=$ length $\times$ breadth
Area of base $= \pi r^2$ $= 2\pi r \times h$
Area of lid and base $= 2\pi r^2$ $= 2\pi rh$

If a cylinder has radius, r, and height, h,
then the formula for the surface area is:

$$\text{Surface area} = 2\pi r^2 + 2\pi rh$$

Area of the top and bottom   Area of the rectangle

The formula for the surface area
is sometimes given as:
Surface area $= 2\pi r(r + h)$

EXAMPLE

Find the surface area of a cylinder with radius 4 cm and height 6 cm.
Take π to be 3.14.

$$\begin{aligned}
\text{Area} &= 2\pi rh + 2\pi r^2 \\
&= 2 \times \pi \times 4 \times 6 + 2 \times \pi \times 4^2 \\
&= 150.796 \ldots + 100.530 \ldots \\
&= 251.327 \ldots \\
&= 251.3 \text{ cm}^2, \text{ correct to 1 d.p.}
\end{aligned}$$

Exercise 36.5

Take π to be 3.14 or use the π key on your calculator.

1 Find the surface areas of these cylinders.

(a)   (b)   (c)

2 Show that the curved surface area of this can
is approximately 75 cm².

3 A bucket is in the shape of a cylinder.
   (a) Calculate the area of the bottom of the bucket.
   (b) Calculate the curved surface area of the bucket.
   (c) What is the volume of the bucket?

50 cm

40 cm

4 A cylinder is 15 cm high.
The curved surface area of the cylinder is 377 cm².
Calculate the volume of the cylinder.

5 A cylinder has a radius of 3.6 cm. The volume of the cylinder is 346 cm³.
Calculate the total surface area of the cylinder.
Give your answer to an appropriate degree of accuracy.

6 A concrete pipe is 150 cm long.
It has an internal radius of 15 cm and an external radius of 20 cm.
Calculate, giving your answers to 3 significant figures,
   (a) the area of the curved surface inside of the pipe,
   (b) the curved surface area of the outside of the pipe.

150 cm

20 cm

15 cm

What you need to know

- **Faces**, **vertices** (corners) and **edges**.
  For example, a cube has 6 faces, 8 vertices and 12 edges.

vertex
edge
face

- A **net** can be used to make a solid shape.

-    **Isometric paper** is used to make
  2-dimensional drawings
  of 3-dimensional shapes.

- Volume is the amount of space occupied by a 3-dimensional shape.

- Plans and Elevations.
  The view of a 3-dimensional shape looking from above is called a **plan**.
  The view of a 3-dimensional shape from the front or sides is called an **elevation**.

- The formula for the volume of a **cuboid** is:
     Volume = length × breadth × height
       $V = l \times b \times h$

  height
  breadth
  length

- To find the **surface area** of a cuboid find
  the area of the six rectangular faces
  and add the answers together.

- Volume of a **cube** is: Volume = (length)³
              $V = l^3$

- If you make a cut at right angles to the length of a **prism**
  you will always get the same cross-section.

  cross-section
  length

- Volume of a prism = area of cross-section × length

-    r
     h
     A **cylinder** is a prism.
     Volume of a cylinder is: $V = \pi \times r^2 \times h$
     Surface area of a cylinder is: Surface area $= 2\pi r^2 + 2\pi rh$

Volumes and Surface Areas

36

3-dimensional coordinates

One coordinate identifies a point on a line.
Two coordinates identify a point on a plane.
Three coordinates identify a point in space.

The diagram shows a cuboid drawn in 3-dimensions.

Using the axes *x*, *y* and *z* shown:

Point *A* is given as (0, 2, 0).

Point *B* is given as (2, 2, 0).

Point *C* is given as (2, 2, 3).

Give the 3-dimensional coordinates of
points, *D*, *E*, *F*, and *G*.

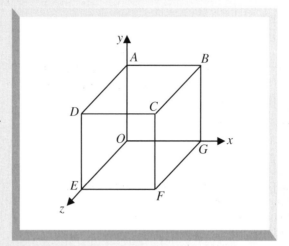

3-dimensional noughts and crosses

The diagram shows a 3-dimensional game which can be used by two people to
play "noughts" and "crosses".

To play the game each player takes it
in turn to give the 3-dimensional
coordinates of a point.
The first player to get three points in
a line wins.

Winning lines can be horizontal,
vertical or diagonal.
eg. (1, 0, 1), (1, 1, 1) and (1, 2, 1)
would be a winning line.

Use a copy of the diagram to play
"3-dimensional noughts and crosses".

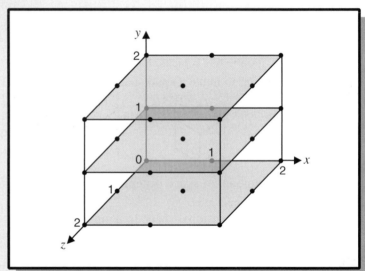

Review Exercise 36

Do not use a calculator for questions 1 to 8.

 Jane uses one centimetre cubes to make a model.
Two views of her model are shown.
(a) How many cubes has Jane used?

Jane places her model inside a box.
The box is in the shape of a cube with sides 3 cm.
(b) Calculate the volume of space left in the box,
stating your units.

AQA

2 The diagram shows a cuboid.

(a) Calculate the volume of the cuboid.
(b) (i) Draw a net of this cuboid.
    (ii) Calculate the area of the net.

Not to scale

2 cm
3 cm
5 cm

AQA

3

The diagram shows a square based pyramid.
Each edge of the pyramid is 4 cm long.
Draw an accurate net of the pyramid.

AQA

4 This 3-dimensional shape has been made using
linking cubes of side 1 cm.
On squared paper, draw diagrams to show:
(a) the plan of the shape,
(b) the elevation from **X**.

X

5

3 cm
5 cm
2 cm

The diagram shows a box made to hold a toy.
On dotty paper, draw a similar box, but with all dimensions
twice the length of the original dimensions.   AQA

6 A block of wood measures 15 cm by 8 cm by 3 cm.
A letter F is cut out of the block of wood, as shown.

(a) Calculate the shaded area.
(b) Calculate the volume of the letter F.

8 cm
3 cm
3 cm
3 cm
15 cm
3 cm
3 cm

7

Not to scale

2 cm
6 cm
4.5 cm

This block of jelly measures 2 cm by 6 cm by 4.5 cm.

(a) What is the volume of this block of jelly?
(b) A shopkeeper buys a box of these jellies.
The box measures 6 cm by 12 cm by 9 cm.
How many blocks of jelly fill the box?

AQA

Volumes and Surface Areas

8 The diagram shows a prism.
The cross section of the prism is a trapezium.
Calculate the volume of the prism.

4 cm
5 cm
14 cm
6 cm

AQA

9

The diagram shows a cuboid which is just big enough to hold six tennis balls.
Each tennis ball has a diameter of 6.8 cm.
Calculate the volume of the cuboid.

AQA

10 Ice cream is sold in a box that is the shape of a prism.
The ends are parallelograms.
The size of the prism is shown in the diagram.
The length of the prism is 12 cm.
Calculate the volume of the ice cream in the box.

4 cm
3 cm
12 cm
6 cm

AQA

11

The volume of a cube is given by the formula $V = L^3$.
(a) A cube has volume 5832 cm³.
What is the length of each edge?
(b) The area of each face of a different cube is 625 cm².
What is the volume of this cube?

L
L
L

AQA

12 Lentil soup is sold in cylindrical tins.
Each tin has a base radius of 3.8 cm and
a height of 12.6 cm.
Calculate the surface area of a tin.
Give your answer to a suitable degree of accuracy.

12.6 cm
3.8 cm
Not to scale

13

8.4 cm
7 cm

"Bradley's Soup" is canned by a small family business.
Each morning they make 200 litres of soup.
This is put in cylindrical tins, each of which is 8.4 cm high and
has a diameter of 7.0 cm.
How many of these tins can be filled from the 200 litres of soup.

AQA

14 To feed a lawn, one box of fertilizer is needed
for every 9 m².
(a) How many boxes are needed to fertilize
a circular lawn of radius 4 m?

The fertilizer is also sold in cylindrical drums.
The volume of a drum is 3060 cm³.
The height of a drum is 12 cm.
(b) Calculate the radius of a drum.

AQA

12 cm
Fitsons
Not to scale

CHAPTER 37

Enlargements and Similar Figures

Enlargement

When a shape is enlarged:

all **lengths** are multiplied by a **scale factor**, angles remain unchanged.

For example:

Shape **B** is an enlargement of Shape **A**.
The scale factor is 2.

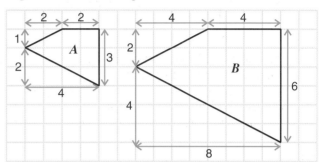

Scale factor = $\dfrac{\text{new length}}{\text{original length}}$

This can be rearranged to give
new length = original length × scale factor.

Similar figures

When one figure is an enlargement of another, the two figures are **similar**.

Sometimes one of the figures is rotated or reflected.
For example:

Figures **C** and **E** are enlargements of figure **A**.
Figures **A**, **C** and **E** are similar.

| A | B | C | D | E |

When two figures are **similar**:

their **shapes** are the same,
their **angles** are the same,
corresponding **lengths** are in the same ratio,
this ratio is the **scale factor** of the enlargement.

Activity

Figures *X* and *Y* are similar.

Y is an enlargement of *X*.

The ratio (or scale factor) is given by

$\dfrac{\text{new length}}{\text{original length}}$

Check that this ratio is the same for all four pairs of corresponding sides.

Check that the angles are the same in the two figures.

1 A photo has width 6 cm and height 10 cm.
An enlargement is made, which has
width 8 cm.
Calculate the height of the enlargement.

Scale factor = $\frac{8}{6}$

$h = 10 \times \frac{8}{6}$

$h = 13.3$ cm, correct to 1 d.p.

2 These two figures are similar.
Calculate the lengths of x and y.
Write down the size of the angle marked a.

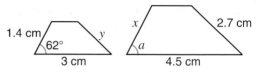

The scale factor = $\frac{4.5}{3}$ = 1.5

Lengths in the large figure are given by:
length in small figure × scale factor
$x = 1.4 \times 1.5$
$x = 2.1$ cm

Lengths in the small figure are given by:
length in large figure ÷ scale factor
$y = 2.7 \div 1.5$
$y = 1.8$ cm

The angles in similar figures are the same,
so $a = 62°$.

Exercise **37.1**

1 Copy each diagram onto squared paper and draw an enlargement with the given scale factor.

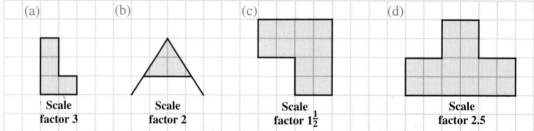

(a) Scale factor 3

(b) Scale factor 2

(c) Scale factor $1\frac{1}{2}$

(d) Scale factor 2.5

2 The shapes in this question have been drawn accurately.
(a) Explain why these two shapes are not similar to each other.

(b) Which two of these shapes are similar to each other?

P   Q   R

3 Which of the following must be similar to each other?
(a) Two circles.   (b) Two kites.   (c) Two parallelograms.
(d) Two squares.   (e) Two rectangles.

4 These two kites are similar.
  (a) What is the scale factor of their lengths?
  (b) Find the length of the side marked x.
  (c) What is the size of angle a?

5 In each part, the two figures are similar. Lengths are in centimetres.
Calculate the lengths and angles marked with letters.

(a)

(b)

(c)

6 These two tubes are similar.

The width of the small size is 2.4 cm and
the height of the small size is 10 cm.
The width of the large size is 3.6 cm.
Calculate the height of the large size.

7 A shape has width 0.8 cm and length 2.4 cm.
It is enlarged to give a new shape with width 1 cm.
Calculate the length of the new shape.

8 A castle has height 30 m.
The height of the castle wall is 6 m.
A scale model of the castle has height 25 cm.
Calculate the height of the castle wall in the scale model.

9 The dimensions of three sizes of paper are given.

Length (cm)	24	30	y
Width (cm)	x	20	32

All the sizes are similar.
Calculate the values of x and y.

Similar triangles

For any pair of similar triangles:
  corresponding lengths are opposite equal angles,
  the scale factor is the ratio of corresponding sides.

$$\frac{AB}{PQ} = \frac{BC}{QR} = \frac{CA}{RP} = \text{scale factor}$$

Enlargements and Similar Figures

1 These two triangles are similar, with the equal angles marked.

Calculate the lengths x and y.

Scale factor $= \frac{6}{5} = 1.2$

$x = 2 \times 1.2$
$x = 2.4\,\text{cm}$

$y = 4.8 \div 1.2$
$y = 4\,\text{cm}$

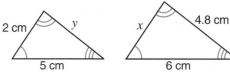

2 Triangles ABC and PQR are similar.

Calculate the lengths of AC and PQ.

BC and PR are corresponding sides.

Scale factor $= \frac{4.48}{3.20} = 1.4$

$AC = 6.04 \div 1.4$
$AC = 4.31\,\text{m}$, correct to 2 d.p.

$PQ = 1.70 \times 1.4$
$PQ = 2.38\,\text{m}$

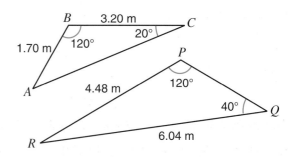

Exercise 37.2

Question 1 should be done without a calculator.

1 In each part, the triangles are similar, with equal angles marked. Lengths are in centimetres. Calculate lengths x and y.

(a)

(b)

(c)

(d)

2 Triangles ABC and ADE are similar. Lengths are in centimetres.
$\angle AED = \angle ACB$.

Calculate the lengths of AB and AE.

3 Triangles PST and PQR are similar. Lengths are in centimetres.
$\angle PTS = \angle PRQ$.

(a) Write down the length of PR.
(b) Calculate QR, PQ and QS.

4 In each part the triangles are similar.
Calculate the unknown lengths in both triangles.

(a)

(b)

(c)

(d)

Showing that two triangles are similar

To show that two triangles are similar you have to show that:

either they have equal angles

or corresponding lengths are all in the same ratio.

If you can show that one of these conditions is true then the other one is also true.

1 *AB* and *CD* are parallel lines. *AD* and *BC* meet at *X*.
(a) Prove that triangles *ABX* and *DCX* are similar.
(b) Which side in triangle *DCX* corresponds to *AX* in triangle *ABX*?
(c) Calculate the length of *AX*.

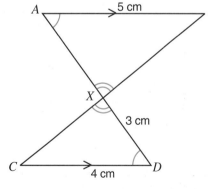

(a) $\angle BAX = \angle CDX$ (alternate angles)
$\angle AXB = \angle DXC$ (vertically opposite angles)
Triangles *ABX* and *DCX* contain two pairs of equal angles and so they are similar.
If two pairs of angles are equal then the third pair must be equal. Why?

(b) $\angle ABX = \angle DCX$.
Sides *AX* and *DX* are opposite these equal angles.
So *DX* corresponds to *AX*.

(c) $\frac{AX}{3} = \frac{5}{4}$ (or scale factor $= \frac{5}{4}$)

$AX = \frac{5}{4} \times 3$

$AX = 3.75$ cm

> You **must** give reasons for any statements you make.
> Alternate angles, corresponding angles and vertically opposite angles were covered in Chapter 27.

EXAMPLE

2 Show that these two triangles are similar.

$\frac{5}{2} = 2.5$

$\frac{3.75}{1.5} = 2.5$

$\frac{2.5}{1} = 2.5$

All three pairs of corresponding sides are in the same ratio, so the triangles are similar.

Exercise **37.3**

1 *BC* is parallel to *PQ*.
Show that triangles *ABC* and *APQ* are similar and calculate the required lengths.

(a)

Calculate *AC* and *AP*.

(b)

Calculate *AC* and *BP*.

(c)

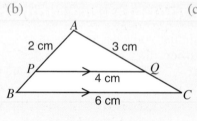

Calculate *BC* and *BP*.

(d)

Calculate *AQ* and *BC*.

(e)

Calculate *AQ* and *BP*.

2 Show that these pairs of triangles are similar and find angle *x*.

(a)

(b)

3 All marked lengths are in centimetres.

(a) In each part show that triangles ABC and APQ are similar and find angle x.

(i)

(ii)

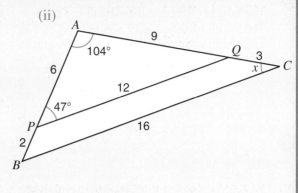

(b) In each part find the perimeters of triangles ABC and APQ.
What do you notice about the ratio of the perimeters of the triangles and the ratio of the lengths of corresponding sides?

4 (a) Explain why triangles ABC and PQR are similar.
(b) Calculate the length of AB.
(c) The perimeter of triangle ABC is 7.5 cm.
Find the perimeter of triangle PQR.

5

Triangles XYZ and PQZ are similar.
$\angle ZXY = \angle ZPQ = 90°$.
$PZ = 4$ cm and $XY = 4.5$ cm.
The ratio $QZ : YZ$ is $2 : 3$.
Calculate the area of triangle XYZ.

What you need to know

● When a shape is **enlarged**: all **lengths** are multiplied by a **scale factor**,
                                angles remain unchanged.

● When two figures are **similar**:
    their **shapes** are the same,
    their **angles** are the same,
    corresponding **lengths** are in the same ratio,
    this ratio is the **scale factor** of the enlargement.

● Scale factor $= \dfrac{\text{new length}}{\text{original length}}$

● All circles are similar to each other.

● All squares are similar to each other.

● For **similar triangles**:
    corresponding lengths are opposite equal angles,
    the scale factor is the ratio of the corresponding sides.

$$\frac{AB}{PQ} = \frac{BC}{QR} = \frac{CA}{RP} = \text{scale factor}$$

Enlargements and Similar Figures

1 Two similar solid shapes are made.
The height of the smaller shape is 7 cm.
The width of the smaller shape is 6 cm.
The width of the larger shape is 9.6 cm.

Calculate the height of the larger shape.

Not to scale

7 cm   6 cm   9.6 cm

AQA

2 Explain why triangles *ABX* and *PQX* are similar.

2 cm   1 cm   54°   36°

Not drawn accurately

3 In the diagram *AB* is parallel to *CD*.
AB = *OC* = 12 cm.   *OB* = 10 cm.

Use similar triangles to calculate the length of *CD*.

Not to scale

12 cm   10 cm   12 cm

AQA

4 All of these triangles are similar.

2 cm   3 cm   46°   29°   4 cm

6 cm   *x*   *z*   3 cm

5 cm   105°   *y*   29°

(a)   Calculate the length *x*.
(b)   Calculate the length *y*.
(c)   What is the value of angle *z*?

AQA

5

A   2 cm   **B**   3 cm

These shapes are similar.
The height of shape **A** is 1.6 cm.
(a)   What is the height of shape **B**?

The perimeter of shape **B** is 13.5 cm.
(b)   Find the perimeter of shape **A**.

6

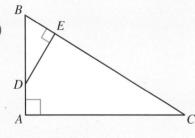

In the triangle *ABC*, *AB* = 10 cm.
AC = 24 cm and *BC* = 26 cm.
Angle *BAC* = 90°.
D is the midpoint of *AB*. *DE* is perpendicular to *BC*.
Use similar triangles to calculate the distance *DE*.   AQA

7 *ABC* is a triangle.
The point *P* lies on *AB* and the point *Q* lies on *AC*.
PQ is parallel to *BC*.
BC = 12 cm,   *PQ* = 8 cm   and   *AQ* = 6 cm.
Calculate the length *QC*.

6 cm   8 cm   12 cm

AQA

CHAPTER 38

Pythagoras' Theorem

The longest side in a right-angled triangle is called the **hypotenuse**.

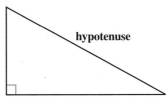

hypotenuse

In any right-angled triangle it can be proved that:

"The square on the hypotenuse is equal to the sum of the squares on the other two sides."

This is known as the **Theorem of Pythagoras**, or **Pythagoras' Theorem**.

Checking the Theorem of Pythagoras

Look at this triangle.

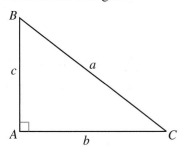

Notice that: the side opposite angle A is labelled a,
the side opposite angle B is labelled b,
the side opposite angle C is labelled c.

ABC is a right-angled triangle because $\angle BAC = 90°$.
$a = 5\,\text{cm}$, so $a^2 = 25\,\text{cm}^2$.
$b = 4\,\text{cm}$, so $b^2 = 16\,\text{cm}^2$.
$c = 3\,\text{cm}$, so $c^2 = 9\,\text{cm}^2$.

$a^2 = b^2 + c^2$

Activity

Use a ruler and a pair of compasses to draw the following triangles accurately.

(a)

(b)

(c)

(d)

(e)

(f)

For each triangle: Measure angle BAC.
Is angle $BAC = 90°$?
Does $a^2 = b^2 + c^2$?
Explain your answers.

When we know the lengths of two sides of a right-angled triangle, we can use the Theorem of Pythagoras to find the length of the third side.

Finding the hypotenuse

EXAMPLE

The roof of a house is 12 m above the ground. What length of ladder is needed to reach the roof, if the foot of the ladder has to be placed 5 m away from the wall of the house?

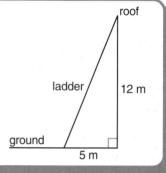

Using Pythagoras' Theorem.

$l^2 = 5^2 + 12^2$
$l^2 = 25 + 144$
$l^2 = 169$

Take the square root of both sides.

$l = \sqrt{169}$
$l = 13 \text{ m}$

The ladder needs to be 13 m long.

Exercise 38.1

1 These triangles are right-angled. Calculate the length of the hypotenuse.

(a)   8 cm, 6 cm

(b) 7 cm, 24 cm

(c)   10 cm, 24 cm

2 These triangles are right-angled. Calculate the length of side a to one decimal place.

(a)   6 cm, 5 cm, a

(b) a, 8 cm, 10 cm

(c)   5 cm, a, 9 cm

3 AB and CD are line segments, drawn on a centimetre-squared grid. Calculate the exact length of

(a) AB,   (b) CD.

4 Calculate the distance between the following points.

(a) $A(2, 0)$ and $B(6, 3)$.
(b) $C(6, 3)$ and $D(0, 10)$.
(c) $E(2, 2)$ and $F(-3, -10)$.
(d) $G(-2, -2)$ and $H(-6, 5)$.
(e) $I(3, -1)$ and $J(-3, -5)$.

5 The coordinates of the vertices of a parallelogram are $P(1, 1)$, $Q(3, 5)$, $R(x, y)$ and $S(7, 3)$.

(a) Find the coordinates of R.
(b) X is the midpoint of PQ. Find the coordinates of X.
(c) Y is the midpoint of PS. Find the coordinates of Y.
(d) Calculate the distance XY.

Finding one of the shorter sides

To find one of the shorter sides we can rearrange the Theorem of Pythagoras.

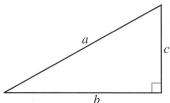

To find b we use:
$b^2 = a^2 - c^2$

To find c we use:
$c^2 = a^2 - b^2$

○○○○○○○○○○○○○○○○○○○
To find the length of a shorter side of a right-angled triangle:
Subtract the square of the known short side from the square on the hypotenuse.
Take the square root of the result.

EXAMPLE

A wire used to keep a radio aerial steady is 9 metres long.
The wire is fixed to the ground 4.6 metres from the base of the aerial.
Find the height of the aerial, giving your answer correct to one decimal place.

Using Pythagoras' Theorem. $9^2 = h^2 + 4.6^2$

Rearranging this we get:
$h^2 = 9^2 - 4.6^2$
$h^2 = 81 - 21.16$
$h^2 = 59.84$

Take the square root of both sides.
$h = \sqrt{59.84}$
$h = 7.735...$
$h = 7.7$ m, correct to 1 d.p.

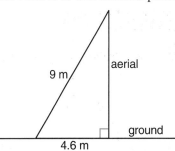

The height of the aerial is 7.7 m, correct to 1 d.p.

Exercise 38.2

1 Work out the length of side b.

(a)

10 cm
6 cm
b

(b)

6.5 cm
2.5 cm
b

(c)

2.5 cm
1.5 cm
b

2 Work out the length of side c, correct to one decimal place.

(a)

8 cm
4 cm
c

(b)

5 cm
12 cm
c

(c)

10 cm
3 cm
c

3 Two boats A and B are 360 m apart.
Boat A is 120 m due east of a buoy.
Boat B is due north of the buoy.
How far is boat B from the buoy?

4   The diagram shows a right-angled triangle, *ABC*, and a square, *ACDE*.

$AB = 2.5\,\text{cm}$ and $BC = 6.5\,\text{cm}$.
Calculate the area of the square *ACDE*.

5

The diagram shows a right-angled triangle, *ABC*, and a square, *XYBA*.

$BC = 6\,\text{cm}$.
The square *XYBA* has an area of $23.04\,\text{cm}^2$.
Calculate the length of *AC*.

Problems involving the use of Pythagoras' Theorem

Questions leading to the use of Pythagoras' Theorem often involve:
Understanding the problem.
     What information is given?
     What are you required to find?
Drawing diagrams.
     In some questions a diagram is not given.
     Drawing a diagram may help you to understand the problem.
Selecting a suitable right-angled triangle.
     In more complex problems you will have to select a right-angled triangle which can be used to
     answer the question. It is a good idea to draw this triangle on its own, especially if it has been
     taken from a three-dimensional drawing.

EXAMPLE

The diagram shows the side view of a swimming pool.
It slopes steadily from a depth of 1 m to 3.6 m.
The pool is 20 m long.
Find the length of the sloping bottom of the pool,
giving the answer correct to three significant figures.

$\triangle CDE$ is a suitable right-angled triangle.
$CD = 3.6 - 1 = 2.6\,\text{m}$

Using Pythagoras' Theorem in $\triangle CDE$.
$DE^2 = CD^2 + CE^2$
$DE^2 = 2.6^2 + 20^2$
$DE^2 = 6.76 + 400$
$DE^2 = 406.76$
$DE = \sqrt{406.76}\ \text{m}$
$DE = 20.1682\ldots\ \text{m}$

The length of the sloping bottom of the pool is 20.2 m, correct to 3 sig. figs.

1 In each of the following, work out the length of the side marked *x*.

(a)   (b)   (c)   (d)

2 A rectangle is 8 cm wide and 15 cm long.
Work out the length of its diagonals.

3 The length of a rectangle is 24 cm. The diagonals of the rectangle are 26 cm.
Work out the width of the rectangle.

4 A square has sides of length 6 cm.
Work out the length of its diagonals.

5 The diagonals of a square are 15 cm.
Work out the length of its sides.

6 The height of an isosceles triangle is 12 cm. The base of the triangle is 18 cm.
Work out the length of the equal sides.

7 An equilateral triangle has sides of length 8 cm.
Work out the height of the triangle.

8 The diagram shows the side view of a car ramp.
The ramp is 110 cm long and 25 cm high.
The top part of the ramp is 40 cm long.
Calculate the length of the sloping part of the ramp.

9 The top of a lampshade has a diameter of 10 cm.
The bottom of the lampshade has a diameter of 20 cm.
The height of the lampshade is 12 cm.
Calculate the length, *l*, of the sloping sides.

10 The top of a bucket has a diameter of 30 cm.
The bottom of the bucket has a diameter of 16 cm.
The sloping sides are 25 cm long.
How deep is the bucket?

11

ABCD is a kite.
AB = 8.5 cm, *BC* = 5.4 cm   and   *BD* = 7.6 cm.
(a)   Calculate the length of *AC*.
(b)   Calculate the area of the kite.

Pythagoras' Theorem

- The longest side in a right-angled triangle is called the **hypotenuse**.
- The **Theorem of Pythagoras** states:
  "In any right-angled triangle the square on the hypotenuse is equal to the sum of the squares on the other two sides."

  $a^2 = b^2 + c^2$

  Rearranging gives:

  $b^2 = a^2 - c^2$

  $c^2 = a^2 - b^2$

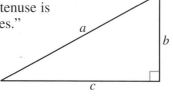

- When we know the lengths of two sides of a right-angled triangle, we can use the Theorem of Pythagoras to find the length of the third side.

Investigate the relationship between the areas of the semi-circles *A*, *B* and *C*.

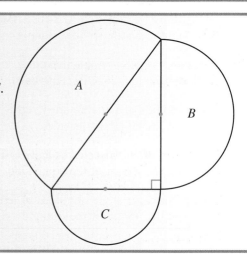

Review Exercise 38

1 Pauline is building a greenhouse.
The base, *PQRS* of the greenhouse should be a rectangle measuring 2.6 m by 1.4 m.
To check the base is rectangular Pauline has to measure the diagonal *PR*.

(a) Calculate the length of *PR* when the base is rectangular.

(b) When building the greenhouse Pauline finds angle *PSR* > 90°. She measures *PR*.
Which of the following statements is **true**?

X: *PR* is greater than it should be.

Y: *PR* is less than it should be.

Z: *PR* is the right length.　　　　AQA

2 The diagram shows the position of a ferry sailing between Folkestone and Calais.
The ferry is at *X*.
The position of the ferry from Calais is given as:

North of Calais 15 km,
West of Calais 24 km.

Calculate the distance of the ferry from Calais.
Give your answer correct to **one** decimal place.
AQA

3 The coordinates of the points A and B are $(6, 8)$ and $(1, 1)$.

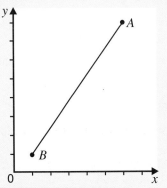

Work out the length of AB.　　　AQA

4 The sketch shows triangle ABC.
$AB = 40$ cm,　$AC = 41$ cm and　$CB = 9$ cm.

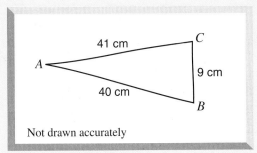

Not drawn accurately

By calculation, show that triangle ABC is a right-angled triangle.　　　AQA

5 John is standing 200 m due west of a power station and 300 m due north of a pylon. Calculate the distance of the power station from the pylon.

6 The diagram shows the position of a camp, a supply hut and a heliport.

Not drawn accurately

(a) What is the bearing of the supply hut from the camp?

(b) Calculate the distance from the camp to the supply hut. Give your answer correct to 2 significant figures.　　　AQA

7 The diagram shows a trapezium $ABCD$.

Not to scale

Calculate the **exact** length of the line AB.

8 A helicopter flies from its base on a bearing of 045° for 20 km before landing. How far east of its base is the helicopter when it lands?

9 Helena is playing golf.

North

Not to scale

Her golf ball is 146 m due west of the 18th hole on a golf course.
She hits the ball, which lands 53 m due south of the hole.
Calculate the shortest distance that she will have to walk from where she hit the ball to where it landed.　　　AQA

CHAPTER 39

Trigonometry

We use **trigonometry** to find the lengths of sides and the sizes of angles in right-angled triangles.

We already know that the longest side of a right-angled triangle is called the **hypotenuse**.

In order to understand the relationships between sides and angles the other sides of the triangle also need to be named.

The **opposite** side is the side directly opposite the angle being used and the **adjacent** side is the side next to the angle.

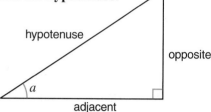

Look at this diagram.
It shows how the height of a kite changes as more and more string is let out.

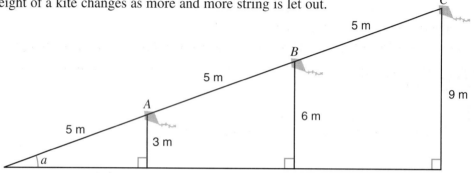

When the kite is at A, the string is 5 m long and the kite is 3 m high.

At A, the ratio $\dfrac{\text{height of kite}}{\text{length of string}}$, is therefore $\frac{3}{5} = 0.6$.

Calculate the value of the same ratio at B and C.

What do you notice?

When the kite is flying at angle a, the ratio $\dfrac{\text{height of kite}}{\text{length of string}}$ will always be the same whatever the length of the kite string and is called the **sine** of angle a.

Finding the length of the opposite side

The sine ratio

For any right-angled triangle: $\sin a = \dfrac{\text{opposite}}{\text{hypotenuse}}$

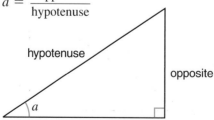

The sine ratio links three pieces of information:

the size of an **angle**,
the length of the side **opposite** the angle,
the length of the **hypotenuse**.

If we are given the values for two of these we can find the value of the third.

EXAMPLE

Find the height of a kite when it is flying at an angle of 40° and the kite string is 12 m long.
Give the answer correct to 3 significant figures.

$$\sin a = \frac{\text{opp}}{\text{hyp}}$$

Substitute known values.

$$\sin 40° = \frac{h}{12}$$

Multiply both sides by 12.

$$h = 12 \times \sin 40°$$

Mathematical shorthand	
Word	**Abbreviation**
sine	sin
opposite	opp
hypotenuse	hyp

Using your calculator, press: [1] [2] [×] [sin] [4] [0] [=]

$$h = 7.713...$$
$$h = 7.71 \text{ m, correct to 3 s.f.}$$

The height of the kite is 7.71 m, correct to 3 s.f.

Exercise **39.1**

1 Find the height, h, of these kites.
Give your answers correct to 3 significant figures.

(a)

(b)

(c)

2 Calculate the lengths marked x.
Give your answers correct to 3 significant figures.

(a)

(b)

(c)

3 In $\triangle ABC$, angle $ACB = 90°$.

(a) If $\angle BAC = 47.5°$ and $AB = 4.6$ m find BC.
(b) If $\angle ABC = 67.4°$ and $AB = 12.4$ m find AC.
(c) If $\angle BAC = 15.8°$ and $AB = 17.4$ cm find BC.
(d) If $\angle BAC = 35°$ and $AB = 8.5$ cm find the size of $\angle ABC$ and then find AC.
Give your answers correct to 3 significant figures.

Finding an angle

If you are given the sine of an angle and asked to find the angle, use the inverse sine function, $\sin^{-1}$, on your calculator.

Using your calculator, press:
The display should read 0.5.
Clear the display and press: sin⁻¹ 0 . 5 =
What do you notice?

EXAMPLE

Find the size of angle a when the kite string is 12 m long and the kite is flying 7 m above the ground.
Give the answer correct to one decimal place.

$$\sin a = \frac{\text{opp}}{\text{hyp}}$$

Substitute known values.

$$\sin a° = \frac{7}{12}$$

$$a = \sin^{-1} \frac{7}{12}$$

Using your calculator, press: sin⁻¹ (7 ÷ 1 2) =

$a = 35.685...$
$a = 35.7°$, correct to 1 d.p.

Exercise 39.2

1 Find the size of angle a for each of these kites.
Give your answers correct to one decimal place.

(a) (b) (c)

2 Find the size of angle x in each of these triangles.
Give your answers correct to one decimal place.

(a) (b) (c)

3 In $\triangle PQR$ angle $PQR = 90°$.
(a) If $QR = 4$ m and $PR = 10$ m find the size of $\angle QPR$.
(b) If $PQ = 4.7$ cm and $PR = 5.2$ cm find the size of $\angle PRQ$.
(c) If $QR = 7.2$ m and $PR = 19.4$ m find the size of $\angle QPR$.
(d) If $PQ = 3.7$ cm and $PR = 9.1$ cm find the size of $\angle QRP$
and then find the size of $\angle QPR$.
Give your answers correct to one decimal place.

EXAMPLE

Find the length of the string, l, when a kite is 6 m high and the string makes an angle of $50°$ with the ground.
Give the answer correct to 3 significant figures.

$$\sin a = \frac{\text{opp}}{\text{hyp}}$$

Substitute known values.

$$\sin 50° = \frac{6}{l}$$

Multiply both sides by l.

$$l \times \sin 50° = 6$$

Divide both sides by $\sin 50°$.

$$l = \frac{6}{\sin 50°}$$

Using your calculator, press: $\boxed{6}$ $\boxed{\div}$ $\boxed{\sin}$ $\boxed{5}$ $\boxed{0}$ $\boxed{=}$

$$l = 7.832\ldots$$
$$l = 7.83 \text{ m, correct to 3 s.f.}$$

The length of the string is 7.83 m, correct to 3 s.f.

Exercise 39.3

① Find the lengths, l, of these kite strings.
Give your answers correct to 3 significant figures.

(a)

5.2 m, $48°$, l

(b)

l, 3.4 m, $27°$

(c)

l, 2.9 m, $36°$

② Calculate the length of side x in each of these triangles.
Give your answers correct to two decimal places.

(a)

2.6 cm, $23.6°$, x

(b)

x, $47.3°$, 3.9 cm

(c)

4.7 cm, $63.7°$, x

③ In $\triangle ABC$ angle $ACB = 90°$.

(a) If $\angle BAC = 36.2°$ and $BC = 4.5$ m   find AB.
(b) If $\angle ABC = 64.7°$ and $AC = 15.8$ cm   find AB.
(c) If $\angle BAC = 12.7°$ and $BC = 14.7$ cm   find AB.
(d) If $\angle BAC = 72.8°$ and $AC = 7.6$ m
find the size of $\angle ABC$ and then find AB.
Give your answers correct to 3 significant figures.

We have found that **sine** is the ratio $\dfrac{\text{opposite}}{\text{hypotenuse}}$.

In a similar way we can find two other ratios, the **cosine** of angle a and the **tangent** of angle a.

The cosine ratio

For any right-angled triangle:

$$\cos a = \frac{\text{adjacent}}{\text{hypotenuse}}$$

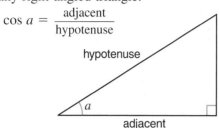

The cosine ratio links three pieces of information:
  the size of an **angle**,
  the length of the side **adjacent** to the angle,
  the length of the **hypotenuse**.
If we are given the values of two of these we can find the value of the third.

The tangent ratio

For any right-angled triangle:

$$\tan a = \frac{\text{opposite}}{\text{adjacent}}$$

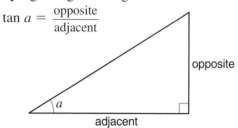

The tangent ratio links three pieces of information:
  the size of an **angle**,
  the length of the side **opposite** to the angle,
  the length of the side **adjacent** to the angle.
If we are given the values of two of these we can find the value of the third.

EXAMPLE

1 Write down the sin, cos and tan ratios for angle a in the triangle.

$$\sin a = \frac{\text{opp}}{\text{hyp}} = \frac{8}{17}$$

$$\cos a = \frac{\text{adj}}{\text{hyp}} = \frac{15}{17}$$

$$\tan a = \frac{\text{opp}}{\text{adj}} = \frac{8}{15}$$

Mathematical shorthand	
Word	**Abbreviation**
adjacent	adj
opposite	opp
hypotenuse	hyp
sine	sin
cosine	cos
tangent	tan

How to select and use the correct ratio

There are only 3 different types of question for each of the ratios.
Selecting the correct ratio is most important.
To do this:

1. Go to the angle you know (or want to find).

2. Name sides (opp, adj, hyp).
   If you are trying to find the length of a side, name that side first together with one other side of known length.
   If you are trying to find the size of an angle, name two sides of known length.

3. Select the correct ratio and write it down.

$$\sin a = \frac{\text{opp}}{\text{hyp}} \qquad \cos a = \frac{\text{adj}}{\text{hyp}} \qquad \tan a = \frac{\text{opp}}{\text{adj}}$$

   One way to remember the ratios is to use the initial letters, SOHCAHTOA.
   You may know another method.

4. Substitute known values from the question.

5. Rearrange to isolate the angle, or side, you are trying to find.

6. Use your calculator to find the size of the angle, or side, writing down more figures than you need for the final answer.

7. Correct to the required degree of accuracy.

8. Give the answer, stating the degree of approximation and giving the correct units. When giving the answer to a problem you should use a short sentence.

EXAMPLES

2 Find the length, h, giving the answer to 3 significant figures

$$\tan a = \frac{\text{opp}}{\text{adj}}$$

Substitute known values.

$$\tan 28° = \frac{h}{12.4}$$

Multiply both sides by 12.4.

$$h = 12.4 \times \tan 28°$$

Using your calculator, press: [1] [2] [.] [4] [×] [tan] [2] [8] [=]

$$h = 6.593...$$
$$h = 6.59 \, \text{m, correct to 3 s.f.}$$

3 Find the size of angle a, correct to one decimal place.

$$\cos a = \frac{\text{adj}}{\text{hyp}}$$

Substitute known values.

$$\cos a° = \frac{11}{16}$$

$$a = \cos^{-1} \frac{11}{16}$$

Using your calculator, press: [cos⁻¹] [(] [1] [1] [÷] [1] [6] [)] [=]

$$a = 46.56...$$
$$a = 46.6°, \text{correct to 1 d.p.}$$

Exercise **39.4**

1 Write down the sin, cos and tan ratios for angle p in each of the following triangles.

(a)

(b)

(c)

2 By choosing the correct ratio, calculate angle p in each of the following triangles. Give your answers correct to one decimal place.

(a)

(b)

(c)

(d)

(e)

(f)

3 By choosing the correct ratio, calculate side *a* in each of the following triangles.

(a)

7.3 cm 37.8° *a*

(b)

3.1 cm 25.6° *a*

(c)

53.5° 5.2 cm *a*

(d)

a 72.4° 3.6 cm

(e)

3.2 cm *a* 42.7°

(f)

6.3 cm *a* 57.3°

4 An equilateral triangle has sides of length 5 cm.
Calculate the height of the triangle.

5 An isosceles triangle has sides of length 10 cm, 10 cm and 6 cm.
Calculate the angles of the triangle.

6 Calculate
(a) the length of *AC*, (b) the length of *CE*.

C 5 cm 20° *E* *D* 50° *B* 5 cm *A*

7 Calculate
(a) the length of *RQ*, (b) angle *SPR*.

S 3.6 cm *R* 74° 10 cm *Q* *P*

8 Calculate the length of *WX*.

Y 30° 8 cm *Z* 10 cm 25° *W* *X*

448

9 Calculate the length of *PQ*.

P   4 cm

55°

Q

3.5 cm

20°

10 Calculate the length of *CD*.

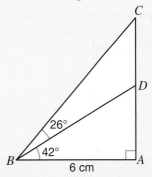

C

D

26°

42°

B   6 cm   A

Angles of elevation and depression

When we look **up** from the horizontal the angle we turn through is called an **angle of elevation**.

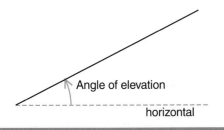

Angle of elevation

horizontal

When we look **down** from the horizontal the angle we turn through is called an **angle of depression**.

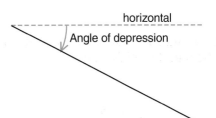

horizontal

Angle of depression

EXAMPLES

1 From a point on the ground, 30 m from the base of a pylon, the angle of elevation to the top of the pylon is 50°.

h
(opp)

50°

30 m (adj)

Find the height of the pylon.

$$\tan a = \frac{\text{opp}}{\text{adj}}$$

$$\tan 50° = \frac{h}{30}$$

$$h = 30 \times \tan 50°$$
$$h = 35.75\ldots$$
$$h = 35.8 \text{ m, correct to 3 s.f.}$$

The height of the pylon is 35.8 m, correct to 3 s.f.

2 Staten Island Ferry is 270 m away from the base of the Statue of Liberty.
The ferry can be seen from a viewing point in the lantern, 85 m above the ground.

horizontal

d

Alternate to angle of depression

d

85 m (opp)

270 m (adj)

What is the angle of depression to the ferry from the viewing point?

$$\tan a = \frac{\text{opp}}{\text{adj}}$$

$$\tan d° = \frac{85}{270}$$

$$d = \tan^{-1} \frac{85}{270}$$

$$d = 17.47\ldots$$
$$d = 17.5°, \text{ correct to 1 d.p.}$$

The angle of depression to the ferry from the viewing point is 17.5°, correct to 1 d.p.

1 From a point on the ground 20 m from the base of a tree, the angle of elevation to the top of the tree is 47°. Calculate the height of the tree.

2 From a point on the ground 10 m from a block of flats, the angle of elevation to the top of the block is 76°. Calculate the height of the block of flats.

3 A fishing boat is 200 m from the bottom of a vertical cliff. From the top of the cliff the angle of depression to the fishing boat is 34°.
(a) Calculate the height of the cliff.
(b) A buoy is 100 m from the bottom of the cliff. Calculate the angle of depression to the buoy from the top of the cliff.

4 A yacht is 20 m from the bottom of a lighthouse. From the top of the lighthouse the angle of depression to the yacht is 48°. Calculate the height of the lighthouse.

5 A cat is on the ground 25 m from the foot of a house. A bird is perched on the gutter of the house 15 m from the ground. Calculate the angle of elevation from the cat to the bird.

6 A tree, 6 m high, casts a shadow of 4.8 m on horizontal ground. Calculate the angle of elevation to the sun.

7 From a point, A, on the ground, the angle of elevation to a hot air balloon is 9°. The balloon is 150 m above the ground. Calculate the distance from A to the balloon.

8 From the top of a cliff, 36 m high, the angles of depression of two boats at sea are 17° and 25°. The boats are in a straight line from the foot of the cliff. Calculate the distance between the two boats.

Three-figure bearings

Remember:
Bearings are used to describe the direction in which you must travel to get from one place to another.
They are measured from the North line in a clockwise direction.
A bearing can be any angle from 0° to 360° and is written as a three-figure number.

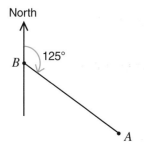

A is on a bearing of 125° from B.

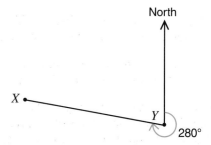

X is on a bearing of 280° from Y.

EXAMPLE

A plane flies 300 km on a bearing of 132° from an airport.
How far South and East is it from the airport?
Give the answers correct to 3 significant figures.

x is the distance South.
y is the distance East.
Using supplementary angles:
$\angle PAB = 180° - 132° = 48°$.

To find x

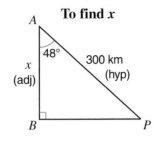

$\cos a = \dfrac{\text{adj}}{\text{hyp}}$

$\cos 48° = \dfrac{x}{300}$

$x = 300 \times \cos 48°$

$x = 200.73\ldots$ km

$x = 201$ km, correct to 3 s.f.

To find y

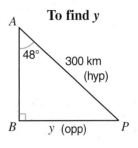

$\sin a = \dfrac{\text{opp}}{\text{hyp}}$

$\sin 48° = \dfrac{y}{300}$

$y = 300 \times \sin 48°$

$y = 222.94\ldots$ km

$y = 223$ km, correct to 3 s.f.

The plane is 201 km South and
223 km East of the airport,
correct to 3 s.f.

*How can you use Pythagoras'
Theorem to check the answer?*

Sketch diagrams

Drawing a sketch diagram may help you to
understand the question.
More information can be added to the diagram as you
answer the question.

Exercise **39.6**

1 A plane flies 250 km on a bearing of 050°.
   (a) How far north is it from its original position?
   (b) How far east is it from its original position?

2 A helicopter leaves its base and flies 23 km on a bearing of 285°.
   How far west is it from its base?

3 A ship at A is 3.8 km due north of a lighthouse.
   A ship at B is 2.7 km due east of the same lighthouse.
   What is the bearing of the ship at B from the ship at A?

4 A helicopter has flown from its base on a bearing of 153°. Its distance east of base is 19 km.
   How far has the helicopter flown?

5 A fishing boat leaves port and sails on a straight course.
   After 2 hours its distance south of port is 24 km and its distance east of port is 7 km.
   On what bearing did it sail?

6 A yacht sails 15 km on a bearing of 053°, then 7 km on a bearing of 112°.
   How far north is the yacht from its starting position?

7 A plane flies 307 km on a bearing of 234°, then 23 km on a bearing of 286°.
   How far south is the plane from its starting position?

8 Jayne sails 1.5 km on a bearing of 050°.
   She then changes course and sails 2 km on a bearing of 140°.
   On what bearing must she sail to return to her starting position?

- **Trigonometry** is used to find the lengths of sides and the sizes of angles in right-angled triangles.

- You must learn the **sine**, **cosine** and **tangent** ratios.

$$\sin a = \frac{\text{opposite}}{\text{hypotenuse}} \qquad \cos a = \frac{\text{adjacent}}{\text{hypotenuse}} \qquad \tan a = \frac{\text{opposite}}{\text{adjacent}}$$

- Each ratio links the size of an angle with the lengths of two sides.
  If we are given the values for two of these we can find the value of the third.

- When we look **up** from the horizontal the angle we turn through is called the **angle of elevation**.

- When we look **down** from the horizontal the angle we turn through is called the **angle of depression**.

- **Three-figure bearings.**
  Bearings are used to describe the direction in which you must travel to get from one place to another. They are measured from the North line in a clockwise direction.
  A bearing can be any angle from 0° to 360° and is written as a three-figure number.

Review Exercise 39

1 When Colin is 10 m from a haystack, the angle of elevation to the top of the haystack is 18°.
Calculate h, the height of the haystack.

Not to scale

h

18°

10 m

2 The design for a children's slide, *ABCD*, for a playground is shown.
The height of the slide, *BD*, is 136 cm.
The distance *DC* is 195 cm.

(a) Calculate the angle *BCD*.

(b) Angle *ABD* is 28°.
Calculate the distance *AB*.

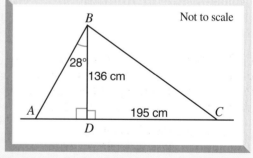

Not to scale

B

28°

136 cm

A 195 cm *C*

D

AQA

3 The diagram shows the positions of Leeds and Newcastle.
Calculate how far south Leeds is from Newcastle, the distance marked x on the diagram.
Give your answer to an appropriate degree of accuracy.

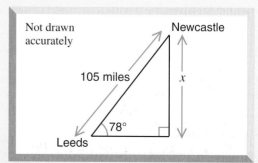

Not drawn accurately

Newcastle

105 miles

x

78°

Leeds

AQA

4 This quadrilateral is made from two right-angled triangles.
  (a) Calculate the length *x*.
  (b) Calculate the angle *A*.

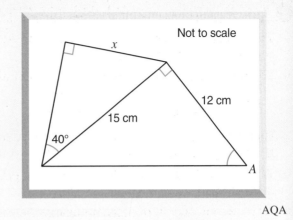

Not to scale

x

12 cm

15 cm

40°

A

AQA

5 The diagram shows part of a framework for a roof.
Triangles *ABC* and *CED* are right-angled.
AC = 3.2 m. *CE* = 4.1 m.
Angle *ACB* is 49°. Angle *EDC* is 58°.

  (a) Calculate the length *BC*.
  (b) Calculate the length *CD*.

A

Not to scale

3.2 m

E

4.1 m

49°   58°

B   *C*   *D*

AQA

6 The diagram shows a side view of two buildings.
The length *DE* = 15 m. Angle *FDE* = 20°.
  (a) Calculate the height *EF*.

A telephone wire stretches from *C* to *F*.
The length *CF* = 20.9 m.
  (b) Calculate the size of angle *CFD*.

B   *C*

20.9 m

Not to scale

F

20°

A   *D*   15 m   *E*

AQA

7 A lift at the seaside takes people from sea level to the top of a cliff, as shown.
From sea level to the top of the cliff, the lift travels 23 m and rises a height of 21 m.

  (a) Calculate the distance *AC*.
  (b) Calculate the angle *BCA*.

Cliff top   *B*

Not to scale

21 m   23 m

Sea level

A   *C*

AQA

8 Cos *PQR* = $\frac{12}{13}$

  (a) Find (i) tan *PQR*,
             (ii) sin *PQR*.

  (b) *PQ* = 6 cm.
      What are the lengths of *QR* and *PR*?

R

Q   *P*

9 (a) Calculate the length, *l*, of this ladder.

Not to scale

2.4 m

l

0.7 m

(b) A health and safety directive says:
'*A ladder must be placed at an angle of between 70° and 80° to the ground.*'
   (i) A ladder is required to reach a height of 4.7 metres.
       Calculate the length of the longest ladder that can be used safely.
   (ii) The same ladder is used to reach a height of 4.9 metres.
        Calculate whether or not the ladder is safe.

AQA

10 A ship sails on a two stage journey from *A* to *B* to *C*.
The first stage of the journey from *A* to *B* is shown.
A to *B* is a journey of 90 km on a bearing of 032°.

(a) Calculate the distance travelled east during the
    first stage of this journey.

N

B

90 km

32°

A

Not to scale

N

90°

B

150 km

C

90 km

32°

A

Not to scale

The second stage of the journey from *B* to *C* is a distance 150 km on
a bearing of 090°.
(b) Find the total distance travelled east on the journey from *A* to *C*.
    Hence calculate the bearing of *C* from *A*.

AQA

11 A group of geography students need to calculate the width of a river.
They measure the angle of elevation to the top of an electricity pylon from opposite banks of
the river, *P* and *L*.
The pylon is 70 metres high.

70 m

43°

36°

P

River

L

Calculate the width of the river *PL*.

70 m

43°

36°

P

L

River

Not to scale

AQA

Understanding and Using Measures

Units of measurement

Different units can be used to measure the same quantity. For example:

The same **length** can be measured using centimetres, kilometres, inches, miles, …

The same **mass** can be measured using grams, kilograms, pounds, ounces, …

The same **capacity** can be measured using litres, millilitres, gallons, pints, …

There are two sorts of units in common use — **metric** units and **imperial** units.

Activity Which of the units mentioned in these statements are metric and which are imperial?

This sheet is 8 foot by 4 foot and 6 millimetres thick.

I did about 300 miles last week so I'll need about 8 gallons to fill the tank. How many litres is that?

An Olympic champion runs 100 metres at an average speed of nearly 25 miles per hour.

I weigh 8 stone 2 pounds or 52 kilograms.

Metric units

The common metric units used to measure length, mass (weight) and capacity (volume) are shown below.

Length	Mass	Capacity and volume
1 kilometre (km) = 1000 metres (m)	1 tonne (t) = 1000 kilograms (kg)	1 litre = 1000 millilitres (ml)
1 m = 100 centimetres (cm)	1 kg = 1000 grams (g)	1 cm³ = 1 ml
1 cm = 10 mm		

Kilo means thousand, 1000.   So, a **kilo**gram is one thousand grams.

For example: 3 kilograms = 3000 grams.

Centi means hundredth, $\frac{1}{100}$.   So, a **centi**metre is one hundredth of a metre.

For example: 2 centimetres = $\frac{2}{100}$ metre.

Milli means thousandth, $\frac{1}{1000}$.   So, a **milli**litre is one thousandth of a litre.

For example: 5 millilitres = $\frac{5}{1000}$ litre.

Changing from one metric unit to another

Changing from one metric unit to another involves multiplying, or dividing, by a power of 10 (10, 100 or 1000). Multiplying and dividing by powers of 10 was covered in Chapter 8.

EXAMPLES

1

| 1 centimetre (cm) = 10 millimetres (mm) |

(a) Change 6.3 cm into millimetres.

To change centimetres into millimetres, multiply by 10.
$6.3 \times 10 = 63$
6.3 cm = 63 mm

(b) Change 364 mm into centimetres.

To change millimetres into centimetres, divide by 10.
$364 \div 10 = 36.4$
364 mm = 36.4 cm

2

| 1 kilogram (kg) = 1000 grams (g) |

(a) Change 19.4 kg into grams.

To change kilograms into grams, multiply by 1000.
$19.4 \times 1000 = 19\ 400$
19.4 kg = 19 400 g

(b) Change 245 g into kilograms.

To change grams into kilograms, divide by 1000.
$245 \div 1000 = 0.245$
245 g = 0.245 kg

Changing units - areas and volumes

$1\,m = 100\,cm$

$1\,m^2 = 100 \times 100\,cm^2 = 10\ 000\,cm^2$

$1\,m^3 = 100 \times 100 \times 100\,cm^3 = 1\ 000\ 000\,cm^3$

How many mm equal 1 cm?

How many mm² equal 1 cm²?

How many mm³ equal 1 cm³?

Exercise 40.1   Do not use a calculator.

1 Change each of the following lengths into millimetres.
(a) 8.6 cm   (b) 0.8 cm   (c) 0.08 cm

2 Change each of the following lengths into centimetres.
(a) 90 mm   (b) 210 mm   (c) 2 mm

3 Change each of the following lengths into metres.
(a) 200 cm   (b) 4550 cm   (c) 66 cm

4 Change each of the following lengths into centimetres.
(a) 6 m   (b) 0.9 m   (c) 0.07 m

5 Change each of the following lengths into kilometres.
(a) 4000 m   (b) 35 000 m   (c) 455 m

6 Change each of the following lengths into metres.
(a) 6 km   (b) 650 km   (c) 0.35 km

7 Change each of the following masses into grams.
(a) 2 kg   (b) 7.5 kg   (c) 0.6 kg

8 Change each of the following masses into kilograms.
(a) 3000 g   (b) 32 000 g   (c) 220 g

9 Copy and complete each of the following.
(a) 320 000 ml = ... *l*
(b) 0.32 t   = ... kg = ... g
(c) 3200 g   = ... kg = ... t
(d) 320 mm   = ... cm = ... m
(e) 32 000 cm   = ... m   = ... km
(f) 3.2 km   = ... m   = ... cm

10 Find the number of metres in:
   (a) 8000 mm   (b) 8.6 cm   (c) 0.04 km

11 Find the number of millilitres in:
   (a) 2 l (b) 0.85 l (c) 0.03 l

12 Which two lengths are the same?
   2000 m   20 km   200 m   2 km   0.02 km

13 Which two weights are the same?
   8 g   8 kg   8000 g   0.8 kg   80 kg

14 Which length is longest?
   0.5 km   50 m   5000 mm   500 cm

15 Which weight is heaviest?
   0.3 t   3000 g   3 kg   30 kg

16 How many:
   (a) metres are there in 3123 mm?
   (b) centimetres are there in 4.5 m?
   (c) metres are there in 3.24 km?
   (d) grams are there in 1 tonne?
   (e) litres are there in 400 ml?

17 Which area is larger?
      0.5 m^2 or 500 cm^2
   Give a reason for your answer.

18 Which volume is larger?
      0.08 m^3 or 800 000 cm^3
   Give a reason for your answer.

19 A can of coke contains 330 ml.
How many litres of coke are there in 6 cans?

20 One lap of a running track is 400 m.
How many laps are run in an 8 km race?

21 Twenty children at a party share equally 1 kg of fruit pastilles.
How many grams of pastilles does each child receive?

22 A recipe for a dozen biscuits uses 240 g of flour.
James has 1.2 kg of flour.
How many biscuits can he make?

23 Ben takes two 5 ml doses of medicine four times a day.
Ben stops taking the medicine after 5 days.
Originally, there was $\frac{1}{4}$ of a litre of medicine.
How much medicine is left?

Estimating with sensible units using suitable degrees of accuracy

It is a useful skill to be able to estimate length, mass and capacity. These facts might help you.

Length
Most adults are between 1.5 m and 1.8 m tall. The door to your classroom is about 2 m high.
Find some more facts which will help you to estimate length and distance.

Mass
A biro weighs about 5 g. A standard bag of sugar weighs 1 kg.
Find some more facts which will help you to estimate weight or mass.

Capacity
A teaspoon holds about 5 ml. A can of pop holds about 330 ml.
Find some more facts which will help you to estimate volume and capacity.

EXAMPLES

1 The Great Wall of China, the longest man-made structure in the world, is about 2350 km long.
Degree of accuracy: nearest 50 km.

2 Earthquake shock waves travel through rock at a speed of approximately 25 000 km/hour.
Degree of accuracy: nearest 1000 km/hour.

3 The smallest mammal is the Kitti's hog-nosed bat. It weighs about 1.5 g.
Degree of accuracy: nearest 0.1 g.

4 The current Olympic record for the men's 100 m is 9.92 seconds.
Degree of accuracy: nearest 0.01 seconds.

Understanding and Using Measures

1 Which of the following is the best estimate for the mass of a banana?

| 1 kg | 5 g | 250 g |
| 30 g | 3 kg | 750 g |

2 Which of the following is the best estimate for the diameter of a football?

| 2 m | 50 mm | 30 cm |
| 1.5 m | 0.6 m | 800 mm |

3 Which of the following would be the best estimate for the capacity of a mug?

| 15 ml | 1200 ml | 2 l |
| 0.5 l | 200 ml | 800 ml |

4 Give a sensible estimate using an appropriate unit for the following measures:
(a) the length of a matchstick,
(b) the length of a football pitch,
(c) the weight of a 30 cm ruler,
(d) the weight of a double decker bus.
In each case state the degree of accuracy you have chosen for your estimate.

5 The diagram, which is drawn to scale, shows a man standing next to a tree. Using an appropriate metric unit estimate the height of the tree. State the degree of accuracy that you have used in making your estimate.

6 How much milk is in this jug?

Give your answer in an appropriate unit and state the degree of accuracy you have used.

7 "My teacher's height is about 1.7 mm."
This statement is incorrect.

It can be corrected by changing the unit:
"My teacher's height is about 1.7 m,"
or it can be corrected by changing the quantity:
"My teacher's height is about 1700 mm."

Each of these statements is also incorrect.
"Tyrannosaurus, a large meat-eating dinosaur, is estimated to have been about 12 cm long."
"The tallest mammal is the giraffe which grows up to about 5.9 mm tall."
"My car used 5 ml of petrol on a journey of 35 miles."
"The area of the school hall is about 500 mm²."

Correct each statement:
(a) by changing the unit,
(b) by changing the quantity.
For each statement give the degree of accuracy that is used.

Imperial units

The following imperial units of measurement are in everyday use.

Length	**Mass**	**Capacity and volume**
1 foot = 12 inches	1 pound = 16 ounces	1 gallon = 8 pints
1 yard = 3 feet	14 pounds = 1 stone	

Metric and imperial conversions

In order to convert to and from metric and imperial units you need to know these facts.

Length	**Mass**	**Capacity and volume**
5 miles is about 8 km	1 kg is about 2.2 pounds	1 litre is about 1.75 pints
1 inch is about 2.5 cm		1 litre is about 0.2 gallons
1 foot is about 30 cm		

EXAMPLES

1 Convert 40 cm to inches.

1 inch is about 2.5 cm.
40 cm is about 40 ÷ 2.5 inches.
40 cm is about 16 inches.

2 How many pints are there in a 4 litre carton of milk?

1 litre is about 1.75 pints.
4 litres is about 4 × 1.75 pints.
4 litres is about 7 pints.

3 Change 5 kg to pounds.

1 kg is about 2.2 pounds.
5 kg is about 5 × 2.2 pounds.
5 kg is about 11 pounds.

4 Tim is 6 feet 2 inches tall.
Estimate Tim's height in centimetres.

6 feet 2 inches = 6 × 12 + 2 = 74 inches.
74 inches is about 74 × 2.5 cm.
6 feet 2 inches is about 185 cm.

5 The capacity of a car's petrol tank is 12 gallons.
How much does the petrol tank hold in litres?

1 litre is about 0.2 gallons.
12 gallons is about 12 ÷ 0.2 litres.
12 gallons is about 60 litres.

6 How far is 32 km in miles?

There are 32 ÷ 8 = 4 lots of 8 km in 32 km.
So there must be 4 lots of 5 miles in 32 km.
4 × 5 = 20.
There are 20 miles in 32 km.

Exercise 40.3

1 Change these lengths into centimetres.
   (a) 2 inches   (b) 2 feet

2 Change these lengths into inches.
   (a) 2 m   (b) 20 cm

3 Change these lengths into kilometres.
   (a) 5 miles   (b) 45 miles

4 Change these lengths into miles.
   (a) 8 km   (b) 40 km

5 Change these weights into pounds.
   (a) 25 kg   (b) 1 t

6 Change these weights into kilograms.
   Give your answers to the nearest kilogram.
   (a) 100 pounds
   (b) 6 stones 11 pounds

7 How many litres are there in
   (a) 5 pints,   (b) 2 gallons 3 pints?

8 Convert each quantity to the units given.
   (a) 15 kg to pounds.
   (b) 20 litres to pints.
   (c) 5 metres to inches.
   (d) 6 inches to millimetres.
   (e) 50 cm to inches.
   (f) 6 feet to centimetres.

9 A box contains 200 balls.
   Each ball weighs 50 g.
   Estimate the total weight of the balls in pounds.

10 Kelvin is 5 feet 8 inches tall.
   Estimate Kelvin's height in centimetres.

11 Kelvin weighs 9 stones 12 pounds.
   Estimate Kelvin's weight in kilograms.

12 Estimate the number of:
   (a) metres in 2000 feet,
   (b) kilometres in 3 miles,
   (c) feet in 150 centimetres,
   (d) pounds in 1250 grams,
   (e) litres in 10 gallons.

13 A sheet of card measures 12 inches by 20 inches.
   What is the area of the card in square centimetres?

14 The height of a pile of magazines is 20 inches.
   Each magazine is 5 mm thick.
   How many magazines are in the pile?

15 Lauren says 10 kg of potatoes weighs the same as 20 lb of sugar.
   Is she correct? Show all your working.

16 Alfie cycles 6 miles. Jacob cycles 10 kilometres.
Alfie claims that he has cycled further than Jacob. Is he correct?
Show all your working.

17 Nick weighs 10 stones 6 pounds. Last year he weighed 10 kg more.
How much did Nick weigh last year?

18 Lubna has 250 g of butter. She uses 4 oz of butter to make a cake.
What weight of butter is left?

19 A stair carpet is 85 cm wide and 4.5 m in length.
Calculate the area of the carpet in square feet.

20 Convert the following speeds to kilometres per hour.
(a) 30 miles per hour.   (b) 50 miles per hour.   (c) 30 metres per second.

21 Convert the following speeds to miles per hour.
(a) 60 km per hour.   (b) 40 metres per second.

22 Convert a speed of 60 miles per hour to metres per second.
Give your answer to a suitable degree of accuracy.

23 (a) A car does 40 miles to the gallon. How many kilometres does it do per litre?
(b) A car does 9.6 kilometres to the litre. How many miles does it do per gallon?

24 30 g of grass seed is needed to sow 1 m² of lawn.
What weight of grass seed is needed to sow a rectangular lawn measuring 40 foot by 30 foot?

25 Concrete is sold by the cubic metre.
A path, 31 feet long, 5 feet wide and 1 foot 6 inches deep, is to be made of concrete.
How many cubic metres of concrete are needed?

Discrete and continuous measures

Discrete measures

Discrete measures can only take particular values.

For example: The number of people on a bus is 42.
Two ice skating judges give scores of 5.1 and 5.2.

The number of people on a bus must be a whole number.
The ice skating scores show that a discrete measure does not need to be a whole number.
They are discrete because scores are not given between numbers like 5.1 and 5.2.

Continuous measures
James was 14 on the day of his 14th birthday.
He will still be called 14 years old right up to the day before his 15th birthday.
So, although James is 14, his actual age is any age within a range of 1 year.

I am 14.

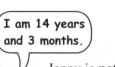

I am 14 years and 3 months.

Jenny is **not** exactly 14 years and 3 months old.
However, Jenny's age is given to a greater degree of accuracy than James' age because the range of possible ages in her case is smaller.
What is the range of possible ages in Jenny's measurement of her age?

Measures which can lie within a range of possible values are called **continuous measures**.
The value of a continuous measure depends on the accuracy of whatever is making the measurement.

460

EXAMPLES

1 Jane is 160 cm tall to the nearest 10 cm.
What are the limits between which her actual height lies?

When rounding to the nearest 10:

      The smallest value that rounds to 160 is 155.
      155 cm is the smallest height that Jane can be.
      The largest value that rounds to 160 is $164.\dot{9}$.
      $164.\dot{9}$ cm is the largest height that Jane can be.
      For ease the value $164.\dot{9}$ is normally called 165 (even though 165 rounds to 170).

So Jane's actual height is any height from 155 cm to 165 cm.
This can be written as the inequality: 155 cm ≤ Jane's height < 165 cm

2 Jane is 162 cm tall to the nearest 1 cm.
What are the limits between which her actual height lies?

When rounding to the nearest 1:

      The smallest value that rounds to 162 is 161.5.
      161.5 cm is the smallest height that Jane can be.
      The largest value that rounds to 162 is $162.4\dot{9}$.
      $162.4\dot{9}$ cm is the largest height that Jane can be.
For ease the value $162.4\dot{9}$ is normally called 162.5 (even though 162.5 rounds to 163).

So Jane's actual height is any height from 161.5 cm to 162.5 cm.
This can be written as the inequality: 161.5 cm ≤ Jane's height < 162.5 cm

Exercise **40.4**

1 State whether each of the following are discrete or continuous measures.
  (a) The volume of wine in a wine glass.
  (b) The votes cast for the Independent Party candidate in a local election.
  (c) The number of pages in a newspaper.
  (d) The time it takes to walk to school.
  (e) The number of beds in a hospital.
  (f) The weight of your best friend.

2 For each of the following measures state whether the value given is an exact value or give the limits within which it could lie.
  (a) A book has 224 pages.
  (b) A bus was 5 minutes late.
  (c) Tom has two brothers.
  (d) I weigh 63 kg.
  (e) Judy is 153 cm tall.

3 What are the slowest and fastest possible times:
  (a) of Derek who runs exactly 100 metres in 13 seconds measured to the nearest second,
  (b) of Jan who swims exactly 100 metres in 82.6 seconds measured to the nearest tenth of a second?

4 Tina is 1.53 m tall.
  (a) To what degree of accuracy is Tina's height given?
  (b) What are the limits between which her true height lies?

5 (a) What is the minimum weight of a 62 kg parcel measured to the nearest kilogram?
(b) What is the minimum length of a 2.3 m shelf measured to the nearest 0.1 m?
(c) What is the minimum time for a race timed at 12.63 seconds measured to the nearest one hundredth of a second?

6 What degree of accuracy has been used to make these estimates of the length of a corridor:
(a) About 120 m. The smallest possible length is 115 m.
(b) About 100 m. The smallest possible length is 75 m.
(c) About 200 m. The smallest possible length is 150 m.

Dimensions and formulae

Formulae can be used to calculate perimeters, areas and volumes of various shapes. By analysing the **dimensions** involved it is possible to decide whether a given formula represents a perimeter, an area or a volume.

Length (L) has **dimension 1**.
Length (L) × Length (L) = **Area** (L²) has **dimension 2**.
Length (L) × Length (L) × Length (L) = **Volume** (L³) has **dimension 3**.

The size of this square based cuboid depends on:
  x, the length of the side of the square base, y, the height of the cuboid.

The total **length** of the edges of the cuboid is given by the formula: $E = 8x + 4y$
This formula involves: Numbers: 8 and 4
                       Lengths (L): x and y The formula has **dimension 1**.

The total **surface area** of the cuboid is given by the formula: $S = 2x^2 + 4xy$
This formula involves: Numbers: 2 and 4
                       Areas (L²): $x \times x$ and $x \times y$ The formula has **dimension 2**.

The **volume** of the cuboid is given by the formula: $V = x^2y$
This formula involves: Volume (L³): $x \times x \times y$ This formula has **dimension 3**.

EXAMPLE

In each of these expressions the letters a, b and c represent lengths. Use dimensions to check whether the expressions could represent a perimeter, an area or a volume.

(a) $2a + 3b + 4c$ (b) $3a^2 + 2b(a + c)$
(c) $2a^2b + abc$ (d) $3a + 2ab + c^3$

> **Note**
> When checking formulae and expressions, numbers can be ignored because they have no dimension.
> ≡ means 'is equivalent to'.

(a) $2a + 3b + 4c$
Write this using dimensions.
$L + L + L \equiv 3L \equiv L$
$2a + 3b + 4c$ has dimension 1
and could represent a perimeter.

(b) $3a^2 + 2b(a + c)$
Write this using dimensions.
$L^2 + L(L + L)$
$\equiv L^2 + L(2L)$
$\equiv L^2 + 2L^2$
$\equiv 3L^2$
$\equiv L^2$
$3a^2 + 2b(a + c)$ has dimension 2
and could represent an area.

(c) $2a^2b + abc$
Write this using dimensions.
$L^2 \times L + L \times L \times L$
$\equiv L^3 + L^3$
$\equiv 2L^3$
$\equiv L^3$
$2a^2b + abc$ has dimension 3 and
could represent a volume.

(d) $3a + 2ab + c^3$
Write this using dimensions.
$L + L \times L + L^3$
$\equiv L + L^2 + L^3$
The dimensions are **inconsistent**.
$3a + 2ab + c^3$ does not represent a perimeter, an area or a volume.

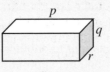

1 p, q, r and x, y, z represent lengths.
For each formula state whether it represents
a length, an area or a volume.

   (a) pq (b) $2\pi x$ (c) $p + q + r$ (d) πz
   (e) pqr (f) $2(pq + qr + pr)$ (g) $\pi x^2 y$ (h) $2\pi x(x + y)$

2 In each of the expressions below, x, y and z represent lengths.
By using dimensions decide whether each expression could represent a perimeter, an area,
a volume or none of these. Explain your answer in each case.

   (a) $x + y + z$ (b) $xy + xz$ (c) xyz (d) $x^2(y^2 + z^2)$

   (e) $x(y + z)$ (f) $\dfrac{x^2}{y}$ (g) $\dfrac{xz}{y}$ (h) $x + y^2 + z^3$

   (i) $xy(y + z)$ (j) $x^3 + x^2(y + z)$ (k) $xy(y^2 + z)$ (l) $x(y + z) + z^2$

3 The diagram shows a discus. x and y are the lengths shown on the diagram.
These expressions could represent certain quantities relating to the discus.

     $\pi(x^2 + y^2)$ $\pi x^2 y^2$ πxy $2\pi(x + y)$

   (a) Which of them could be an expression for:
       (i)   the longest possible distance around the discus,
      (ii) the surface area of the discus.
   (b) Use dimensions to explain your answers to part (a).

4 x, y and z represent lengths.
   (a) $A = xyz + z(x - y) + 2y$
       This is not a formula for perimeter, area or volume. Use dimensions to explain why.
   (b) $P = 3z(x + y)$
       This could be a formula for area. Use dimensions to explain why.
   (c) $V = x^2 y + z^2(2x - y) + 2y^3$
       This could be a formula for volume. Use dimensions to explain why.

5 p, q, r and s represent the lengths of the edges of this triangular prism.
Match the formulas to the measurements.

   Formulas $\frac{1}{2} pqs$ $2\left(p + q + r + \frac{3s}{2}\right)$ $s(p + q + r) + pq$

   Measurements Edge length   Surface area   Volume

6 These arrows are similar.

   w represents the width of any arrow.
   k and c are numbers.
   H represents the height of the arrow and A its area.
   Which of the following statements could be correct and which **must** be wrong.
   (a) $H = kw$ (b) $H = ckw$ (c) $H = kw + c$
   (d) $A = cw$ (e) $A = kw^2$ (f) $A = kw^3$
   Give a reason for each of your answers and where you think the formula **must** be wrong
   suggest what it might be for.

7 In these formulae a, b and c represent lengths and A represents an area.
   (a) $a = b + c$ (b) $a^2 = bc$ (c) $A = a^2 + bc$
   (d) $c = A + ab$ (e) $Ab = a^3$ (f) $A = \dfrac{a^2}{c} + b^2$
   Which of the formulae have consistent dimensions?

What you need to know

- The common units — both **metric** and **imperial** — used to measure **length**, **mass** and **capacity**.

- How to convert from one unit to another. This includes knowing the connection between one metric unit and another and the approximate equivalents between metric and imperial units.

Metric Units	Imperial Units	Conversions
Length 1 kilometre (km) = 1000 metres (m) 1 m = 100 centimetres (cm) 1 cm = 10 mm **Mass** 1 tonne (t) = 1000 kilograms (kg) 1 kg = 1000 grams (g) **Capacity and volume** 1 litre = 1000 millilitres (ml) 1 cm³ = 1 ml	**Length** 1 foot = 12 inches 1 yard = 3 feet **Mass** 1 pound = 16 ounces 14 pounds = 1 stone **Capacity and volume** 1 gallon = 8 pints	**Length** 5 miles is about 8 km 1 inch is about 2.5 cm 1 foot is about 30 cm **Mass** 1 kg is about 2.2 pounds **Capacity and volume** 1 litre is about 1.75 pints 1 litre is about 0.2 gallons

- How to change between units of area. For example $1 \text{ m}^2 = 10\,000 \text{ cm}^2$.

- How to change between units of volume. For example $1 \text{ m}^3 = 1\,000\,000 \text{ cm}^3$.

- How to estimate measurements using sensible units and a suitable degree of accuracy.

- Be able to recognise limitations on the accuracy of measurements.
  A **discrete measure** can only take a particular value and a **continuous measure** lies within a range of possible values which depends upon the degree of accuracy of the measurement.

- By analysing the **dimensions** of a formula it is possible to decide whether a given formula represents a **length** (dimension 1), an **area** (dimension 2) or a **volume** (dimension 3).

Shoe size is a discrete measure.
Foot size is a continuous measure.

Investigate the connection between foot size and shoe size.

Review Exercise 40

1 How many magazines, each 0.6 cm thick, will fit on a bookcase shelf which is exactly 1.2 m wide?

1.2 m

2 One glass of lemonade contains 300 ml.
How many glasses of lemonade can be poured from a jug which contains 2.4 litres?

3 (a) How many centimetres are there in 39 millimetres?
(b) The distance from London to Edinburgh is 400 miles.
How many kilometres is this?

AQA

4 One litre of water weighs 1 kg. One litre of water is approximately 0.22 of a gallon.
(a) Estimate the weight of one gallon of water in pounds.
(b) Calculate how many litres are equivalent to one gallon.
Give your answer correct to one decimal place.

AQA

5 Tim is 5 feet 10 inches tall and weighs 72 kg.
Sam is 165 cm tall and weighs 11 stone 7 pounds.
Who is taller? Who is heavier?

6 Ben buys 4 lb 4 oz of apples which cost £1.24 per kg. 454 grams is equal to 1 lb.
  (a) Calculate the weight of the apples in kilograms, writing down all the figures shown on your calculator display.
  (b) (i) For the purpose of calculating the cost, write this weight to an appropriate degree of accuracy.
       (ii) Explain why you used this degree of accuracy.   AQA

7 Convert an area of $25\,\text{m}^2$ to: (a) cm^2,   (b)   square feet.

8 Convert a speed of 30 miles per hour into feet per second.   1 mile = 5280 feet.   AQA

9 James runs at an average speed of 12 miles/hour.
Tim runs at an average speed of 320 m/minute.
Who runs the fastest?

10 According to the instructions Vinyl Matt paint covers about $13\,\text{m}^2$/litre.
  (a) Estimate the area covered with 2 gallons of paint?
  (b) Estimate how many litres of paint is needed to cover a wall which measures 18 feet by 10 feet.

11 The total surface area of the Earth's oceans is 362 million square kilometres.
To what degree of accuracy is this measurement given?

12 Which of these measurements is discrete and which is continuous?
  (a) Two pints of milk.   (b) Two 1 pint bottles of milk.
Explain your answer.

13 A blue whale weighs 140 tonnes to the nearest 10 tonnes.
What is the smallest possible weight of a blue whale?

14 What is the greatest possible difference between the times of two runners who both run a race in 12.2 seconds timed to the nearest tenth of a second?

15 What is the smallest possible length of a piece of string which measures 25 cm to the nearest centimetre.

16 One of these formulae gives the volume of an egg of height H cm and width w cm.

Formula **A**: $\frac{1}{6}\pi H^2 w^2$ Formula **B**: $\frac{1}{6}\pi H w^2$ Formula **C**: $\frac{1}{6}\pi H w$

  (a) Which is the correct formula?
  (b) Explain how you can tell that this is the correct formula.   AQA

17 The diagram shows a prism.
The following formulae represent certain quantities connected with the prism.

$wx + wy$ $\frac{1}{2}z(x+y)w$ $\frac{z(x+y)}{2}$ $2(v + 2w + x + y + z)$

  (a) Which of these formulae represents length?
  (b) Which of these formulae represents volume?   AQA

18 In the following expressions, r, a and b represent lengths.
For each expression, state whether it represents a **length**, an **area**, a **volume**, or **none** of these.

  (a) πab (b) $\pi r^2 a + 2\pi r$ (c) $\frac{\pi r a^3}{b}$ AQA

1 Find the size of the angles *a*, *b* and *c*.

2

(a) Which of these diagrams has only one line of symmetry?
(b) Which of these diagrams has rotational symmetry but no lines of symmetry?   AQA

3

The diagram shows an open box.
(a) Draw an accurate net of the open box.
(b) Calculate the total outside surface area of the open box.

AQA

4 This 3-dimensional shape has been made
using linking cubes of side 1 cm.
On squared paper, draw diagrams to show:
(a) the plan of the shape,
(b) the elevation of the shape from **X**.

5

The diagram shows triangles **P**, **Q** and **R**.
(a) Describe the single transformation which takes **P** onto **Q**.
(b) Describe the single transformation which takes **P** onto **R**.

Copy triangle **P** onto squared paper.
(c) Draw an enlargement of triangle **P** with scale factor 2,
centre (0, 0).

6 By drawing at least six shapes, show how
this shape can be used to make a tessellation.

7 A triangle has sides of length 7 cm, 5 cm and 4 cm.
(a) Make an accurate drawing of the triangle.
(b) Work out the area of the triangle.

8 The diagram shows a parallelogram and a rectangle.
Both shapes have the same area.
Calculate the length of the rectangle.

4 cm

6 cm

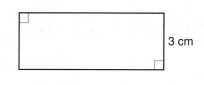

3 cm

9 (a) Which of these shapes are similar to each other?

P

Q

R

S

(b) This shape is enlarged with scale factor 2.
(i) What is the perimeter of the enlarged shape?
(ii) What is the area of the enlarged shape?

10

A

56°

x

B   *C*

(a) Triangle *ABC* is isosceles. *AB = AC*.
Work out the size of angle *x*.

(b) *BE* is parallel to *CD*.
(i) Write down the size of angle *p*.
(ii) Work out the size of angle *q*.

A
q
B   *E*
130°   155°
C   *p*   *D*

AQA

11 (a) Adrian is 6 feet 3 inches tall.
Calculate Adrian's height in centimetres.
(b) Adrian weighs 78 kg, correct to the nearest kilogram.
What are the limits between which his true weight must lie?

12 A table top is a circle of radius 50 cm.
(a) Calculate the circumference of the table top.
(b) Calculate the area of the table top.

13 The diagram shows a rectangle *ABCD*.
The coordinates of *A*, *B* and *C* are given.
(a) Write down the equations of the lines of
symmetry of the rectangle *ABCD*.

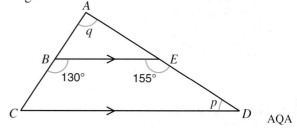

y
A (5, 5)   *B* (11, 5)
D   *C* (11, 2)
O   *x*

(b) The rectangle *ABCD* has been translated
9 units to the left and 4 units down.
Its new position is shown by the rectangle *EFGH*.
(i) Write down the coordinates of *E*.
(ii) Describe the translation that would
move the rectangle back to its
original position.

y
A (5, 5)   *B* (11, 5)
E   *F*   *D*   *C* (11, 2)
x
H   *G*

AQA

14 The diagram shows a circular paddling pool with a vertical side.
The radius of the pool is 35 cm.
The water in the pool is 8 cm deep.
Calculate the volume of water in the pool.

35 cm

AQA

15

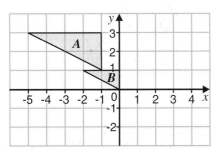

(a) Describe fully the single transformation which maps A onto B.

(b) B is mapped onto C by a translation with vector $\begin{pmatrix} 3 \\ -2 \end{pmatrix}$.

Draw a diagram to show the positions of B and C.

(c) B is mapped onto D by a rotation, 90° clockwise about (2, 1).
Show the position of D on your diagram.

16 Y is 50 m from X on a bearing of 080°.
Z is 70 m from Y on a bearing of 110°.
(a) Make a scale drawing to show the positions of X, Y and Z.   Use a scale of 1 cm to 10 m.
(b) Find by measurement the distance and bearing of X from Z.

17 The diagram shows part of a garden path.
Each shape in the path is a regular polygon.
Work out the size of each lettered angle.

18 Two straight roads are shown on the diagram.
A new gas pipe is to be laid from
Bere equidistant from the two roads.
The diagram is drawn to a scale of 1 cm to 1 km.
(a) Copy the diagram and construct the path of the gas pipe.

Alton

Cole

Bere

(b) The gas board needs a construction site depot.
The depot must be equidistant from Bere and Cole.
The depot must be less than 2 km from Alton.
Draw loci on your diagram to represent this information.
(c) The depot must be nearer the road through Cole than the road through Alton.
Mark on your diagram, with a cross, a possible position for the site depot.

19 Colin and Dexter are standing next to each other in the sunshine.
Colin is 150 cm tall and his shadow is 240 cm long.
Dexter is 165 cm tall. How long is his shadow?

20 (a) Calculate the area of this trapezium.
(b) Calculate the perimeter of this trapezium.

17 cm
6 cm
8 cm

AQA

21 The following formulae represent certain quantities connected with containers, where a, b and c are dimensions.

$\pi a^2 b$ $\qquad$ $2\pi a(a + b)$ $\qquad$ $2a + 2b + 2c$ $\qquad$ $\frac{1}{2}(a + b)c$ $\qquad$ $\sqrt{a^2 + b^2}$

(a) Which formulae represent area?
(b) Which formulae represent volume?

AQA

22 Wendy sketches a toy boat.

  (a) **Using ruler and compasses only,** draw an accurate diagram of sail *A*. **You must show your construction lines.**

  (b) Calculate the height *h* of sail *B*.

  (c) Calculate the angle *x*.

AQA

23

In the diagram, *QR* is parallel to *ST*.

  (a) Explain why triangles *PQR* and *PST* are similar.

  (b) $PR = 6\,\text{cm}$, $RT = 4\,\text{cm}$ and $ST = 12.5\,\text{cm}$. Calculate the length of *QR*.

AQA

24 The diagram shows the course sailed by a yacht from *O* to *A* and then from *A* to *B*.

A is 3 km from *O*.
B is 5 km from *A* on a bearing of 150°.
Angle *OAB* is 90°.

Calculate the bearing on which the yacht must sail to return directly from *B* to *O*.

Not drawn accurately

AQA

25

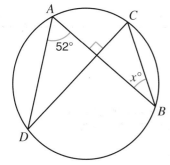

In the diagram, the chords *AB* and *CD* are perpendicular. Angle $DAB = 52°$.

Calculate the value of *x*.
You must give a reason for your answer.

AQA

26 The diagram shows a right-angled triangle, *ABC*.

Angle $ABC = 90°$. $\text{Tan}\, x = \frac{3}{4}$.

  (a) Calculate sin *x*.

ABC and *PQR* are similar triangles.

PQ is the shortest side of triangle *PQR*.
Angle $PQR = 90°$ and $PR = 15\,\text{cm}$.

  (b) (i) What is the value of cos *y*?
     (ii) What is the length of *PQ*?

AQA

Do not use a calculator for this exercise.

1
(a) Simplify $b \times b \times b$.
(b) Multiply out $2(a - 3)$.
(c) Drinks cost 35 pence each. How much will d drinks cost?

2 The diagram shows four patterns.

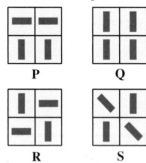

P   **Q**

R   **S**

(a) Which of these patterns has line symmetry and not rotational symmetry?
(b) Which of these patterns has line symmetry and rotational symmetry of order 2?

AQA

3 A sequence begins: 15, 7, 3, ...
The rule for continuing the sequence is shown.

> Subtract 1 from the last number and then divide by 2.

Write down the next three numbers in the sequence.

4
(a) Calculate the volume of this cuboid.

3 cm
4 cm
6 cm

(b) Calculate the surface area of the cuboid.

5
(a) Solve (i) $8x + 4 = 20$,
        (ii) $3x - 2 = 10$.
(b) Simplify $5 - 5n + n$.

6
(a) Work out the value of $2p^2$ when $p = 3$.
(b) Simplify $2(x - 3) + 5$.
(c) Solve $3y - 7 = 5$.

7 The diagram has been drawn to a scale of 1 cm to 200 m.

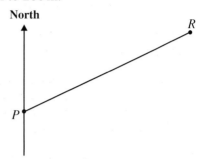

North

R

P

(a) What is the bearing of R from P?
(b) Calculate the distance PR, in metres.

8 $y = 5x + 2$.
(a) Find the value of y when $x = -1$.
(b) Find the value of x when $y = 17$.

9
(a) Copy and complete the table of values for $y + 2x = 5$.

x		-1		1		3
y						

(b) Draw a graph of $y + 2x = 5$ for values of x from -1 to 3.
(c) Use your graph to find the value of x when $y = 2$.

10 $ABCD$ is a rectangle.

A B

63°

x

D C

What is the size of angle x?   *AQA*

11
(a) What is the value of $3p - q$ when $p = -1$ and $q = 2$?
(b) What is the value of $x^2 - 2x$ when x is -3?

12 Solve the equations.
(a) $2 - a = 5$
(b) $5x - 7 = 9$
(c) $3t + 1 = 7 - t$

13
(a) Simplify. (i) $c^2 \times c^3$ (ii) $d^6 \div d^2$
(b) Factorise. $2m - 6$

14 A triangle has sides of length 6 cm, 5 cm and 4 cm.
  (a) Make an accurate drawing of the triangle.
  (b) By taking measurements from your diagram, calculate the area of the triangle.

15 In the diagram, *PQR* is an isosceles triangle.
The lines *PQ* and *RS* are parallel.
  (a) Work out the size of angle *x*.
  (b) (i) What is the size of angle *y*?
      (ii) Give a reason for your answer.

16 A circle has a radius of 4.87 cm.
Use approximation to estimate the area of the circle in terms of π.

17 (a) Sarah thinks of a number. She doubles it and then subtracts 3.
      (i) What was her number when the answer is 27?
      (ii) What was her number when the answer is -1?
  (b) Solve the equation $2(2x - 3) = 6$.

AQA

18 The graph shows Zak's journey to work.
He starts on the motorway but is held up by an accident.
The police move traffic onto side roads where Zak continues his journey.
He arrives at work at 8.45 am.

  (a) What is his average speed before he is held up by the accident?
  (b) How long was he held up by the accident?
  (c) How far was his journey in miles?
  (d) What was Zak's average speed for the whole journey?

AQA

19 (a) Which of the following is a net of a cube?

P   Q   R   S

  (b) A cube has edges of length 3 cm.
      Calculate the surface area of the cube.

  (c) Cubes of edge 3 cm are stored in a box, as shown.

      The box is a cuboid with dimensions
      15 cm by 20 cm by 30 cm.
      What is the maximum number of cubes
      that can be stored inside the box?

AQA

20 (a) Draw the graph of $y = 2x^2 - 5x + 1$ for values of *x* from -2 to $+4$.
  (b) Use your graph to solve the equation $2x^2 - 5x + 1 = 6$.

AQA

21 A sequence begins: 5, 8, 11, 14, ...
Write an expression in terms of n for the nth term in the sequence.

22 (a) Multiply out $4(2x - 1)$.
(b) Make k the subject of the formula $m = 3k + 7$.
(c) Solve the equation $(m - 3)(m + 8) = 0$. AQA

23 The diagram shows the positions of shapes **T**, **M** and **N**.

(a) Describe fully the single transformation which maps **T** onto **M**.
(b) Describe fully the single transformation which maps **T** onto **N**.
(c) **M** is mapped onto **P** by an enlargement, scale factor 2, centre $(-5, 1)$.
Draw a diagram to show the positions of **M** and **P**.

24 In triangle LMN, $\cos L = \frac{3}{5}$.

Calculate the length of NL.

25 (a) Solve the equation $5(x - 3) = x + 7$.
(b) Solve the simultaneous equations $2x - y = 4$ and $x + 2y = -3$.
(c) Solve the equation $x^2 - 2x - 8 = 0$
(d) Factorise $a^2 - a$. AQA

26 DE is the diameter of a circle and F is another point on the circumference.

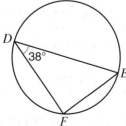

Calculate angle DEF.
You must explain your working. AQA

27 You are given the formula $V = \sqrt{\dfrac{P}{R}}$.
(a) Work out the value of V when $P = 0.35$ and $R = \frac{5}{7}$.
(b) Rearrange the formula to give P in terms of V and R.

28 The diagram shows a sketch of the line $2y = x - 2$.

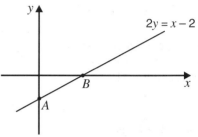

(a) Find the coordinates of points A and B.
(b) Find the gradient of the line $2y = x - 2$.
(c) Explain why the simultaneous equations $2y = x - 2$ and $2y = x - 3$ have no solution.
(d) Another line passes through B and through the point $(0, 2)$.
Find the equation of this line. AQA

29 The dimensions of a cone are given.

The following formulae represent certain quantities connected with the cone.

$$\pi a \qquad \frac{\pi a^2 c}{12} \qquad 2\pi ab \qquad \frac{\pi a^2}{4}$$

Which of these formulae represents volume? AQA

30 The diagram shows a shape, in which all the corners are right angles.

The area of the shape is 48 cm^2.
(a) Form an equation, in terms of x, for the area of the shape.
Show that the equation can be simplified to $x^2 + x - 12 = 0$.
(b) Solve the equation $x^2 + x - 12 = 0$ and hence calculate the perimeter of the shape. AQA

You may use a calculator for this exercise.

1 (a) Simplify $t + 2t + 3t$.
(b) Solve $4x + 3 = 5$.

2 Triangle PQR is isosceles, with $PQ = PR$ and angle $PQR = 48°$.

Show that angle $QPR = 84°$.

3 The nth term of a sequence is $3n + 2$.
(a) Write down the first and second terms of the sequence.
(b) Which term of the sequence is equal to 23?   AQA

4 The diagram shows a triangular prism.

(a) Draw an accurate net of the prism on 1 cm squared paper.
(b) Calculate the total surface area of the prism.   AQA

5 (a) Mark buys and sells vegetables. He works out the selling price, S pence per kg, using the formula $S = \frac{3C}{2} + 15$ where C is the cost in pence per kg of buying the vegetables.
(i) Find the selling price of carrots which he buys for 22p per kg.
(ii) He sells parsnips at 69p per kg. What is the cost of buying parsnips?
(b) One day Mark sold 100 kg of onions. What weight in pounds is 100 kg?

6

A   **B**   **C**

Which of these shapes **cannot** be used to form a tessellation? Explain why.

7 Solve these equations.
(a) $\frac{x}{5} = 3$ (b) $4y - 3 = 2$

8 The length of a rectangle is 7.9 cm. The perimeter of the rectangle is 26.8 cm. Calculate the area of the rectangle.

9

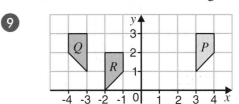

(a) Describe fully the single transformation which maps P onto Q.
(b) Describe fully the single transformation which maps P onto R.

10 (a) Simplify $3m + 5n + 4m - 3n$.
(b) Multiply out $3(x - 1)$.
(c) Solve the equations
(i) $4x + 11 = 7$,
(ii) $2 + 3y = 9 - 2y$.

11 (a) The words in this list are used to describe angles.

alternate   corresponding
exterior   interior   opposite

Choose a word in the list to describe each of the following pairs of angles.
(i) p and q,   (ii) d and e.
(b) Angle $x = 112°$. What is the size of angle y?   AQA

12 In triangle ABC, the side AB is 8 cm. Angle $A = 33°$ and angle $B = 100°$. Make an accurate drawing of the triangle.   AQA

13 Solve the equations.
(a) $2g = 9$ (b) $2(g + 1) = 9$

14 On graph paper draw and label the lines $y = 2x$ and $y = 6 - x$ for values of x from -1 to 4.

15

(a) Write down an expression, in terms of p and q, for the **perimeter** of this shape. Give your answer in its simplest form.

(b) Express the **area** of the shape in terms of p and q. AQA

16 A candle weighs x grams.

(a) Write an expression, in terms of x, for the weight of 20 candles.

(b) A box of 20 candles weighs 3800 g. The box weighs 200 g. By forming an equation, find the value of x.

17 A penny farthing bicycle is shown.

(a) The large wheel has a diameter of 160 cm. Find the circumference of the wheel.

(b) The small wheel has a circumference of 137 cm. The large wheel rotates once. How many complete rotations does the small wheel make? AQA

18 Sticks are used to make patterns of triangles.

Pattern 1   **Pattern 2**   **Pattern 3**

Write an expression, in terms of n, for the number of sticks used to make Pattern n.

19 Carpet tiles measure 45 cm by 45 cm.

45 cm

45 cm

How many tiles are needed to cover a floor which measures 4.05 m by 5.4 m?

20 (a) Solve $3x - 9 = 7 - 2x$.

(b) Factorise $3a - 6b$.

(c) Simplify $5x - 2(x + 3)$.

21 The graph represents a coach journey from Bath.

The coach completed its journey at 1130.

(a) At what time did the coach leave Bath?

(b) How far did the coach travel?

(c) How many times did the coach stop on the journey?

(d) What was the average speed of the coach between 1030 and 1100?

22 Find the value of $\frac{1}{x} + y^3$ when $x = 5$ and $y = 0.5$.

23 A sequence begins: 5, 3, 1, −1, …
Write an expression, in terms of n, for the n th term of the sequence.

24 (a) This diagram shows a kite $ABCD$.

$AB = 15$ cm, $BC = 36$ cm and $AC = 39$ cm.
Explain why angle $B = 90°$.

(b) The diagram shows two regular polygons.

Work out the size of angle x. AQA

25 Factorise. (a) $6p - 3$ (b) $p^2 + 2p$

26 Draw a graph to show the region where:
$3x + y \geqslant 6$, $x \leqslant 2$ and $y \leqslant 4$.

27 (a) Solve (i) $\dfrac{x - 7}{3} = -2$

   (ii) $8 - 3x = 2(x + 5)$.

(b) Use trial and improvement to solve the equation $x^3 + 2x = 400$.
Show all your trials.
Give your answer correct to one decimal place.

28 PQR is the cross-section of a roof, with $PR = RQ$. $PQ = 8.6$ m. R is 3.6 m above the level of PQ.

Calculate the length RQ. AQA

29 A formula for calculating distance is

$$d = \frac{(u + v)t}{2}$$

(a) Make t the subject of the formula.
(b) Find the value of t when
$d = 60$, $u = 5.8$ and $v = 10.2$.
AQA

30 The diagram shows a road, ML, which slopes downhill for 800 m to a lake.
The top of the road, M, is 190 m above the lake.

Calculate x, the angle of the slope of the road. AQA

31 (a) Solve the inequality $3m - 5 > 7$.
(b) Write down all the solutions of the inequality $-6 < 3n \leqslant 5$ where n is an integer.
(c) Solve the simultaneous equations
$3x - 2y = 15$ and $2x - 4y = 2$.

32 Gilda is standing 75 m away from a building.
She measures the angle of elevation to the top of the building as $18°$.
Calculate the height of the building. AQA

33 (a) Simplify.
   (i) $a^6 \div a^3$ (ii) $3xy^2 \times 2x^3y^5$
   (iii) $(p^3)^2$
(b) Multiply out and simplify.
   (i) $5t(t + 3)$ (ii) $(x + y)(x - 3y)$

34 In the diagram AB is parallel to ED.
Angle $CED = 54°$ and angle $BCD = 100°$.

Not drawn accurately

(a) Find the size of
   (i) angle x.
   (ii) angle y.
(b) Triangle ABC is similar to triangle DEC.
$AC : CD$ is $3 : 2$. $AB = 5.4$ cm.
Calculate the length of DE. AQA

35 A water trough has a semi-circular cross-section, as shown.

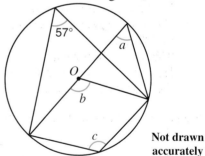

The diameter of the end of the trough is 38 cm. The trough is 3 m long.
Calculate the volume of water in the trough when it is full. Give your answer in litres.
AQA

36 O is the centre of the circle.
Work out the size of angles a, b and c.

Not drawn accurately

37 A piece of land is bounded by three straight roads PQ, QR and RP.
P is due north of R.
Q is on a bearing of $063°$ from R.
PQR is a right angle.

(a) What is the bearing of P from Q?

The length of QR is 4.7 km.
(b) Calculate the area of the piece of land.
AQA

38 Find the equation of the straight line drawn through the points $(0, -4)$ and $(4, 8)$.

EP

Answers

CHAPTER 1

Exercise **1.1**   Page 1

1. qualitative

2. quantitative, continuous

3. quantitative, discrete

4. qualitative

5. quantitative, discrete

6. quantitative, continuous

7. quantitative, discrete

8. qualitative

9. quantitative, discrete

10. quantitative, continuous

Exercise **1.2**   Page 2

1. (a)

Colour of car	Frequency
Black	1
Blue	9
Green	4
Grey	2
Red	11
Silver	4
White	9
Total	40

(b) red
(c) 8 more

2. (a)

Day	Frequency
Monday	8
Tuesday	7
Wednesday	6
Thursday	7
Friday	7
Saturday	3
Sunday	5
Total	43

(b) 43
(c) Monday
(d) 8

3. (a)

Age	Tally	Frequency
0 - 9	||||	4
10 - 19	卌 ||	7
20 - 29	卌 卌 |	11
30 - 39	卌 卌	10
40 - 49	||||	4
50 - 59	||||	4

(b) 10 years   (c) 10   (d) 11   (e) 8

4. (a)

Height h cm	Frequency
$145 \leqslant h < 150$	2
$150 \leqslant h < 155$	2
$155 \leqslant h < 160$	7
$160 \leqslant h < 165$	9
$165 \leqslant h < 170$	6
$170 \leqslant h < 175$	8
$175 \leqslant h < 180$	2
Total	36

(b) 5 cm   (c) 7   (d) 11   (e) 32

Exercise **1.3**   Page 4

1. (a) Francis   (b) Louisa   (c) Alistair

2. (a) (i)

Make	Frequency
Ford	4
Nissan	3
Vauxhall	5
Total	12

Colour	Frequency
Blue	2
Green	1
Grey	2
Red	3
White	4
Total	12

Number of doors	Frequency
2	2
3	5
4	2
5	3
Total	12

(ii)

Mileage (m)	Frequency
$0 \leqslant m < 5000$	0
$5000 \leqslant m < 10\,000$	2
$10\,000 \leqslant m < 15\,000$	0
$15\,000 \leqslant m < 20\,000$	2
$20\,000 \leqslant m < 25\,000$	1
$25\,000 \leqslant m < 30\,000$	2
$30\,000 \leqslant m < 35\,000$	4
$35\,000 \leqslant m < 40\,000$	1
Total	12

(b) (i) Vauxhall (ii) 2 (iii) 5 (iv) 5

Exercise 1.4   Page 5

1. (a) Too personal   (b) Leading
   (c) (i) Groups overlap
       (ii) ▢ less than 5   ▢ 5 to 9   ▢ 10 or more
2. (a) Too open   (b) Too open
   (c) Leading
3. (a) Too personal   (b) Too open
   (c) Too open   (d) Too open

Exercise 1.5   Page 7

1. Small sample. One data collection time.
2. Women only. One location.
   One data collection time.
3. Advantage: confidential, wider circulation, etc.
   Disadvantage: slow, non-response, etc.
8. (a) 8   (b) 16   (c) 20
   (d) 40   (e) 50%
9. (a) 5   (b) 8
   (c) 3   (d) 10
10. (a) 14   (b) 20
    (c) 70%   (d) 80%
    (e) Disprove. 80% is greater than 70%.
11. Disprove, Boys $\frac{3}{21} = \frac{1}{7}$, Girls $\frac{2}{14} = \frac{1}{7}$,
    same proportion
12. (a) 20   (b) 27
    (c) Prove, Maths ABC = 27,
        English ABC = 32, English > Maths
13. (a)

	Yes	No
Men	47	11
Women	18	24

  (b) Yes. Taller: $\frac{47}{58} \times 100 = 81\%$

14. (a) (i) 10   (ii) No. Less 8, More 12
    (b) (i) 37   (ii) No. Girls 37, Boys 37, same
15. E.g. Fewer females than males.
    No-one under 18.

Review Exercise 1   Page 10

1. For example:

		Colour		
		Blue	Green	Red
Make	Ford			
	Nissan			
	Vauxhall			

2.

Weight (g)	Frequency
$80 \leqslant g < 120$	7
$120 \leqslant g < 180$	9
$180 \leqslant g < 250$	8

3. (a) **B, C**   (b) **E, H**
4. (a) **Question 1** - too open
       Question 2 - leading
   (b) Do you think that smoking is bad for
       your health? YES/NO
5. E.g. Only males asked.
   No-one under 11.
   Mainly adults surveyed.
6. (a) 219
   (b) Do you take part in any exercise outside
       school? YES/NO
       How many times a week do you exercise?
       0 ▢   1 - 5 ▢   6 - 10 ▢   more than 10 ▢
   (c) Girls only. All take part in sport.
   (d) (i) Leading
       (ii) Response classes are not precise.
7. Do not support.
   Women 75%   Men 75%   Same proportion
8. (a) 6   (b) 5   (c) 38

CHAPTER 2

Exercise 2.1   Page 13

1. (a) Saturday   (b) 5 hours   (c) 41 hours
   (d) Sunday   (e) $\frac{1}{4}$ (f) 6 hours
2. (b) £5   (c) £7   (d) 20%
3. (a) 15   (b) 1   (c) 5   (d) 20%
4. (a) 38   (b) Monday
   (c)

Day of birth	S	M	T	W	T	F	S
Number of boys	1	3	4	4	1	5	1

Exercise 2.2   Page 15

1. (a) 7 hours   (b) 5 hours   (c) 3
   (d) (i) 20   (ii) 20%
   (e) E.g. Boys have higher mode and
       larger range.

2. (a) 5 (b) 7 (c) 7 (d) $33\frac{1}{3}\%$
(e) 35% (f) 4 (g) 5
(h) Boys have higher mode and larger range.

Exercise 2.3 Page 16

1.

Tree	Ash	Beech	Maple
Angle	120°	150°	90°

2.

Colour	Brown	Blue	Green	Other
Angle	160°	100°	60°	40°

3.

Ice cream	Vanilla	Strawberry	99
Angle	188°	74°	98°

4.

Takeaway	Fish & Chips	Chicken & Chips	Chinese Meal	Pizza
Angle	110°	136°	52°	62°

5.

TVChannel	BBC1	BBC2	ITV	CH4	CH5
Angle	119°	50°	115°	47°	29°

6.

Cereal	Cornflakes	Muesli	Porridge	Bran Flakes
Angle	125°	100°	60°	75°

Exercise 2.4 Page 18

1. (a) 12 (b) 8 (c) Hotel
2. (a) 20 (b) 15 (c) Sauze d'Oulx
3. (a) France (b) 45 (c) 55 (d) 20
4. (a) 5 (b) 2 (c) 18
5. (a) 288 (b) 174°

Exercise 2.5 Page 19

1. 1 | 0 means 10 litres
```
1 | 0 2 6 6 7 9
2 | 3 3 4 5 5 6 7 9
3 | 1 3 5 5
4 | 1 2
```

2. 3 | 2 means 3.2 seconds
```
1 | 5
2 | 4 4 5 6 7 8 8 9
3 | 0 1 2 2 3 5 5 6 7
4 | 2 2 3
5 | 6 6 8
```

3. 1 | 6 means 16 press-ups
```
0 | 9
1 | 6 8
2 | 0 1 2 4 5 7 8
3 | 2 2 3 6 6 6
4 | 0 1
```

4. 2 | 7 means 2.7 cm
```
1 | 8
2 | 0 1 4 5 6 6 7
3 | 1 4 5 5 6 9
4 | 0 2 2 5
5 | 4
6 | 0
```

5. (a) 12 (b) 23 pence (c) 39 pence

Exercise 2.6 Page 21

1. (a) 9 (b) 50 (c) 17
(d) Highest mark scored by a boy.
Lowest mark scored by a girl.
Boys have a greater range of marks.

2. (a) Adults | Children 4 | 7 means 4.7 mins
```
              4 |  7 9
            9 4 |  5 | 1 3 4 9
        7 5 4 1 0 |  6 | 2 3 4 5 5 6 8
  9 8 7 3 3 3 0 |  7 | 1 4 6 7 9
          2 2 0 |  8 | 0 2
            4 2 |  9 |
              1 | 10 |
```

(b) Adults have larger range.
Fastest time recorded by child,
slowest time recorded by adult.

Review Exercise 2 Page 22

1. (b) Bed & Breakfast (c) 50 (d) 34%

2.

Item	TVs	VCRs	Computers	Other
Angle	140°	120°	68°	32°

3. (a) $\frac{1}{3}$ (b) 1836 (c) 357

4. (a)

Fuel	Solid fuel	Electricity	Gas
Angle	24°	126°	210°

(b) (i) $\frac{5}{36}$ (ii) 72
(c) Gas. Town has larger population and
proportion of gas users greater than 50%.

5. 5 | 4 means 5.4 grams
```
2 | 8
3 | 5 9
4 | 2 4 6 6 7 8 8
5 | 0 1 4 4 6 6 8
6 | 0 3 7
```

6. (a)

Grade	A	B	C	Ungraded
Angle	60°	90°	135°	75°

(b) 9
(c)

Grade	A	B	C	Ungraded
Number of girls	3	4	5	2

7. (a) 2 : 3   (b) 20%
   (c) Boys: range = 3,   mode = size 5.
        Girls: range = 4,   mode = size 4.
        Girls: higher range.   Boys: higher mode.

CHAPTER 3

Exercise **3.1**   Page 25

1. (a) 7   (b) 4   (c) 4
2. (a) 1   (b) 2   (c) 3
3. (a) 3   (b) 5
   (c) 3.5   (d) 3.9
4. (a) 135   (b) 135   (c) 133
5. (a) 39   (b) 23   (c) 38.8
6. (a) 10   (b) 9   (c) 9.3
7. 86.9 kg   **9.** 129 cm
8. 4   **10.** 15.2

Exercise **3.2**   Page 27

1. (a) 5   (b) 4   (c) 5   (d) 5
2. (a)

Number of keys	2	3	4	5	6
Frequency	2	3	8	5	2

   (b) 20   (c) 4   (d) 4   (e) 4.1
3. (a)

Wage (£)	25	30	35	40	45
Frequency	6	4	5	1	3

   (b) £20   (c) £25   (d) 19
   (e) £30   (f) £620   (g) £32.63
4. (a) 9   (b) 9   (c) 30   (d) 8.5
5. (a) 2, 2.5, 2.7   (b) 2, 2, 2.1
   (c) 0, 5, 4.5

Exercise **3.3**   Page 29

1. (a) £10 000 ≤ s < £20 000, £20 350
   (b) 30 - 40 hours, 29.4 hours
2. 5.3 kg   **4.** 4.3 m
3. £94 000   **5.** 27.7

Exercise **3.4**   Page 31

1. Moneymaker larger range and higher mean than Cherry.
2. (a) (i) 0.5 minutes   (ii) 1.95 minutes
   (b) Girls a little slower on average and more varied.
3. Jays: mean 1.9, range 5
    Wasps: mean 2.4, range 3
    Wasps scored more on average and had less spread.
4. Women: mean 1.6, range 6
    Men: mean 1.5, range 2
    Women made more visits to the cinema, though the number of visits is more spread.

5. Average: Boys 6.2, Girls 7.2
    Range: Boys 4,   Girls 4½
    No.   Girls' average greater than boys'.
    Correct about variation.
6. (a) MacQuick 20 - 29,   Pizza Pit 30 - 39
   (b) MacQuick - mean 26 years
          (Pizza Pit 36.5 years)
   (c) Exact ages not known.
7. Before: median 3,   range 4
    After: median 3,   range 5
    Would have been better to calculate the means. Before 2.2, After 3.0

Exercise **3.5**   Page 32

1. Mode trainers. Cannot calculate others.
2. Mode 15s, median 12s, mean 22.15s
    Median most sensible, not affected by 200 as is mean, mode not much use.
3. Mode 81, median 83, mean 69.8
    Median most sensible, not affected by 5 and 6 as is mean, mode not much use.
4. Swimmer A.
    Mean is lower (A 30.88s, B 31.38s)
    Range less (A 1.7s, B 15s)
    Median is higher (A 30.9s, B 30.0s)
5. Batsman B.
    Higher median (B 31.5, A 21)
    Higher mean (B 36, A 35)
6. He should use the median mark.
    The median mark is the middle mark, so half of the students will get the median mark or higher.
7. (a) Mode.
        Represents the lowest cost for these data.
   (b) Median.
        Mean affected by **one** much higher cost.
        Mode is equal to the lowest cost.

Review Exercise **3**   Page 34

1. (a) (i) 9 minutes   (ii) 9.5 minutes
   (b) Trains are more variable, but less late on average.
2. (a) Range 6p,   mode 33p
   (b) Median 32p,   mean 32.1p
3. (a) (i) 2   (ii) 2.28
   (b) (i) 2.5   (ii) 2.63
   (c) The calculation for the mean involves the number of runs scored off every ball.
4. (a) 52   (b) 11   (c) Increase. 62 ÷ 9 = 6.9
5. (a) 24 cm   (b) 24.3 cm
   (c) 1st group had higher mode (1st 25, 2nd 23), but lower range (1st 7, 2nd 13).
6. (a) £200 - £300   (b) £300 - £400
   (c) Mean, influenced by 12 people earning £600 - £1000.

7. 16.9 minutes

8. (a) $150 \leqslant p < 155$
(b) 156 litres
(c) Estimated mean – uses all values

CHAPTER 4

Exercise 4.1   Page 36

1. (a) 15°C
(b) Temperature variations during each day are not known.
Line only indicates trend in midday temperatures.

2. (a) 8   (b) Jan, Feb, June
(c) No information given about when cars are sold during the month.

3. (b) (i) 154 cm   (ii) 15 years 4 months

4. (a) 82 kg   (b) 82 kg
(c) 5 kg   (d) Week 4

Exercise 4.2   Page 39

1. 35, 34, 35, 36, 39, 37, 40

2. 28.8, 28.6, 28.2, 28.6, 30.6, 33

3. 18, 17.5, 17, 16, 15, 14, 13, 12, 11.25

4. 6.6

5. 3-point moving averages are:
370, 365, 375, 390, 400, 390, 400

Exercise 4.3   Page 40

1. (a) (c)

(b) 51.5, 45, 44, 50.5, 51.5, 64.5, 77.5, 62.5, 49.5
(d) There is an upward trend in the amount of water used.

2. (a) (c)

(b) £65.61, £64.55, £65.11, £62.27, £62.17, £67.39, £67.70, £68.18, £66.74
(d) There is an upward trend in the quarterly bills.

3. (a) (c)

(b) 3-point moving averages are:
35, 36, 62, 63, 65, 40, 44, 43, 41, 46
(d) Trend shows steady level of absence, greatly affected by Spring figure for Year 9.

4. (a) (c) (d)

(b) 47.8, 44.7, 43.8, 44, 43.6, 44.5, 46, 46.8, 47.3, 47.8, 49.7, 50.7, 52.2
(e) The trend shows a general increase in sales.
(f) £4800

5. (a) (c) (d)

(b) 4-point moving averages are:
27.5, 27, 24, 22, 21, 20, 19, 17.5, 16.25
(e) The trend shows a general decrease in the number of new homes being built.
(f) 11

Exercise 4.4   Page 42

1. (a) 36   (b) 24
(c) 40   (d) 80 - 90 kg

2. (a) 5   (b) 5

3. (a) Entries are: 4, 7, 9, 4
(c) 6.00 and less than 6.50

6. (a) 0   (b) 26
(c) 27   (d) 95

7.

Mark	0 - 9	10 - 19	20 - 29	30 - 39
Frequency	3	12	19	6

8. (a)

Mark	Frequency
20 and less than 30	5
30 and less than 40	8
40 and less than 50	9
50 and less than 60	6
60 and less than 70	2

   (b) 40 and less than 50

10. (b) Females have smaller range in weight
      than males.
      Males have higher modal class.

11. (c) English results have smaller range.
      English modal class is higher.

12. (b) 2002 results have a larger range.
      2001 results have higher modal class.

Exercise 4.5   Page 46

1. Axes not labelled.

2. Bars not equal width.

3. Vertical axis does not begin at zero.

4. Pass rate not given.
    Advert implies you "pass" after 8 lessons.

5. 10% increase in price, disproportionate
    increase in diagram size.

6. Horizontal axis does not begin at zero and is
    not a uniform scale.

7. Vertical scale not uniform.
    Size of diagrams disproportionate to increase
    in sales.

8. Horizontal scale not uniform.
    Vertical scale not calibrated.

Review Exercise 4   Page 47

1. (b) £87 000
    (c) Prices of houses rise and fall,
        future prices unpredictable.

2. (a) (c) (d)

    (b) 5.4, 5, 4.6, 4.4, 4.6, 5, 5.2, 5.2, 5.4, 5.4,
        5.2
    (e) Trend shows no change in the number of
        absences.

3. Vertical axis does not begin at zero.
    Horizontal axis is not uniform.

4. (a) 3 km but less than 4 km
    (b) 31
    (c) 190

5.

Time (seconds)	Frequency
10 and less than 20	4
20 and less than 30	6
30 and less than 40	2

6. (a) More than 4 hours but less than or equal
       to 5 hours
    (b) Ann gained 20 points $(4 \leqslant t < 5)$,
       Ben gained 10 points $(5 \leqslant t < 6)$.

7. (b) 34

8. (b) Type Y
    (c) (i)   Type X
        (ii) Weights spread over more weight
           class intervals.

CHAPTER 5

Exercise 5.1   Page 50

1. (a) 2   (b) 164 cm   (c) No
    (d) Taller girls usually have larger shoe sizes
       than shorter girls.

2. (a) 72
    (b) (i)   English 46, French 88
        (ii) French could be her first language.

3. (a) 4 (b) 43 kg (c) Tend to be higher

Exercise 5.2   Page 52

1. (a) **B**   (b) **C**   (c) **D**

2. (a) Negative (b) Positive (c) Zero
    (d) Positive (e) Negative

3. (b) Positive correlation
    (c) Different conditions, types of road, etc.

4. (b) Negative correlation
    (c) Different road surfaces, driving styles, etc.

Exercise 5.3   Page 54

1. (b) Positive correlation (d) 4.8 to 4.9 kg

2. (b) Negative correlation (d) 38 minutes

3. (b) Negative correlation
    (d) (i)   27 to 28 (ii) 91 to 92 kg

4. (b) (i)   88 - 89 (ii) 49 - 50
    (c) (ii), as estimated value is within the
           range of known values.

5. (b) Scatter of points suggests correlation is
       close to zero.

Review Exercise 5   Page 55

1. 1 B, 2 C, 3 A

2. (a) Books with more pages tend to be more
       expensive. Positive correlation.
    (c) (i)   £10.70 - £10.90 (ii) 130 - 140

3. (a) (i) 10 to 12 cm   (ii) 21 to 23 cm
  (b) (ii), as estimated value is between known values.
4. (b) Very strong negative correlation.
  (d) 11 to 12
5. (b) Positive correlation.
  (d) 90 to 100 beats per minute.
6. (b) Perfect negative correlation.
  (d) £2600 - £3000
7. (c) (i) 80 - 85 km   (ii) 11 - 13 litres
  (d) (i), as estimated value is between known values.

CHAPTER 6

Exercise 6.1 — Page 60

1. (a) Entries are: 0, 4, 16, 34, 49, 57, 60
  (c) (i) 14 mins   (ii) 18 to 19 mins
   (iii) 9 to 10 mins
  (d) 9 mins
2. (a) 52   (c) (i) 61 g   (ii) 28 g
3. (b) (i) 6 to 7 mins   (ii) 8 mins

Exercise 6.2 — Page 62

1. (a) Entries are: 0, 7, 28, 65, 77, 80
  (c) (i) 6 minutes   (ii) 12
2. (a) 26 to 27   (b) 7 to 8 marks
  (c) 15 to 16%   (d) 17
3. (a) 95
  (c) (i) 89 cm   (ii) 10 to 11 cm   (iii) 19
  (d) 83 cm
4. (b) 9 to 10 hours   (c) 12%
5. (a) 175 cm, 14.5 cm   (b) 3   (c) 41
  (d) 172.5 cm   (e) 185.5 cm

Exercise 6.3 — Page 64

1. (a) 40   (b) 13 cm   (c) 8.5 cm
  (d) Girls heights are more varied, etc.   (e) 1
2. (b) (i) 18 litres   (ii) 10 litres
  (c) Neighbour's cows have higher average yield, but the yield is more varied, etc.
3. Variety X, median 350 g, IQR 100 g.
  Variety Y, median 350 g, IQR 220 g.
  Same median, but weight of Variety Y is more varied, etc.

Exercise 6.4 — Page 66

1.

Temperature (°C)

2.

Weight (kg)

3.

Distance (km)

4.

Height (cm)

5. (a) 0.06 s   (b) 0.08 s
6. (a) 72%   (b) 18%
  (c) English   (d) 21%
  (e) English mark has a higher median, Maths marks more spread.
7. (b) Males have lower median time and not spread out. Females have higher median time and greater variation.
8. (a) median = £52,   lower quartile = £33, upper quartile = £65

Review Exercise 6 — Page 69

1. (a) 3 miles
  (b) 0.5 miles
  (c) Range is affected by a few long journeys, etc.
2. (b) (i) 57 marks   (ii) 22 marks
  (c) Paper 2. Higher median, less variation.
3. (a) Entries are: 2, 5, 13, 22, 28, 35, 40
  (c) 78.5g
  (d) 19g
  (e) The spread of the second sample is greater (IQR 38 g compared with 19 g), etc.
4. (a) Lettuces planted by hand have a greater mean diameter.
  (b) Lettuces planted by machine have a smaller diameter and are less varied in size.
5. (a) 13p   (b) 29p   (c) 5p
6.

Time (minutes)

CHAPTER 7

Exercise 7.1 — Page 71

1. (a) Evens   (b) Impossible
  (c) Likely   (d) Unlikely
  (e) Certain   (f) Unlikely
  (g) Likely
2.

1. (a) $\frac{1}{3}$ (b) $\frac{2}{3}$ (c) $\frac{2}{3}$

2. (a) $\frac{3}{10}$ (b) $\frac{7}{10}$

3. (a) $\frac{1}{5}$ (b) $\frac{2}{5}$

4. (a) $\frac{1}{11}$ (b) $\frac{4}{11}$ (c) $\frac{2}{11}$

5. (a) $\frac{1}{12}$ (b) $\frac{1}{6}$

6. (a) $\frac{1}{2}$ (b) $\frac{1}{4}$ (c) $\frac{1}{52}$

7. (a) $\frac{2}{5}$ (b) $\frac{3}{5}$ (c) 1   (d) 0

8. (a) $\frac{2}{3}$ (b) $\frac{1}{3}$ (c) $\frac{3}{4}$

9. (a) $\frac{2}{5}$ (b) $\frac{3}{5}$ (c) $\frac{4}{25}$ (d) $\frac{4}{15}$ (e) $\frac{2}{5}$

10. The events are not equally likely.

11. (a) $\frac{1}{3}$ (b) $\frac{1}{15}$ (c) $\frac{11}{24}$
     (d) $\frac{17}{50}$ (e) $\frac{21}{25}$ (f) $\frac{4}{5}$

1. $\frac{7}{25}$ **3.** $\frac{21}{30} = \frac{7}{10}$

2. $\frac{9}{10}$ **4.** (a) $\frac{1}{10}$ (b) 10

5. (a) Tom $\frac{1}{3}$,   Sam $\frac{1}{2}$,   Kim $\frac{3}{4}$,   Pam $\frac{9}{20}$
     (b) Pam - because she has played the most games.
     (c) Pam - because $\frac{9}{20}$ is greater than $\frac{1}{3}$.

6. 9

7. (a) $\frac{1}{500}$ (b) 25

8. (a) 300   (b) 120   (c) 150

9. 8

10. (a) $\frac{52}{100} = 0.52$ $\frac{102}{200} = 0.51$ $\frac{141}{300} = 0.47$
     (b) 0.47

11. (a) Relative frequency close to theoretical probability (0.25).
     (b) Varies around 0.5

1. $\frac{3}{5}$

2. 0.4   **5.** 0.6

3. 0.04   **6.** (a) 0.04   (b) 0.97

4. $\frac{47}{50}$ **7.** (a) 0.5   (b) 0.3

8. (a) (i) The probabilities add to 105%
         (ii) 5%
     (b) (i) 45%   (ii) 75%   (iii) 80%

9. (a) 0.4
     (b) 0.6
     (c) (i) Yes   (ii) No
     (d) (i) 0.6   (ii) 0.6   (iii) 0.7

1. (a) RBG, RGB, GBR, GRB, BGR, BRG
     (b) $\frac{1}{3}$

2. (a)

	1	2	3	4	5	6
1	2	3	4	5	6	7
2	3	4	5	6	7	8
3	4	5	6	7	8	9
4	5	6	7	8	9	10
5	6	7	8	9	10	11
6	7	8	9	10	11	12

     (b) (i) $\frac{1}{12}$ (ii) $\frac{1}{12}$ (iii) $\frac{5}{6}$
     (c) They cover all possible scores.

3.

	Dice					
	1	2	3	4	5	6
Coin H	H1	H2	H3	H4	H5	H6
T	T1	T2	T3	T4	T5	T6

     (a) $\frac{1}{12}$ (b) $\frac{1}{4}$ (c) $\frac{1}{12}$
     (d) $\frac{1}{4}$ (e) $\frac{1}{6}$ (f) $\frac{1}{2}$

4. (a)

Stage 1	Stage 2
Bus	Bus
Bus	Walk
Train	Bus
Train	Walk
Lift	Bus
Lift	Walk

     (b) $\frac{1}{6}$

5. (a)

		2nd spin			
		1	2	3	4
	1	2	3	4	5
1st	2	3	4	5	6
spin	3	4	5	6	7
	4	5	6	7	8

     (b) (i) $\frac{1}{16}$ (ii) $\frac{1}{8}$ (iii) $\frac{3}{16}$

6. (a)

		Bag A		
		R	R	W
	W	RW	RW	WW
Bag B	W	RW	RW	WW
	R	RR	RR	WR

     (c) $\frac{4}{9}$

7. (a)

A	1	1	2	2	3	3
B	2	3	2	3	2	3

     (b) (i) $\frac{2}{6} = \frac{1}{3}$ (ii) $\frac{4}{6} = \frac{2}{3}$ (c) $\frac{4}{5}$

8. (a) Maths, English
Maths, Science
Maths, Art
English, Science
English, Art
Science, Art

(b) $\frac{3}{6} = \frac{1}{2}$ (c) $\frac{1}{3}$

9. (a)

2nd spin					
W	RW	GW	BW	YW	WW
Y	RY	GY	BY	YY	WY
B	RB	GB	BB	YB	WB
G	RG	GG	BG	YG	WG
R	RR	GR	BR	YR	WR
	R	G	B	Y	W

1st spin

(b) (i) $\frac{1}{25}$ (ii) $\frac{9}{25}$ (iii) $\frac{5}{25} = \frac{1}{5}$

10. (a)

	1	2	3	4	5	6
1	2	3	4	5	6	7
2	3	4	5	6	7	8
3	4	5	6	7	8	9

(b) $\frac{1}{18}$ (c) $\frac{1}{6}$

Exercise 7.6 — Page 83

1. (a)
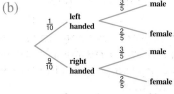

(b) (i) $\frac{4}{25}$ (ii) $\frac{16}{25}$

2. (a)
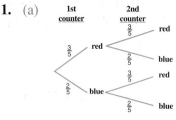

(b) (i) 0.01   (ii) 0.18   (c) 810

3. (a) (i) $\frac{5}{50} = \frac{1}{10}$ (ii) $\frac{45}{50} = \frac{9}{10}$
(iii) $\frac{20}{50} = \frac{2}{5}$ (iv) $\frac{30}{50} = \frac{3}{5}$

(b)

(c) (i) $\frac{2}{50} = \frac{1}{25}$ (ii) $\frac{29}{50}$

4. (a)

(b) $\frac{9}{50}$ (c) $\frac{21}{50}$

5. (a) Lights   Brakes

(b) $\frac{7}{25}$

6. (a) 0.7   (b) 0.49   (c) 0.58

7. (a) $\frac{3}{20}$ (b) $\frac{5}{8}$

8. (a) 0.14   (b) 0.06

9. (a) $\frac{1}{3}$ (b) $\frac{1}{2}$

10. (a) (i) 0.1   (ii) 0.7   (iii) 0.6
(b) (i) 0.01   (ii) 0.09

11. (a) (i) 0.3   (ii) 0.1   (iii) 0.5
(b) 0.34

Review Exercise 7 — Page 87

1. (a)

	1	2	3	4
1	2	3	4	5
2	3	4	5	6
3	4	5	6	7

(b) (i) $\frac{2}{12} = \frac{1}{6}$ (ii) $\frac{10}{12} = \frac{5}{6}$
(c) $\frac{4}{12} = \frac{1}{3}$

2. (a) $\frac{1}{4}$ (b) $\frac{3}{8}$
(c) They do not have an equal chance of winning.

3. (a) $\frac{1}{5}$ (b) $\frac{3}{4}$

4. (a)

Turban	Shirt
white	green
white	red
white	yellow
blue	green
blue	red
blue	yellow

(b) (i) $\frac{1}{2}$ (ii) $\frac{1}{6}$ (iii) $\frac{1}{3}$
(c) (ii) $\frac{5}{11}$

5. Red 1, White 2, Blue 3

6. (a) 0.3   (b) 0.6

7. (a) $\frac{12}{20} = \frac{3}{5}$ (c) 500

8. (a) $\frac{7}{9}$ (b) $\frac{4}{5}$

     (c) 0.24

     (d) No. 0.8 of men can drive.
        0.76 of women can drive. $0.8 > 0.76$

9. $\frac{1}{36}$

10. (a)

     (b) (i) 0.48   (ii) 0.52

11. (a) 0.72   (b) 0.26

12. (a) $\frac{1}{25}$ (b) $\frac{1}{5}$ (c) $\frac{10}{25} = \frac{2}{5}$

Exam Practice: Module 1
Non-calculator Paper   Page 89

1. (a) (i) 132   (ii) 280
     (b) (i) Overslept   (ii) 8

2. (a) 15   (b) 18 cm   (c) 26 cm

3. (a) Highest − lowest = 8
       10, 10, and 2 other numbers
     (b) Sum of four numbers = 36
       10, 10 and 2 other numbers
     (c) E.g. 4, 10, 10, 12
         Sum of four numbers = 36 **and**
         highest − lowest = 8

4. (a) $\frac{3}{20}$ (b) $\frac{7}{20}$

5. (a) 35   (b) 3   (c) 5.1
     (d) Males have greater range,
       7 compared with 3.
       Females have greater average,
       5.1 compared with 3.6.

6. (a)

Painting	A	B	C	D
Angle	90°	120°	60°	90°

     (b) $\frac{20}{60} = \frac{1}{3}$

7. (a) $\frac{1}{6}$
     (b) Probably not, as 2 occurs twice as many
       times as any other number.

8. Set A   Set B
     1   X
     1   Y
     2   X
     2   Y
     3   X
     3   Y

9. (a) $\frac{7}{9}$ (b) $\frac{6}{25}$

     (c) Can swim: girls 0.76, boys 0.8.
       Not true. $0.8 > 0.76$

10. (a) 0.4   (b) 18

11. (b) Positive correlation
     (c) (ii) 6 to 6.3 years

12. (a) Q1: Too open, vague.
       Q2: Too long **and** leading.
     (b) How many hours per week do you read?
       ☐ less than 1   ☐ 1 to 3   ☐ more than 3

13. Estimated total weight
     $= (8 \times 40) + (10 \times 60) + (4 \times 80) = 1240\,\text{kg}$
     Likely to be overloaded.

14. (a)

     (b) 120 g   (c) (i) 0   (ii) 20

15. (a) $\frac{4}{25}$ (b) $\frac{6}{25}$ (c) $\frac{4}{25}$

Exam Practice: Module 1
Calculator Paper   Page 92

1. (a)

Dice

Coin		1	2	3	4	5	6
	Heads	1	2	3	4	5	6
	Tails	2	4	6	8	10	12

     (b) $\frac{1}{12}$ (c) $\frac{7}{12}$

2. (a) 5.9 cm
     (b)

					4	7 means 4.7 cm
4	7	9				
5	0	3	6	8		
6	1	4	5	5	7	
7	2					

3. (a) 40
     (b) Yes. Pensioners 40%, students $33\frac{1}{3}\%$

4. (c) (i) 3500 g
        (ii) Required information lies beyond
           known values.
           Chicken may have stopped growing.

5. (a) 0.6   (b) 0.2

6. 1. No answer for 7 am and 8 am.
    2. No response box for other items.
    3. Too open. No time boxes given.

7. (a) **B**   (b) **C**   (c) **D**

8. (a) E.g. Most people travel to out-of-town
        shopping supermarkets by car and
        so a high proportion of drivers will
        be included.
     (b) 23 000

9. (a) 400
　　(b) There are three terms to a cycle of one year, so a 3-point moving average will smooth out termly variations.

10. (a)

Day 1　　　　Day 2
0.7 On time
　　0.7 On time
　　　　0.3 Late
0.7 On time
　0.3 Late
　　　0.3 Late

　　(b) 0.51

11. (a)

0　10　20　30　40　50　60　70　80　90　100
Boys

　　(b) E.g. Average mark (median) similar but girls have a smaller interquartile range (marks closer together).

12. (a) 13.4 minutes

13. (b) 50　　(c) (i) 53　(ii) 29
　　(d) E.g. Town has lower median and ages are more closely grouped.

14. (b) 26, 26.5, 27.5, 29, 30.5, 31.5, 34, 37, 45.5
　　(e) Upward trend in sale of phones.
　　(f) 30

15. $\frac{4}{7}$

CHAPTER 8

Exercise 8.1　　　　Page 95

1. (a) 396　　　　(b) 5010
　　(c) 70 200　　(d) 9 002 051
　　(e) 762 504 019　(f) 20 202 020

2. (a) eighty-four
　　(b) twenty-three thousand five hundred and ninety
　　(c) ninety-three million one hundred and forty-five thousand six hundred and seventy
　　(d) seven hundred and sixty-four thousand eight hundred and nine
　　(e) six thousand and forty-nine
　　(f) nine million eighty thousand and four

3. (a) 1004　(b) 1035　(c) 1014

4. (a) 30　　(b) 3 000 000　(c) 600
　　(d) 2000　(e) 4000　　(f) 6

5. (a) 203　(b) 28

6. (a) 39, 74, 168, 421
　　(b) 3801, 3842, 3874, 4765, 5814

7. (a) 429, 425, 399, 103, 84
　　(b) 9951, 9653, 9646, 9434

8. (a) 76541 (digits in descending order)
　　(b) 14567 (digits in ascending order)

9. (a) 9654　(b) 4569

10.

3458	4358	5348	8345
3485	4385	5384	8354
3548	4538	5438	8435
3584	4583	5483	8453
3845	4835	5834	8534
3854	4853	5843	8543

6 numbers beginning with 8

Exercise 8.2　　　　Page 97

1. (a) 28　　(b) 33
2. (a) 29　　(b) 31　　(c) 43
　　(d) 43　　(e) 53　　(f) 46
3. (a) 91　　(b) 4　　(c) 55
　　(d) 63　　(e) 38　　(f) 17
4. (a) 788　(b) 83　　(c) 174
　　(d) 952　(e) 2002　(f) 12 203
　　(g) 201　(h) 1541　(i) 3451
　　(j) 1 000 000
5. (a) 27　　(b) 56　　(c) 35
　　(d) 54　　(e) 74　　(f) 70
　　(g) 120　(h) 112
6. 112 miles　　**10.** 256
7. £539　　　　**11.** 1030 grams
8. £306　　　　**12.** 1378
9. 520 km　　　**13.** 81 030

Exercise 8.3　　　　Page 98

1. (a) 33　　(b) 27
2. (a) 28　　(b) 46　　(c) 25
　　(d) 35
3. (a) 5　　(b) 92　　(c) 43
　　(d) 68　　(e) 76　　(f) 17
　　(g) 59　　(h) 21
4. (a) 16　　(b) 17　　(c) 50
　　(d) 49　　(e) 90　　(f) 105
　　(g) 150　(h) 301　(i) 575
　　(j) 4
5. (a) 354　(b) 428　(c) 1284
　　(d) 158　(e) 2224　(f) 469
　　(g) 6268　(h) 3277
6. 89　　　　　**7.** 384
8. Car C
　　Car A 8479,　Car B 11 643,　Car C 13 859
9. (a) £74　(b) £60

Exercise 8.4　　　　Page 100

1. 40　　　　　**3.** 144
2. 72　　　　　**4.** £5.52
5. (a) 84　　(b) 85　　(c) 252
　　(d) 549　(e) 2112　(f) 15 895
　　(g) 24 072　(h) 42 084
6. (a) 1320　(b) 12 300
　　(c) 47 000　(d) 38 400
7. (a) 2310　(b) 514　　(c) 100
8. (a) 240　(b) £3.90
9. (a) 210 chairs　　(b) 140 tables

10. (a) 300 seconds (b) 1140 seconds
11. 1600 kg
12. 720 chairs **13.** 10 000 metres
14. (a) 7590 (b) 7140 (c) 21 480
(d) 12 300 (e) 13 020 (f) 21 510
(g) 32 960 (h) 9940 (i) 18 960
(j) 13 000
15. (a) E.g. To multiply by 200, multiply by 2
and then by 100.
(b) E.g. To multiply by 2000, multiply by 2
then by 1000.
(c) (i) 173 500 (ii) 4 458 000

Exercise 8.5 — Page 102

1. 49p
2. 6 **4.** 12p
3. £14 **5.** 15 packets
6. (a) 17 (b) 157 (c) 136
(d) 75 remainder 5
(e) 393 remainder 2
(f) 206 (g) 1098 (h) 20 140
7. (a) 456 (b) 465
(c) 64 (d) 654
8. (a) 100 (b) 702 000 (c) 10
9. 8
10. 15 **12.** 25 boxes
11. 12 **13.** 7 minutes
14. (a) 253 (b) 79 (c) 537
(d) 126 (e) 45 (f) 613
15. (a) E.g. To divide by 200, divide by 100
then by 2.
(b) (i) 26 (ii) 412

Exercise 8.6 — Page 103

1. (a) 204 (b) 345 (c) 1344
(d) 2432 (e) 4862 (f) 38 772
2. 216 **5.** 1316
3. 255 **6.** £1392
4. £966 **7.** £5191
8. (a) 43 (b) 32 (c) 27
(d) 32 (e) 48 (f) 41
(g) 21 (h) 29
9. (a) 16 remainder 10 (b) 25 remainder 7
(c) 17 remainder 35 (d) 13 remainder 13
10. 14 pints, 24p change
11. (a) 41 (b) 16
12. (a) 20 (b) 35, 10p change
(c) 14, 10p change

Exercise 8.7 — Page 104

1. (a) 37 (b) 3 (c) 9 (d) 58
(e) 6 (f) 30 (g) 5 (h) 19
(i) 14 (j) 20 (k) 24 (l) 4
(m) 0 (n) 56 (o) 56 (p) 6
(q) 28 (r) 0

2. (a) $5 \times 6 + 7 = 37$
(b) $5 + 6 \times 7 = 47$
(c) $15 + 8 \times 9 = 87$
(d) $15 \times 8 + 9 = 129$
(e) $15 \times 8 - 9 = 111$
(f) $15 \div 5 + 3 = 6$
(g) $5 - 24 \div 6 = 1$
(h) $19 \div 19 + 7 \times 0 = 1$
(i) $4 \times 4 + 7 \times 2 = 30$
3. Many answers, for example:
$6 - 3 \times 2 + 1 = 1$ $6 - 3 - 2 + 1 = 2$
$6 \div 3 + 2 - 1 = 3$ $6 \div 3 + 2 \times 1 = 4$
$6 - 3 + 2 \times 1 = 5$ $6 + 3 - 2 - 1 = 6$
$6 + 3 - 2 \times 1 = 7$ $6 \times 3 \div 2 - 1 = 8$
$6 \times 3 \div 2 \times 1 = 9$ $6 + 3 + 2 - 1 = 10$
4. 25
5. 148 cm
6. (a) 36 (b) 43

Review Exercise 8 — Page 105

1. (a) eight hundred and seventy thousand
three hundred and two
(b) 3 027 409
2. (a) 987 542 (b) 245 789
3. (a) 97, 404 (b) 114, 306
(c) 92, 209
4. (a) 2059 (b) 587
5. (a) 73 500 (b) 6420
(c) 3020 (d) 462
6. 298 miles
7. (a) 6462 (b) 241
8. (a) 50 (b) 50
(c) 10 (d) 2
9. £547.50
10. 14 664 **14.** £3427
11. 120 **15.** £17
12. (a) 166 (b) 4 **16.** 32
13. £14 522 **17.** 50

CHAPTER 9

Exercise 9.1 — Page 108

1. (a) $7 + 0.6 + 0.02$
(b) $30 + 7 + 0.9 + 0.02 + 0.008$
(c) $7 + 0.5 + 0.04 + 0.001$
(d) $20 + 0.5 + 0.003$
2. (a) 0.4 (b) 0.009
(c) 80 (d) 0.05
3. (a) 1.68 (b) 1.39 (c) 1.04
4. (a) 0.07 (b) 0.6
5. (a) A 10.5, B 11 (b) C 5.2, D 5.6
(c) E 0.54, F 0.59 (d) G 0.751, H 0.757

6. 47.5074   **7.** 93.07

8. (a) 3.001, 3.01, 3.1, 3.15, 3.2
    (b) 3.567, 3.576, 3.657, 3.675
    (c) 0.1, 0.15, 0.45, 0.5, 0.55

9. (a) 9.87, 9.78, 8.97, 8.79
    (b) 1.5, 0.15, 0.015, 0.00015
    (c) 2.701, 2.7, 2.67, 2.599

Exercise 9.2   Page 110

1. (a) (i) 8.86 (ii) 12.449 (iii) 17.49
    (b) (i) $8.86 - 3.72 = 5.14$
        (ii) $12.449 - 5.384 = 7.065$
        (iii) $17.49 - 5.69 = 11.8$

2. (a) (i) 6.23 (ii) 24.32 (iii) 24.68
    (b) (i) $6.23 + 3.24 = 9.47$
        (ii) $24.32 + 13.28 = 37.6$
        (iii) $24.68 + 20.36 = 45.04$

3. (a) 10.9   (b) 1.65   (c) 0.9
    (d) 11   (e) 1.2   (f) 0.6
    (g) 0.24   (h) 8.9

4. (a) 6.84   (b) 86.33 (c) 5.22
    (d) 5.003 (e) 3   (f) 1.24
    (g) 15.781 (h) 8.28 (i) 16.033
    (j) 6.273

5. (a) (i) £3.30   (ii) £1.70
    (b) (i) £11.24   (ii) £3.76
    (c) (i) £0.83   (ii) £9.17
    (d) (i) £16.24   (ii) £33.76

6. 4.35 kg   **7.** 4.88 m   **8.** 1.55 m

9. (a) Team A 148.93 s
        Team B 149.08 s
        Team C 149.53 s
    (b) A, B, C

10. 0.719 s   **11.** (a) 95.21 s (b) 47.72 s

Exercise 9.3   Page 111

1. (a) 250.6   (b) 2506   (c) 25 060
    (d) 9.3   (e) 93   (f) 930
    (g) 0.623 (h) 6.23   (i) 62.3
    (j) 94.51 (k) 945.1 (l) 9451

2. (a) 3.77   (b) 0.377 (c) 0.0377
    (d) 0.027 (e) 0.0027 (f) 0.00027
    (g) 18.902 (h) 1.8902 (i) 0.18902
    (j) 0.9   (k) 0.09   (l) 0.009

3. (a) (i) 0.64 (ii) 6.4   (iii) 64
    (b) (i) 0.64 (ii) 0.064 (iii) 0.0064

4. (a) £13.50   (b) £135   (c) £1350

5. (a) £2.50   (b) £25   (c) £250

6. (a) 5.04 km (b) 50.4 km (c) 504 km

7. (a) £7.95   (b) £0.12   (c) 76.9p

8. 12.3×1000 and $12.3 \div 0.001$
    $12.3 \div 100$ and 12.3×0.01
    12.3×0.1 and $12.3 \div 10$
    $12.3 \div 0.01$ and 12.3×100
    12.3×10 and $12.3 \div 0.1$
    12.3×0.001 and $12.3 \div 1000$

Exercise 9.4   Page 113

1. (a) 8.5   (b) 0.36
    (c) 1.3   (d) 0.48
    (e) 0.06   (f) 1.44

2. (a) 8.75   (b) 54.53
    (c) 1.03   (d) 29.808
    (e) 0.0007 (f) 0.01
    (g) 0.0001 (h) 97.82
    (i) 57.78   (j) 0.000 177 6

3. (a) (i) 3   (ii) 1.5
        (iii) 0.24 (iv) 15
    (b) Each answer is less than the original
        number.

4. (a) 21p   (b) £1.84
    (c) 78p

5. (a) £20.93   (b) £14.58
    (c) £54.21   (d) £26.24

6. (a) (i) 5.22 euros (ii) 0.87 euros
        (iii) 78.59 euros
    (b) (i) $12.30   (ii) $1.23
        (iii) $59.86

7. (a) (i) £4.34   (ii) £5.12
        (iii) £2.60   (iv) £2.34
    (b) £3.97

Exercise 9.5   Page 115

1. (a) 4   (b) 15   (c) 15
    (d) 4   (e) 50

2. (a) 1.75   (b) 1.6   (c) 2.4
    (d) 1.75   (e) 1.125

3. (a) 12.3   (b) 2.92 (c) 6.05
    (d) 1430   (e) 0.05 (f) 12.5
    (g) 6.54   (h) 37.5

4. (a) 37   (b) 5.6   (c) 43.75
    (d) 46.9   (e) 10.62 (f) 34.2

5. (a) (i) 10   (ii) 6   (iii) 0.3
    (b) Each answer is greater than the original
        number.

6. 47p   **9.** 120

7. 9p   **10.** 67

8. 75.6p   **11.** 45

Exercise 9.6   Page 116

1. (a) $\frac{1}{4}$ (b) $\frac{1}{2}$ (c) $\frac{3}{4}$ (d) $\frac{1}{10}$

2. (a) $\frac{7}{10}$ (b) $\frac{2}{5}$ (c) $\frac{1}{100}$ (d) $\frac{1}{5}$
    (e) $\frac{1}{20}$ (f) $\frac{3}{20}$ (g) $\frac{13}{25}$ (h) $\frac{7}{100}$
    (i) $\frac{1}{8}$ (j) $\frac{13}{20}$ (k) $\frac{3}{5}$ (l) $\frac{19}{20}$

3. (a) $1\frac{7}{10}$ (b) $2\frac{3}{10}$ (c) $1\frac{2}{5}$ (d) $3\frac{1}{4}$
    (e) $4\frac{4}{5}$ (f) $12\frac{1}{10}$ (g) $16\frac{3}{4}$ (h) $5\frac{1}{20}$

4. (a) $\frac{2}{3}$ (b) $\frac{1}{9}$ (c) $\frac{5}{9}$

Review Exercise 9 — Page 117

1. (a) (i) 20.745   (b) (i) 0.87
   (ii) 14.407   (ii) 4.33
   (iii) 179.22   (iii) 1.53

2. 40 s

3. 2.37 m

4. (a) (i) 76.2   (b) (i) 0.762
   (ii) 762   (ii) 0.0762
   (iii) 7620   (iii) 0.007 62

5. (a) (i) 1746   (b) (i) 4.365
   (ii) 2619   (ii) 2.91
   (iii) 3492   (iii) 2.1825

6. (a) £247.50 (b) £12.99

7. (a) 46.62 (b) 10.152 (c) 105.9

8. (a) 7.2 (b) 1235 (c) 13 700

9. 11

10. 28p   12. 240.159574…

11. 4.63   13. 24.86052632…

CHAPTER 10

Exercise 10.1 — Page 119

1. (a) 50 (b) 50 (c) 70
2. (a) 4870 (b) 4900 (c) 5000
3. (a) 360 (b) 400
4. (a) 7480 (b) 7500 (c) 7000

5.

Number	Nearest 10	Nearest 100	Nearest 1000
7613	7610	7600	8000
977	980	1000	1000
61 115	61 120	61 100	61 000
9714	9710	9700	10 000
623	620	600	1000
9949	9950	9900	10 000
5762	5760	5800	6000
7509	7510	7500	8000
7499	7500	7500	7000

6. Nearest 1000.

7. (a) 19 000 (nearest thousand)
   (b) 260 (nearest ten)
   (c) 140 (nearest ten)
   (d) £50 (nearest pound)
   (e) 130 (nearest ten)
   (f) 24 100 (nearest hundred)
   (g) 309 000 km² (nearest thousand km²)
   (h) 190 km (nearest ten kilometres)
   (i) £51 (nearest pound)
   (j) 700 (nearest hundred)

8. (a) 745, 746, 747, 748, 749
   (b) 750, 751, 752, 753, 754
   (c) Any number from 8450 to 8499
   (d) Any number from 8500 to 8549

9. (a) 35   (b) 44

10. (a) 1950   (b) 2049   11. 42 500

12. smallest: 135, greatest: 144   13. 2749

Exercise 10.2 — Page 120

1. 4   4. 5   7. 29
2. 5   5. 9   8. 19   10. 7
3. 10   6. 24   9. 5   11. 5

Exercise 10.3 — Page 121

1. (a) 3.962 (b) 3.96 (c) 4.0
2. (a) 567.65 (b) 567.7 (c) 568
3. Missing entries:
   0.96, 0.97, 15.281, 0.06, 4.99, 5.00
4. 5.71   5. 4.86
6. (a) (i) 46.1   (ii) 59.7
   (iii) 569.4   (iv) 17.1   (v) 0.7
   (b) (i) 46.14   (ii) 59.70
   (iii) 569.43 (iv) 17.06   (v) 0.66
   (c) (i) 46.145 (ii) 59.697
   (iii) 569.434 (iv) 17.059 (v) 0.662
7. (a) £12.16, nearest penny
   (b) £3.57, nearest penny
   (c) £2.37, nearest penny
   (d) 35.7 cm, nearest millimetre
   (e) £1.33, nearest penny
   (f) £12.70, nearest penny

Exercise 10.4 — Page 123

1. (a) 20   (b) 500   (c) 0.3
   (d) 0.02   (e) 20

2.

Number	sig. fig.	Answer
456 000	2	460 000
454 000	2	450 000
7 981 234	3	7 980 000
7 981 234	2	8 000 000
1290	2	1300
19 602	1	20 000

3.

Number	sig. fig.	Answer
0.000567	2	0.00057
0.093748	2	0.094
0.093748	3	0.0937
0.093748	4	0.09375
0.010245	2	0.010
0.02994	2	0.030

489

4. 485.7

5. (a) (i) 83 000   (ii) 83   (iii) 1000
     (iv) 0.0073   (v) 0.0019
   (b) (i) 82 700   (ii) 82.7   (iii) 1000
     (iv) 0.00728   (v) 0.00190
   (c) (i) 82 660   (ii) 82.66   (iii) 1001
     (iv) 0.007281   (v) 0.001899

6. 472 m² (3 s.f.)

7. (a) 51 cm² (2 s.f.)
   (b) 157 cm² (3 s.f.)
   (c) 6100 m² (2 s.f.)
   (d) 1.23 m (nearest cm)
   (e) 154 000 m² (3 s.f.)

Exercise 10.5   Page 125

1. (a) $30 \times 40 = 1200$,   1312
   (b) $10 \times 70 = 700$,   792
   (c) $60 \times 30 = 1800$,   1972
   (d) $70 \times 50 = 3500$,   3240
   (e) $30 \times 80 = 2400$,   2652
   (f) $20 \times 200 = 4000$,   3723
   (g) $300 \times 60 = 18\,000$,   16 296
   (h) $300 \times 20 = 6000$,   7176

2. (a) $600 \div 20 = 30$,   33
   (b) $600 \div 20 = 30$,   29
   (c) $300 \div 20 = 15$,   16
   (d) $800 \div 40 = 20$,   24

3. (a) $4 \times 2 = 8$,   7.56
   (b) $9 \times 3 = 27$,   27.59
   (c) $50 \times 4 = 200$,   202.02
   (d) $100 \times 3 = 300$,   299.86

4. (a) $10 \div 5 = 2$,   2.2
   (b) $20 \div 4 = 5$,   4.8
   (c) $30 \div 3 = 10$,   9.5
   (d) $200 \div 5 = 40$,   39.9

5. (a) 30 is bigger than 29 and 50 is bigger
     than 48.
     So, 30×50 is bigger than 29×48
   (b) $200 \div 10 = 20$, 14, estimate is bigger

6. (a) £8000 + £1000 = £9000
   (b) £9312

7. (a) 6.4, 6.41875
   (b) 20, 18.709677…
   (c) 20, 20.45631…

Exercise 10.6   Page 126

1. 167.5 cm

2. 8.5 m ≤ height of building < 9.5 m

3. Minimum weight: 835 g
    maximum weight: 845 g

4. 11.55 seconds

5. 9.35 kg

6. Least length: 2.65 m,   greatest length: 2.75 m

7. 94 ml

8. Minimum weight: 7.5 kg
    maximum weight: 8.5 kg

Review Exercise 10   Page 127

1. (a) 8480   (b) 8500   (c) 8000

2. (a) (i) 6 700 000
     (ii) 100 000
   (b) 109 500

3. (a) $20 \times 30 = 600$
   (b) $2000 \div 40 = 50$

4. (a) $90 \times 2 = 180$
   (b) $2000 \div 50 = 40$

5. 18.7 is less than 19, but rounds to 19.
   0.96 is less than 1, but rounds to 1.
   $19 \times 1 = 19$,   so 18.7×0.96 must be less
   than 19.

6. $40 \times 0.03 = 1.2$

7. $100 \times £20 = £2000$

8. 15

9. Smallest: 85,   largest: 94

10. (a) 25.57   (b) 25.6   (c) 30

11. (a) 17.5 m
   (b) 17.5 m ≤ length of bus < 18.5 m

12. 4.13

13. (a) 24.8605263…
   (b) $\dfrac{5 \times 20}{6 - 2} = \dfrac{100}{4} = 25$

14. (a) 19 m²
   (b) Round up to the nearest square metre for
     enough carpet to cover whole floor.

15. 18.9 kg

CHAPTER 11

Exercise 11.1   Page 129

1. (a) Warmer   (b) Colder
   (c) Warmer   (d) Colder

2. (a) Less   (b) More
   (c) Less   (d) More

3. (a) Colombo   (b) Moscow
   (c) −22°C, −17°C, −7°C, 0°C, 3°C, 15°C,
     21°C.

4. (a) −28°C, −13°C, −3°C, 19°C, 23°C.
   (b) −11°C, −9°C, −7°C, 0°C, 10°C, 12°C.
   (c) −29°C, −15°C, 2°C, 18°C, 27°C.
   (d) −20°C, −15°C, −5°C, 0°C, 10°C, 20°C.

5. (a) −78, −39, −16, −9, 11, 31, 51.
   (b) −5, −3, −2, −1, 0, 1, 2, 4, 5.
   (c) −103, −63, −19, −3, 5, 52, 99, 104.
   (d) −50, −30, −20, 0, 10, 30, 40.
   (e) −30, −15, −10, 0, 8, 17, 27.

Exercise 11.2   Page 130

1. (a) −3   (b) −4   (c) −7
   (d) −32   (e) 0   (f) −27
   (g) −61   (h) −1

2. (b) (i) -1 (ii) -4 (iii) -4

3. (a) 9 (b) 1 (c) 12
(d) -10 (e) 30 (f) 15

4. (a) $-£75$ (£75 overdrawn)
(b) £40 (£40 in credit)

5. (a) $-80\,$m (b) $-200\,$m (c) $60\,$m
(d) $60\,$m (e) $120\,$m (f) $70\,$m
(g) $300\,$m (h) $50\,$m (i) $130\,$m
(j) $240\,$m (k) $250\,$m

Exercise 11.3 — Page 131

1. (a) 2 (b) 1 (c) -9
(d) 8 (e) 4 (f) -5
(g) -7 (h) 7 (i) 1
(j) -15 (k) -3 (l) -6

2. (a) 13 (b) 6 (c) 7
(d) 7 (e) 5 (f) -12
(g) -1 (h) 13 (i) -11
(j) 11 (k) 9 (l) 0

3. (a) 5 (b) 3 (c) 3
(d) -7 (e) -6 (f) -1

4. (a) 6 (b) -8 (c) -28
(d) 0 (e) -35 (f) 19

5. (a) 7 (b) -1 (c) 36
(d) -6 (e) 38 (f) 15
(g) -15 (h) 25 (i) 15
(j) -6

6. $-15°$C

7. (a) $10°$C (b) $10°$C
(c) $5°$C (d) $37°$C

Exercise 11.4 — Page 133

1. (a) 35 (b) -35 (c) 35
(d) 10 (e) -10 (f) 10
(g) 1 (h) -24 (i) -24
(j) -45 (k) 64 (l) -42
(m) 42 (n) -80 (o) -80
(p) 32

2. (a) -20 (b) 60 (c) -30
(d) 60 (e) -60 (f) -100

3. (a) -4 (b) 4 (c) 5
(d) -5 (e) -5 (f) 5
(g) 6 (h) -6 (i) 4
(j) -8 (k) 6 (l) -5

4. (a) -1.8 (b) 3 (c) -1.6
(d) 3.2 (e) -20 (f) 12
(g) -10 (h) 5

5. (a) -0.5 (b) -0.8 (c) 0.7
(d) -15 (e) -4 (f) 4

Review Exercise 11 — Page 133

1. 132, 34, 17, -11, -21.

2. (a) Poole (b) Selby

3. (a) -18 (b) 4 (c) 4

4. (a) 5 (b) -2

5. (a) 13 degrees (b) $-8°$C

6. 5 degrees

7. 11 degrees

8. 24 degrees

9. 33 m

10. $-£33.75$ (£33.75 overdrawn)

11. (a) 24 (b) -24
(c) -24 (d) 24
(e) 40 (f) -40
(g) -40 (h) 40

12. (a) -5 (b) 2
(c) -6 (d) 4

13. (a) E.g. (i) $\boxed{-5} \times \boxed{2} = \boxed{-10}$
(ii) $\boxed{1} \div \boxed{-1} = \boxed{-1}$
(b) -28

14. (a) $21°$C (b) $-0.4°$F

15. 4

CHAPTER 12

Exercise 12.1 — Page 135

1. (a) 10, 20, 30, 40, 50
(b) 3, 6, 9, 12, 15
(c) 7, 14, 21, 28, 35
(d) 6, 12, 18, 24, 30
(e) 9, 18, 27, 36, 45
(f) 20, 40, 60, 80, 100

2. (a) 20 (b) 42
(c) third (d) seventh
(e) 10 (f) 9

3. (a) second (b) second
(c) fifth (d) eighth
(e) third

4. (a) 35 (b) 48

5. (a) (i) Answers are even numbers.
(ii) Answers are even numbers.
(iii) Answers are even numbers.
(iv) Answers are odd numbers.

(b) (i)

×	2	3	6	7	9
2	E	E	E	E	E
3	E	O	E	O	O
6	E	E	E	E	E
7	E	O	E	O	O
9	E	O	E	O	O

(ii)

×	O	E
O	O	E
E	E	E

(c) Only **O** × **O** gives an odd number.

491

1. (a) 1, 2, 3, 4, 6, 12
   (b) $12 \div 8 = 1.5$
      To be a factor, 8 would need to divide
      into 12 a whole number of times.
2. (a) $1 \times 18, 2 \times 9, 3 \times 6$
   (b) 1, 2, 3, 6, 9, 18
3. (a) $1 \times 20, 2 \times 10, 4 \times 5$
   (b) 1, 2, 4, 5, 10, 20
4. (a) 1, 2, 4, 8, 16
   (b) 1, 2, 4, 7, 14, 28
   (c) 1, 2, 3, 4, 6, 9, 12, 18, 36
   (d) 1, 3, 5, 9, 15, 45
   (e) 1, 2, 3, 4, 6, 8, 12, 16, 24, 48
   (f) 1, 2, 5, 10, 25, 50
   (g) 1, 2, 3, 4, 5, 6, 10, 12, 15, 20, 30, 60
   (h) 1, 2, 4, 5, 8, 10, 16, 20, 40, 80
5. (a) (i) 1, 2 (ii) 1, 3 (iii) 1, 5
      (iv) 1, 7 (v) 1, 11 (vi) 1, 13
   (b) 17, 19, 23, 29, 31, …
6. (a) (i) 1, 2, 4, (ii) 1, 3, 9
      (iii) 1, 5, 25 (iv) 1, 7, 49
   (b) 121, 169, 289, 361, …
7. (a) (i) 1, 2, 3, 6 (ii) 1, 2, 5, 10
      (iii) 1, 2, 7, 14 (iv) 1, 2, 13, 26
      (v) 1, 5, 11, 55 (vi) 1, 2, 19, 38
   (b) 15, 21, 22, 33, 35, …
8. 6, 36
9. (a) 1, 5 (b) 1, 2, 4 (c) 1, 2
   (d) 1, 2, 3, 4, 6, 12 (e) 1, 2, 3, 6
10. (a) 5 (b) 27 (c) 3, 5
11. (a) 4 (6, 12, 18, 36)
   (b) 8 (5, 10, 15, 20, 30, 40, 60, 120)
   (c) 6 (2, 4, 10, 20, 50, 100)
   (d) 8 (4, 8, 12, 16, 24, 32, 48, 96)
12. (i) 2, 3, 5, 7, 11, 13, 17, 19, 23, 29, 31, 37,
      41, 43, 47
      Each number has 2 factors.
      Prime numbers.

1. (a) 4^4 (b) 3^8 (c) 8^7
   (d) 0.3^3 (e) 1.6^5 (f) 12^7
2. (a)

Expression	Index form	Value
$10 \times 10 \times 10 \times 10 \times 10 \times 10$	10^6	1 000 000
$10 \times 10 \times 10 \times 10 \times 10$	10^5	100 000
$10 \times 10 \times 10 \times 10$	10^4	10 000
$10 \times 10 \times 10$	10^3	1000
10×10	10^2	100
10	10^1	10
1	10^0	1

(b) (i)

Expression	Index form	Value
$5 \times 5 \times 5 \times 5 \times 5 \times 5$	5^6	15 625
$5 \times 5 \times 5 \times 5 \times 5$	5^5	3125
$5 \times 5 \times 5 \times 5$	5^4	625
$5 \times 5 \times 5$	5^3	125
5×5	5^2	25
5	5^1	5
1	5^0	1

(ii)

Expression	Index form	Value
$4 \times 4 \times 4 \times 4 \times 4 \times 4$	4^6	4096
$4 \times 4 \times 4 \times 4 \times 4$	4^5	1024
$4 \times 4 \times 4 \times 4$	4^4	256
$4 \times 4 \times 4$	4^3	64
4×4	4^2	16
4	4^1	4
1	4^0	1

(c) 1
3. (a) 8 (b) 36 (c) 81
   (d) 144 (e) 625 (f) 10 000 000
4. (a) $2^2 \times 3^2$ (b) $2 \times 3^3 \times 5$
   (c) $2 \times 3 \times 5^2$ (d) $2^4 \times 3 \times 5^2$
   (e) $3^4 \times 5^2 \times 7$

1. (a) 2, 3 (b) 2, 5 (c) 2, 7
   (d) 3, 5 (e) 2, 3, 11
2. (a) $2^2 \times 3$ (b) $2^2 \times 5$ (c) $2^2 \times 7$
   (d) $3^2 \times 5$ (e) $2 \times 3 \times 11$
3. (a) 1, 2, 2×3, 2×3^2, 2×3^3, 2^2, $2^2 \times 3$,
      $2^2 \times 3^2$, $2^2 \times 3^3$, 2^3, $2^3 \times 3$, $2^3 \times 3^2$,
      $2^3 \times 3^3$, 2^4, $2^4 \times 3$, $2^4 \times 3^2$, $2^4 \times 3^3$, 2^5,
      $2^5 \times 3$, $2^5 \times 3^2$, $2^5 \times 3^3$, 3, 3^2, 3^3
   (b) 1, 5, 5×7, 5×7^2, 5×7^3, 5×7^4, 5^2,
      $5^2 \times 7$, $5^2 \times 7^2$, $5^2 \times 7^3$, $5^2 \times 7^4$, 5^3,
      $5^3 \times 7$, $5^3 \times 7^2$, $5^3 \times 7^3$, $5^3 \times 7^4$, 7, 7^2,
      7^3, 7^4
4. 1000 1 000 000 2700
   56 250 000 3 294 225 926 859 375
5. 2700, 3528, 4500
6. 56, 88, 104 **7.** 126, 132, 150

1. (a) 24 (b) 160 (c) 20
   (d) 90 (e) 90 (f) 24
   (g) 40 (h) 630
2. (a) 6 (b) 8 (c) 2
   (d) 4 (e) 11 (f) 4
   (g) 3 (h) 15

4. (a) 3   (b) 2×3^4
    (c) 54   (d) 324

5. (a) $2^3 \times 3^3$ (b) $2^5 \times 3^2$
    (c) 72   (d) 864

6. 9.18 am

Exercise 12.6   Page 144

1. (a) 1, 4, 9, 16, 25, 36, 49, 64, 81, 100, 121, 144, 169, 196, 225, 256, 289, 324, 361, 400
    (c) $21^2 = 400 + 41 = 441$

2. (a) 1, 8, 27, 64, 125, 216, 343, 512, 729, 1000

3. (a) (i) 9   (ii) −8   (iii) 16   (iv) −125
    (b) The result of squaring a negative number is a positive number.
        The result of cubing a negative number is a negative number.

4. 64

5. (a) 44.89   (b) 39.304   (c) 0.49
    (d) 0.000064   (e) 0.16   (f) −0.125

6. (a) 1   (b) 0.027   (c) 0.4   (d) 0.25

7. (a) 1.69   (b) 4.913   (c) 1   (d) 4.8

8. (a) (i) 169   (ii) 289   (iii) 6.25
        (iv) 0.64   (v) 94.09
    (b) (i) 216   (ii) 3375   (iii) 13.824
        (iv) 0.343   (v) 175.616
    (c) (i) 2187   (ii) 16 807   (iii) 531 441
        (iv) 0.0625   (v) 792.35168

9. (a) 79.62624   (b) −1.728   (c) 0.49
    (d) 90   (e) 60   (f) 864
    (g) 1944   (h) 128   (i) 8192
    (j) 0.860 518 4

10. (a) 30   (b) 66
     (c) 2592   (d) 1440
     (e) 1080   (f) 6.770 83…
     (g) 126 216   (h) 0.281 25
     (i) 20 000

11. (a) (i) 0.5   (ii) 0.2   (iii) 0.1
       (iv) 2   (v) 10   (vi) 5
     (b) (i) 0.25   (ii) 0.05   (iii) 0.04
       (iv) 4   (v) 2.5   (vi) 6.25

13. (a) 0.5   (b) 0.25   (c) 1.25   (d) 4

14. (a) 3   (b) 0   (c) 1   (d) 2
     (e) 6   (f) 3   (g) 4   (h) 3

Exercise 12.7   Page 146

1. (a) 5   (b) 10   (c) 8   (d) 7

2. (a) 2   (b) 4   (c) 5   (d) 3

3. (a) 5   (b) 3   (c) 4

4. (a) (i) 4.5   (ii) 10.4   (iii) 2.8

5. (a) 3.6   (b) 5.8   (c) 1.7

6. 7.4 m

7. 16.51 mm

Exercise 12.8   Page 147

1. (a) 2^7 (b) 4^9 (c) 6^3
    (d) 8^7 (e) $9^0 = 1$ (f) 2^{-2}
    (g) 5^{-2} (h) 3^{-1} (i) 8^{-5}

2. (a) 2^3 (b) 4^2 (c) 6
    (d) 8   (e) 3^6 (f) 2^{-4}
    (g) 5^{12} (h) 11^{-5} (i) 7^{-1}

3. (a) 8^2 (b) 7^{-5} (c) 2.5^{-1}
    (d) $4^0 = 1$ (e) 10^{-1} (f) 6^{-4}
    (g) 0.1^{-12} (h) 5^{-15} (i) 4^5

4. (a) $4^2 \times 8^7$ (b) 4×5^{-2}
    (c) $2^{-2} \times 5^5$ (d) $3^{-3} \times 8^4$

5. (a) 2^3 (b) 3   (c) 5^3

Exercise 12.9   Page 148

1. (a) $\sqrt{2}$ surd   (b) $\sqrt{9} = 3$
    (c) $\sqrt{7}$ surd   (d) $\sqrt{1} = 1$
    (e) $\sqrt{18}$ surd   (f) $\sqrt{25} = 5$

2. (a) $2\sqrt{2}$ (b) $2\sqrt{3}$ (c) $2\sqrt{7}$
    (d) $3\sqrt{3}$ (e) $5\sqrt{3}$ (f) $3\sqrt{5}$
    (g) $2\sqrt{5}$ (h) $6\sqrt{2}$

3. (a) $2\sqrt{2}$ (b) $\sqrt{5}$ (c) $7\sqrt{3}$ (d) $2\sqrt{2}$

4. (a) $\frac{3}{2}$ (b) $\frac{5}{4}$ (c) $\frac{\sqrt{6}}{2}$
    (d) $\sqrt{2}$ (e) $\frac{2}{\sqrt{5}}$

5. (a) 3   (b) 6   (c) 6   (d) 4
    (e) 6   (f) 6   (g) $5\sqrt{2}$ (h) $3\sqrt{2}$

Review Exercise 12   Page 150

1. (a) 1, 2, 3, 4, 6, 12
    (b) 1, 2, 3, 5, 6, 10, 15, 30
    (c) 1, 2, 3, 4, 6, 8, 12, 16, 24, 32, 48, 96

2. Only two factors, 1 and 19.

3. (a) 9, 18   (b) 3, 6   (c) 3

4. 36

5. (a) 9, 25, 100   (b) 20, 25, 100
    (c) 3, 29

6. (a)   8: 1, 2, 4, 8
          9: 1, 3, 9
       11: 1, 11
       17: 1, 17
    121: 1, 11, 121
    (b) (i) 11, 17   (ii) prime numbers
    (c) (i) 9, 121   (ii) square numbers

7. (a) 108   (b) 1, 3, 37, 111
    (c) 103   (d) 2

8. (a) (i) $2 \times 3^2 \times 7$ (b) 630
       (ii) $2 \times 3^2 \times 5$ (c) 18
       (iii) $2 \times 3 \times 5 \times 7$

9. (a) 4   (b) $2^3 \times 3^2$
    (c) 24   (d) 144

10. 90 seconds

11. (a) 16   (b) 3

12. (a) 125   (b) 64

13. 3

14. (a) 7   (b) 289

15. (a) $2\sqrt{5}$ (b) $\frac{6}{5}$
    (c) 6

16. 3^3 greater, $\sqrt{625} = 25$, $3^3 = 27$

17. (a) 0.09   (b) 0.125

18. 2 significant figures.
$2^{10} = 1024$, $10^3 = 1000$

19. 7.1

20. 5.8

21. (a) 32 768   (b) 0.167

22. 2.57

23. (a) 10^2 (b) 10^6
    (c) 10^0 (d) 10^{-1}
    (e) 10^{-3}

24. (a) 1   (b) 625
    (c) 272   (d) 90
    (e) 500   (f) 50
    (g) 50   (h) 40

25. (a) 5   (b) 5
    (c) 1

26. (a) 31 104   (b) 0.02943
    (c) 0.00006561   (d) 8145
    (e) -16384 (f) 786 432

27. (a) 3^8 (b) 5^{11}
    (c) 9^6 (d) 4^5
    (e) 7^5 (f) 6^4
    (g) 2^{-3} (h) 5^{-7}
    (i) 4^{-3} (j) $2^{-7} \times 7^2$
    (k) 3^9

28. (a) 2.65   (b) 7
    (c) 343

CHAPTER 13

Exercise 13.1   Page 153

1. Missing entries:
    (a) 7.5×10^4
    (b) 800 000 000, 8×10^8
    (c) 35 000 000 000 000,
        $3.5 \times 10\ 000\ 000\ 000\ 000$
    (d) $6.23 \times 10\ 000\ 000\ 000\ 000$, 6.23×10^{13}
    (e) 5 400 000 000, $5.4 \times 1\ 000\ 000\ 000$
    (f) 69 300 000, 6.93×10^7
    (g) $4.531 \times 100\ 000\ 000\ 000$, 4.53×10^{11}
    (h) 697 000, $6.97 \times 100\ 000$
    (i) $4.5312 \times 100\ 000$, 4.5312×10^5
    (j) 109 700, 1.097×10^5

2. (a) 6 E 13, 6×10^{13}, 60 000 000 000 000
    (b) 9.6 E 12, 9.6×10^{12}, 9 600 000 000 000
    (c) 1.05 E 13, 1.05×10^{13},
        10 500 000 000 000
    (d) 1.3 E 14, 1.3×10^{14},
        130 000 000 000 000
    (e) 2.4 E 14, 2.4×10^{14},
        240 000 000 000 000
    (f) 2.5 E 12, 2.5×10^{12}, 2 500 000 000 000
    (g) 1.408 E 16, 1.408×10^{16},
        14 080 000 000 000 000
    (h) 2.288 E 14, 2.288×10^{14},
        228 800 000 000 000
    (i) 8.073 E 11, 8.073×10^{11},
        807 300 000 000
    (j) 1.1 E 15, 1.1×10^{15},
        1 100 000 000 000 000

3. (a) 3×10^{11} (b) 8×10^7
    (c) 7×10^8 (d) 2×10^9
    (e) 4.2×10^7 (f) 2.1×10^{10}
    (g) 3.7×10^9 (h) 6.3×10^2
    (i) 3.219×10^9 (j) 6.5412×10^8
    (k) 8.97213×10^5 (l) 4.267×10^{10}

4. (a) 600 000   (b) 2000
    (c) 50 000 000   (d) 900 000 000
    (e) 3 700 000 000   (f) 28
    (g) 99 000 000 000   (h) 71 000
    (i) 397   (j) 817.2
    (k) 7 431 200   (l) 1 234 000 000

5. (a) (i) 4.5×10^3 (ii) 7.8×10^7
        (iii) 5.3×10^5 (iv) 3.25×10^4
    (b) (i) 4500   (ii) 78 000 000
        (iii) 530 000   (iv) 32 500

6. (a) (i) Brazil   (ii) 250 000 000
    (b) 1.288×10^9

Exercise 13.2   Page 155

1. (a) -1 (b) -5 (c) -9
    (d) -3 (e) -11 (f) -13

2. Missing entries:
    (b) 7.5×10^{-3}
    (c) 8.75×10^{-6}
    (d) $3.5 \times 0.000\ 000\ 001$, 3.5×10^{-9}
    (e) $6.23 \times 0.000\ 000\ 000\ 001$, 6.23×10^{-12}
    (f) $5 \times 0.000\ 000\ 1$, 5×10^{-7}
    (g) $4.725 \times 0.000\ 000\ 01$, 4.725×10^{-8}
    (h) 5×0.01, 5×10^{-2}
    (i) $7.85 \times 0.000\ 001$, 7.85×10^{-6}

3. (a) 0.35
    (b) 0.0005
    (c) 0.000 072
    (d) 0.0061
    (e) 0.000 000 000 117
    (f) 0.000 000 813 5
    (g) 0.064 62
    (h) 0.000 000 004 001

4. (a) 7×10^{-3} (b) 4×10^{-2}
     (c) 5×10^{-9} (d) 8×10^{-4}
     (e) 2.3×10^{-9} (f) 4.5×10^{-8}
     (g) 2.34×10^{-2} (h) 2.34×10^{-9}
     (i) 6.7×10^{-3} (j) 3×10^{-1}
     (k) 7.395×10^{-8} (l) 3.4×10^{-13}

5. (a) 0.000 005 5
     (b) 0.000 000 065
     (c) 32 000 000
     (d) 290
     (e) 0.000 000 000 031 67
     (f) 11 150
     (g) 0.000 014 12
     (h) 40

6. (a) $6 \text{ E} -12$, 6×10^{-12}, 0.000 000 000 006
     (b) $1.35 \text{ E} -10$, 1.35×10^{-10}, 0.000 000 000 135
     (c) $3 \text{ E} -11$, 3×10^{-11}, 0.000 000 000 03
     (d) $1.15 \text{ E} -10$, 1.15×10^{-10}, 0.000 000 000 115
     (e) $4.24 \text{ E} -09$, 4.24×10^{-9}, 0.000 000 004 24
     (f) $9.728 \text{ E} -11$, 9.728×10^{-11}, 0.000 000 000 097 28
     (g) $2.891 \text{ E} -13$, 2.891×10^{-13}, 0.000 000 000 000 289 1
     (h) $3 \text{ E} -10$, 3×10^{-10}, 0.000 000 000 3
     (i) $1.055 \text{ E} 11$, 1.055×10^{11}, 105 500 000 000
     (j) $9.25 \text{ E} 11$, 9.25×10^{11}, 925 000 000 000

Exercise 13.3   Page 157

1. (a) 262 500
     (b) 105 000 000 000 000
     (c) 72 250 000 000 000
     (d) 0.000 000 125
     (e) 30 000 000 000
     (f) 263 160 000 000 000 000 000

2. (a) 9.38×10^{19} (b) 1.6×10^{1}
     (c) 2.25×10^{26} (d) 1.25×10^{-37}
     (e) 2.4×10^{20} (f) 5×10^{-2}

3. (a) 2.088×10^{9} (b) $1.525\,965 \times 10^{16}\,\text{km}$

4. (a) Pluto, Saturn, Jupiter
     (b) $1.397 \times 10^{5}\,\text{km}$, 139 700 km

5. (a) $9.273 \times 10^{6}\,\text{km}^2$ (b) $4.93 \times 10^{5}\,\text{km}^2$

6. 2.52×10^{12}

7. 2.2×10^{-5} **9.** 2.85×10^{-3}

8. 2.3×10^{-7} **10.** 9×10^{-28} grams

11. (a) 4.55×10^{9} years
      (b) About 6.6×10^{3} times

Exercise 13.4   Page 158

1. (a) 5.2×10^{3} (b) 8.4×10^{6}
     (c) 4×10^{4} (d) 5×10^{4}

2. (a) 2.8×10^{3} (b) 9×10^{5}
     (c) 3×10^{7} (d) 9.5×10^{8}

3. (a) 8×10^{7} (b) 6×10^{7}
     (c) 2.4×10^{8} (d) 2.7×10^{15}

4. (a) 3×10^{3} (b) 3×10^{3}
     (c) 5×10^{1} (d) 2×10^{11}
     (e) 4×10^{5} (f) 3×10^{-3}

5. (a) 1.5×10^{0} (b) 2.7×10^{13}
     (c) 4.5×10^{4} (d) 1.25×10^{-13}
     (e) 6×10^{8}

6. (a) 1.5×10^{11} (b) 2.4×10^{3}
     (c) 4.2×10^{-8} (d) 6.4×10^{7}
     (e) 5×10^{1} (f) 3×10^{9}
     (g) 6.25×10^{-6} (h) 2.5×10^{4}

Review Exercise 13   Page 159

1. (a) (i) 3.9×10^{5} (ii) 390 000
     (b) (i) 6.7×10^{-3} (ii) 0.0067

2. (a) 4×10^{4} (b) 1.6×10^{7}

3. (a) 3.45×10^{10} (b) 5.43×10^{-7}
     (c) 1.125×10^{2}

4. (a) 4.746×10^{7} (b) 2.67×10^{8}

5. (a) 5.137×10^{6} (b) 7.115×10^{4}

6. £1.81×10^{4}

7. (a) £4.01×10^{10} (b) £1070 (3 s.f.)

CHAPTER 14

Exercise 14.1   Page 161

1. (a) $\frac{4}{9}$ (b) $\frac{2}{8} = \frac{1}{4}$ (c) $\frac{8}{16} = \frac{1}{2}$ (d) $\frac{3}{18} = \frac{1}{6}$

2. E.g. $\frac{15}{24}$, $\frac{30}{48}$, $\frac{45}{72}$, …, $\frac{10}{16}$, $\frac{20}{32}$, …
     simplest form $\frac{5}{8}$

3. (a) **P**   (b) **P**   (c) **R**
     (d) **R**   (e) **Q**   (f) **S**

4. (a) $\frac{1}{3}$ (b) $\frac{1}{3}$ (c) $\frac{1}{3}$ (d) $\frac{1}{3}$ (e) $\frac{1}{2}$

5. (a) E.g. $\frac{2}{6}$, $\frac{3}{9}$, $\frac{4}{12}$
     (b) E.g. $\frac{4}{18}$, $\frac{6}{27}$, $\frac{8}{36}$
     (c) E.g. $\frac{10}{16}$, $\frac{15}{24}$, $\frac{20}{32}$
     (d) E.g. $\frac{8}{10}$, $\frac{12}{15}$, $\frac{16}{20}$
     (e) E.g. $\frac{6}{20}$, $\frac{9}{30}$, $\frac{12}{40}$
     (f) E.g. $\frac{14}{24}$, $\frac{21}{36}$, $\frac{28}{48}$

6. (a) 2   (b) 3   (c) 6   (d) 3   (e) 8   (f) 7

7. (a) $\frac{3}{4}$ (b) $\frac{4}{5}$ (c) $\frac{2}{3}$ (d) $\frac{2}{9}$
     (e) $\frac{2}{3}$ (f) $\frac{2}{5}$ (g) $\frac{6}{25}$ (h) $\frac{4}{5}$

8. (a) $\frac{1}{5}$ (b) $\frac{1}{4}$ (c) $\frac{2}{3}$ (d) $\frac{2}{5}$ (e) $\frac{4}{7}$

9. (a) $\frac{7}{10}$ (b) $\frac{1}{5}$

10. (a) 24   (b) $\frac{1}{6}$

1. (a) $1\frac{3}{10}$ (b) $1\frac{1}{2}$ (c) $2\frac{1}{8}$
   (d) $3\frac{3}{4}$ (e) $4\frac{3}{5}$ (f) $4\frac{6}{7}$

2. (a) $\frac{27}{10}$ (b) $\frac{8}{5}$ (c) $\frac{35}{6}$
   (d) $\frac{63}{20}$ (e) $\frac{41}{9}$ (f) $\frac{53}{7}$

3. (a) 3   (b) 4   (c) 3
   (d) 8   (e) 8   (f) 9
   (g) 12   (h) 20

4. (a) $2\frac{2}{5}$ (b) $7\frac{1}{2}$
   (c) $7\frac{1}{2}$ (d) $9\frac{3}{5}$

5. £60

6. 28

7. £48

8. £92

9. £132.50

10. (a) 9   (b) 10   (c) $\frac{5}{24}$

11. (a) (i) 10 (ii) 25 (iii) 12
    (b) $\frac{13}{60}$

12. £2656.25

1. (a) $\frac{3}{8}$ (b) $\frac{7}{12}$ (c) $\frac{7}{10}$
   (d) $\frac{8}{15}$ (e) $\frac{9}{14}$ (f) $\frac{9}{20}$

2. (a) $\frac{1}{8}$ (b) $\frac{1}{12}$ (c) $\frac{3}{10}$
   (d) $\frac{2}{15}$ (e) $\frac{5}{14}$ (f) $\frac{1}{20}$

3. (a) $1\frac{1}{4}$ (b) $1\frac{1}{2}$ (c) $1\frac{11}{20}$
   (d) $1\frac{8}{21}$ (e) $1\frac{5}{24}$ (f) $1\frac{3}{20}$

4. (a) $\frac{1}{8}$ (b) $\frac{8}{15}$ (c) $\frac{5}{8}$
   (d) $\frac{17}{45}$ (e) $\frac{5}{24}$ (f) $\frac{19}{48}$

5. (a) $4\frac{1}{4}$ (b) $3\frac{5}{6}$ (c) $4\frac{3}{8}$
   (d) $5\frac{17}{20}$ (e) $6\frac{13}{30}$ (f) $5\frac{9}{20}$

6. (a) $1\frac{1}{10}$ (b) $\frac{5}{12}$ (c) $\frac{5}{8}$
   (d) $3\frac{3}{10}$ (e) $1\frac{27}{40}$ (f) $\frac{47}{48}$

7. (a) $\frac{5}{6}$ (b) $\frac{1}{6}$

8. $\frac{11}{20}$

9. (a) $\frac{7}{20}$ (b) $\frac{17}{20}$

10. $\frac{7}{60}$

11. (a) $\frac{27}{80}$ (b) Andy

12. $\frac{3}{10}$

1. (a) $\frac{1}{6}$ (b) $\frac{1}{20}$ (c) $\frac{1}{10}$
   (d) $\frac{5}{21}$ (e) $\frac{1}{6}$ (f) $\frac{1}{4}$
   (g) $\frac{4}{5}$ (h) $\frac{7}{16}$

2. (a) $\frac{3}{8}$ (b) $\frac{3}{10}$ (c) $\frac{1}{3}$
   (d) $\frac{1}{3}$ (e) $\frac{3}{16}$ (f) $\frac{2}{35}$
   (g) $\frac{1}{2}$ (h) $\frac{1}{4}$

3. (a) $1\frac{1}{8}$ (b) 2   (c) $3\frac{3}{4}$
   (d) $3\frac{17}{20}$ (e) $4\frac{7}{8}$ (f) $1\frac{13}{15}$
   (g) 14   (h) $13\frac{1}{2}$

4. (a) $2\frac{3}{5}$ (b) $3\frac{1}{2}$ (c) $5\frac{2}{5}$
   (d) $2\frac{1}{2}$ (e) $1\frac{1}{3}$ (f) $3\frac{4}{7}$
   (g) $\frac{2}{3}$ (h) $1\frac{1}{3}$

5. (a) $\frac{1}{8}$ (b) $\frac{1}{8}$

6. (a) $\frac{4}{15}$ (b) $\frac{2}{5}$

7. (a) $\frac{4}{15}$ (b) 15

1. (a) $\frac{1}{10}$ (b) $\frac{3}{8}$ (c) $\frac{1}{10}$
   (d) $\frac{1}{3}$ (e) $\frac{4}{7}$ (f) $\frac{4}{9}$

2. (a) 2   (b) $\frac{2}{5}$ (c) $2\frac{5}{8}$
   (d) $3\frac{1}{3}$ (e) 22   (f) $7\frac{1}{3}$

3. (a) $\frac{5}{6}$ (b) $\frac{9}{16}$ (c) $\frac{4}{5}$
   (d) $1\frac{1}{3}$ (e) $\frac{2}{3}$ (f) $1\frac{1}{2}$
   (g) $\frac{2}{3}$ (h) $1\frac{1}{6}$ (i) $1\frac{1}{2}$
   (j) $1\frac{4}{5}$

4. (a) $\frac{2}{3}$ (b) $1\frac{3}{8}$ (c) $1\frac{1}{7}$
   (d) $4\frac{2}{3}$ (e) $13\frac{1}{2}$ (f) $\frac{4}{5}$
   (g) $1\frac{1}{2}$ (h) $1\frac{1}{4}$ (i) $2\frac{2}{7}$
   (j) $3\frac{6}{25}$

5. (a) $21, \frac{17}{20}$ cm   (b) $23, \frac{1}{2}$ cm

6. (a) $\frac{32}{45}$ (b) $2\frac{2}{5}$

7. $\frac{16}{21}$

1. £3.20   4. £6

2. 70 km   5. 96 cm

3. £3.20   6. 189

Exercise 14.7   Page 172

1. (a) $\frac{3}{25}$ (b) $\frac{3}{5}$ (c) $\frac{8}{25}$
   (d) $\frac{7}{40}$ (e) $\frac{9}{20}$ (f) $\frac{13}{20}$
   (g) $\frac{11}{50}$ (h) $\frac{101}{500}$ (i) $\frac{7}{25}$
   (j) $\frac{111}{200}$ (k) $\frac{5}{8}$ (l) $\frac{21}{25}$

2. (a) (i) 0.25   (ii) 0.5   (iii) 0.75
   (b) (i) 0.1   (ii) 0.3   (iii) 0.7
   (c) (i) 0.4   (ii) 0.6   (iii) 0.8

3. (a) (i) 0.15   (ii) 0.35   (iii) 0.95
   (b) (i) 0.16   (ii) 0.36   (iii) 0.92
   (c) (i) 0.07   (ii) 0.23   (iii) 0.53

4. (a) 0.125   (b) 0.625
   (c) 0.225   (d) 0.725

5. (a) $0.\dot{7}$ (b) $0.\dot{1}$ (c) $0.\dot{3}\dot{6}$
   (d) $0.8\dot{2}$ (e) $0.1\dot{3}\dot{5}$ (f) $0.\dot{2}1\dot{6}$
   (g) 0.16 (h) $0.\dot{2}8571\dot{4}$

6. (a) $0.\dot{8}$ (b) $0.\dot{4}$ (c) $0.5\dot{1}$
   (d) $0.7\dot{2}$ (e) $0.\dot{1}4285\dot{7}$ (f) $0.\dot{8}5714\dot{2}$
   (g) $0.0\dot{3}$ (h) $0.4\dot{6}$ (i) $0.8\dot{3}$
   (j) $0.7\dot{7}\dot{2}$

7. (a) 0.33   (b) 0.67   (c) 0.43
   (d) 0.45   (e) 0.78   (f) 0.38

Review Exercise 14   Page 173

1. (a) 24   (b) 10   (c) 4
2. 15
3. (a) £270   (b) £405
4. (a) $\frac{11}{12}$ (b) $\frac{11}{40}$
5. $\frac{4}{15}$
6. $\frac{7}{10}$
7. (a) $\frac{2}{5}$ (b) $\frac{6}{25}$ (c) $\frac{9}{20}$ (d) $\frac{1}{8}$
8. $\frac{1}{4}$
9. (a) $6\frac{1}{12}$ (b) $4\frac{10}{63}$ (c) $2\frac{1}{10}$
   (d) $2\frac{19}{30}$ (e) $4\frac{1}{2}$ (f) 10
   (g) $1\frac{5}{7}$ (h) $2\frac{1}{2}$
10. (a) $2\frac{1}{12}$ m   (b) $\frac{1}{4}$ m²
11. $\frac{1}{10}$
12 £80
13. (a) 0.8   (b) 0.45
    (c) 0.42   (d) 0.402
14. (a) 0.143
    (b) 1.014, 1.14, $1\frac{1}{7}$, 1.41, 11.14
15. (a) 64   (b) $\frac{7}{16}$
16 208 km

CHAPTER 15

Exercise 15.1   Page 175

1. (a) (i) $\frac{1}{10}$ (ii) $\frac{1}{5}$ (iii) $\frac{1}{4}$ (iv) $\frac{3}{4}$
   (b) (i) 0.1   (ii) 0.2
   (iii) 0.25   (iv) 0.75

2. (a) $\frac{3}{20}$ (b) $\frac{1}{20}$ (c) $\frac{9}{50}$
   (d) $\frac{13}{25}$ (e) $\frac{23}{100}$ (f) $\frac{1}{8}$

3. (a) 0.15   (b) 0.05   (c) 0.47
   (d) 0.72   (e) 0.875   (f) 1.5

4. Missing entries: 30%, 40%, 12%, 35%
5. Missing entries: 70%, 45%, 5%, 120%
6. $33\frac{1}{3}\%$
7. (a) 34%   (b) 48%   (c) 15%
   (d) 80%   (e) 27%   (f) 65%
   (g) $66\frac{2}{3}\%$ (h) $22\frac{2}{9}\%$
8. (a) 15%   (b) 32%   (c) 12.5%
   (d) 7%   (e) 112%   (f) 1.5%
9. (a) $\frac{2}{5}$, $\frac{1}{2}$, 0.55, 60%
   (b) 0.42, 43%, $\frac{11}{25}$, $\frac{9}{20}$
   (c) 28%, 0.2805, $\frac{57}{200}$, $\frac{23}{80}$
10. 80%
11. (a) 90%   (b) 85%   (c) 88%   (d) 80%
12. Team A

Exercise 15.2   Page 176

1. (a) 60%   (b) 16%   (c) 70%
   (d) 21%   (e) 21%
2. (a) 32%   (b) 10%   (c) 60%
   (d) 15%   (e) 30%
3. 32%   6. 12.5%
4. 30%   7. 37.5%
5. (a) 40%   (b) 60%   8. 3%
9. (a) $33\frac{1}{3}\%$ (b) $66\frac{2}{3}\%$ (c) $12\frac{1}{2}\%$
   (d) $42\frac{1}{2}\%$ (e) $56\frac{1}{2}\%$
10. 9.5%   11. 25%

Exercise 15.3   Page 177

1. (a) 50   (b) 40   (c) 140
   (d) 60   (e) 240   (f) 110
   (g) 2.5   (h) 12   (i) 19.5
   (j) 17   (k) 60   (l) 64
2. (a) £16   (b) £15   (c) £66
   (d) £52.50   (e) £25   (f) £30
   (g) £27   (h) 4 m   (i) 24 kg
   (j) 280 m   (k) £11.25   (l) 12p
3. (a) 60   (b) 105   (c) 45%

4. £20

5. 270 **8.** £10.50

6. £42 **9.** (a) 660 (b) 198

7. £2.70 **10.** 24 g

Exercise 15.4 — Page 178

1. (a) £480 (b) £420 (c) £2800
(d) £1080 (e) £3450 (f) £1260
(g) £80 (h) £13 (i) £16.50
(j) £57.50

2. (a) £420 (b) £600 (c) £2000
(d) £150 (e) £10 200 (f) £4550
(g) £510 (h) £5.50 (i) £33.60
(j) £40.95

3. 40p per minute **8.** £4706

4. £215 **9.** £5622.50

5. 759 g **10.** £14 560

6. £18.45 **11.** £10 530

7. £244.64 **12.** £492

Exercise 15.5 — Page 179

1. £19.38 **4.** $83\frac{1}{3}$%

2. 32p per pint **5.** 17.3%

3. 79.9p per litre **6.** £109 520

7. (a) £34.13 (b) £41.39

8. (a) 36.3% (b) 23.7% (c) 37.8%

9. (a) 270 (b) 7.5%

10. 4.55×10^5 km² (455 000 km²)

11. 1.35×10^9 km³ **13.** 30%

12. 1.49×10^9 square miles **14.** 2.53%

Exercise 15.6 — Page 181

1. 20%

2. 6% **4.** $12\frac{1}{2}$%

3. 20% **5.** 28%

6. (a) $12\frac{1}{2}$% (b) 12%
Rent went up by a greater percentage.

7. Becky Sam's increase = 32%
Becky's increase = 40%

8. 30.8%

9. Car A 13.8%, Car B 18.2%

10. 1998 - 1999 (9.2%) **14.** 5.9% decrease

11. 19.5% **15.** 8% increase

12. 3.51% **16.** 19%

13. 18.6% **17.** 3.5%

Exercise 15.7 — Page 182

1. 600 ml **7.** 67.5 mg

2. £600 **8.** £1420

3. £220 **9.** £8000

4. (a) 50 **10.** School A 425,
(b) 90 School B 450

5. 1.89 m **11.** £400

6. £312 500 **12.** £150

Review Exercise 15 — Page 184

1. (a) 18 **4.** 180
(b) 20% **5.** $37\frac{1}{2}$%

2. £780 **6.** 57.3%

3. 90% **7.** 3080

8. (a) 166.4 cm (b) 13.7%

9. (a) 8.80 m (b) 15%

10. (a) £2434.50 (b) 73.9%

11. (a) 6900
(b) Yes. $6000 \times 1.15^4 = 10\,500$

12. 43 200 **14.** £85

13. £36 **15.** £212.31

CHAPTER 16

Exercise 16.1 — Page 186

1. (a) 1030 (b) 2230 (c) 0145
(d) 1345 (e) 0750 (f) 2350

2. (a) 2.15 pm (b) 5.25 am (c) 11.20 pm
(d) 10.05 am (e) 9.40 am (f) 5.05 pm

3. (a) 1835, 1920, 2000, 2050
(b) 40 minutes (c) 45 minutes

4. (a) 1.15 pm (b) 2 hours 50 minutes

5. (a) 1325 (b) 4 hours 15 minutes

6. (a) 1.30 pm (b) 1330

7. (a) 1441 (b) 2.41 pm

Exercise 16.2 — Page 187

1. (a) 49 minutes (b) 1 hour 35 minutes
(c) 1.42 pm (d) 0815

2. (a) 1215 (b) 1 hour 48 minutes
(c) 5.42 pm

3. (a) 0900 (b) 44 minutes
(c) 2 hours 20 minutes

4. (a) (i) 1520 (ii) 1610
(b) 1650

Exercise 16.3 — Page 189

1. 36 hours **6.** £22 500

2. £582.40 **7.** £31 900

3. £374 **8.** £1610

4. £305.10 **9.** £800 000

5. £10.20 **10.** £1440

Exercise 16.4 — Page 190

1. £19 409 **5.** £108.09

2. (a) £1185 **6.** £38.87
(b) £118.50 **7.** £420.13

3. (a) £1638 **8.** £3524.27
(b) £13.65 **9.** £10 980.80

4. £3963.50 **10.** £610.40

Exercise 16.5 — Page 191

1. £15.99
2. 90p
3. £1.60
4. 90p
5. £4.80
6. (a) £47 (b) 10 days
7. (a) £39 (b) 120 miles
8. £26
9. £638
10. £165
11. £40.50

Exercise 16.6 — Page 192

1. (a) 4p (b) 3.5p
2. Small: 5.2 g per penny.
   Large: 5.1 g per penny.
   Small tin is better buy.
3. Small: 8.7 g per penny.
   Large: 8.5 g per penny.
   Small pot is better buy.
4. 700 g
5. Large: 2.3 g per penny.
   Small: 2.2 g per penny.
   Large pot is better buy.
6. 1 kg
7. Medium
8. 1.5 litre bottle
9. Small: 0.882 ml per penny.
   Medium: 0.862 ml per penny.
   Large: 0.878 ml per penny.
   Small size is better value for money.
10. (a) Daisy's £448, Alfie's £438
    (b) Alfie's

Exercise 16.7 — Page 194

1. (a) £300
   (b) £25
2. £74.84
3. 810
4. £6.30
5. £112
6. £46.76
7. £402.40
8. (a) £72 (b) £187.50 (c) £84 000
   (d) £95 (e) £284 (f) £178
9. £12 400

Exercise 16.8 — Page 195

1. £6
2. (a) £3.50 (b) £73.50
3. (a) £59.50 (b) £399.50
4. (a) £15.75 (b) £105.75
5. (a) £8.97 (b) £188.50
6. £291.40
7. £170.37
8. £216.20
9. £88.27
10. £428.87
11. £69.32
12. £183.75
13. £3.20
14. £293.75
15. £2928.10

Exercise 16.9 — Page 197

1. £10
2. (a) £30 (b) £15
3. £2
4. £225
5. £48
6. £225
7. £242
8. £330.75
9. (a) earns 78p more interest
10. (a) £11 576.25 (b) £11 910.16
    (c) £12 250.43 (d) £12 597.12
11. (a) £2420 (b) £1938.66

Exercise 16.10 — Page 197

1. (a) 310 euros (b) 34 600 yen
   (c) 126 liri (d) 2496 krone
   (e) 460 francs (f) 284 dollars
2. (a) £39.13 (b) £28.90
   (c) £48.39 (d) £18.03
   (e) £24.65
3. (a) 38.75 euros (b) £15
4. (a) 276 francs (b) £10.65
5. (a) £387.10 (b) 46.5 euros
6. (a) £240.38 (b) 561.6 krone
7. (a) 710 dollars (b) £18.13
8. £131.92
9. France: £5806.45, Japan: £5780.35
   Cheaper in Japan by £26.10

Review Exercise 16 — Page 199

1. (a) 5.05 pm (b) 1 hour 44 minutes
2. 56p
3. (a) £32.16 (b) 150 miles
4. £417.54
5. (a) £720 (b) £60
6. £40.72
7. (a) £47.23 (b) 300
8. Large: 9.34 g per penny.
   Small: 9.66 g per penny.
   Small pot is better value.
9. £6.20
10. £586.32
11. £120
12. 4 hours
13. Rome: 75p, London: 95p.
    Rome is cheaper, by 20p.
14. (a) 39 euros (b) £13.78
15. £1619.75
16. £5.76
17. £2450.09
18. (a) 29 000 (b) 61 000 (c) 1989

CHAPTER 17

Exercise 17.1 — Page 201

1. (a) 8 SMILERS and 2 GLUMS
   (b) (i) 8 SMILERS and 4 GLUMS
       (ii) 3 SMILERS and 9 GLUMS
   (c) (i) 16 SMILERS and 4 GLUMS
       (ii) 8 SMILERS and 12 GLUMS

2. (a) (i) 75 (ii) 200
   (b) (i) 12 (ii) 32
   (c) (i) 56 (ii) 140
3. (a) (i) 16 (ii) 80
   (b) (i) 9 (ii) 45
   (c) (i) 84 (ii) 112
4. (a) (i) 14 SMILERS and 6 GLUMS
   (ii) 35 SMILERS and 15 GLUMS
   (b) (i) 9 SMILERS and 6 GLUMS
   (ii) 30 SMILERS and 20 GLUMS

Exercise 17.2 — Page 203

1. (a) E.g. 12 : 2, 18 : 3, 24 : 4.
   (b) E.g. 14 : 4, 21 : 6, 28 : 8.
   (c) E.g. 6 : 10, 9 : 15, 12 : 20.
2. (a) 1 : 2 (b) 1 : 3 (c) 3 : 4
   (d) 2 : 5 (e) 3 : 4 (f) 2 : 5
   (g) 3 : 7 (h) 9 : 4 (i) 4 : 9
   (j) 7 : 3
3. (a) 12 (b) 28
   (c) 100 (d) 20
4. 198 cm   **8.** 2 : 3
5. 400 g   **9.** 5 : 2
6. 64   **10.** 1 : 250
7. 18 years old   **11.** 1 : 1500
12. (a) 4 : 1 (b) 2 : 25 (c) 11 : 2
   (d) 5 : 2 (e) 4 : 1 (f) 40 : 17
   (g) 9 : 20 (h) 25 : 1 (i) 1 : 15
   (j) 2 : 1
13. 40 : 9
14. 1 : 3   **16.** 1 : 2
15. 2 : 3   **17.** 3 : 2

Exercise 17.3 — Page 204

1. (a) 6, 3 (b) 15, 5
   (c) 7, 28 (d) 90, 10
2. 18
3. Sunny £36, Chandni £12
4.

	4 : 1	3 : 2
(a)	32, 8	24, 16
(b)	16, 4	12, 8
(c)	64 kg, 16 kg	48 kg, 32 kg
(d)	160 g, 40 g	120 g, 80 g
(e)	£960, £240	£720, £480

5. (a) £14, £21 (b) £32, £24
   (c) £3.50, £2 (d) £1.80, £3
6. 45
7. £192   **11.** $\frac{5}{8}$
8. 2 033 000   **12.** 60%
9. $\frac{1}{4}$ **13.** 48%
10. 80%   **14.** 170 000 km²

15. (a) Jenny 50, Tim 30 (b) 10
16. (a) 5 : 2 (b) 6 (c) 55
   (d) 32 is not a multiple of 5 + 2 = 7
17. 8 cm, 12 cm, 18 cm
18. 200 kg
19. 40°, 60°, 80°
20. 45%
21. (a) $12\frac{1}{2}$%, $37\frac{1}{2}$%, 50%
   (b) $\frac{1}{3}$ (c) $\frac{3}{5}$

Exercise 17.4 — Page 206

1. (a) 16p (b) £1.28
2. (a) £6 (b) £60
3. £2.85
4. (a) 120 cm (b) 2 kg
5. £201.60
6. (a) 250 g (b) 150 g
7. £61
8. £2.85
9. £14.76
10. (a) 50 g (b) 720 g
11. £44.64
12. £32.41
13. (a) £3.08 (b) 12 minutes
14. (a) 180 g (b) 637.5 ml
   (c) 210 g
15. (a) 12 minutes (b) 16 miles
16. (a) 12 m² (b) 12 litres
17. (a) £260 (b) 32
18. $17\frac{1}{2}$ minutes
19. (a) 168.75 g (b) 36 (c) 540 ml
20. £8.35

Review Exercise 17 — Page 208

1. 3 : 4   **9.** £4
2. 9   **10.** (a) 25 g (b) 750 g
3. 12   **11.** (a) 375 g (b) 360
4. £262.50, £157.50 **12.** £1.45
5. 12   **13.** 1 : 200 000
6. (a) 18 (b) 35% **14.** (a) $\frac{3}{4}$
7. (a) 24 (b) 5 : 3   (b) $12\frac{1}{2}$%
8. £276   (c) 200 cm³

CHAPTER 18

Exercise 18.1 — Page 210

1. 8 mph
2. (a) 20 km/h (b) 50 km/h
   (c) 4 km/h
3. 14 km/h
4. 8 km

5. (a) 150 km   (b) 400 m
    (c) 1500 m

6. 3 km

7. (a) 3 hours   (b) 2 minutes
    (c) 20 seconds

8. $1\frac{1}{2}$ hours   **11.** 25 m per minute

9. 15 minutes   **12.** 6 km

10. $2\frac{1}{4}$ hours   **13.** 27 minutes

14. (a) $2\frac{1}{2}$ hours   (b) 50 minutes

15. (a) 57.5 km/hour   (b) 1 hour

16. (a) 8 m/s   (b) 100 km
    (c) 12 cm   (d) 1 hour
    (e) 5 s

17. (a) 300 km   (b) 5 hours
    (c) 60 km/h

18. 5 m/s   **20.** 10.30 am

19. 10 km/hour   **21.** 11.09 am

22. (a) 13.8 km/h   (b) 1.10 pm

23. (a) 8 hours   (b) 111 km/h

24. (a) 4.81 m/s   (b) 17.3 km/h

25. 100 m

26. 3×10^8 m/s

27. 2 hours 17 minutes

Exercise 18.2   Page 212

1. 8 g/cm³   **5.** 9360 g

2. 9 g/cm³   **6.** 2000 cm³

3. 28.6 g/cm³   **7.** 0.8 g/cm³

4. 7200 g   **8.** 100 g

9. 118.3 people/km²

10. (a) 30 530 km²   (b) 104.2 people/km²
    (c) 5.74×10^7

Review Exercise 18   Page 213

1. 94 km/h   **3.** $1\frac{1}{2}$ hours

2. 240 miles   **4.** 8 mph

5. (a) 200 miles   (b) 30 minutes

6. 63.3 miles per hour

7. 18 miles per hour

8. (a) 9 km/h   (b) 36 minutes

9. 45 km/h   **13.** 24 km/h

10. 36 minutes   **14.** 125 m

11. 5 hours 48 minutes   **15.** 4.35 cm³

12. 25 km/h   **16.** 2.92 g/cm³

17. Steel 2.5 g/cm³, Concrete 1600 cm³,
    Foam 200 g

18. Europe 0.065 people/km²
    Asia 0.068 people/km²
    Asia

19. 40 minutes

Exam Practice: Module ③
Non-calculator Paper   Page 215

1. (a) 1 hour 54 minutes
    (b) 0759   (c) 0823

2. 14 pence

3. (a) 17.5   (b) 2.95

4. Large (500 g) = 2 × Standard (250 g)
    2 × £1.39 = £2.78   and   £2.78 > £2.69.
    Large size is better value for money.

5. (a) (i) 3   (ii) 2
    (b) −9, −3, 0.6, 2, 10
    (c) 0.06

6. £3978

7. (a) 12 000 000   (b) 50
    (c) 0.5

8. 7 boxes

9. (a) 11 degrees Celsius
    (b) −2°C

10. (a) (i) 6, 9   (ii) 2, 5, 7   (iii) 2, 5
    (b) (i) 500   (ii) 93 000
    (c) 25 796

11. 1310

12. (a) 14   (b) 48

13. 62p

14. (a) 30 000   (b) 27 000

15. (a) $\frac{3}{10}$, $\frac{1}{3}$, $\frac{2}{5}$, $\frac{5}{8}$
    (b) 40%   (c) 20

16. 4

17. Minimum: 395,   maximum 404

18. £90

19. (a) 260   (b) 65%

20. 40 scones

21. $\frac{£2000}{80}$ = £25 per guest

22. (a) $\frac{5}{8}$ (b) $\frac{3}{8}$ (c) 80

23. (a) $\frac{1}{6}$ (b) $1\frac{11}{20}$

24. (a) 49   (b) 9   (c) $\frac{2}{3}$

25. (a) Any decimal between 0.25 and $0.\dot{3}$.
    (b) $\frac{1}{2}$

26. (a) 72p   (b) £78

27. (a) 51   (b) 8

28. (a) 13   (b) 24.9

29. 3^4 is bigger. $2^6 = 64$, $3^4 = 81$.

30. $\frac{80 \times 5}{20 - 10} = \frac{400}{10} = 40$

31. 90%

32. (a) 17.1911   (b) 171.911

33. (a) 12 mph (b) 13 mph

34. (a) 4.2 (b) 0.08 (c) $1\frac{17}{20}$

35. 15

36. Least: 74.5 m, greatest: 75.5 m

37. (a) $2^3 \times 3^2$ (b) 24

38. 240 mph

39. (a) $\dfrac{600 \times 5}{0.2} = 15\ 000$

   (b) E.g. 99 and 100: $\dfrac{99 \times 100}{50} = 198$

40. 32

41. No.
   Year 1: £500 × 0.04 = £20
   Year 2: £520 × 0.04 = £20.80
   Total interest = £20 + £20.80 = £40.80

42. £7.20 per hour

43. Andi is correct.
   Increase of 10% = 110% of original speed
   = 1.1 × original speed
   Decrease of 10% = 90% × 1.1 = 0.99
   = 99% of original speed

44. (a) $10^2 \div 0.4 = 250$
   (b) (i) $p = 2$, $q = 3$
      (ii) $2 \times 3 \times 3 = 2 \times 3^2$
      (iii) 72

45. A: False. The prime numbers will be factors
      of the product.

   B: True. Even number + Odd number
      = Odd number + Even number
      = Odd number.

46. 3 hours 30 minutes

47. 54 890 000 (or 5.489×10^7)

48. (a) 1.5×10^3 (b) 6×10^5

49. £40

50. (a) 2.4×10^3 (b) 8×10^3
   (c) 1.6×10^{11}

Exam Practice: Module 3

Calculator Paper — Page 218

1. 39p

2. 21 minutes

3. (a) 4, 6 (b) 24
   (c) 7 (d) 216

4. £349.20

5. £6.46

6. (a) Yum. Yum 8.4 g/p, Core 8.3 g/p
   (b) 39p

7. (a) 28.7 (b) 30

8. (a) 2.25
   (b) 2.035, $\sqrt{4.78}$, 2.21, $2\frac{1}{4}$, 1.53^2

9. (a) 0.43 (b) 50 000

10. (a) 6 (b) 27%

11. £1.26

12. If 1st number is odd, last number is odd.
   Odd + Odd = Even
   If 1st number is even, last number is even.
   Even + Even = Even

13. £57.34

14. 300 euros is £97.30 less than £300

15. 15 pence   **20.** 200 m²

16. 50 mph   **21.** (a) £4
17. £107.50   (b) 35 g

18. £1660   **22.** £70.21

19. (a) £87.80   **23.** (a) 39.520…
   (b) 119.5%   (b) $\dfrac{20^2}{7+3} = \dfrac{400}{10} = 40$

24. (a) 48 marks (b) 45%
   (c) 12 boys (d) $2000 \div 30 \approx 67$

25. (a) 75 g (b) 40%

26. £16.80

27. 95.8%

28. (a) 1 953 125 (b) 0.143
   (c) 0.0074

29. 1 hour $27\frac{1}{2}$ minutes

30. Yes, she does have enough money.
   400 000 dollars = £291 971
   450 000 euros = £288 462

31. 2 hours 40 minutes

32. 3.21

33. 31.6%   **35.** £3434.70

34. Angela £20   **36.** (a) 250 g
   Fran £35   (b) 125 g
   Dan £45   **37.** 16.4%

38. (a) 0.000 37
   (b) (i) 1.012×10^6 (ii) 3.28×10^{-1}

39. (a) 220 (b) 2.401×10^7

40. (a) 18 (b) 7560

41. 4.78×10^{-1} **44.** 57.5 kg

42. (a) 6.5   **45.** £27
   (b) 1.27 seconds   **46.** 5 104 000

43. 51.8 cm³   **47.** 15.7%

CHAPTER 19

Exercise 19.1 — Page 221

1. $n + 4$ **9.** $25p$

2. $n - 3$ **10.** $6k$

3. $3n$ **11.** $5b$ pence

4. $m + 6$ **12.** $\dfrac{c}{3}$ pence

5. $m - 12$ **13.** $\dfrac{a}{5}$ pence

6. $8m$ **14.** $\dfrac{36}{g}$

7. $p - 1$ **15.** (a) $2t$

8. $p + 5$ (b) $10t$

1. (a) $2y$ (b) $3c$ (c) $5x$
(d) $7p$ (e) $2t$ (f) $3d$
(g) $3n$ (h) $5y$ (i) $10g$
(j) $8m$ (k) $13z$ (l) $2r$
(m) $5t$ (n) $4y$ (o) $3j$
(p) $4c$ (q) $7x$ (r) w
(s) 0 (t) $-5y$ (u) $-5x$
(v) $-14a$ (w) $6b$ (x) $2m$

2. (a) $4x$ (b) $6a$ (c) $9y$ (d) $6u$

3. (a) Can be simplified, $2v$.
(b) Cannot be simplified, different terms.
(c) Can be simplified to $3v + 4$.
(d) Cannot be simplified, different terms.

4. (a) $8x + y$ (b) $w + 2v$ (c) $2a - 2b$
(d) $5x + 3y$ (e) $3 + 7u$ (f) $p + 4q$
(g) $3d - 7c$ (h) $2y + 1$ (i) $a + b$
(j) $4m + n$ (k) $9c - d$ (l) $x + y$
(m) $6p$ (n) $5 - 5k$ (o) $a + 3$

5. (a) $8a + 3b$ (b) $3p + 3q$ (c) $3m + 2n$
(d) $x - 2y$ (e) $2x + 3y$ (f) $d + 3$
(g) $3b - 2a$ (h) 7 (i) $a + 2b$
(j) $-2f$ (k) $v - 4w$ (l) $-2 - 5t$
(m) $4q - 4p$ (n) $1 - 7k$ (o) $c - d + 11$

6. (a) $4x + 2$ (b) $4a + 6b$
(c) $3x$ (d) $6y + 9$

7. (a) $2xy$ (b) $2pq$
(c) $3ab$ (d) $2x^2$
(e) $9y^2$ (f) $4a^2$
(g) $2d^2 - 3g^2$ (h) $5t^2 - t$
(i) $6m - m^2$ (j) $2p^2 - p$

1. (a) $3a$ (b) $7b$ (c) $8c$
(d) $9d$ (e) $4e$ (f) $8f$
(g) $6p$ (h) $15q$ (i) r^2
(j) g^2 (k) $2g^2$ (l) $6g^2$
(m) $4t^2$ (n) $12t^2$ (o) $15u^2$
(p) $9d^2$

2. (a) $-3y$ (b) $-5y$ (c) $2y$
(d) $-6y$ (e) $-t^2$ (f) $-2t^2$
(g) $-10t^2$ (h) $10t^2$

3. (a) $5a$ (b) $4b$ (c) 12 (d) 20
(e) $2y$ (f) 8 (g) 2 (h) 18
(i) $3p$ (j) 3 (k) 9 (l) 6
(m) 4 (n) 5 (o) 4 (p) 9

4. (a) $-2y$ (b) $-3y$ (c) -5 (d) m
(e) -3 (f) -2 (g) -3 (h) 1

5. (a) ab (b) xy (c) y^2 (d) $2pq$
(e) $2a^2$ (f) $3xy$ (g) $6ab$ (h) $12gh$
(i) $6d^2$ (j) $3g^2$ (k) $5ab$ (l) $6gh$
(m) abc (n) m^3 (o) $2d^3$ (p) $3g^3$
(q) $6x^3$ (r) $10m^2n$ (s) $3abc$ (t) $18pqr$

6. (a) a^2 (b) $4x^2$ (c) $6g^2$ (d) $10y^2$

1. (a) y^3 (b) t^5 (c) a^6
(d) g^{10} (e) a^4 (f) m^6
(g) $2y^3$ (h) $6d^5$ (i) $8x^5$
(j) $25y^6$ (k) $6t^5$ (l) $24r^6$
(m) m^3n^2 (n) a^4b^2 (o) $6r^3s^4$
(p) $10x^5y^3$

2. (a) t^6 (b) y^6 (c) g^9
(d) x^8 (e) $9a^2$ (f) $8h^3$
(g) $2m^6$ (h) $4m^6$ (i) $3d^6$
(j) $9d^6$ (k) $27a^6$ (l) $8k^9$
(m) x^2y^2 (n) m^3n^6 (o) $8s^3t^3$
(p) $9p^4q^2$

3. (a) y^2 (b) a (c) 1
(d) t^4 (e) g^{-1} (f) h^{-2}
(g) $6b^2$ (h) $5m$ (i) $4x^6$
(j) $4t$ (k) $5y^4$ (l) $3h^{-1}$
(m) y (n) m^2n^{-1} (o) $\frac{2}{3}p^2q^{-1}$
(p) $3rs^2$

4. (a) t (b) g^{-1} (c) m^2 (d) y
(e) y^2 (f) m^{-1} (g) $2t^2$ (h) 3

1. (a) $2x + 10$ (b) $3a + 18$
(c) $8y + 12$

2. (a) $3x + 6$ (b) $2y + 10$
(c) $4x + 2$ (d) $3p + 3q$

3. (a) $a^2 + a$ (b) $2d + d^2$
(c) $2x^2 + x$

4. (a) $2x + 8$ (b) $4b + 4$
(c) $8x + 4$ (d) $3t - 6$
(e) $20 - 4a$ (f) $6 - 12p$
(g) $6b + 12c$ (h) $6m - 15n$

5. (a) $x^2 + 3x$ (b) $2y + y^2$
(c) $t^2 - 5t$ (d) $2g^2 + 3g$
(e) $2m - 3m^2$ (f) $3a^2 + 4a$
(g) $2p^2 + 6p$ (h) $6d - 9d^2$
(i) $2x^2 + 2xy$ (j) $5xy - 10y^2$

6. (a) $2x + 5$ (b) $3a + 11$
(c) $6w - 17$ (d) $10 + 2p$
(e) $3q$ (f) $7 - 3t$
(g) $5z + 8$ (h) $8t + 15$
(i) $2c - 6$ (j) $5a - 9$
(k) $3y - 10$ (l) $2x + 6$
(m) $8a + 23$ (n) $10x - 12$
(o) $2p - 11$ (p) $5a + 2b$
(q) $3x + y$ (r) $2p - 5q$
(s) $5x - x^2$ (t) $a^2 - 2a$
(u) $2y$

7. (a) $5x + 8$ (b) $5a + 13$
(c) $9y + 23$ (d) $9a + 5$
(e) $26t + 30$ (f) $5z + 13$
(g) $12q + 16$ (h) $11x - 3$
(i) $20e - 16$ (j) $12d + 6$
(k) $3m^2 - 3m$ (l) $5a^2 - 4a$

8. (a) $-3x + 6$ (b) $-3x + 6$
(c) $-2y + 10$ (d) $-6 + 2x$
(e) $-15 + 3y$ (f) $-4 - 4a$
(g) $3 - 2a$ (h) $2d + 6$
(i) $2b - 6$ (j) $-6p - 9$
(k) $m - 6$ (l) $5d + 1$
(m) $-a^2 + 2a$ (n) $d - d^2$
(o) $2x^2$ (p) $-6g^2 - 9g$
(q) $7t^2 - 6t$ (r) $8m - 2m^2$

Exercise 19.6 — Page 228

1. (a) $2(x + y)$ (b) $3(a - 2b)$
(c) $2(3m + 4n)$ (d) $x(x - 2)$
(e) $a(b + 1)$ (f) $x(2 - y)$
(g) $2a(b - 2)$ (h) $2x(2x + 3)$
(i) $dg(1 - g)$

2. (a) $2(a + b)$ (b) $5(x - y)$
(c) $3(d + 2e)$ (d) $2(2m - n)$
(e) $3(2a + 3b)$ (f) $2(3a - 4b)$
(g) $4(2t + 3)$ (h) $5(a - 2)$
(i) $2(2d - 1)$ (j) $3(1 - 3g)$
(k) $5(1 - 4m)$ (l) $4(k + 1)$

3. (a) $x(y - z)$ (b) $g(f + h)$
(c) $b(a - 2)$ (d) $q(3 + p)$
(e) $a(1 + b)$ (f) $g(h - 1)$
(g) $a(a + 3)$ (h) $t(5 - t)$
(i) $d(1 - d)$ (j) $m(m + 1)$
(k) $r(5r - 3)$ (l) $x(3x + 2)$

4. (a) $3(y + 2)$ (b) $t(t - 1)$
(c) $2d(d + 2)$ (d) $3m(1 - 2n)$
(e) $2g(f + 2g)$ (f) $4q(p - 2)$
(g) $3y(2 - 5y)$ (h) $2x(3x + 2y)$
(i) $2n(3n - 1)$ (j) $2b(2a + 3)$
(k) $\frac{1}{2}a(1 - a)$ (l) $x(w + 2 - x)$

Review Exercise 19 — Page 229

1. $6t$ pence
2. $(x + 3)$ years old
3. (a) $(n - 2)$ years old (b) $3n$ years old
(c) $(3n + 4)$ years old (d) $(8n + 2)$ years
4. (a) £1.50 (b) $25n$ pence
(c) $x = 25y$
5. (a) (i) $3w$ (ii) $w + 2$ (iii) w^2
(b) $7d + 3$
6. (a) (i) $5x$ (ii) $3x$ (iii) $3y^2$
(b) (i) $4x + 4y$ (ii) $5x - 10y$
7. (a) $3ab$ (b) $a^2 + 2a$
(c) $2x - 6$
8. (a) $t(t - 3)$ (b) $3a(2 + b)$
9. (a) $5a - 3b$ (b) $3y$ pence
10. (a) $5x + 10y$ (b) $6x^2 - 3x + 4$
11. (a) p^4 (b) $24abc$ (c) 1
12. (a) t^8 (b) p^4 (c) a^4
13. (a) $13 - 2x$ (b) $2y(3x - 1)$ (c) $5m^2$
14. a^4c^{-1}

15. (a) $6x + 4xy$ (b) $4a^5 - 4a^3b$
16. (a) $3(2x - 5)$ (b) $y(y + 7)$
17. (a) $2x^2 - x$ (b) $1 - 3x$
18. (a) $6y^5$ (b) $2t^3$ (c) $8a^3$
19. (a) (i) $3y(2x - y)$ (ii) $2m(2m + 3)$
(b) (i) $10y^5$ (ii) $3x^4$
20. $2a^2b^2c$

CHAPTER 20

Exercise 20.1 — Page 230

1. (a) 3 (b) 4 (c) 9 (d) 16
2. (a) $x = 4$ (b) $a = 3$ (c) $y = 8$
(d) $t = 6$ (e) $h = 22$ (f) $d = 1$
(g) $z = 30$ (h) $p = 0$ (i) $c = 99$
3. (a) 5 (b) 5
(c) 18 (d) 21
4. (a) $a = 4$ (b) $e = 6$
(c) $p = 4$ (d) $d = 16$
5. (a) 1 (b) 4 (c) 4
(d) 2 (e) 3 (f) 5
6. (a) $x = 3$ (b) $y = 2$
(c) $d = 1$ (d) $x = 5$

Exercise 20.2 — Page 231

1. 3 **6.** 5
2. 14 **7.** 4
3. 5 **8.** 3
4. 6 **9.** 4
5. 11 **10.** 7
11. (a) 2 (b) $2(x + 3) = 2x + 6$
12. (a) 9 (b) $3(x - 2) = 3x - 6$
13. (a) 6 (b) $2x + 3$

Exercise 20.3 — Page 233

1. (a) $y = 3$ (b) $x = 6$ (c) $a = 10$
(d) $e = 15$ (e) $d = 11$ (f) $c = 20$
(g) $x = 2$ (h) $y = 19$ (i) $m = 7$
2. (a) $q = 7$ (b) $m = 10$ (c) $n = 16$
(d) $p = 18$ (e) $x = 31$ (f) $y = 17$
(g) $a = 2$ (h) $k = 4$ (i) $h = 12$
3. (a) $x = 14$ (b) $t = 28$ (c) $f = 18$
(d) $y = 19$ (e) $b = 7$ (f) $x = 29$
(g) $m = 4$ (h) $k = 5$ (i) $y = 7$
4. (a) $c = 4$ (b) $a = 4$ (c) $f = 3$
(d) $p = 3$ (e) $h = 5$ (f) $u = 2$
(g) $d = 10$ (h) $e = 7$ (i) $f = 9$
5. (a) $p = 4$ (b) $t = 3$ (c) $h = 7$
(d) $b = 2$ (e) $d = 10$ (f) $x = 6$
(g) $c = 5$ (h) $n = 3$ (i) $x = 2$
6. (a) $c = 7$ (b) $x = 4$ (c) $y = 4$
(d) $x = 2$ (e) $b = 6$ (f) $x = 4$
(g) $k = 2$ (h) $b = 3$ (i) $c = 2$

7. (a) $a = 3$ (b) $x = 9$ (c) $a = 0$
(d) $p = 1$ (e) $y = 5$ (f) $p = 4$
(g) $x = 9$ (h) $k = 4$ (i) $m = 3$

5. (a) $n = 2$ (b) $z = 6$ (c) $w = 3$
(d) $m = 4$ (e) $h = 2$ (f) $x = -3$
(g) $w = 3$ (h) $y = 1\frac{1}{2}$ (i) $v = -8$
(j) $c = -1\frac{1}{2}$ (k) $x = -18$ (l) $x = -7$

Exercise 20.4   Page 234

1. (a) $k = \frac{1}{2}$ (b) $a = -3$ (c) $d = -4$
(d) $n = -\frac{1}{2}$ (e) $t = -5$ (f) $n = 1$
(g) $m = 1\frac{1}{2}$ (h) $x = 2\frac{1}{3}$ (i) $y = -\frac{1}{2}$

2. (a) $x = -2$ (b) $y = -3$ (c) $t = -2$
(d) $a = -2$ (e) $d = -3$ (f) $g = -3$
(g) $t = \frac{1}{2}$ (h) $x = 7\frac{1}{2}$ (i) $d = 1\frac{2}{5}$
(j) $a = 1\frac{1}{2}$ (k) $g = \frac{1}{5}$ (l) $b = 4\frac{1}{2}$

3. (a) $x = -2$ (b) $n = -\frac{1}{2}$ (c) $x = -1$
(d) $y = -3$ (e) $x = -1$ (f) $x = -3$
(g) $x = -1\frac{1}{2}$ (h) $x = -4$ (i) $x = -1\frac{1}{2}$

Exercise 20.5   Page 235

1. (a) $x = 3$ (b) $a = 2$ (c) $t = 2$
(d) $y = 0$ (e) $e = 5$ (f) $x = 2$

2. (a) $p = 5$ (b) $c = 6$ (c) $x = 3$
(d) $y = 9$ (e) $g = 11$ (f) $q = 8$

3. (a) $a = 4$ (b) $b = 6$ (c) $c = 1$
(d) $d = 9$ (e) $e = 5$ (f) $f = 4$

4. (a) $w = 2$ (b) $s = 3$ (c) $x = 2$
(d) $g = 3$ (e) $q = 4$ (f) $t = 3$
(g) $w = 4$ (h) $x = 3$ (i) $y = 5$

5. (a) $p = -1$ (b) $d = -2$ (c) $g = -2$
(d) $x = 8\frac{1}{2}$ (e) $y = \frac{2}{5}$ (f) $t = \frac{1}{2}$
(g) $t = 1\frac{3}{4}$ (h) $a = 2\frac{1}{2}$ (i) $m = 2\frac{3}{5}$

6. (a) $x = 4$ (b) $a = 2$ (c) $m = -\frac{1}{2}$
(d) $y = 2\frac{1}{2}$ (e) $w = -3$ (f) $e = 2$
(g) $a = 1\frac{1}{2}$ (h) $t = -11$ (i) $x = 1$

Exercise 20.6   Page 236

1. (a) $x = 5$ (b) $q = 2$ (c) $t = 3$
(d) $e = 3$ (e) $g = 4$ (f) $y = 1$
(g) $x = 2$ (h) $k = 1$ (i) $a = 4$
(j) $p = 6$ (k) $m = 2$ (l) $d = 5$
(m) $y = 5$ (n) $u = 3$ (o) $q = 0$

2. (a) $d = 8$ (b) $q = 3$ (c) $c = 2$
(d) $t = 3$ (e) $w = 2$ (f) $e = 3$
(g) $g = 5$ (h) $z = 4$ (i) $m = 6$
(j) $a = 5$ (k) $x = 4$ (l) $y = 3$

3. (a) $m = -4$ (b) $t = -2$ (c) $p = -2$
(d) $x = 3\frac{1}{2}$ (e) $a = \frac{1}{2}$ (f) $b = \frac{4}{5}$
(g) $y = \frac{4}{5}$ (h) $d = \frac{3}{4}$ (i) $f = -3\frac{1}{2}$

4. (a) $t = -5$ (b) $y = 2$ (c) $s = \frac{1}{2}$
(d) $p = -\frac{1}{3}$ (e) $a = 1.8$ (f) $c = 0.11$
(g) $p = 5$ (h) $x = -6$ (i) $x = 32$

Exercise 20.7   Page 237

1. (a) 3 (b) 8 (c) 12 (d) 15

2. (a) $x = 6$ (b) $y = 8$ (c) $a = 24$
(d) $d = -10$ (e) $a = 6$ (f) $x = 4\frac{1}{2}$
(g) $m = -2$ (h) $t = \frac{4}{9}$

3. (a) $h = 11$ (b) $x = 8$ (c) $a = -3$
(d) $d = -3$ (e) $x = \frac{3}{4}$ (f) $a = \frac{1}{10}$
(g) $d = 5\frac{1}{2}$ (h) $h = 1\frac{1}{2}$ (i) $x = -3$
(j) $x = \frac{7}{9}$ (k) $a = 5$ (l) $x = 1\frac{1}{4}$

4. (a) $x = 1\frac{1}{3}$ (b) $x = 12$ (c) $x = -1\frac{3}{5}$
(d) $x = -4$ (e) $x = 1$ (f) $x = 19$

Exercise 20.8   Page 238

1. (a) $12x$ (b) $x = 15$
2. (a) $6k\,\text{kg}$ (b) $2\frac{1}{2}\,\text{kg}$
3. (a) $2x$ pence (b) 64 pence
4. (a) $(3y + 15)\,\text{cm}$ (b) $y = 8$
5. (a) $6a + 3$ (b) 7
6. (a) $(n - 7)$ years old
(b) Dominic is 25 years old
Marcie is 18 years old
7. (a) $(4y - 2)\,\text{cm}$ (b) 19 cm
8. (a) (i) £$(p + 4)$ (ii) £$(p - 3)$
(iii) £$(3p + 1)$
(b) Aimee £12, Grace £8, Lydia £5
9. (a) $(x + 10)$ pence
(b) $(3x + 20)$ pence
(c) 15 pence
10. (a) $(7x - 4)\,\text{cm}$ (b) $x = 9$
(c) 13 cm, 17 cm, 29 cm
11. (a) $18x = 540°$ (b) $150°$
12. Cake costs 37 pence.
13. 105 cm²
14. (a) $5x + 12$
(b) $5x + 12 = 2(x + 12)$ so $x = 4$.
Sarah has 32 CDs now.

Review Exercise 20   Page 240

1. (a) 4 (b) 3
(c) 6 (d) 4
2. (a) $x = 7$ (b) $x = 4$
3. (a) 7 (b) 4
4. 29
5. (a) $y = 2$ (b) $t = -3$
(c) $g = \frac{1}{2}$ (d) $x = \frac{3}{5}$
6. (a) $x = 4$ (b) $y = -1\frac{1}{2}$

7. (a) $x = 7$ (b) $x = -2$

8. (a) $x = 8$ (b) $x = 1\frac{3}{5}$
 (c) $x = 5$

9. (a) $x = 1\frac{1}{4}$ (b) $x = 1\frac{1}{2}$

10. (a) $x = 6$ (b) $x = \frac{1}{2}$
 (c) $x = 23$

11. (a) $x = -1$ (b) $x = 2\frac{4}{5}$

12. (a) $q = -2$ (b) $t = 1\frac{1}{2}$
 (c) $x = 10\frac{1}{2}$

13. (a) 13 years old (b) 26 years old

14. 2.5 litres

15. (a) $(x - 15)$ pence (b) 42 pence

16. (a) $(3x + 2)\,\text{cm}$ (b) $x = 7$

CHAPTER 21

Exercise 21.1 — Page 242

1. (a) 5 (b) 2
 (c) 12 (d) 9

2. (a) 10 (b) -2
 (c) 10 (d) 25

3. (a) 8 (b) 0
 (c) 12 (d) 32

4. (a) 24 (b) -3 (c) 2
 (d) 18 (e) 18

5. (a) 15 (b) 0 (c) 2
 (d) 50 (e) 15

6. (a) 27 (b) -3 (c) $2\frac{1}{2}$
 (d) 90 (e) 54

Exercise 21.2 — Page 243

1. (a) -1 (b) -4
 (c) -12 (d) 3

2. (a) 0 (b) -8
 (c) -10 (d) -16

3. (a) -8 (b) -8
 (c) -12 (d) 2

4. (a) 12 (b) -9 (c) -2
 (d) -18 (e) 6

5. (a) -5 (b) -20 (c) -2
 (d) -50 (e) -45

6. (a) 3 (b) -21 (c) $-2\frac{1}{2}$
 (d) -90 (e) 54

Exercise 21.3 — Page 244

1. (a) $5y$ pence
 (b) $(y + 8)$ pence

2. $12e$

3. (a) $(a + 1)$ years old
 (b) $(a - 4)$ years old
 (c) $(a + n)$ years old

4. $b - 3$

5. $(h + 12)\,\text{cm}$

6. (a) $2d$
 (b) $2d + 5$

7. (a) $P = y + 5$ (b) $P = y - 2$
 (c) $P = 2y$

8. Ben: $A = d - 2$ Charlotte: $A = 2d$
 Erica: $A = \dfrac{d}{2}$

9. (a) $P = 4g$ (b) $P = 4y + 4$
 (c) $P = 3x - 1$ (d) $P = 2a + 2b$

10. $C = 25d$

11. (a) £44 (b) £80
 (c) $C = 12x + 8$

12. (a) 115 (b) 175
 (c) 45 (d)

n	$n + 1$	$n + 2$
	$n + 11$	
	$n + 21$	

 (e) $S_n = 5n + 35$

Exercise 21.4 — Page 246

1. (a) 10 (b) 1

2. (a) 28 (b) -12

3. (a) 2 (b) -6

4. (a) -2 (b) 8

5. (a) 13 (b) -7

6. (a) -2 (b) 10

7. (a) 2 (b) $\frac{1}{2}$

8. (a) 1 (b) 2.5

9. (a) 6 (b) 5.8

10. (a) 0 (b) 1

11. (a) 3.5 (b) 4

12. $F = 75$

13. $V = 26$ **14.** $P = -9$

15. (a) $C = 104$ (b) $C = 32$

16. (a) $T = 35$ (b) $T = -2$
 (c) $T = -18$ (d) $T = 6$

17. (a) $K = -1$ (b) $K = 13$

18. (a) $L = 10$ (b) $L = -11$

19. 33

20. (a) $96\,\text{m}$ (b) $36\,\text{m}$

21. (a) $-10°C$ (b) $-20°C$ (c) $-40°C$

22. (a) $50°F$ (b) $14°F$ (c) $-40°F$

23. 138 minutes

24. 240 volts **26.** £40.14

25. $F = 4100$ **27.** 0.3

Exercise 21.5 — Page 247

1. (a) $S = 9$ (b) $S = 9$

2. (a) $S = 18$ (b) $S = 18$

3. (a) $S = 36$ (b) $S = 36$

4. (a) $S = 32$ (b) $S = 32$

5. (a) $S = 16$ (b) $S = 16$

6. (a) 39 (b) 66
 (c) 39 (d) 66

7. (a) 27 (b) -27
 (c) 125 (d) -125

8. (a) 128 (b) -128

9. (a) -2 (b) 2

10. (a) $\frac{3}{4}$ (b) $1\frac{1}{2}$

11. (a) 4   (b) 1.5   (c) -3

12. (a) $L = 10$ (b) $L = 0.5$

13. (a) 26.0   (b) 3.2

14. (a) 12   (b) 1.4

15. $F = 144$

16. $h = 307.5$ **17.** $R = 2.25$

18. (a) $T = 1.80$ (b) $T = 2.5$

19. (a) $v = 6.3$ (b) $v = 7.4$

Exercise 21.6   Page 248

1. (a) £13   (b) $C = 2k + 3$
   (c) 2 km

2. (a) 140 minutes   (b) $C = 40k + 20$
   (c) 2 kg

3. (a) $F = 42$ (b) $F = 2C + 30$
   (c) $C = 14$

4. (a) 410   (b) $b = 3n + 50$
   (c) 140

5. (a) £51   (b) $T = 15d + 6$
   (c) 6 days

6. (a) £295   (b) $C = 45n + 70$
   (c) 9 days

Exercise 21.7   Page 250

1. (a) $m = a - 5$ (b) $m = a - x$
   (c) $m = a + 2$ (d) $m = a + b$
   (e) $m = 2 - a$ (f) $m = x - a$

2. (a) $x = \frac{y}{4}$ (b) $x = \frac{y}{a}$
   (c) $x = -\frac{y}{a}$ (d) $x = 2y$
   (e) $x = ay$ (f) $x = -ay$
   (g) $x = \frac{2}{y}$ (h) $x = -\frac{n}{y}$

3. (a) $p = \frac{1}{2}y - 3$ (b) $p = \frac{t - q}{5}$
   (c) $p = \frac{m + 2}{3}$ (d) $p = \frac{q + r}{4}$
   (e) $p = \frac{3 - a}{2}$ (f) $p = \frac{g - d}{3}$
   (g) $p = 2m - 6$ (h) $p = 3y - 3x$
   (i) $p = 5t + 10$ (j) $p = 2h - 2g$
   (k) $p = \frac{3}{s - q}$ (l) $p = \frac{a}{x - y}$

4. $K = \frac{P}{0.45}$ **6.** $n = \frac{C - 35}{24}$

5. $c = \frac{F - 32}{1.8}$ **7.** $a = \frac{2A}{h} - b$

8. (a) $c = \pm\sqrt{y}$ (b) $c = y^2$
   (c) $c = \pm\sqrt{\frac{y}{d}}$ (d) $c = 9y^2$
   (e) $c = \pm\sqrt{y - x}$ (f) $c = (y - x)^2$
   (g) $c = \pm\sqrt{dy - dx}$ (h) $c = (ax + ay)^2$

9. (a) $V = IR$ (b) $m = \frac{E}{c^2}$
   (c) $x = \pm\sqrt{\frac{y - b}{a}}$ (d) $v = \pm\sqrt{\frac{2e}{m}}$

10. (a) $a = b - c^2$ (b) $a = \pm\sqrt{b}$
   (c) $a = 2b + \frac{1}{4}c$ (d) $a = \frac{1}{3}b$
   (e) $a = \frac{4b}{15}$ (f) $a = \frac{3b}{2}$
   (g) $a = \frac{p - d}{m}$ (h) $a = \pm\sqrt{\frac{F}{m}}$

11. $t = \pm s\sqrt{R}$

12. $m = \frac{b - a}{2}$

13. (a) $x = \frac{3a}{2}$ (b) $x = \frac{3b - 2a}{5}$
   (c) $x = \frac{2a}{3}$

14. $q = \frac{p}{2}$

Exercise 21.8   Page 251

1. (a) $d = \frac{P}{4}$ (b) $d = 0.7$ cm

2. (a) $l = \frac{A}{b}$ (b) $l = 6$ cm

3. (a) (i) $D = ST$ (ii) $D = 24$ km
   (b) (i) $T = \frac{D}{S}$ (ii) $T = 1.25$ hours

4. (a) $p = \frac{2A}{3q}$ (b) $p = 3.2$ cm

5. (a) $b = \frac{1}{2}P - l$ (b) $b = 4.2$ cm

6. (a) $x = \frac{y - c}{m}$ (b) $x = 3$

7. (a) $b = \frac{2A}{h}$ (b) $b = 23$

8. (a) $d = \pm\sqrt{\frac{C}{I}}$ (b) $d = \pm 1.17$

9. (a) $q = \pm\sqrt{p^2 - r^2}$ (b) $q = \pm 6.8$

10. (a) $r = \sqrt[3]{\frac{3V}{4\pi}}$ (b) $r = 33.7$

11. (a) $x = \pm\sqrt{ab}$ (b) $x = \pm 4.0 \times 10^4$

Review Exercise 21   Page 252

1. 4   **5.** $S = -14$

2. $V = 7$ **6.** (a) 6   (b) -6

3. (a) 1   (b) 5   **7.** 17.4 cm
   (c) -5 (d) -6 **8.** 7 rolls

4. $P = 7.5$ **9.** 5

10. (a) 340   (b) $N = 2T + 20$ (c) 140

11. (a) $v = 9\frac{1}{5}$ (b) $t = \frac{v - u}{a}$

12. $p = \frac{t + 50}{7}$ **14.** $V = 66$

13. $x = \frac{y - c}{m}$ **15.** $p = \frac{7}{4}r - 3$

16. (a) $y = 27$ (b) $x = \pm 7$
   (c) $x = \pm\sqrt{\frac{y}{3}}$

17. $r = st^2$

CHAPTER 22

Exercise 22.1 — Page 253

1. (a) 17, 21, 25   (b) 14, 16, 18
(c) 16, 13, 10   (d) 28, 33, 38
(e) 48, 96, 192   (f) $1\frac{1}{2}$, $1\frac{3}{4}$, 2
(g) 2, 1, $\frac{1}{2}$ (h) 0.9, 1.0, 1.1
(i) 2, 0, -2 (j) 5, 2.5, 1.25
(k) 21, 28, 36   (l) 29, 47, 76

2. (a) 8, 14   (b) 10, 22
(c) 8, 32   (d) 16, -2
(e) 16, 36   (f) 8, 21
(g) 2, 20, 26

3. (a) Add 7; 37, 44
(b) Add 2; 13, 15
(c) Add 4; 21, 25
(d) Subtract 5; 11, 6
(e) Divide by 2; 2, 1
(f) Multiply by 3; 81, 243
(g) Subtract 2; -10, -12
(h) Subtract 3; -5, -8

4. (a) 28
(b) Keep on adding 3 to the last term until you get to the 10th term, 28.

5. (a) David multiplies the last term by 2, $4 \times 2 = 8$.
Tony adds the next counting number, $4 + 3 = 7$.
(b) 512   (c) 46

6. No.
To find the next number, add 6 to the last term. All numbers in the sequence will be odd.

Exercise 22.2 — Page 255

1. (a) 1, 5, 9, 13, 17   (b) 1, 2, 4, 8, 16
(c) 40, 35, 30, 25, 20   (d) 4, 5, 7, 11, 19
(e) 47, 23, 11, 5, 2   (f) 2, 6, 4, 5, 4.5

2. (a) 2, 4, 8   (b) 6, 12, 24
(c) $-2, -4, -8$

3. (a) 4, 10, 22   (b) 8, 18, 38
(c) $-4, -6, -10$

4. (a) (i) 21 (ii) 3   (b) 37

5. (a) (i) 36 (ii) 123   (b) 10

6. (a) 37, 60   (b) 1, 4

7. $-6, -27$

8. (a) 49, 97   (b) 1537

Exercise 22.3 — Page 257

1. (a) 3   (b) 3   (c) 6
(d) 8   (e) -2 (f) -4

2. (a) $3n$ (b) $8n$
(c) $12n$ (d) $2n$

3. (a) 3   (c) $3n + 1$ (d) 25

4. (a) 2   (c) $2n + 7$ (d) 47

5. (a) -4 (c) $24 - 4n$

6. (a) $3n - 2$ (b) $22 - 3n$ (c) $4n + 1$
(d) $4n$ (e) $2n - 1$ (f) $4n + 3$
(g) $8 - 2n$ (h) $3n + 2$ (i) $5n - 2$
(j) $45 - 5n$ (k) $n - 1$ (l) $2n - 3$

Exercise 22.4 — Page 260

1. (a) 10   (b) 27 is an odd number
(c) $2p$ (d) 240

2. (a) 17   (b) 4
(c) $4n + 1$ (d) 81

3. (a) (i) 15 (ii) 30 (iii) 300   (b) $3n$

4. (a) (i) 18 (ii) 82
(b) Pattern 7   (c) $4n + 2$

5. (a) (i) 51 (ii) 100
(b) (i) $x + 1$ (ii) $2x$

6. (a) $22\,\text{cm}^2$ (b) $42\,\text{cm}^2$ (c) $4n + 2\,\text{cm}^2$

7. (a) 27   (b) $T = 5n + 2$
(c) 52   (d) 15

8. (a) 11   (b) Pattern 18
(c) $m = 2p + 1$

9. (a) 25   (b) $4^2 = 16, 5^2 = 25$
(c) n^2 (d) 225

10. (a) (i) 37, add 2 more than last time.
(ii) 35, add 2 more than last time.
(iii) 39, add 2 more than last time.
(iv) 72, add 4 more than last time.
(v) 42, add 2 more than last time.
(b) (i) $n^2 + 1$ (ii) $n^2 - 1$ (iii) $n^2 + 3$
(iv) $2n^2$ (v) $n^2 + n$

11. (a) $T = n^2 + n = n(n + 1)$
(b) 110

12. (a) 15   (b) $\frac{4 \times 5}{2} = 10$, $\frac{5 \times 6}{2} = 15$
(c) $\frac{n(n + 1)}{2}$ (d) 55

13. (a) 32   (b) $2^4 = 16$, $2^5 = 32$
(c) 2^n (d) 1024   (e) 8th

14. (a) 10, 100, 1000, 10 000, 100 000
(b) 10^n (c) 10^6

15. (a) 3^n (b) 59 049

Review Exercise 22 — Page 262

1. (a) 38   (b) $\frac{1}{4}$

2. (a) 81   (b) Yes. $196 = 14^2$

3. (a) 6, 7   (b) No. $\frac{8 + 4}{2} = 6$, $\frac{4 + 6}{2} = 5$

4. 5, 16, 8

5. (a) 19   (b) (i) $x + 4$ (ii) $x - 4$

6. (a) 14   (b) 59   (c) $3n - 1$

7. (a) 33, 45
(b) (i) 65
(ii) Add twice the difference between the two previous terms.
(c) $2n + 1$

8. (a) $3n$ (b) $3n - 2$ (c) n^2

9. (a) 30   (b) 40 is not a multiple of 3.
     (c) $3p$
10. $2n + 3$
11. (a) 28
     (b) Add on one more to last term each time, add on 2, 3, 4, 5, 6, 7, …
     (c) Triangular numbers

CHAPTER 23

Exercise **23.1**   Page 265

1. (a) (1) $y = 4$
        (2) $x = -3$
        (3) $x = 1$
        (4) $y = -1$
        (5) $y = x$
     (b) $(1, 4)$
     (c) $(-3, -1)$

2.

3. (a)

x	0	1	2	3
(i) y	2	3	4	5
(ii) y	0	2	4	6
(iii) y	0	-1	-2	-3
(iv) y	2	1	0	-1

4.

x	-1	0	1	2	3
(a) y	-2	-1	0	1	2
(b) y	-2	1	4	7	10

5. (b) $(0, -2)$
6. (b) Same slope, parallel
     y-intercept is different
7. (b) Same slope, parallel
     y-intercept is different
8. (b) Same y-intercept, 3
     Different slope
10. (b) $x = 0.5$
11. (a) Missing entries: 6, 4, 3
     (b) (i) $y = 2.5$ (ii) $y = 4.5$
12. (b) (i) $y = -2$ (ii) $x = 0.5$
13. (b) $(2, 1)$

Exercise **23.2**   Page 267

1. (a) gradient 3, y-intercept -1
2. $y = 3x$, $y = 3x + 2$
3. gradients: 4, 3, 2, -2, $\frac{1}{2}$, 2, 0, $-\frac{1}{2}$
     y-intercepts: 3, 5, -3, 4, 3, 0, 3, 4
4. (a) $y = 5x - 4$ (b) $y = -\frac{1}{2}x + 6$
5. (1) C   (2) D   (3) B   (4) A
6. (a) $y = x - 2$ (b) $y = 2x - 2$
     (c) $y = -2x - 2$
7. (c) 1   (d) $(0, -4)$ (e) $y = x - 4$
8. (c) $y = -2x - 1$

9. (a) Line slopes up from left to right.
     (b) Line slopes down from left to right.
     (c) Line is horizontal.
10. $y = 3x$
11. $y = 3x + 8$
12. (a) £25   (b) £15 per hour
     (c) $y = 15x + 25$ (d) £145
13. $y = 13 - 3x$
14. (a) $f = 0.8d + 2.4$ (b) £6.40
15. (a) $l = 0.06w + 8$ (b) 26 mm

Exercise **23.3**   Page 270

1. $y = \frac{3x}{2} + 3$
2. (a) $y = -\frac{1}{2}x + 2$ (b) $y = -\frac{4}{5}x + 4$
     (c) $y = -\frac{2}{3}x + \frac{4}{3}$ (d) $y = \frac{2}{7}x - 2$
3. (a) $\frac{1}{2}$ (b) 1   (c) 2
     (d) $-\frac{1}{3}$ (e) $\frac{3}{4}$ (f) $-\frac{2}{5}$
4. (a) $a = 0$ (b) $a = \frac{1}{2}$ (c) $a = -2$
     (d) $a = 2\frac{1}{2}$ (e) $a = 2$ (f) $a = \frac{2}{5}$
5. (a) $y = x +$ (any number)
     (b) $y = 2x +$ (any number)
     (c) $y = \frac{1}{2}x +$ (any number)
6. $y = -\frac{3}{2}x +$ (any number)
7. (a) $\frac{4}{5}$ (b) 2
     (c) $y =$ (any number)$x + 2$
8. (a) $(0, 5)$ (b) $(3, 0)$
9. (a) $(0, 4), (5, 0)$
     (b) $(0, -2), (0.5, 0)$
     (c) $(0, 5), (7.5, 0)$
10. (a) $A(0, 2), B(-4, 0)$
     (b) $\frac{1}{2}$
     (c) (ii) $y = \frac{1}{2}x +$ (any number)
11. (a) $P(0, 3), Q(6, 0)$
     (b) $-\frac{1}{2}$
     (c) (ii) $y = -\frac{1}{2}x +$ (any number)

Exercise **23.4**   Page 272

1. (a)

x	1	2	3
$y = x + 2$	3	4	5
$y = 5 - x$	4	3	2

     (c) $x = 1.5$
2. (b) $x = 2.5$
3. (b) $x = 0.5$
4. $x = 1.2$
5. (b) $y = 9$ (c) $x = 3$

Exercise **23.5**   Page 273

1. B
2. 1: C,   2: B,   3: E,   4: A

3.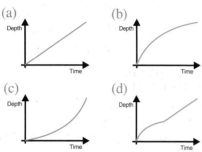

4. (d) B
(e) A
(f) 6 days

5. (a)
(b)
(c)
(d)

1. (a) 1005 (b) 24 miles (c) 3
2. (a) 1042 (b) 28 km
(c) (i) 1115 (ii) 8 km
3. (a) 50 km/h (b) 20 m/s
(c) 9 miles/hour
4. (a) 10 km/h (b) 6.7 km/h
(c) 8 km/h
5. (a) (b) (i)
(b) (ii) 1110
6. (a) 1118 (b) 1230 (c) Twice
(d) 42 minutes
(e) Between 1200 and 1230
(f) 4 km/h
7. (a) 9 miles/hour
(b) (i)
(ii) 1415
8. (a)
(b) 15 km/h
9. (a)
(b) (i) 1220 (ii) 1102 (iii) 14 km/hour

1. (a) Any point with coordinates $(x, x + 1)$,
i.e., y coordinate is one more than
x coordinate.
(b)

2.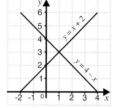

3. (a)

x	-1	1	3
y	-3	1	5

(c) $x = 1.75$

4.
(b) $x = 2$

5. (b) (2, 4)
6. (b) (0, 3)
7. (a) 12 cm
(b) 2
(c) 10 kg

8. $y = -1\frac{1}{2} x + 6$

9. (a) Nina
(b) Polly passed Nina and went into the lead.
(c) Nina stopped running.
(d) Nina

10. (a) $y = 3x + 5$ (b) (i) $\frac{2}{3}$ (ii) (0, −2)

11. $A: W$, $B: Z$, $C: X$

12. (a) (i) (ii) (b)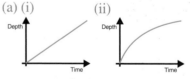

13. (a) Twice
(b) (i) 2 km (ii) 12 km/h
(c) Between D and E

14.

CHAPTER 24

Exercise **24.1** — Page 282

1. $x = 4$, $y = 2$
2. $x = 3$, $y = 5$
3. $x = 2$, $y = 3$
4. $x = 2$, $y = 3$
5. $x = 3$, $y = 1$
6. $x = 4$, $y = 3$
7. $x = -2$, $y = 3$
8. $x = 5$, $y = 0.5$

Exercise **24.2** — Page 283

1. (a) Both lines have gradient -1.
   (b) Both lines have gradient 4.
   (c) Both lines are the same.
   (d) Both lines have gradient 0.4.
2. (a) $y = -2x + 6$, $y = -2x + 3$
   (b) $y = 2x + 3.5$, $y = 2x + 2$
   (c) $y = 2.5x - 4$, $y = 2.5x + 1.75$
   (d) $y = -3x + 1.25$, $y = -3x + 0.5$
3. (b) and (d) have no solution.
   (a) $x = 0.4$, $y = 4$
   (c) $x = -0.125$, $y = 1.875$

Exercise **24.3** — Page 285

1. $x = 1$, $y = 2$
2. $x = 3$, $y = 4$
3. $x = 2$, $y = 1$
4. $x = 1$, $y = 7$
5. $x = 3$, $y = 1$
6. $x = 2$, $y = 3$
7. $x = 5$, $y = 2$
8. $x = 4$, $y = 2$
9. $x = 5$, $y = 4$
10. $x = 3$, $y = 2$
11. $x = 4$, $y = 1$
12. $x = 4$, $y = 2$
13. $x = 2$, $y = 3$
14. $x = 4$, $y = -2$
15. $x = 2$, $y = -1.5$
16. $x = -1$, $y = 3$
17. $x = -5$, $y = 6$
18. $x = 2.5$, $y = -1$
19. $x = -6$, $y = 2.5$
20. $x = 3$, $y = -1.5$
21. $x = -1$, $y = -3$
22. $x = 3.5$, $y = -1$
23. $x = 1.5$, $y = -0.5$
24. $x = -0.5$, $y = -2.5$

Exercise **24.4** — Page 286

1. $x = 2$, $y = 1$
2. $x = 2$, $y = 3$
3. $x = 3$, $y = 1$
4. $x = 4$, $y = 2$
5. $x = 2$, $y = -1$
6. $x = 4$, $y = -3$
7. $x = 4$, $y = 0.5$
8. $x = -3$, $y = 0.5$
9. $x = 4$, $y = 1$
10. $x = 2.2$, $y = 5.6$
11. $x = 1.5$, $y = 2$
12. $x = 1$, $y = 2$
13. $x = 5$, $y = 2$
14. $x = 1$, $y = -2$
15. $x = -1$, $y = 2$
16. $x = 2$, $y = 1$
17. $x = -1$, $y = 1$
18. $x = -2$, $y = 3$
19. $x = -1$, $y = 7$
20. $x = 4$, $y = -1$
21. $x = 2.5$, $y = 3$
22. $x = 2$, $y = -1$
23. $x = 1$, $y = -2$
24. $x = -2$, $y = 0.5$

Exercise **24.5** — Page 287

1. $x = 2$, $y = 6$
2. $x = 9$, $y = 18$
3. $x = 8$, $y = 2$
4. $x = 3$, $y = 6$
5. $x = 2$, $y = 13$
6. $x = 0$, $y = 2$
7. $x = 2$, $y = 4$
8. $x = 7$, $y = 6$
9. $x = 4$, $y = 8$
10. $x = 10.5$, $y = 0.5$
11. $x = -68$, $y = -122$
12. $x = 8$, $y = 6$

Exercise **24.6** — Page 288

1. (a) $6x + 3y = 93$, $2x + 5y = 91$
   (b) Pencil 8p, pen 15p
2. (a) $5x + 30y = 900$, $10x + 15y = 1260$
   (b) Apples £1.08 per kg, oranges 12p each
3. $x = 95$, $y = 82$
4. 32 children, 3 adults
5. $x = 100$, $y = 70$
6. Coffee 80p, Tea 70p
7. $x = 160$, $y = 120$

Review Exercise **24** — Page 289

1. (a) $x = 3$, $y = 7$ (b) $x = 4.5$, $y = 1.25$
2. (a) $x = 3$, $y = 2$ (b) $x = 4$, $y = -2$
   (c) $x = 1$, $y = 2$ (d) $x = -2$, $y = 1$
3. $x = 1$, $y = -2$
4. $x = 2.5$, $y = -1$
5. $x = -1$, $y = -2$
6. (a) Same gradient, 2
   $y = 2x - 2$, $y = 2x + \frac{3}{2}$
   (b) Same gradient, $\frac{1}{4}$
   $y = \frac{1}{4}x + \frac{1}{4}$, $y = \frac{1}{4}x + \frac{3}{8}$
   (c) $a = 3$, $b =$ any number, except 2
   (d) $\frac{q}{p} = -3$, $\frac{r}{p} \neq 2$
7. $x = 1.2$, $y = 1.4$
8. $x = -0.5$, $y = 6.5$
9. $x = 7$, $y = 3$
10. (a) $4x + y = 58$, $6x + 2y = 92$
    (b) $x = 12$, $y = 10$

CHAPTER 25

Exercise **25.1** — Page 291

1. (a) True (b) True (c) True (d) False
   (e) True (f) False (g) False (h) True
2. (a) E.g. 5, 4, 3, …
   (b) E.g. -2, -1, 0 …
   (c) E.g. 5, 4, 3, …
   (d) E.g. 7, 6, 5, …
   (e) E.g. 11, 12, 13, …   (f) -1 (g) 5
   (h) One of: -6, -5, -4, -3, -2

3. (a) 2, 3, 4
(b) −1, 0, 1, 2, 3
(c) −4, −3, −2, −1
(d) −1, 0, 1, 2

4. (a) $x \geqslant 2$
(b) $-6 \leqslant x < -2$
(c) $-2 < x < 1$
(d) $x < 5$ and $x \geqslant 8$

5. (a)
(b)
(c)

Exercise **25.2** Page 292

1. (a) $n > 2$ (b) $a < 4$ (c) $d \leqslant 3$
(d) $t < -3$ (e) $g > -2$ (f) $y \geqslant 0$

2. (a) $a < 4$ (b) $b \geqslant 1$ (c) $b \leqslant 1$
(d) $c > 5$ (e) $d < -3$ (f) $a \geqslant 6$
(g) $b < 15$ (h) $c \leqslant 3$ (i) $d > 4$
(j) $f < -2$ (k) $g \leqslant \frac{1}{2}$ (l) $h < 2$
(m) $j \geqslant 2\frac{1}{2}$ (n) $k > -4$ (o) $m > -6\frac{1}{2}$
(p) $n \leqslant 2$ (q) $p > 8$ (r) $q > 1$
(s) $r \geqslant -1\frac{1}{2}$ (t) $t > 13$ (u) $u \leqslant 9$
(v) $v < -1\frac{1}{2}$ (w) $w > 8$ (x) $x < 1\frac{2}{5}$

Exercise **25.3** Page 293

1. $a < -2$ **6.** $f < 1$ **11.** $m < -3$
2. $b \geqslant 3$ **7.** $g > -4$ **12.** $n > -4$
3. $c \leqslant -4$ **8.** $h \geqslant 2$ **13.** $p \geqslant \frac{5}{9}$
4. $d > -1$ **9.** $j \leqslant 1$ **14.** $q > -2\frac{1}{5}$
5. $e \geqslant 2$ **10.** $k > -\frac{1}{3}$ **15.** $n < 9$

Exercise **25.4** Page 294

1. (a) $1 < x \leqslant 5$ (b) $-1 \leqslant x < 9$
(c) $-7 < x \leqslant 4$

2. (a) $1 < x \leqslant 3$ (b) $-2 \leqslant x < 4$
(c) $3 < x < 4\frac{1}{2}$ (d) $-\frac{1}{3} \leqslant x \leqslant 4$
(e) $2 < x \leqslant 5$ (f) $-3 \leqslant x < 6$
(g) $-2 < x < 2$ (h) $3 \leqslant x < 6$
(i) $-4\frac{1}{2} \leqslant x \leqslant -1$

3. (a) 6, 7, 8
(b) −2, −1, 0, 1, 2, 3, 4
(c) 0, 1, 2
(d) 4, 5, 6, 7
(e) 5
(f) 2, 3
(g) −2, −1, 0
(h) −1, 0, 1, 2, 3
(i) −4, −3, −2, −1, 0, 1, 2, 3, 4, 5, 6
(j) 8, 9, 10, 11, 12, 13, 14, 15, 16
(k) −4, −3, −2, −1, 0, 1, 2, 3
(l) −6

Exercise **25.6** Page 296

3.

4. A : ③,   B : ①,
C : ④,   D : ②.

5. $y \geqslant 1$, $y \leqslant x$

6. (a) $x \geqslant 1$, $y < 5$ and $y > x + 2$
(b) $y < 4$, $x \leqslant 3$, $y \leqslant 2x$ and $y > x$
(c) $x \leqslant 2$, $x + y > 3$, $y \leqslant x + 3$
(d) $y > 1$, $1 \leqslant x < 3$, $x + y \leqslant 5$

7. (a)

(b) (2, 2), (3, 2)

Review Exercise **25** Page 298

1. (a) $x \geqslant -5$ (b) $x < 3$
(c) $x \leqslant 6$ (d) $x > -2$

2. (a)
(b)
(c)

3. −3, −2, −1, 0, 1, 2, 3, 4

4. −1, 0, 1

5. (a) $x < 4$ (b) $-1 < x \leqslant 2$
(c) $-1 \leqslant x < 1$ (d) $-3 < x < -1$

6. (a) −1, 0, 1, 2, 3, 4
(b) −3, −2, −1, 0, 1
(c) −2, −1

7. (a) −4, −3, −2, −1, 0, 1   (b) $x < \frac{1}{2}$

8. $-1 \leqslant x < 1$

9. $x > 2$

10. $a > 5$

11. (a) $x < 6$ (b) $x > 0$

12. (a) $x \leqslant 1$
(b) (i) $x \geqslant -1\frac{2}{5}$ (ii) −1

13. (a) (b) (c)

14. A2, B4, C1, D3   **15.** (2, 5), (3, 5)

16.

17. (a)   (b)

(c)

---

CHAPTER 26

7. (a) $(x - 2)^2$ (b) $(x + 5)(x + 6)$
(c) $(x - 2)(x + 4)$ (d) $(x - 7)(x + 3)$
(e) $(x - 4)(x + 5)$ (f) $(x + 3)(x + 4)$
(g) $(x + 4)^2$ (h) $(x - 1)^2$
(i) $(x - 7)(x + 7)$ (j) $t(t + 12)$
(k) $(x - 2)(x - 7)$ (l) $(x - 6)(x - 1)$
(m) $(x + 2)(x + 9)$ (n) $(x + 3)(x + 8)$
(o) $(x + 1)(x + 18)$ (p) $(x - y)(x + y)$
(q) $(x + 3)(x - 2)$ (r) $y(y + 4)$
(s) $(y - 5)^2$ (t) $(x - 6)^2$

Exercise **26.3**   Page 304

1. $3(x + 4y)$
2. $(t - 4)(t + 4)$
3. $(x + 1)(x + 3)$
4. $y(y - 1)$
5. $2(d^2 - 3)$
6. $(p - q)(p + q)$
7. $a(a - 2)$
8. $(x - 1)^2$
9. $2y(y - 4)$
10. $(a - 3)^2$
11. $3(m - 2)(m + 2)$
12. $(v - 3)(v + 2)$
13. $a(x - y)(x + y)$
14. $-2(4 + x)$
15. $(2 - k)^2$
16. $2(3 - x)(3 + x)$
17. $2(5 - x)(5 + x)$
18. $3(2x - 3y)(2x + 3y)$
19. $3a(2a - 1)$
20. $(x - 7)(x - 8)$

Exercise **26.4**   Page 305

1. (a) $2d + 3$ (b) $3x + 2$
(c) $4a + 5b$ (d) $3m - 2n$
(e) $4x - 2y$ (f) $a + b$
(g) $x - 1$ (h) $x^2 - 2$
(i) $\dfrac{x}{3x - 2}$ (j) $\dfrac{x}{2x^2 - 1}$
(k) $\dfrac{1}{2x - 1}$ (l) $\dfrac{1}{3x}$
(m) $\dfrac{3}{2}$ (n) $\dfrac{m}{3}$
(o) $\dfrac{x - 3}{x + 2}$ (p) $2x$
(q) $\dfrac{2(x - 1)}{2x - 1}$ (r) $-\dfrac{5}{3}$

2. (a) **E** (b) **C** (c) **B** (d) **A** (e) **D**

3. (a) $\dfrac{x}{x + 1}$ (b) $\dfrac{x + 2}{x + 3}$ (c) $\dfrac{x}{x + 3}$
(d) $\dfrac{x - 5}{x + 3}$ (e) $\dfrac{x - 2}{x - 3}$ (f) $\dfrac{x - 5}{x + 4}$
(g) $x - 1$ (h) $\dfrac{1}{x + 2}$ (i) $\dfrac{x + 1}{2}$

Exercise **26.1**   Page 301

1. $x^2 + 7x + 12$
2. $x^2 + 6x + 5$
3. $x^2 - 3x - 10$
4. $2x^2 - 3x - 2$
5. $3x^2 - 20x + 12$
6. $6x^2 + 7x + 2$
7. $x^2 + 6x - 16$
8. $x^2 + 3x - 10$
9. $x^2 + 2x - 3$
10. $x^2 - 5x + 6$
11. $x^2 - 5x + 4$
12. $x^2 - 5x - 14$
13. $2x^2 + x - 3$
14. $3x^2 + 14x - 5$
15. $12x^2 + 14x - 10$
16. $x^2 - 9$
17. $x^2 - 25$
18. $x^2 - 49$
19. $x^2 - 100$
20. $x^2 + 6x + 9$
21. $x^2 + 10x + 25$
22. $x^2 - 6x + 9$
23. $x^2 - 14x + 49$
24. $4x^2 - 12x + 9$

Exercise **26.2**   Page 303

1. (a) $x(x + 5)$ (b) $x(x - 7)$
(c) $y(y - 6)$ (d) $2y(y - 6)$
(e) $t(5 - t)$ (f) $y(8 + y)$
(g) $x(x - 20)$ (h) $3x(x - 20)$

2. (a) $(x - 3)(x + 3)$ (b) $(x - 9)(x + 9)$
(c) $(y - 5)(y + 5)$ (d) $(y - 1)(y + 1)$
(e) $(x - 8)(x + 8)$ (f) $(10 - x)(10 + x)$
(g) $(6 - x)(6 + x)$ (h) $(x - a)(x + a)$

3. (a) $(x + 5)(x + 1)$ (b) $(x + 7)(x + 2)$
(c) $(x + 2)(x + 4)$ (d) $(x + 3)(x + 6)$
(e) $(x - 5)(x - 1)$ (f) $(x - 5)(x - 2)$
(g) $(x - 4)(x - 3)$ (h) $(x + 4)(x - 1)$
(i) $(x + 7)(x - 2)$ (j) $(x - 5)(x + 1)$

4. (a) $(x + 1)(x + 2)$ (b) $(x + 1)(x + 7)$
(c) $(x + 3)(x + 5)$ (d) $(x + 2)(x + 6)$
(e) $(x + 1)(x + 11)$ (f) $(x + 4)(x + 5)$
(g) $(x + 4)(x + 6)$ (h) $(x + 4)(x + 9)$

5. (a) $(x - 3)^2$ (b) $(x - 4)(x - 2)$
(c) $(x - 10)(x - 1)$ (d) $(x - 15)(x - 1)$
(e) $(x - 5)(x - 3)$ (f) $(x - 8)(x - 2)$
(g) $(x - 10)(x - 2)$ (h) $(x - 8)(x - 3)$

6. (a) $(x - 3)(x + 2)$ (b) $(x - 6)(x + 1)$
(c) $(x - 4)(x + 6)$ (d) $(x - 3)(x + 8)$
(e) $(x - 5)(x + 3)$ (f) $(x - 3)(x + 6)$
(g) $(x - 8)(x + 5)$ (h) $(x - 6)(x + 2)$

Exercise **26.5**   Page 306

1. (a) $x = 2$ or 3 (b) $x = -4$ or -6
(c) $x = 3$ or -1 (d) $x = 5$ or -2
(e) $x = 0$ or 4 (f) $x = 0$ or -2

2. (a) $x = 1$ or 2 (b) $y = -3$ or -4
(c) $m = 4$ or -2 (d) $a = 3$ or -4
(e) $n = 9$ or -4 (f) $z = 6$ or 3
(g) $k = -3$ or -5 (h) $c = -7$ or -8
(i) $b = 4$ or -5 (j) $v = 12$ or -5
(k) $w = 4$ or -12 (l) $p = 9$ or -8

3. (a) $x = 0$ or 5 (b) $y = 0$ or -1
   (c) $p = 0$ or -3 (d) $a = 0$ or 4
   (e) $t = 0$ or 6 (f) $g = 0$ or 4

4. (a) $x = 2$ or -2 (b) $y = 12$ or -12
   (c) $a = 3$ or -3 (d) $d = 4$ or -4
   (e) $x = 10$ or -10 (f) $x = 6$ or -6
   (g) $x = 7$ or -7 (h) $x = 1.5$ or -1.5

5. (a) $y = 5$ or -1 (b) $x = 0$ or 1
   (c) $x = 4$ (d) $x = 5$ or -3
   (e) $n = 12$ or -2 (f) $m = 7$ or 1
   (g) $a = 8$ or -3 (h) $x = 1$ or 3

6. (a) $x(x - 4) = 21$
   (b) $x = 7$ (x cannot equal -3)

7. $x = 9$ or -7

8. 7 and 8

Exercise 26.6   Page 308

1. (a)

x	-3	-2	-1	0	1	2	3
y	9	4	1	0	1	4	9

   (c) $y = 2.25$

2. (a)

x	-3	-2	-1	0	1	2	3
y	7	2	-1	-2	-1	2	7

   (c) $y = 0.25$ (d) $(-1.4, 0)$, $(1.4, 0)$

3. (b) $y = -1.75$
   (c) $x = -2$ and $x = 2$

4. Graphs have same shape, different positions.

5. (b) $y = 7.25$
   (c) $x = -1.7$ and $x = 1.7$

6. (b) $x = \pm 1.6$

7. (a) Entries are: 6, 2, 0, 0, 2, 6
   (c) $x = -1$ or 0
   (d) $\left(-\frac{1}{2}, -\frac{1}{4}\right)$

8. (a) Entries are: 5, 1, -1, -1, 1, 5
   (c) $x = -0.6$ or 1.6

9. (a) Entries are: -3, 7, 13, 15, 13, 7, -3
   (c) $x = \pm 2.7$

10. (b) $x = -3$ or 1

11. (b) $x = \pm 3.2$ (c) $(0, 10)$

12. (a) $x = \pm 2.8$ (b) $x = \pm 2.2$
   (c) $x = 0$ (d) $x = \pm 2.4$

14. (a) Entries are: -24, 0, 8, 6, 0, -4, 0, 18
   (c) $x = -3$ or 0 or 2

15. (b) $x = -2.7$

Exercise 26.7   Page 310

1. $x = 3.8$

2. (a) $w = 4.2$
   (b) $x = 2.3$

3. $x = 3.2$

4. $x = 9.4$

5. (a) $x = 6.2$
   (b) $x = 6.22$

6. (a) $2x^2(x + 2)$
   (b) $x = 5.3$

7. $x = 1.82$

Review Exercise 26   Page 311

1. $x^2 + 3x - 10$

2. (a) $(x - 5)(x + 2)$ (b) $x = 5$ or -2

3. $2x^2 + 5x - 12$

4. (a) $x = 4$ (b) $x = -3$ or 4

5. $x = -2$ or -6

6. (a) $(x - 4)(x + 2)$ (b) $a = 0$ or -4

7. (a) $x(x + 3) = 2(x + 1)$ (b) 1 cm

8.

9. (b)

x	-2	-1	0	1	2
y	8	2	0	2	8

   (d) $(1.4, 3.6)$, $(-1.9, 6.9)$

10. (a)

x	-2	-1	0	1	2	3	4
y	6	1	-2	-3	-2	1	6

   (c) $x = -0.7$ or 2.7

11. $x = 6.7$ **12.** $x = 2.59$

Section Review   Page 312

1. (b) $M(-1, 1)$

2. (a) £22   (b) 9 days

3. (a) 50   (b) 4   (c) 5

4. $12m$

5. (a) $3x$ pence   (b) $(x + 7)$ pence

6. (a) $y = 8$ (b) $a = 8$

7. (a) 18   (b) $\frac{1}{2}$

8. (a) -4 (b) 120

9. (a) -22 (b) 2

10. 6.5

11. (a) $3 - a$ (b) $t = 4$ (c) 2

12. (a) Even number.
   (b) Could be even or odd.
       When n is even, $3n$ is even, $3n + 1$ is odd.
       When n is odd, $3n$ is odd, $3n + 1$ is even.

13. (a) 70°F   (b) $F = 2C + 30$
   (c) $C = 35$

14. (a)

        (b) $(3, 3)$

15. (a) $x = 2$ (b) $x = \frac{1}{2}$

16. (a) 8
    (b) 7.5
    (c) Any two multiples of 4.
    (d) Starting numbers are multiples of 4.

17. **A** and **Q**, **B** and **P**, **C** and **S**, **D** and **R**

18. (a) (i) 40 miles.
       (ii) The cyclist was not moving.
       (iii) 10 miles per hour.
    (b) $2\frac{1}{2}$ hours.

19. (a) $x = 6$ (b) $5x - 12$

20. (a) $(5a + 3)$ cm   (b) $5a + 3 = 23, \ a = 4$

21. (a) $2x$ pence   (b) $3(x + 5)$ pence
    (c) 16 pence

22. (a) $2(2a + b)$ (b) $t(3 - t)$

23. (a) 18   (b) $4n - 2$

24. (a) (b)

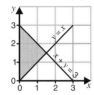

25. (a) $x = -\frac{1}{2}$ (b) $m(m - 7)$
    (c) 6, 7, 8   (d) $x = -2, \ y = 1.5$

26. (a) $G(0, 5), H(10, 0)$
    (b) (i)   (ii) $x = 2, \ y = 4$

               (c) $x = \dfrac{y - b}{a}$

27. (a)

x	-1	0	1	2	3
y	5	2	1	2	5

    (c) $x = -0.4$ and 2.4

28. (a) $y = 0.4x + 18$ (b) £58

29. (a) (i) $13x + 1$ (ii) $x^2 + 2x - 8$
    (b) (i) $(x + 3)(x + 5)$
       (ii) $x = -3$ or $x = -5$

30.

31. (a) $6y^5$
    (b) $2y^4$
    (c) $9y^6$

32. (a) $x = 6$
    (b) $x = 3.5, \ y = 0.5$
    (c) 2, 3
    (d) $x = 2$ or $x = 3$

33. (a) $r = \sqrt[3]{\dfrac{3V}{4\pi}}$ (b) $r = 6$

34. $x = 2.6$

35. (a) $6x^2 + 7x - 20$
    (b) $5xy(x + 3y^2)$

36. (a) $(x + 3)(x + 2) = 42$
         $x^2 + 5x + 6 = 42$
        $x^2 + 5x - 36 = 0$
    (b) $x = 4, \ 16 \text{ cm}^2$

37. (a) $y = 0$ or -5
    (b) $m = 3$ or $m = 4$

38. $x(15 - x) = 54$
       $15x - x^2 = 54$
   $x^2 - 15x + 54 = 0$

39. (a) $\dfrac{a}{5}$ (b) $2(x - 3)(x + 3)$

40. $(x + 2)(x + 1) = 6$
    $x^2 + 3x + 2 = 6$
    $x^2 + 3x - 4 = 0$

CHAPTER 27

Exercise **27.1**   Page 316

1. (a) 180°   (b) 90°   (c) 270°
    (d) 90°   (e) 120°   (f) 6°
    (g) 42°   (h) 720°   (i) 540°
    (j) 810°

2. (a) 45°   (b) 315°

3. (a) 45°   (b) 360°

4. Acute: **A**, **G**   Obtuse: **B**, **C**, **F**, **H**
   Reflex: **D**, **I**   Right: **E**

Exercise **27.2**   Page 317

1. (a) 39°   (b) 118°   (c) 42°

3. (a) 217°   (b) 234°

Exercise **27.3**   Page 319

1. (a) $a = 30°$ (b) $b = 150°$
    (c) $c = 42°$ (d) $d = 20°$
    (e) $e = 126°$ (f) $f = 203°$
    (g) $g = 133°, \ h = 47°$ (h) $i = 112°$
    (i) $j = 127°, \ k = 53°, \ l = 37°$
    (j) $m = 96°$
    (k) $n = 47°, \ p = 43°$

2. (a) 45° (b) 30° (c) 60° (d) 36°
    (e) 40° (f) 80° (g) 20° (h) 30°

Exercise **27.4**   Page 322

1. (a) $a = 65°$ (b) $b = 115°$
    (c) $c = 105°$ (d) $d = 100°$

2. (a) $a = 130°, \ b = 130°$
    (b) $c = 60°, \ d = 120°$
    (c) $e = 40°, \ f = 40°$
    (d) $g = 65°, \ h = 65°$

3. (a) $a = 63°$ (b) $b = 68°, \ c = 112°$
    (c) $d = 87°$ (d) $e = 124°$
    (e) $f = 65°$ (f) $g = 54°$
    (g) $h = 113°$ (h) $i = 124°$

4. (a) $a = 125°, \ b = 125°$
    (b) $c = 62°, \ d = 118°, \ e = 62°$
    (c) $f = 74°, \ g = 106°$
    (d) $h = 52°, \ i = 128°$

5. (a) $m = 84°$, $n = 116°$
(b) $p = 56°$, $q = 116°$
(c) $r = 61°$
(d) $s = 270°$

Exercise 27.5   Page 323

1. (a) $\angle BAC$ (b) $\angle RQS$ (c) $\angle XZY$
2. $a = \angle QPS$, $b = \angle PQS$, $c = \angle RQS$,
$d = \angle QRS$, $e = \angle QSR$, $f = \angle PSQ$
3. (a) $93°$ (b) $108°$ (c) $52°$ (d) $110°$
(e) $65°$ (f) $295°$ (g) $283°$ (h) $326°$
4. (a) (i) $43°$ (ii) supplementary angles
(b) (i) $125°$ (ii) vertically opposite angles
(c) (i) $63°$ (ii) corresponding angles
5. (a) $132°$ (b) $126°$ (c) $141°$
(d) $85°$ (e) $65°$
(f) $\angle QSP = 105°$, $\angle STU = 105°$
6. (a) $\angle AOB = 153°$, $\angle COD = 37°$
(b) $\angle QTU = 48°$, $\angle QTS = 132°$
(c) reflex $\angle TUV = 280°$

Exercise 27.6   Page 325

1. (a) $45°$ (b) $135°$ (c) $90°$
(d) $90°$ (e) $180°$
2. (a) South (b) North
3. (a) North-west (b) North-east
4. Entries are: south-east, south-east, south,
north-west

Exercise 27.7   Page 327

1. (a) $065°$ (b) $140°$ (c) $249°$
(d) $228°$ (e) $300°$ (f) $090°$
2. (b) (i) $230°$ (ii) $305°$ (iii) $015°$
(iv) $080°$ (v) $125°$ (vi) $355°$
3.
4. (a) $315°$
(b) $135°$
(c) $285°$
(d) $105°$
(e) $230°$
(f) $050°$

Exercise 27.8   Page 328

1. 16.8 km
2. 3.2 cm
3. (a) 7 m (b) 30 cm
4. 12.5 m
5. 70 cm
6. (a) 1 : 20 (b) 5.8 m (c) 22.5 cm
7. (a) (i) $128°$ (ii) $308°$
(b) (i) 4.7 cm (ii) 47 km
8. (a) 240 m (b) $063°$
9. 19.8 km
10. (a) 8 km (b) $114°$ (c) $294°$
11. (a) 6300 km (b) $248°$
12. (a) 50 km (b) $347°$ (c) $167°$

516

Review Exercise 27   Page 331

1. (a) $a = 57°$, supplementary angles
(b) $x = 30°$
2. (a) $p = 55°$, $q = 125°$ (b) $y = 85°$
3. (a) $a = 71°$ (b) $b = 63°$ (c) $c = 117°$
4. (a) $x = 30°$ (b) $y = 30°$ (c) $z = 80°$
5. (a) (i) $153°$ (ii) $63°$ (b) $\angle BOQ$
6. (a) $230°$ (b) $140°$
(c) (i) 3.7 cm (ii) 740 m
7. (b) $245°$ (c) (i) 64 km (ii) $197°$

CHAPTER   28

Exercise 28.1   Page 333

1. (a) Yes (b) Yes (c) No
(d) No (e) Yes (f) No
2. (a) Yes, obtuse-angled
(b) No
(c) Yes, acute-angled
(d) Yes, right-angled
(e) Yes, obtuse-angled
(f) No
3. (a) $a = 70°$ (b) $b = 37°$
(c) $c = 114°$ (d) $d = 43°$

Exercise 28.2   Page 334

1. $x + 45° = 80°$ (ext. $\angle$ of a Δ)
$x = 80° - 45° = 35°$
2. (a) $a = 120°$ (b) $b = 110°$
(c) $c = 50°$ (d) $d = 80°$
(e) $e = 88°$ (f) $f = 55°$
3. (a) $a = 32°$, $b = 148°$
(b) $c = 63°$
(c) $d = 52°$, $e = 64°$

Exercise 28.3   Page 335

1. (a) Isosceles (b) Equilateral (c) ΔBCE
2. (b) (i) Acute-angled, scalene
(ii) Right-angled, scalene
(iii) Acute-angled, isosceles
(iv) Obtuse-angled, isosceles
3. $AC = BC$ $\angle BAC = \angle ABC$
4. (6, 2), (6, 8)
5. (a) $a = 60°$ (b) $a = 85°$
(c) $a = 75°$ (d) $a = 50°$
6. $a = 40°$, $b = 120°$, $c = 62°$, $d = 128°$,
$e = 18°$, $f = 144°$, $g = 85°$, $h = 116°$,
$i = 26.5°$, $j = 153.5°$
7. (a) Isosceles (b) $74°$
(c) $46°$
8. (a) $\angle BCD = 120°$
(b) $\angle PRQ = 80°$, $\angle QRS = 160°$
(c) $\angle MNX = 50°$

5. (b) 9.3 cm   (c) 39°

1. (a) 13 cm   (b) 13.3 cm
    (c) 19.9 cm

2. ΔPQR = 33 cm, ΔQRS = 32 cm,
    ΔRST = 35 cm. ΔRST has greatest perimeter

3. (a) a = 7 cm   (b) d = 3.8 cm
    (c) f = 3 cm

4. (a) 9 cm²   (b) 6 cm²
    (c) 3.6 cm²   (d) 7.2 cm²
    (e) 4.16 cm²   (f) 11.52 cm²

5. (a) 3.8 cm²   (b) 8 cm²
    (c) 3.24 cm²

6. (a) a = 8 cm   **7.** 67.5 cm²
    (b) b = 4 cm   **8.** 30 cm
    (c) c = 16 cm   **9.** 4 cm

1. (b) (i) Isosceles   (ii) 8 cm²
    (c) Point S on line y = 5.

2. (a) x = 116°   (b) y = 52°

3. (a) $\angle DCA$ = 53°   (b) $\angle BAC$ = 50°

4. x = 20°, $\angle DAC$ = 40°   **6.** 9.6 cm²

5. (b) 103°   **7.** (b) 16 cm²

8. (a) 45 cm   (b) 75 cm²   (c) 10 cm

CHAPTER   **29**

3. (a) 5   (b) 3   (c) 0

4. 1, 1, 1, 2, 0

5. (a) 2   (b) 3   (c) 4
    (d) 2   (e) 6   (f) 8

6. (a) MY   (b) NZ   (c) NXZ   (d) JP

7. (a) 1   **8.** (a) 1
    (b) (i) (ii)   (b) (i)

                          (ii) 3

9. (a) (i) 0   (ii) 2   (b) (i) 1   (ii) 1
    (c) (i) 2   (ii) 2   (d) (i) 0   (ii) 4
    (e) (i) 1   (ii) 1

1. 9

2. (a) 4   (b) 4   (c) 2   (d) Infinite

3. (a) 2   (b) 2   (c) 4

4. (a) 4   (b) 1, 4

5. (a) 4   (b) 4

1. A, O   F, L   C, G   H, J   D, P

2. **D**, **E**

3. (a) ΔCED (b) *CBFE*

4. ΔAXZ and ΔZYC, ΔBXZ and ΔZYB

1. **A**, **D** (SSS)

2. **A**, **D** (ASA)

3. (a) Yes, ASA   (b) No
    (c) Yes, SAS   (d) Yes, SSS
    (e) No   (f) Yes, RHS
    (g) Yes, SAS   (h) No
    (i) Yes, ASA

4. (a) No   (b) No
    (c) Yes, RHS   (d) No
    (e) Yes, ASA   (f) Yes, ASA
    (g) Yes, SSS   (h) Yes, SAS
    (i) Yes, ASA

5. No lengths given, one triangle is larger than the other.

6. DE = PQ (given) DF = PR (given)
    $\angle EDF$ = $\angle QPR$ (70°)   Congruent, SAS

7. (a) $\angle BDC$ = 25°
    (b) BD is common
       AB = CD (7 cm)
       $\angle ABD$ = $\angle BDC$ (alt. $\angle$s)
       Congruent, SAS
    (c) $\angle ADB$

1.

2. (a) Y   (b) Z

3. (a) **A**   (b) **C**

4. (a) 5

5.

6. (a) ΔCDE
    (b) ΔCEF
    (c) *CDEF*

7. (a) x = 70°   (b) y = 10 cm

8. **A** and **D**,   SSS

9. **A** and **E**,   ASA

CHAPTER   **30**

1. (b) (i) Isosceles trapezium
      (ii) Parallelogram
      (iii) Rhombus
      (iv) Kite
      (v) Square

2. $M(1, 4)$

3. $S(3, 1)$ **6.** $A(1, 3)$

4. $C(5, 4)$ **7.** $L(2, 3)$

5. $Y(6, 4)$ **8.** $(3, 1), (3, 5)$

9. (a) $a = 90°$ (b) $a = 35°$
    (c) $a = 140°$ (d) $a = 114°$

10. (a) $a = 90°$, $b = 53°$, $c = 37°$
    (b) $d = 42°$, $e = 48°$
    (c) $f = 27°$, $g = 117°$
    (d) $h = 16°$, $i = 99°$, $j = 65°$

11. (a) $a = 36°$, $b = 144°$
    (b) $c = 124°$, $d = 56°$
    (c) $e = 130°$, $f = 23°$, $g = 23°$
    (d) $h = 42°$, $i = 84°$

12. (a) $a = 110°$, $b = 100°$ (b) $c = 95°$
    (c) $d = 46°$ (d) $e = 96°$

13. $a = 115°$, $b = 44°$

14. $\angle WXY = 72°$, $\angle XYZ = 108°$

15. (a) $a = 62°$
    (b) $b = 54°$, $c = 36°$
    (c) $d = 62°$
    (d) $e = 116°$, $f = 86°$
    (e) $g = 124°$
    (f) $h = 75°$
    (g) $i = 38°$, $j = 42°$
    (h) $k = 55°$, $l = 45°$

Exercise 30.2   Page 356

1.

A	B	C	D	E	F	G	H	I
1	0	1	4	2	2	0	0	1
1	1	1	4	2	2	1	2	1

2. (a) 4   (b) 2   (c) 1

3. (a) 2   (b) 2   (c) 1

4. (b) 2   (c) 2

Exercise 30.3   Page 358

1. (a) **B** and **C**   (b) **B** and **D**

2. **A** $8\,cm^2$ **B** $12\,cm^2$ **C** $12\,cm^2$ **D** $9\,cm^2$
    E $8\,cm^2$ **F** $12\,cm^2$

3. (a) $8\,cm$, $3.75\,cm^2$ (b) $8\,cm$, $2.79\,cm^2$
    (c) $11.2\,cm$, $7.84\,cm^2$ (d) $5.6\,cm$, $1.96\,cm^2$

4. (a) $12.25\,cm^2$ (b) $3.92\,cm^2$ (c) $4.68\,cm^2$
    (d) $12.24\,cm^2$ (e) $4.35\,cm^2$ (f) $5.75\,cm^2$

5. $14\,m^2$ **8.** $20\,cm^2$

6. $84\,cm^2$ **9.** $8\,cm$

7. $4\,cm$ **10.** $4\,cm$

11. $h = 5.4\,cm$, $l = 9\,cm$

12. (a) $a = 4\,cm$ (b) $b = 5\,cm$
    (c) $c = 10\,cm$ (d) $d = 4\,cm$
    (e) $e = 3\,cm$ (f) $f = 11\,cm$
    (g) $g = 8\,cm$ (h) $h = 10\,cm$
    (i) $i = 8\,cm$ (j) $j = 2\,cm$

Review Exercise 30   Page 360

1. (a) 2   (b) **A**   (c) 2

2. $Q(3, 6)$

3. $\angle ADC = 180° - (87° + 44°) = 49°$
    $\angle ABC = \angle ADC$ (opp. $\angle$'s in a parallelogram)
    $\angle ABC = 49°$

4. $x = 63°$, $y = 27°$ **7.** $64\,cm^2$

5. (a) 1   (b) $56°$ **8.** $25\,cm^2$

6. (a) $a = 115°$, $b = 44°$ **9.** $29.4\,cm$

10. (a) $13.5\,m^2$ (b) $8.1\,m^2$

11. (a) $50\,m^2$ (b) $17.5\,cm^2$

CHAPTER   31

Exercise 31.1   Page 363

1. (a) $x + 130° = 180°$ (supp. $\angle$'s)
      $x = 180° - 130° = 50°$
    (b) $y + 130° + 70° + 100° = 300°$
      (sum of $\angle$'s in a quad. $= 360°$)
      $y = 360° - 300° = 60°$

2. (a) $a = 63°$ (b) $b = 55°$, $c = 62°$
    (c) $d = 95°$, $e = 76°$

3. (a) $a = 60°$ (b) $b = 103°$
    (c) $c = 100°$ (d) $d = 128°$

4. (a) $a = 120°$ (b) $b = 62°$
    (c) $c = 76°$ (d) $d = 120°$, $e = 50°$

5. (a) $540°$ (b) $900°$
    (c) $1080°$ (d) $1260°$

6. (a) $d = 60°$ (b) $e = 120°$
    (c) $f = 130°$

Exercise 31.2   Page 365

1. (a) (i) $120°$ (ii) $90°$ (iii) $60°$ (iv) $45°$
    (b) (i) $60°$ (ii) $90°$ (iii) $120°$ (iv) $135°$

2. 20

3. (a) 40 (b) 15 (c) 9 (d) 6

4. 8

5. (a) 5 (b) 20 (c) 40 (d) 4

6. (a) $72°$ (b) $108°$ (c) $540°$

7. (a) $a = 90°$, $b = 60°$, $c = 210°$
    (b) $d = 90°$, $e = 120°$, $f = 150°$
    (c) $g = 90°$, $h = 135°$, $i = 135°$
    (d) $j = 105°$ (e) $k = 162°$
    (f) $l = 192°$ (g) $m = 132°$
    (h) $n = 96°$

8. (a) $a = 60°$ (b) $b = 135°$, $c = 45°$
    (c) $d = 36°$, $e = 72°$

9. (a) $a = 720°$ (b) $180°$

10. $y = 180 - \dfrac{360}{x}$

11. (a) $150°$ (b) $210°$ (c) $240°$
    (d) $210°$ (e) $330°$

12. (a) 5, 5   (b) 6, 6

4. At any vertex, sum of angles cannot equal 360°.

Review Exercise **31**　　　Page 368

1. (a) Hexagon　　(b)　　　　　　(c) 6

2. (a) Interior angle of equilateral triangle = 60°.
At each vertex, 6 triangles will meet.
(c) $x = 135°$

3. (a) $q = 12°$　　　　　(b) 30 sides

5. $\angle AED = 108°$ (int. ∠ of a pentagon)
$\angle CAE = 108° - 36° = 72°$
$\angle CAE + \angle AED = 180°$ (allied angles)
So AC is parallel to ED.

6. $x = 105°$

7 (a) Line of symmetry is a perpendicular bisector.
(b) $y = 45°$　　(c) $z = 125°$

8. (a) $x = 22.5°$, isosceles triangle
(b) Isosceles trapezium

9. (a) $p = 45°$　　　(b) $q = 135°$

10. (a) Hexagon　　(b) $x = 60°$
(c) 720°

11. (a) (i) $x = 36°$ (ii) $y = 18°$
(b) (i) parallel (ii) $z = 36°$

CHAPTER ⟨32⟩

Exercise 32.1　　　Page 372

1. (a) $a = 90°$, $b = 50°$ (b) $c = 45°$
(c) $d = 40°$, $e = 54°$ (d) $f = 20°$

2. (a) $a = 77°$　　(b) $b = 72°$
(c) $c = 38°$　　(d) $d = 40°$
(e) $e = 25°$　　(f) $f = 65°$, $g = 65°$
(g) $h = 130°$, $i = 65°$
(h) $j = 94°$, $k = 43°$

3. (a) $k = 106°$, $l = 62°$
(b) $m = 70°$, $n = 140°$
(c) $p = 108°$, $q = 105°$
(d) $r = 117°$, $s = 84°$
(e) $t = 292°$, $u = 56°$
(f) $v = 140°$
(g) $w = 110°$, $x = 75°$
(h) $y = 130°$, $z = 82°$

4. 47°　　　**5.** $\angle BCD = 70°$, $\angle CAD = 76°$

6. 119°　　　**7.** $\angle PQR = 105°$, $\angle QRS = 118°$

8. $\angle PSR = 45°$, $\angle TPQ = 95°$

9. (a) 140°　　(b) 70°

10. (a) 100°　　(b) 40°　　(c) 25°

11. 25°　　　**12.** 90°

1. (a) $a = 90°$, $b = 50°$
(b) $c = 35°$, $d = 35°$
(c) $e = 90°$, $f = 49°$, $g = 49°$
(d) $h = 63°$
(e) $j = 67°$
(f) $k = 50°$
(g) $l = 65°$, $m = 65°$
(h) $n = 146°$

2. (a) $a = 65°$, $b = 25°$
(b) $c = 67°$, $d = 23°$, $e = 46°$
(c) $f = 70°$, $g = 20°$

3. (a) 84°　　(b) 42°　　(c) 84°

4. (a) 48°　　(b) 6°

5. (a) 100°　　(b) 40°　　(c) 25°

6. (a) 72°　　(b) 36°　　(c) 54°

7. $p = 42°$, $q = 55°$, $r = 13°$, $s = 55°$

Review Exercise **32**　　　Page 376

1. (a) $a = 59°$　　(b) $b = 45°$
(c) $c = 51°$　　(d) $d = 23°$

2. $x = 37°$, $y = 90°$, $z = 53°$

3. $x = 60°$

4. $\angle TBO = 90°$ (tangent perpendicular to radius)
$\angle TBA = 55°$ (complementary ∠'s)
ΔABT is isosceles
$\angle ABT = 180° - (55° + 55°) = 70°$

5. $x = 18°$

6. $\angle PQS = 45°$, $\angle QRP = 65°$
$\angle QSP = 65°$, $\angle QOP = 130°$

7. $x = 50°$, $y = 60°$, $z = 30°$

8. $x = 92°$, $y = 46°$, $z = 17°$

CHAPTER ⟨33⟩

Exercise 33.1　　　Page 379

1. (a) 12 cm　(b) 24 cm　(c) 39 cm
2. (a) 15 cm　(b) 30 cm　(c) 38.4 cm
3. (a) 1p: 2 cm, 2p: 2.6 cm
(b) 1p: 6 cm, 2p: 7.8 cm
4. (a) 37.7 cm　(b) 22.0 cm　(c) 47.1 cm
5. (a) 28.3 cm　(b) 35.2 cm　(c) 100.5 cm
6. 28 cm　　　**10.** 57.5 m
7. 75.4 cm　　**11.** 5.03 m　　**14.** 30 mm
8. 81.7 cm　　**12.** 31.4 m　　**15.** 60 cm
9. 40.8 cm　　**13.** 3.8 cm　　**16.** 67 m

Exercise 33.2　　　Page 381

1. (a) 75 cm²　(b) 147 cm²　(c) 243 cm²
2. (a) 27 cm²　(b) 75 cm²　(c) 192 cm²
3. (a) 50 cm²　(b) 133 cm²　(c) 452 cm²

4. (a) 32.2 cm² (b) 45.4 cm² (c) 531 cm²

5. 22 167 cm²

6. 16 286 mm²

7. 3421 cm²

8. 491 cm²

9. 1.13 m²

10. 0.79 m²

11. 50.3 cm²

12. 4.0 cm

13. 7.14 m

14. 1.3 cm

Exercise 33.3 — Page 383

1. (a) 56.5 cm
(b) 254.5 cm²

2. (a) 26 cm
(b) 55.4 cm²

3. (a) 56.5 cm
(b) 11.3 m

4. 22.0 cm²

5. 21.5 cm²

6. Circle: 50.3 cm²
Semi-circle: 47.5 cm²
The circle is bigger.

7. (a) 27 m
(b) 56.7 m²

8. 31 cm

9. (a) 225 π cm²
(b) 30 π cm

10. 24.5 times

11. (a) 37.7 m
(b) 17 bags

12. 13.3 cm

13. 18.2 cm²

14. 38.6 cm

15. 18.8 cm

16. 326 cm²

17. 40.1 cm

18. 49 π cm²

19. 24 π cm

20. 8 cm

21. 65 π cm²

Exercise 33.4 — Page 386

1. (a) 134 m² (b) 588 cm² (c) 396 km²

2. (a) 360 cm² (b) 1104 cm² (c) 480 cm²

3. (a) 129 cm² (b) 41.1 cm² (c) 116 m²

4. (a) 22.7 cm² (b) 17.6 cm² (c) 23.9 cm²

5. 54.9 cm²

6. 58 cm²

7. (a) 0.383 m² (b) 2.63 m

8. 13.7 cm², 25.1 cm

9. A 14.1 cm²   B   25.1 cm²
C 39.3 cm²   A + B = C

Review Exercise 33 — Page 388

1. (a) 4.52 cm² (b) 11.0 cm

2. 176.7 cm²

3. π × 5² = 78.5 (less than 84)
So radius must be bigger than 5 m.

4. 372 m²

5. 157 cm²

6. 8510 cm²

7. 2

8. (a) 50.9 cm (b) 380 cm²

9. (a) 16 π cm²
(b) (i) 32 cm² (ii) (4 π − 8) cm²

10. 140 cm²

CHAPTER 34

Exercise 34.1 — Page 390

4.

5.

6.

Exercise 34.2 — Page 392

5. Perpendicular bisectors pass through the centre of the circle.

7.

8.

9.

12.

(d) Yes

Review Exercise 34 — Page 397

1.

2.

3.

4. (b) 43 m

CHAPTER 35

Exercise 35.1 — Page 399

5. (a) (2, −1) (b) (−2, 1) (c) (0, 1)
(d) (2, −3) (e) (1, 2)

6. (a) (3, −4) (b) (−3, 4) (c) (5, 4)
(d) (−5, 4) (e) (4, 3)

4. (a) $(4, -3)$ (b) $(-4, 3)$
    (c) $(-3, -4)$ (d) $(6, 1)$
    (e) $(0, 1)$ (f) $(3, -2)$

3. (a) $(5, 5)$ (b) $(1, 6)$
    (c) $(4, 1)$ (d) $(1, 1)$

4. $T\,(7, 2)$

5. (a) $\begin{pmatrix} 2 \\ 1 \end{pmatrix}$ (b) $\begin{pmatrix} 1 \\ -2 \end{pmatrix}$

    (c) $\begin{pmatrix} -3 \\ 1 \end{pmatrix}$ (d) $\begin{pmatrix} -3 \\ -2 \end{pmatrix}$

6. (b) $\begin{pmatrix} -3 \\ -2 \end{pmatrix}$

7. (a) $(2, 3)$ (b) $\begin{pmatrix} 1 \\ -1 \end{pmatrix}$

8. (a) $A\,(1, 5)$ (b) $\begin{pmatrix} -1 \\ -5 \end{pmatrix}$

2. (a) $(6, 8)$ (b) $(9, 12)$
    (c) $(6, 6)$ (d) $(3, 10)$
    (e) $(5, 5)$ (f) $(5, 4)$

3. (a) scale factor 3, centre $(0, 0)$
    (b) scale factor 3, centre $(5, 0)$
    (c) scale factor 2.5, centre $(0, 5)$

2. (a) scale factor $\frac{1}{3}$, centre $(5, 7)$

    (b) scale factor $\frac{1}{3}$, centre $(1, 7)$

    (c) scale factor $\frac{2}{5}$, centre $(5, 5)$

    (d) scale factor $\frac{1}{2}$, centre $(5, -2)$

    (e) scale factor $\frac{1}{3}$, centre $(0, 7)$

    (f) scale factor $\frac{2}{3}$, centre $(1, 1)$

1. $\mathbf{L_2}$: reflection in x axis
    $\mathbf{L_3}$: rotation, 90° anticlockwise, about $(0, 0)$
    $\mathbf{L_4}$: translation, 3 units right and 2 units up
    $\mathbf{L_5}$: rotation, 180°, about $(0, 0)$
    $\mathbf{L_6}$: reflection in $x = 7$

2. (a) translation $\begin{pmatrix} -7 \\ -4 \end{pmatrix}$

    (b) reflection in $y = -x$
    (c) rotation, 90° anticlockwise, about $(1, 0)$

3. (a) reflection in $x = -1$
    (b) rotation, 90° clockwise, about $(1, -2)$

    (c) translation $\begin{pmatrix} 5 \\ 1 \end{pmatrix}$

4. enlargement, scale factor 2, centre $(1, 2)$

5. enlargement, scale factor $\frac{1}{2}$, centre $(0, 0)$

1. (c) translation $\begin{pmatrix} 8 \\ 0 \end{pmatrix}$

2. (c) rotation, 90° anticlockwise, about $(5, 5)$

3. (d) rotation, 90° anticlockwise, about $(0, 0)$

4. (c) rotation, 180°, about $(1, -1)$

5. (c) translation $\begin{pmatrix} -4 \\ 3 \end{pmatrix}$

6. (d) translation $\begin{pmatrix} 6 \\ 0 \end{pmatrix}$

Review Exercise **35**   **Page 412**

1.

2.

3.

5. (a) (i) **H** (ii) **G** (iii) **F**
    (b) reflection in the y axis

6. (a) reflection in $y = x$
    (b) enlargement, scale factor 2, centre $(-7, 1)$

7. (a) reflection in $x = -1$
    (b) reflection in $y = -1$

    (c) translation $\begin{pmatrix} -4 \\ 1 \end{pmatrix}$

    (d) translation $\begin{pmatrix} 4 \\ -1 \end{pmatrix}$

    (e) enlargement, scale factor 2, centre $(0, 4)$
    (f) enlargement, scale factor $\frac{1}{2}$, centre $(0, 4)$

9. (a) reflection in $y = -1$
    (b) reflection, 90° clockwise, about $(-1, -1)$

10.

    (d) rotation, 90° anticlockwise, about $(1, 3)$

CHAPTER   **36**

2. (a) 4   (b) 2 faces overlap
5. (a) 8   (b) 5
    (c) 12   (d) 120 cm

1. (a)

   (c)

   (b)

2. (a)

        plan   elevation A   elevation B   elevation C

   (b)

        elevation A

        plan

        elevation B   elevation C

   (c)

        plan   elevation A

        elevation B   elevation C

3.

        plan   elevation A

4. (a)

   (b)

5. (a)   (c)

   (b)

1. (b) 52 cm²   (c) 52 cm²
2. (a) (i) 8   (ii) 27
       (iii) 64   (iv) 125
   (b) (i) 24 cm²   (ii) 54 cm²
       (iii) 96 cm²   (iv) 150 cm²
3. (a) 27 cm³, 54 cm²
   (b) 30 cm³, 62 cm²
   (c) 140 cm³, 166 cm²
4. (a) 1 cm × 4 cm × 6 cm,
      1 cm × 2 cm × 12 cm,
      1 cm × 3 cm × 8 cm,
      2 cm × 2 cm × 6 cm,
      2 cm × 3 cm × 4 cm
      Smallest SA: 2 × 3 × 4, 52 cm²
   (b) 9. Largest SA: 1 × 1 × 36, 146 cm²
5. (a) 4 cm³, 18 cm²   (b) 5 cm³, 20 cm²
   (c) 8 cm³, 28 cm²   (d) 7 cm³, 24 cm²
   (e) 14 cm³, 42 cm² (f) 10 cm³, 32 cm²
6. (a) 150 cm³, 190 cm²
   (b) 51.8 cm³, 89.3 cm²
   (c) 19 440 cm³, 4644 cm²
   (d) 96.8 cm³, 132 cm²
   (e) 916 cm³, 612 cm²
7. 10 cm   **9.** 1155 cm²
8. 4.5 cm   **10.** 180 cm³

1. (a) 40 cm³   (b) 140 cm³
   (c) 96 cm³
2. (a) 11 cm², 15.4 cm³
   (b) 6 cm², 15 cm³
   (c) 7.2 cm², 21.6 cm³
3. (a) 5.6 cm², 11.2 cm³
   (b) 314 cm², 6280 cm³
   (c) 3.14 cm², 15.7 cm³
4. (a) 10 cm³   (b) 56 cm³
   (c) 330 cm³   (d) 113 cm³
   (e) 393 cm³   (f) 120 cm³
   (g) 848 cm³   (h) 18 cm³
5. P
6. No. $\pi \times 5 \times 5 \times 10 = 250\pi$ cm³
         $\pi \times 10 \times 10 \times 5 = 500\pi$ cm³
7. 11.5 cm   **9.** 12.0 cm
8. 2.7 cm   **10.** 4.5 cm

1. (a) 339 cm²   (b) 61.3 cm²
   (c) 90.9 cm²
3. (a) 1260 cm²   (b) 6280 cm²
   (c) 62 800 cm³
4. 754 cm³
5. 274 cm²
6. (a) 14 100 cm²   (b) 18 800 cm²

1. (a) 13   (b) 14 cm³
2. (a) 30 cm³ (b) (i)   (ii) 62 cm²

3.

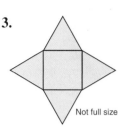

Not full size   Not full size

4. (a)   (b)

6. (a) 75 cm²   **10.** 216 cm³
  (b) 225 cm³   **11.** (a) 18 cm
7. (a) 54 cm³   (b) 15 625 cm³
  (b) 12   **12.** 392 cm²
8. 350 cm³   **13.** 618
9. 1890 cm³   **14.** (a) 6 (b) 9 cm

CHAPTER 37

2. (a) Corresponding lengths not in same ratio.
  (b) **P** and **R**
3. (a) Two circles
  (d) Two squares
4. (a) Scale factor = $\frac{3}{2}$ = 1.5
  (b) $x = 1.8$ cm
  (c) $a = 120°$
5. (a) $x = 1.5$ cm, $y = 2.4$ cm, $a = 70°$
  (b) $x = 5$ cm, $y = 1.5$ cm, $a = 53°$
  (c) $x = 30$ cm, $y = 17.5$ cm, $z = 10$ cm
6. 15 cm   **8.** 5 cm
7. 3 cm   **9.** $x = 16$, $y = 48$

1. (a) $x = 10$ cm, $y = 27$ cm
  (b) $x = 6$ cm, $y = 10$ cm
  (c) $x = 12$ cm, $y = 12$ cm
  (d) $x = 12$ cm, $y = 5$ cm
2. $AB = 8$ cm, $AE = 5$ cm
3. (a) $PR = 10$ cm
  (b) $QR = 5$ cm, $PQ = 7.5$ cm,
     $QS = 4.5$ cm
4. (a) $AB = 2.96$ cm, $QR = 3.25$ cm
  (b) $XZ = 14.4$ m, $BC = 6.25$ m
  (c) $EG = 1.6$ cm, $MN = 4.0$ cm
  (d) $AC = 4.0$ m, $XZ = 2.0$ m

1. (a) $AC = 2.4$ cm, $AP = 2.2$ cm
  (b) $AC = 4.5$ cm, $BP = 1$ cm
  (c) $BC = 4.2$ cm, $BP = 1.6$ cm
  (d) $AP = 2.5$ cm, $BC = 7$ cm
  (e) $AQ = 4\frac{2}{3}$ cm, $BQ = 16\frac{2}{3}$ cm
2. (a) $x = 58°$ (b) $x = 56°$
3. (a) (i) 61°   (ii) 29°
  (b) (i) 13 cm, 5.2 cm
     (ii) 36 cm, 27 cm
    Same
4. (b) $AB = 1.8$ cm (c) 12.5 cm
5. 13.5 cm²

1. 11.2 cm
2. $\angle PQX = 54°$, $\angle AXB = 36°$
  Both triangles have same angles. $PQ = 2AB$
  Triangles are similar.
3. $CD = 14.4$ cm
4. (a) $x = 4.5$ cm (b) $y = 10$ cm
  (c) $z = 46°$
5. (a) 2.4 cm   (b) 9 cm
6. $DE = 4.6$ cm
7. $QC = 3$ cm

CHAPTER 38

1. (a) 10 cm (b) 25 cm (c) 26 cm
2. (a) 7.8 cm (b) 12.8 cm (c) 10.3 cm
3. (a) $\sqrt{52}$ cm (b) $\sqrt{20}$ cm
4. (a) 5   (b) 9.22   (c) 13
  (d) 8.06 (e) 7.21
5. (a) $R(9, 7)$ (b) $X(2, 3)$
  (c) $Y(4, 2)$ (d) 2.24

1. (a) 8 cm   (b) 6 cm   (c) 2 cm
2. (a) 6.9 cm (b) 10.9 cm (c) 9.5 cm
3. 339 m
4. 36 cm²
5. 3.6 cm

1. (a) 2.9 cm (b) 5.7 cm
  (c) 2.1 cm (d) 2.0 cm
2. 17 cm   **5.** 10.6 cm   **8.** 74.3 cm
3. 10 cm   **6.** 15 cm   **9.** 13 cm
4. 8.5 cm   **7.** 6.9 cm   **10.** 24 cm
11. (a) 11.4 cm   (b) 43.5 cm²

1. (a) 2.95 m
   (b) X
2. 28.3 km
3. 8.60
4. $41^2 = 40^2 + 9^2$
   ΔABC is right-angled at C.

5. 361 m
6. (a) 154°
   (b) 2.81 km
7. $\sqrt{18}$ cm
8. 14.1 km
9. 155 m

CHAPTER 39

Exercise 39.1   Page 443

1. (a) $h = 2.27$ m   (b) $h = 4.02$ m
   (c) $h = 8.02$ m
2. (a) $x = 1.50$ cm   (b) $x = 2.99$ cm
   (c) $x = 5.78$ cm
3. (a) $BC = 3.39$ m   (b) $AC = 11.4$ m
   (c) $BC = 4.74$ cm
   (d) $\angle ABC = 55°$, $AC = 6.96$ cm

Exercise 39.2   Page 444

1. (a) $a = 62.1°$ (b) $a = 25.0°$
   (c) $a = 50.9°$
2. (a) $x = 52.3°$ (b) $x = 60.5°$
   (c) $x = 61.4°$
3. (a) $\angle QPR = 23.6°$ (b) $\angle PRQ = 64.7°$
   (c) $\angle QPR = 21.8°$
   (d) $\angle QRP = 24.0°$, $\angle QPR = 66.0°$

Exercise 39.3   Page 445

1. (a) $l = 7.00$ m   (b) $l = 7.49$ m
   (c) $l = 4.93$ m
2. (a) $x = 6.49$ cm   (b) $x = 5.31$ cm
   (c) $x = 10.61$ cm
3. (a) $AB = 7.62$ m   (b) $AB = 17.5$ cm
   (c) $AB = 66.9$ cm
   (d) $\angle ABC = 17.2°$, $AB = 25.7$ m

Exercise 39.4   Page 447

1.

	sin p	cos p	tan p
(a)	$\frac{5}{13}$	$\frac{12}{13}$	$\frac{5}{12}$
(b)	$\frac{7}{25}$	$\frac{24}{25}$	$\frac{7}{24}$
(c)	$\frac{4}{5}$	$\frac{3}{5}$	$\frac{4}{3}$

2. (a) $p = 40.9°$ (b) $p = 38.0°$
   (c) $p = 38.8°$ (d) $p = 53.3°$
   (e) $p = 39.7°$ (f) $p = 35.5°$
3. (a) $a = 5.77$ cm   (b) $a = 6.47$ cm
   (c) $a = 4.18$ cm   (d) $a = 3.78$ cm
   (e) $a = 4.72$ cm   (f) $a = 4.04$ cm
4. 4.33 cm
5. 72.5°, 72.5°, 34.9°

6. (a) 5.96 cm   (b) 1.71 cm
7. (a) 2.76 cm   (b) 19.8°
8. 13.06 cm
9. 4.52 cm   **10.** 9.45 cm

Exercise 39.5   Page 450

1. 21.4 m
2. 40.1 m
3. (a) 135 m   (b) 53.5°
4. 22.2 m

5. 31.0°
6. 51.3°
7. 959 m
8. 40.5 m

Exercise 39.6   Page 451

1. (a) 161 km   (b) 192 km
2. 22.2 km
3. 145°
4. 41.9 km

5. 164°
6. 6.40 km
7. 174 km
8. 283°

Review Exercise 39   Page 452

1. 3.25 m
2. (a) 34.9°   (b) 154 cm
3. 103 miles
4. (a) 9.64 cm   (b) 51.3°
5. (a) 2.10 m   (b) 4.83 m
6. (a) 5.46 m   (b) 64.1°
7. (a) 9.38 m   (b) 65.9°
8. (a) (i) $\frac{5}{12}$ (ii) $\frac{5}{13}$
   (b) $QR = 6.5$ cm, $PR = 2.5$ cm
9. (a) $l = 2.5$ m
   (b) (i) 5.00 m   (ii) Safe, 78.5°
10. (a) 47.7 km   (b) 197.7 km, 069°
11. 21.3 m

CHAPTER 40

Exercise 40.1   Page 456

1. (a) 86 mm   (b) 8 mm   (c) 0.8 mm
2. (a) 9 cm   (b) 21 cm   (c) 0.2 cm
3. (a) 2 m   (b) 45.5 m   (c) 0.66 m
4. (a) 600 cm   (b) 90 cm   (c) 7 cm
5. (a) 4 km   (b) 35 km   (c) 0.455 km
6. (a) 6000 m   (b) 650 000 m   (c) 350 m
7. (a) 2000 g   (b) 7500 g   (c) 600 g
8. (a) 3 kg   (b) 32 kg   (c) 0.22 kg
9. (a) 320 000 ml = 320 l
   (b) 0.32 t = 320 kg = 320 000 g
   (c) 3200 g = 3.2 kg = 0.0032 t
   (d) 320 mm = 32 cm = 0.32 m
   (e) 32 000 cm = 320 m = 0.32 km
   (f) 3.2 km = 3200 m = 320 000 cm
10. (a) 8 m   (b) 0.086 m   (c) 40 m
11. (a) 2000 ml (b) 850 ml   (c) 30 ml

12. 2000 m and 2 km   **14.** 0.5 km

13. 8 kg and 8000 g   **15.** 0.3 t

16. (a) 3.123 m   (b) 450 cm   (c) 3240 km
     (d) 1 000 000 g   (e) 0.4 l

17. 0.5 m² is larger than 500 cm².
     0.5 m² = 5000 cm²

18. 800 000 cm³ is larger than 0.08 m³.
     0.08 m³ = 80 000 cm³

19. 1.98 l **21.** 50 g

20. 20   **22.** 60   **23.** 50 ml

Exercise 40.2   Page 458

1. 250 g   **2.** 30 cm   **3.** 200 ml

5. 6.4 m, nearest 0.1 m

6. 175 ml, nearest 5 ml

7. (a) 12 m, nearest metre
        5.9 m, nearest 100 cm
        5 l, nearest litre
        500 m², nearest 50 m²
     (b) 1200 cm, nearest 100 cm
        5900 mm, nearest 100 mm
        5000 ml, nearest 1000 ml
        500 000 000 mm², nearest 50 000 000 mm²

Exercise 40.3   Page 459

1. (a) 5 cm   (b) 61 cm

2. (a) 78 inches   (b) 8 inches

3. (a) 8 km   (b) 72 km

4. (a) 5 miles   (b) 25 miles

5. (a) 55 pounds   (b) 2200 pounds

6. (a) 45 kg   (b) 43 kg

7. (a) 3 litres   (b) 11 litres

8. (a) 33 pounds   (b) 35 pints
     (c) 195 inches   (d) 150 mm
     (e) 20 inches   (f) 180 cm

9. 22 pounds   **10.** 170 cm   **11.** 62.7 kg

12. (a) 610 m   (b) 4.8 km   (c) 5 feet
     (d) 2.75 pounds   (e) 45.7 litres

13. 1500 cm²

14. 100 magazines

15. No. 10 kg is about 22 pounds.

16. No. 6 miles is about 9.6 km.

17. 12 stones or 76.4 kg

18. 136 g or 4.8 oz

19. 42.5 square feet

20. (a) 48 km/hour   (b) 80 km/hour
     (c) 108 km/hour

21. (a) 37.5 miles per hour
     (b) 90 miles per hour

22. 27 metres per second

23. (a) 12.8 km/litre   (b) 30 miles per gallon

24. 3.35 kg, nearest 10 g

25. 6.8 m³, 1 d.p.

Exercise 40.4   Page 461

1. (a) continuous   (b) discrete
     (c) discrete   (d) continuous
     (e) discrete   (f) continuous

2. (a) exact   (b) 4.5 mins ≤ t < 5.5 mins
     (c) exact   (d) 62.5 kg ≤ w < 63.5 kg
     (e) 152.5 cm ≤ J < 153.5 cm

3. (a) 12.5 s ≤ t < 13.5 s
     (b) 82.55 s ≤ t < 82.65 s

4. (a) nearest 0.01 m (centimetre)
     (b) 1.525 m ≤ h < 1.535 m

5. (a) 61.5 kg   (b) 2.25 m   (c) 12.625 s

6. (a) nearest 10 m   (b) nearest 50 m
     (c) nearest 100 m

Exercise 40.5   Page 463

1. (a) area   (b) length
     (c) length   (d) length
     (e) volume   (f) area
     (g) volume   (h) area

2. (a) perimeter   (b) area
     (c) volume   (d) none
     (e) area   (f) perimeter
     (g) perimeter   (h) none
     (i) volume   (j) volume
     (k) none   (l) area

3. (a) (i) $2\pi(x + y)$
        (ii) $\pi(x^2 + y^2)$, πxy

5. $\frac{1}{2}pqs$, volume
     $2\left(p + q + r + \frac{3s}{2}\right)$, edge length
     $s(p + q + r) + pq$, surface area

6. (a) correct   (b) correct   (c) correct
     (d) wrong   (e) correct   (f) wrong

7. (a), (b), (c), (e)

Review Exercise 40   Page 464

1. 200

2. 8 full glasses

3. (a) 3.9 cm   (b) 640 km

4. (a) 10 pounds   (b) 4.5 l

5. Taller: Tim by about 10 cm,
     heavier: Sam by about 1 kg

6. (a) 1.9295 kg
     (b) (i) 1.93 kg   (ii) nearest 10 g

7. (a) 250 000 cm²   (b) 270 square feet

8. 44 feet per second

9. Both same speed

10. (a) 120 m²   (b) 1.3 litres

11. nearest 1 million square kilometres

12. (a) continuous   (b) discrete

13. 135 tonnes

14. 0.1 s

15. 24.5 cm
16. (a) **B**
    (b) **B** has dimension 3
        $\frac{1}{6} \pi Hw^2 \equiv L \times L^2 = L^3$
17. (a) $2(v + 2w + x + y + z)$ (b) $\frac{1}{2} z(x + y)w$
18. (a) area   (b) none   (c) volume

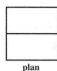 **Section Review**   **Page 466**

1. $a = 153°$, $b = 52°$, $c = 65°$
2. (a) **P**   (b) **R**
3. (b) 40 cm²
4. (a)   (b)

        plan   elevation X

5. (a) Reflection in the y axis
    (b) Rotation, 90° clockwise, about (0, 0)
    (c)

6.

                  7. (b) 9.8 cm²
                  8. 8 cm
9. (a) **P and S**
    (b) (i) 32 cm   (ii) 44 cm²
10. (a) $x = 118°$
    (b) (i) $p = 25°$ (ii) $q = 105°$
11. (a) 190.5 cm
    (b) $77.5 \text{ kg} \leqslant w < 78.5 \text{ kg}$
12. (a) 314 cm   (b) 7854 cm²
13. (a) $x = 8$, $y = 3.5$
    (b) (i) $E(-4, 1)$
         (ii) 9 units to the right and 4 units up.
14. 30 788 cm³
15. (a) Enlargement, scale factor $\frac{1}{2}$,
        centre (1, −1)
    (b) (c)

16. (b) 116 m, 276°
17. $a = 120°$,   **18.**
    $b = 135°$,
    $c = 150°$

19. 264 cm
20. (a) 75 cm²   (b) 41.8 cm
21. (a) $2\pi a(a + b)$, $\frac{1}{2}(a + b)c$
    (b) $\pi a^2 b$
22. (b) $h = 6.9$ cm   (c) $x = 41.8°$
23. (a) $\angle PRQ = \angle PTS$ (corres. $\angle$'s)
        $\angle PQR = \angle PST$ (corres. $\angle$'s)
        Angle P is common.
        Both triangles have same angles.
    (b) $QR = 7.5$ cm
24. 299°
25. $x = 38°$
    $\angle DAB = \angle DCB = 52°$
    $x = 180° - 90° - 52°$
26. (a) $\sin x = \frac{3}{5}$
    (b) (i) $\cos y = \frac{4}{5}$
         (ii) $PQ = 9$ cm

Exam Practice: **Module** **5**

Non-calculator Paper   **Page 470**

1. (a) b^3 (b) $2a - 6$
    (c) $35d$ pence
2. (a) **P**   (b) **Q**
3. $1, 0, -\frac{1}{2}$
4. (a) 72 cm³   (b) 108 cm²
5. (a) (i) $x = 2$ (ii) $x = 4$
    (b) $5 - 4n$
6. (a) 18   (b) $2x - 1$
    (c) $y = 4$
7. (a) 065°   (b) 1000 m
8. (a) $y = -3$ (b) $x = 3$
9. (a)   (b)

x	−1	1	3
y	7	3	−1

    (c) $x = 1.5$

10. $x = 153°$
11. (a) −5   (b) 15
12. (a) $a = -3$ (b) $x = 3.2$
    (c) $t = 1.5$
13. (a) (i) c^5 (ii) d^4
    (b) $2(m - 3)$
14. (b) 9.9 cm²
15. (a) $x = 54°$
    (b) (i) $y = 63°$ (ii) alternate angles
16. $5 \times 5 \times \pi = 25\pi$ cm²
17. (a) (i) 15 (ii) 1
    (b) $x = 3$

18. (a) 80 mph   (b) 45 minutes
     (c) 30 miles   (d) 20 mph

19. (a) **P**   (b) 54 cm^2 (c) 300

20. (b) $x = 3.3$ and $x = -0.8$

21. $3n + 2$

22. (a) $8x - 4$ (b) $k = \dfrac{m - 7}{3}$
     (c) $m = 3$ or $m = -8$

23. (a) Rotation, 90° anticlockwise, centre (0, 0).
     (b) Reflection in $y = x$.
     (c)

24. $NL = 5.4$ cm

25. (a) $x = 5.5$
     (b) $x = 1$, $y = -2$
     (c) $x = -2$ or $x = 4$
     (d) $a(a - 1)$

26. $\angle DEF = 52°$
     $\angle DFE = 90°$ (angle in a semi-circle)
     $\angle DEF = 180° - 90° - 38° = 52°$

27. (a) $V = \pm 0.7$ (b) $P = RV^2$

28. (a) $A\,(0, -1)$, $B\,(2, 0)$
     (b) $\frac{1}{2}$
     (c) Parallel, same gradient $\frac{1}{2}$
     (d) $y = 2 - x$

29. $\dfrac{\pi a^2 c}{12}$

30. (a) $2x \times 2x + 4 \times x = 48$
           $4x^2 + 4x = 48$
        $4x^2 + 4x - 48 = 0$
          $x^2 + x - 12 = 0$
     (b) $x = 3$,   30 cm

Exam Practice: Module 5

Calculator Paper   Page 473

1. (a) $6t$ (b) $x = \frac{1}{2}$

2. $\angle PQR = \angle PRQ = 48°$ (ΔPQR is isosceles)
    $\angle QPR = 180° - 48° - 48° = 84°$

3. (a) 5, 8   (b) 7th term

4. (b) 84 cm^2

5. (a) (i) 48p per kg   (ii) 36p per kg
     (b) 220 pounds

6. Shape **C**.
    The shape cannot be used to cover a surface
    without leaving gaps.

7. (a) $x = 15$ (b) $y = 1.25$

8. 43.45 cm^2

9. (a) Reflection in $y = 0$.
     (b) Translation, 5 units left and 1 unit down.

10. (a) $7m + 2n$ (b) $3x - 3$
     (c) (i) $x = -1$ (ii) $y = 1.4$

11. (a) (i) corresponding   (ii) alternate
     (b) $y = 68°$

13. (a) $g = 4.5$ (b) $g = 3.5$

14.

15. (a) $10p + 4q$
     (b) $6pq$

16. (a) $20x$ grams
     (b) $x = 180$

17. (a) 503 cm
     (b) 3 complete turns

18. $2n + 1$

19. 108

20. (a) $x = 3.2$ (b) $3(a - 2b)$
     (c) $3x - 6$

21. (a) 0945   (b) 38 miles
     (c) Twice   (d) 23 mph

22. 0.325

23. $7 - 2n$

24. (a) If $\angle B$ is a right angle,
       then by Pythagoras on ΔABC.
       $AC^2 = AB^2 + BC^2$
       $(39^2 = 15^2 + 36^2)$
     (b) $x = 105°$

25. (a) $3(p - 1)$ (b) $p(p + 2)$

26.

27. (a) (i) $x = 1$ (ii) $x = -\frac{2}{5}$
     (b) $x = 7.3$

28. $RQ = 5.6$ m

29. (a) $t = \dfrac{2d}{u + v}$ (b) $t = 7.5$

30. $x = 13.7°$

31. (a) $m > 4$ (b) $-1, 0, 1$
     (c) $x = 7$, $y = 3$

32. 24.4 m

33. (a) (i) a^3 (ii) $6x^4y^7$ (iii) p^6
     (b) (i) $5t^2 + 15t$ (ii) $x^2 - 2xy - 3y^2$

34. (a) (i) $x = 54°$ (ii) $y = 46°$
     (b) $DE = 3.6$ cm

35. 170 litres

36. $a = 57°$, $b = 114°$, $c = 123°$

37. (a) 333°   (b) 21.7 km^2

38. $y = 3x - 4$

Index ●●●●●●●●●●●●●●●●●●●●●●●●●●●●●●●●